OPTICAL PUMPING

FRONTIERS IN CHEMISTRY

Ronald Breslow and Martin Karplus, Editors
Columbia University

CONTRIBUTIONS TO THE THEORY OF CHEMICAL KINETICS
T. A. Bak   *Kφbenhavns Universitet*

MOLECULAR ORBITAL THEORY
C. J. Ballhausen   *Kφbenhavns Universitet*
H. B. Gray   *Columbia University*

NONCLASSICAL IONS: Reprints and Commentary
P. D. Bartlett   *Harvard University*

OPTICAL PUMPING: An Introduction
R. A. Bernheim   *The Pennsylvania State University*

ELECTRON PARAMAGNETIC RESONANCE
M. Bersohn   *University of Toronto*
J. Baird   *Brown University*

TOPICS IN BIOORGANIC MECHANISMS
T. C. Bruice   *University of California, Santa Barbara*
S. J. Benkovic   *The Pennsylvania State University*

THERMODYNAMICS OF SMALL SYSTEMS: Parts 1 and 2
T. L. Hill   *University of Oregon*

LECTURES ON QUANTUM THEORY OF MOLECULAR ELECTRONIC STRUCTURE
R. G. Parr   *Johns Hopkins University*

THE BIOSYNTHESIS OF STEROIDS, TERPENES, AND ACETOGENINS
J. H. Richards   *California Institute of Technology*
J. B. Hendrickson   *Brandeis University*

OXIDATION MECHANISMS: Applications to Organic Chemistry
R. Stewart   *University of British Columbia*

MOLECULAR PHOTOCHEMISTRY
N. J. Turro   *Columbia University*

COMPUTER PROGRAMMING FOR CHEMISTS
K. B. Wiberg   *Yale University*

OPTICAL PUMPING

An Introduction

ROBERT BERNHEIM
The Pennsylvania State University

W. A. BENJAMIN, INC.   1965
New York   Amsterdam

OPTICAL PUMPING: An Introduction

Library of Congress Catalog Number 66–10906
Manufactured in the United States of America

*This manuscript was put into production on April 21, 1965;
this volume was published on October 13, 1965*

W. A. BENJAMIN, INC.
New York, New York 10016

Preface

In recent years the words "optical pumping" have been used more and more often, generally in connection with the operation of lasers and masers. However, the concept of optical pumping and the techniques involved have a more general applicability and have been responsible for the success of a large number of fundamental and aesthetically beautiful experiments. Because of this and because it has become evident that an increasing diversity of problems can be investigated with optical pumping, a general survey of the subject seems desirable.

This book contains an elementary discussion of optical pumping techniques and theory suitable for physicists and chemists who wish an introduction to the subject. The first sections of the book describe what optical pumping is and what basic phenomena are involved in an optical pumping experiment. The latter sections of the book are concerned with the application of optical pumping to the investigation of the energy levels of atoms and molecules and with the effect of intermolecular interactions on these energy levels. Most of the discussion is directed at the optical pumping of gases; however, a chapter is included on optical pumping in solids. The emphasis is on the investigation of energy levels, and the application of optical pumping to lasers and masers is only briefly mentioned.

It is not intended that this be an exhaustive review but more a discussion of elementary principles. It is hoped that the inclusion of reprints and a rather complete bibliography will add to the usefulness of this volume.

The author wishes to express his appreciation to the many authors and to the journals for permission to reprint the articles which appear in the last part of this book. Unfortunately, space does not permit the reprinting of all the works that are appropriate for a volume of this sort. As a result, many papers which played important roles in the development of optical pumping could not be included. Likewise, many papers which give the latest experimental and theoretical results do not appear. The articles which are reprinted represent a diverse selection in that some are an extended development of the topics treated in the preceding pages, others contain some thought-provoking ideas on data, while still others represent some of the milestones in the history of optical pumping. The reader will have his own list of favorite papers on this subject, but it is hoped that he will find some of them included here.

ROBERT BERNHEIM

University Park, Pennsylvania
July 1965

Contents

Reprints

1 / Introduction

1-1 WHAT IS OPTICAL PUMPING?

By "optical pumping" we mean the use of light to produce a population of a set of energy levels of a system which is different from the normal Boltzmann distribution at the temperature of the experiment. The energy levels in question might be magnetic energy levels of an atom in which case the optical pumping would refer to either the orientation or the alignment of the atoms by the light beam. On the other hand, the levels might be electronic states which are to be populated in order to establish conditions for laser action. We should like to begin our discussion with atoms and atomic resonance fluorescence as used for the optical pumping of angular momentum substates. Once this process has been explained, various applications will be discussed.

1-2 THE EARLY EXPERIMENTS IN OPTICAL PUMPING

Since a certain amount of the discussion involves the detection of radio-frequency resonances by using the optical resonance transitions of atoms, it might be appropriate to begin our introduction to optical pumping with mention of the first workers to observe the effect of a radiofrequency field upon atomic optical resonance radiation. There were E. Fermi and F. Rasetti (1925 a, b) and G. Breit and A. Ellett (1925) who observed the change in polarization of the resonance fluorescence of mercury vapor upon change in frequency of an applied alternating magnetic field. From such experiments the

1

g-factor and lifetime of the excited state could be determined (Mitchell, 1934, p. 271).

In the following years a great deal of experimental work was done with atomic fluorescence. The reader is referred to two excellent books which describe the early theory and the extensive experimental work (Mitchell, 1934; Pringsheim, 1949).

In the late nineteen forties microwave and radiofrequency spectroscopy began to capture the attention of the physicist and chemist. Magnetic resonance, which had been detected in atomic and molecular beams, had been detected in bulk material; molecular rotational transitions and nuclear electric quadrupole interactions were being observed in the microwave spectra of the vapors of various compounds. These new types of experiments produced many advances in the elucidation of atomic and molecular structure. Another motivation for work in these areas was the desire to be able to determine nuclear spins and moments which, at that time, were two of the few quantities that could be obtained experimentally and which could be used in a discussion of nuclear structure. Most of this work in microwave and radiofrequency spectroscopy was directed at measurements upon the ground electronic states of atoms and molecules.

In 1949 Bitter called attention to the possibility of the optical detection of a radiofrequency resonance. However, the particular detection scheme he proposed was shown to be impractical (Pryce, 1950). Also, Brossel and Kastler, (1949; Kastler, 1950; see reprints) proposed a scheme for the optical orientation of atoms and discussed different ways of detecting the orientation. Successful optical pumping experiments were carried out on the $^3P_1$ state of the mercury isotopes by Brossel and Bitter (1952a) and on the ground state of Na^{23} by Brossel, Kastler, and Winter (1952c) and by Hawkins and Dicke (1953).

1—3 APPLICATIONS OF OPTICAL PUMPING

In the years following these early experiments the principles of optical pumping led to valuable developments, both practical and theoretical. Among the practical devices resulting from these concpets have been the development of various types of frequency standards, the maser, the optical maser (laser), and very sensitive magnetometers, to name a few. The contributions to fundamental knowledge are numerous and include the determination of nuclear spins, magnetic moments, and nuclear electric quadrupole moments; very accurate measurements of the electron magnetic moment and a determination of an upper limit to the electric dipole moment of the electron; the determination of nuclear hyperfine interactions and their "pressure shifts"; the determination of hyperfine interactions and g-factors for excited states of atoms; and the determination of diffusion constants, disorientation cross sections, and spin-exchange cross sections for atomic collisions.

As the field developed, experimental techniques were refined, and new effects were observed. The transmission technique of detecting magnetic resonances in the ground state of alkali metal vapors was introduced (Dehmelt, 1957 a, b,

1958 a, b). Energy level crossing techniques were introduced (Franken, 1958b); the energy shift caused by the intensity of the pumping radiation was considered theoretically (Barrat, 1960) and measured experimentally (Cohen-Tannoudji, 1961 a, b, c); optical masers were proposed (Schawlow, 1958) and made to work (Maiman, 1961); and optical harmonic generation has been accomplished (Franken, 1961b).

In the following pages the fundamental concepts of some of these experiments will be described. However, the emphasis will be on those experiments that yield information about the energy levels of the ground and excited states of the systems considered.

2 / The Optical Pumping Experiment

2–1 A SIMPLE EXAMPLE

(handwritten:) δm = 1, A → D,
(pumping; apply H₀, eventually pump to B,
all same orientation. no absorption - transparent.
atoms)

In order to describe the optical pumping process, we shall first make a few simplifying assumptions which will later be removed. In this example, we shall consider an alkali metal atom which has a $^2S_{1/2}$ ground state and $^2P_{1/2}$ and $^2P_{3/2}$ excited states. The optical transitions between the ground state and these two excited states give rise to the D_1 and D_2 lines, respectively, of alkali metal atomic spectra. For some cases, the D_2 line can be removed from a source of light by means of an interference filter. We shall assume this to be the case for our example.

If an alkali metal atom is placed in a magnetic field H_0, and if the nuclear spin is neglected, the energy levels of the atom pertinent to D_1 spectral lines will be as shown in Figure 2-1. The spin magnetic moment of the valence electron will interact with the magnetic field with energy:

$$E = g\beta H_0 m_S \qquad (2\text{-}1)$$

(handwritten:) $\beta = \dfrac{\hbar e}{2mc}$

where g is the Lande g-factor, β is the Bohr magneton, and m_S is the magnetic quantum number of the atomic state, having a value of $\pm\frac{1}{2}$ for this example.

Next, consider the experimental arrangement shown schematically in Figure 2-2 and which is typical of one method, originally introduced by Dehmelt (1957a), of optically pumping alkali metal atoms. The vapor cell, usually made from a 250-ml flask, is illuminated by a spectral lamp which emits the D_1, D_2 resonance doublet

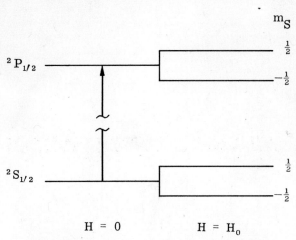

Figure 2-1 Energy levels of a hypothetical
atom with a $^2S_{1/2}$ ground state
and a $^2P_{1/2}$ excited state.

of the alkali metal atom being studied. The light is collimated or focused with
lenses through an interference filter where the D_2 component is attenuated, and
through a circular polarizer. The D_1 light then pases through the vapor cell
which contains the vapor of the alkali metal species. The cell is usually heated
to a temperature that will result in an alkali metal vapor pressure in the region

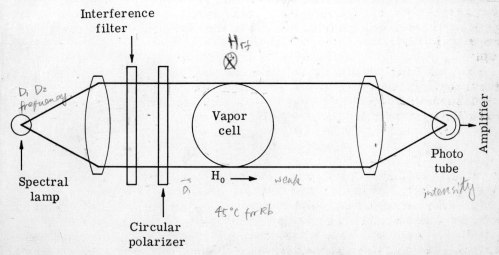

Figure 2-2 Schematic of an optical pumping apparatus that uses transmission detection.

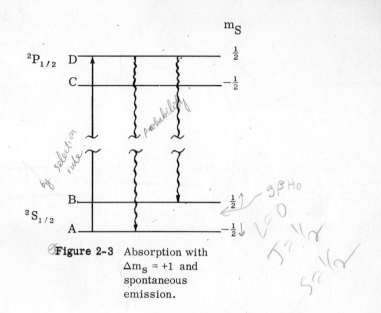

Figure 2-3 Absorption with
$\Delta m_S = +1$ and
spontaneous
emission.

of 10^{-5} mm Hg. Typical operating temperatures are 25°C for Cs, 45°C for Rb,
85°C for K, and 150°C for Na. The vapor cell is placed in a weak magnetic field,
H_0, which is directed along the direction of the light path. The intensity of the D_1
resonance radiation passing through the apparatus can be measured with the photo
tube.

What is the effect of the circularly polarized D_1 radiation upon the atoms in
the vapor cell with the above experimental arrangement? The well-known result
is that the atoms will be excited to the $^2P_{1/2}$ state with a selection rule of
$\Delta m_S = \pm 1$. Furthermore, the selection rule will be either $\Delta m_S = +1$ or
$\Delta m_S = -1$ but not both. Which one holds will depend upon the direction of the
magnetic field with respect to the direction of propagation of the light and the
direction of circular polarization. If the electric vector of the light portrays a
right-handed helix, the light is said to be right circularly polarized. This type
of circularly polarized light is given the notation σ^+ if it produces $\Delta m_S = +1$
transitions.

Inspection of Figure 2-1 reveals that there is only one possible excitation that
can take place; this is shown in Figure 2-3. Excitation with $\Delta m_S = +1$ can occur only from energy level A to energy level D. The lifetimes of the $^2P_{1/2}$ states
of alkali metal atoms are typically of the order of 10^{-8} sec. If we assume that no
disorientation occurs in the excited state of the atom (i.e., that state C is not populated) the atom will fluoresce from state D to states A and B with equal transition probability. For an assembly of atoms the net effect in time will be a transfer of population from state A to state B.

Before the pumping radiation is turned on, the relative populations of states A and B are given by the Boltzmann distribution:

$$\frac{n_B}{n_A} = \exp\left[-(E_B - E_A)/kT\right]$$

which in a typical case gives an excess of about 1 part in 10^6 in state A over state B at room temperature for weak magnetic fields. After the pumping radiation is turned on $n_B \gg n_A$, and the final relative population will be determined by such parameters as the pumping light intensity, relative transition probabilities, and the relaxation time. A concentration of atoms in state B corresponds to a net orientation of the angular momentum of the atoms. The process described above is one example of optical pumping, the pumping being a transfer of atoms from one energy level to another.

2–2 MAGNETIC RESONANCES $\begin{array}{c}AC\\(RF \perp H_0)\end{array}$ ← ~1 gauss

The intensity of light passing through the apparatus in Figure 2-2 will be a function of the amount of orientation of the atoms in the vapor cell. If 100% of the atoms were optically pumped into state B the alkali metal vapor would no longer be able to absorb the D_1 radiation, and the bulb would become transparent. When states A and B are occupied according to their normal Boltzmann distribution, the vapor will absorb the circularly polarized resonance radiation, and the vapor cell will become opaque to the pumping radiation. Thus, one can detect the amount of orientation by simply observing the intensity of D_1 light passing through the apparatus.

If an oscillating magnetic field is applied perpendicular to H_0 and if the frequency of the oscillating field is

$$\nu_0 = \frac{g\beta H_0}{h} \tag{2-3}$$

i.e., the Larmor frequency of the alkali atom, transitions between states A and B can take place. This frequency will fall in the radiofrequency region if H_0 is of the order of 1 gauss. If the radiofrequency radiation is very intense the occupations of states A and B are equalized and the systems of spin energy levels are said to be saturated.

Since the application of the radiofrequency field causes the population of state A to increase, more D_1 resonance radiation will be absorbed, and the bulb will appear to be opaque. If the frequency of the oscillating field is varied and the intensity of D_1 light passing through the apparatus monitored, one will observe the intensity vs. frequency dependence as shown in Figure 2-4. An absorption

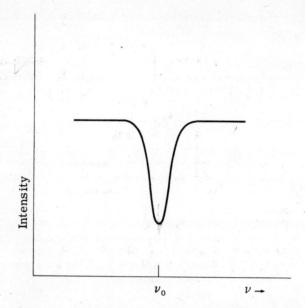

Figure 2-4 Magnetic resonance observed in the intensity of light transmitted through the optical pumping apparatus.

@ ν_0. most B → A, need absorb more light to pump atom to sta align orientation.

of light corresponding to a transition between states A and B will be observed. The central frequency of this line, ν_0, can be measured with high accuracy. The above experiment, then, is a way of performing radiofrequency spectroscopy.

2—3   A MORE GENERAL EXAMPLE

One of the simplifications of the above example was that the ground state of the atom consisted of only two levels — the Zeeman levels of the electron-spin magnetic moment interacting with an externally applied magnetic field. More often, the nucleus of the atom will also have spin angular momentum, and the magnetic sublevels of the ground state of the atom are more complicated. In the case of weak external magnetic fields the sublevels are described in terms of F and m_F, where F is the total angular momentum of an atom and m_F is its projection along an external magnetic field.

As an example, we shall consider an atom with nuclear spin $I = \frac{3}{2}$ and electron spin $S = \frac{1}{2}$ (Na^{23}, Rb^{87}). Here, F = I ± S, and the sublevels of the ground state are shown in Figure 2-5 for the atom in a weak magnetic field. Optical pumping can cause population differences between m_F states and between F states. There is now the opportunity of observing transitions between m_F states

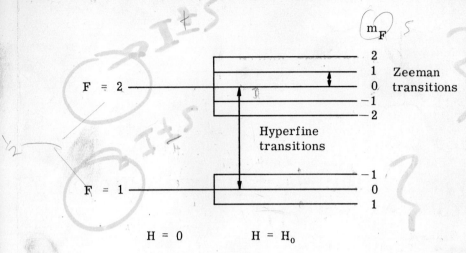

Figure 2-5   Magnetic sublevels of an electronic state of an atom with $L = 0$, $S = \frac{1}{2}$, and $I = \frac{3}{2}$. A positive nuclear moment is assumed.

(Zeeman transitions) and between F states (hyperfine transitions) by applying radio or microwave radiation of the correct frequency to the vapor cell and observing the transmitted light intensity. A discussion of the energy levels and their variation with applied magnetic field is given in Chapter 5.

The extent of the optical pumping or orientation will depend upon several factors. All transitions from the ground-state magnetic sublevels to the excited states must be considered along with their relative transition probabilities. In addition, there exists the possibility of disorientation of the atom in the excited state. Two extreme situations, complete disorientation and no disorientation in the excited state, have been considered by various workers (Franzen, 1957; Hawkins, 1955, 1961). Another factor that influences the extent of orientation is the relaxation among the magnetic sublevels of the ground state. Also, effects arising from the spectral line shape of the pumping radiation must be considered. In the following sections these various contributions to the more general case will be discussed more fully.

3 / The Dynamics of Optical Pumping

3—1 PUMPING AND RELAXATION IN GROUND STATES

We are interested in examining how the occupation of a given magnetic sublevel of the ground state of an atom changes with time. There are two simultaneous rate processes which must be considered: pumping and relaxation. If we let b_{ij} be the probability that the atom will be optically transferred from sublevel i to sublevel j, and w_{ij} be the probability that the atom will be relaxed from sublevel i to sublevel j, then the rate of change of the population of state R will be given by

$$\frac{dn_R}{dt} = + \sum_{i=1}^{Q}{}' (b_{iR} + w_{iR})n_i$$
$$- \sum_{j=1}^{Q}{}' (b_{Rj} + w_{Rj})n_R \tag{3-1}$$

where n_R is the occupation probability of state R, and it is normalized such that

$$\sum_{R=1}^{Q} n_R = 1 \tag{3-2}$$

The summation indices i and j are over the magnetic sublevels of the ground

10

electronic state of the atom which are Q in number. The prime on the summation signs indicates that the terms for $j = R$ and $i = R$ are omitted from the sums. This merely means that processes which take an atom from state R and return it to state R do not change the population of state R.

The first sum in Eq. 3-1 gives the rate at which atoms arrive in state R, whereas the second sum gives the rate at which they leave state R. Equation 3-1 exists simultaneously for each magnetic sublevel, R, of the ground state of the atom. If there are Q sublevels then the set of Eqs. 3-1 plus 3-2 gives $Q - 1$ independent equations. If the transition probabilities b_{ij} and w_{ij} are known the time development of the occupation probability of each state can be computed (Franzen, 1957).

The average probability that the atom will absorb light will be given by

$$B = \frac{1}{Q} \sum_R \sum_j b_{Rj} n_R \qquad (3-3)$$

At thermal equilibrium the n_R's are all nearly equal and Eq. 3-3 can be written

$$B_0 = \frac{1}{Q} \sum_R \sum_j b_{Rj} \qquad (3-4)$$

B_0 is now the average absorption probability per unit time per atom for the non-pumped species. When the atoms have been pumped to a certain degree their absorption will be given by Eq. 3-3. B_0 is a function of the initial light intensity and can be estimated from classical dispersion theory.

In order to obtain the detailed time development of the occupation probabilities of the sublevels, several approximations have to be introduced.

The first of these has to do with the relaxation probabilities in Eq. 3-1. The simplest assumption to make is that the w_{ij} are all equal. Then for each w_{ij} in Eq. 3-1

$$w = \frac{1}{QT_1} \qquad (3-5)$$

where T_1 is the spin-lattice relaxation time for the system, and Q is the total number of magnetic sublevels of the system.

In the absence of optical pumping radiation

$$\frac{dn_R}{dt} = \frac{-1}{T_1}(n_R - 1/Q) \qquad (3-6)$$

In the presence of optical pumping radiation the final time-dependent equations will also be dependent upon whether or not reorientation takes place in the excited state of the atom. The equations can be written down for two cases: (1) no re-orientation in the excited state of the atom and (2) complete reorientation in the excited state (Franzen, 1957). The general equation which holds for both cases is found by using Eq. 3-5 and 3-1:

$$\frac{dn_R}{dt} = - \sum_{j=1}^{Q}{}' b_{Rj} n_R + \sum_{i=1}^{Q}{}' b_{iR} n_i - \frac{n_R}{T_1} + \frac{1}{QT_1} \qquad (3-7)$$

The b_{ij} are then computed according to whether reorientation or no reorientation occurs in the excited state.

The time development of n_R has been solved for a $I = \frac{3}{2}$, $J = \frac{1}{2}$ system, which is the case for Na^{23} (Franzen, 1957), and for a $I = \frac{7}{2}$, $J = \frac{1}{2}$ system, which is the case for Cs^{133} (Hawkins, 1961). In these papers graphs show quite clearly how the population for each state changes as a function of time for each of the two reorientation cases.

3—2 ORIENTATION AND ALIGNMENT

The distribution of atoms among the magnetic sublevels of the ground state is determined by Eq. 3-7 and by the b_{ij}. The b_{ij}, in turn, are determined by the various matrix elements for absorption and emission of the resonance radiation. These will depend upon the given experimental conditions, i.e., whether circularly or linearly polarized light is used, and the direction of magnetic fields at the absorption cell. Therefore, it is not too surprising that a variety of distributions can be obtained with different experimental conditions. These fall into the two main categories mentioned previously: (1) orientation and (2) alignment.

In optical orientation the atoms are pumped in one direction only with regard to the sign of m_F. The atoms can be concentrated in either the $m_F = +F$ level or the $m_F = -F$ level depending upon whether σ^+ or σ^- excitation is utilized. The result of orientation is a net angular momentum of the sample along the light beam. The sample of oriented atoms can also be conveniently characterized by a magnetization.

In optical alignment the atoms are pumped into the highest and lowest m_F levels simultaneously. In this case the net angular momentum along the light beam is zero, and there is no net magnetization.

For the special case of $Q = 2$, optical alignment techniques are not very useful because the most one would be able to do would be to equalize the populations of the two levels; no large population differences would be possible. For $Q = 2$ and optical orientation, Eq. 3-1 takes the form:

$$\frac{dn_A}{dt} = -(b_{AB} + w_{AB})n_A + (b_{BA} + w_{BA})n_B \tag{3-8}$$

$$\frac{dn_B}{dt} = -(b_{BA} + w_{BA})n_B + (b_{AB} + w_{AB})n_A$$

where the level notation of Figure 2-3 has been used. Neglecting the small Boltzmann difference in population at thermal equilibrium, one obtains in the absence of pumping

$$\frac{dn_A}{dt} = \frac{1}{T_1}(n_A - \tfrac{1}{2}) \tag{3-9}$$

and in the presence of pumping

$$dn_A/dt = b_{BA}n_B - n_A/T_1 - b_{AB}n_A + \frac{1}{2T_1} \tag{3-10}$$

A similar set of equations holds for dn_B/dt. If the transition probabilities b_{AB} and b_{BA} are known, the equations can be solved for $n_A(t)$ or $n_B(t)$. After a time long compared to the "optical pumping time," τ, a "stationary state" is reached where dn_A/dt and dn_B/dt are both equal to zero, and the Eqs. 3-8 become

$$\frac{n_A}{n_B} = \frac{1 + 2T_1 b_{BA}}{1 + 2T_1 b_{AB}} \tag{3-11}$$

If $b_{AB} = b_{BA}$, optical orientation cannot occur since the ratio n_A/n_B would be unity. In order for optical pumping to take place $b_{AB} \neq b_{BA}$. Two factors will influence the relative magnitudes of b_{AB} and b_{BA}. These will be (1) the matrix elements connecting the sublevels of the ground electronic state with those of the excited electronic state and (2) the amount of reorientation that occurs while the atom is in the excited electronic state.

For the special example illustrated in Figure 2-3 where only atoms in one of the ground state sublevels are excited and where no disorientation takes place in the excited state, i.e., $b_{BA} = 0$, Eq. 3-11 becomes

$$\frac{n_A}{n_B} = \frac{1}{1 + 2T_1 b_{AB}} \tag{3-12}$$

Here again we see that the population difference between levels A and B becomes larger as T_1 becomes longer. In the case for which Eq. 3-12 holds the transition probability b_{AB} can be replaced by an alternative notation, $1/\tau$, where τ is called the "optical pumping time." Equation 3-12 with this notation becomes

$$\frac{n_A}{n_B} = \frac{1}{1 + (2T_1/\tau)} \tag{3-13}$$

and holds for the steady-state situation. The optical pumping time, then, is associated with the relative transition probabilities between the sublevels of the ground and excited electronic states of the system and the reorientation processes that result from collisions of the atom while it is the excited state.

3—3 OPTICAL PUMPING OF EXCITED STATES

The orientation or alignment of an excited state can be accomplished in two ways. One way is to first populate the excited state and then carry out a pumping scheme similar to that just described for ground states utilizing some still higher excited state. Alternatively, the orientation or alignment can be produced by the same radiation that is used to populate the excited state.

An example of the first procedure is the optical pumping of helium in the $2\,^3S_1$ metastable state (Colegrove, 1960). In this experiment helium atoms are excited from the $2\,^3S_1$ to the $2\,^3P$ states as shown in Figure 3-1. Even if the atoms are redistributed among the $2\,^3P$ states before making the transition back to the $2\,^3S_1$ state, an inequality in population distribution of the $2\,^3S_1$ sublevels can be achieved, those levels with the smallest absorption probability having the highest population. If unpolarized resonance radiation is used, optical alignment in the $2\,^3S_1$ state is produced. This experiment has been used for a magnetic-field stabilizing device (Schearer, 1961), a very sensitive magnetometer, and, more recently, to produce nuclear polarization in He^3 (Colegrove, 1963).

The second type of optical pumping in an excited state is illustrated by the important case of mercury. The very first optical pumping experiment was with mercury vapor (Brossel, 1950, 1952a). Since that time the case of mercury has been exhaustively examined. A typical experimental configuration for the optical pumping of mercury is shown schematically in Figure 3-2. Mercury vapor is irradiated with resonance radiation polarized in the direction of the magnetic field at the vapor cell. The π radiation emitted at right angles to both the incident radiation and the magnetic field passes through an analyzing prism, and its intensity can be measured with a photomultiplier tube. The π resonance radiation causes excitations in which there is no change of components of angular momentum, $\Delta m = 0$. In this way only specific sublevels of the excited state are populated as illustrated in Figure 3-3 for the case of the even isotopes of mercury, i.e., those which have no nuclear spin. The emitted radiation from the $^3P_1$ state is polarized in the same direction as the incident radiation. If a

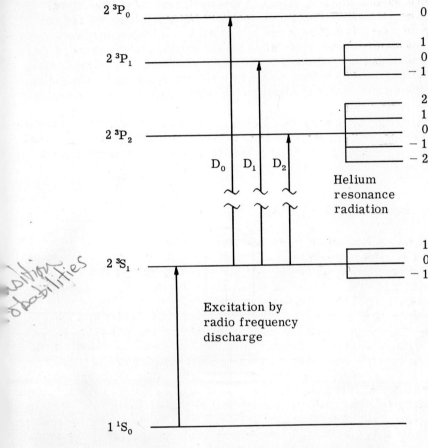

Figure 3-1 Energy levels of the helium atom
pertinent to optical pumping in the
$2\,^3S_1$ state.

transition is produced between magnetic sublevels of the excited state with an applied radiofrequency field, the emitted radiation will contain some σ light, coming
from the $m_J = \pm 1$ states, and the intensity of the π fluorescence from the $m_J = 0$
state will be diminished. This change in intensity of emitted π radiation is, then,
a way of detecting magnetic resonances in the excited state of mercury.

The optical pumping of excited states and the detection of magnetic resonances
has been accomplished in other substances as well. The nuclear electric quadrupole moment of Zn^{67} has been determined by optical methods in the $4\,^3P_1$
metastable state of zinc (Bochmann, 1957). Experiments have been performed on

excited states of singly ionized helium mainly for the purpose of determing the Lamb shift for that system (Series, 1958a). Experiments on the excited states of the alkali metals are usually done for the purpose of determining the nuclear electric quadrupole interaction and the nuclear electric quadrupole moment. Such an experiment is, of course, impossible for the ground state because of the spherical charge distribution of S-state atoms which produces no electric field gradient at the nucleus and, therefore, no nuclear electric quadrupole interaction. Experiments on the excited states of alkali metal vapors have been performed on

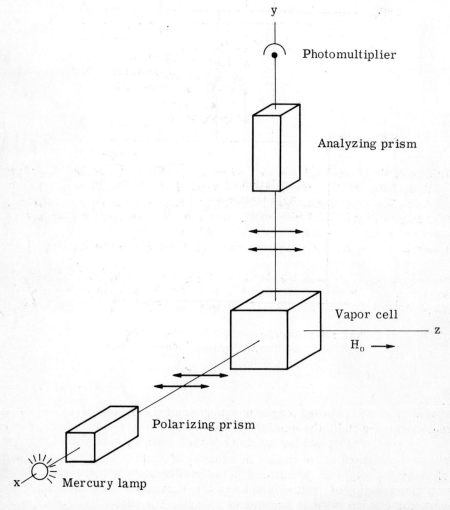

Figure 3-2 Schematic of an apparatus for the optical pumping of the mercury $^3P_1$ state.

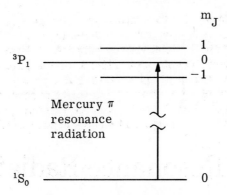

Figure 3-3   Energy levels pertinent to the optical pumping of the $^3P_1$ state of the even isotopes of mercury.

Na^{23} (Krüger, 1958; Sagalyn, 1954), K^{41} (Bucka, 1962a), Rb^{85} and Rb^{87} (K13), and Cs^{133} (Althoff, 1954, 1955; Krüger, 1955b; Bucka, 1956, 1958). It should also be mentioned that the experiments on excited states of atoms were also proposed for atomic beams (Rabi, 1952). Atomic beam experiments have been performed on excited states of Na^{23} (Perl, 1955), and K^{39} (Ritter, 1957).

The nuclear electric quadrupole interaction will be discussed in another section.

In this section we have presented only a very general discussion of the optical pumping process. The reader interested in a careful formalism in terms of the density matrix is referred to the excellent thesis by Cohen-Tannoudji (1962).

4 / Optical Resonance Radiation

4-1 RESONANCE FLUORESCENCE AND LINE FLUORESCENCE

The resonance fluorescence of atoms was first observed in sodium vapor by R. W. Wood about 60 years ago (Wood, 1913). The early explanation of this phenomenon was made on the basis of the classical theory of oscillators whereby light is scattered when its frequency is exactly in tune with a basic frequency of the scattering center. However, the classical theory could not explain the appearance of light of longer wavelengths than that of the exciting light in a fluorescence experiment. For example, it was inconsistent for sodium to emit the yellow D lines when illuminated with ultraviolet light. The advent of the Bohr theory and the concept of emission as a separate process distinct from absorption explained these as well as other anomalous observations in atomic spectra. Strictly speaking, resonance radiation is produced when an excited state of a system emits light by making a transition to the ground state of the system. This occurs for atoms where there is a single ground electronic state such as is the case for S-state atoms (Hg, Na, Ca, etc.), but for systems which have low-lying electronic states, as is usually the case for atoms with P ground states (Tl, Pb, etc.), both resonance radiation and line fluorescence occur. The resonance transition terminates in the ground state, and the line fluorescence occurs when the transition terminates in a state that lies above the ground state. For an S-state atom, irradiation by the resonance lines produces fluorescence of the same lines, whereas for a P-state atom, irradiation by one of the exciting lines will produce at least two lines in the fluorescence as shown in Figure 4-1.

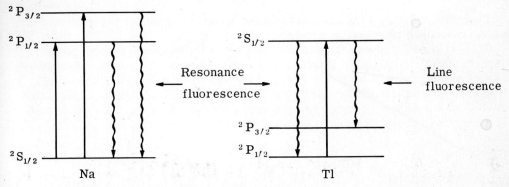

Figure 4-1 Examples showing the difference between resonance
fluorescence and line fluorescence.

An exception to our definition of resonance radiation might occur in the case
of an atom that has a metastable state. If this state is sufficiently well populated
one could have the same situation as described above for resonance radiation
where the metastable state is the lower terminus for a resonance transition.

In order to observe resonance fluorescence one needs a light source and a
cell containing the vapors of the substance which will absorb the light. This cell,
containing the vapors of the unexcited species is sometimes referred to as a
"resonance lamp." A typical experimental arrangement for observation of resonance fluorescence is diagrammed in Figure 4-2. The horn shape of the resonance
lamp, due to R. W. Wood, prevents internal reflections from complicating the observation of the resonance radiation. In Wood's early experiments with sodium,
the light source used for exciting the resonance radiation was a gas flame to which
a solution containing a sodium salt was added. This can be done by inserting into
the flame a piece of asbestos which has been soaked in a salt solution. In modern
experiments the light source is usually a discharge lamp which contains a few

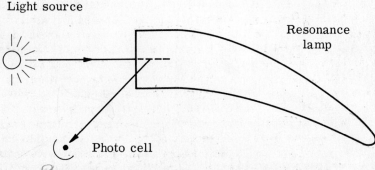

Figure 4-2 Observation of resonance fluorescence.

millimeters pressure of some inert gas and a small quantity of the element whose resonance radiation is required.

It is, of course, beyond the scope of this brief discussion to review all the aspects of resonance light. Instead, only a few topics of immediate consequence to optical pumping will be mentioned, and the reader is referred to the excellent work of Mitchell and Zemansky (1934) on the subject. In addition, a great deal of information concerning experiments with resonance light and about fluorescence and phosphorescence in general can be found in the book by Pringsheim (1949).

4–2 ABSORPTION OF OPTICAL RESONANCE RADIATION

For any spectral absorption line of a gas one can define an absorption coefficient $k(\nu)$ by the relation

$$I(\nu) = I_0 e^{-k(\nu)x} \tag{4-1}$$

where I is the intensity of light of frequency ν transmitted through the absorbing gas, I_0 is the incident light intensity, and x is the thickness of the absorbing

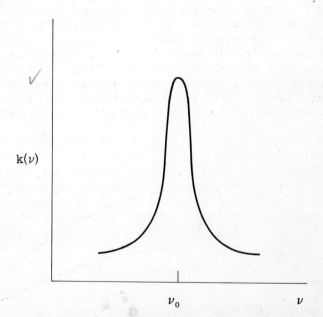

Figure 4-3 Absorption coefficient of a resonance
transition.

gas. If one examines $k(\nu)$ as a function of ν one obtains the absorption line shape as shown for an idealized case in Figure 4-3.

Using the Einstein theory of radiation the integral of the absorption coefficient, which determines the line intensity, is given by

$$\int k(\nu) \, d\nu = \frac{\lambda_0^2 g_2 N}{8\pi g_1 \tau} \tag{4-2}$$

where λ_0 is the wavelength of the center of the line; g_2 and g_1 are the statistical weights of the excited and ground states, respectively; N is the number of absorbing gas atoms per cubic centimeter; and τ is the lifetime of the excited state. The above integral is a constant for a fixed N and can be used to determine τ. However, most tables of spectral lines and transition probabilities describe the line intensity in terms of the oscillator strength, f, defined by a relation due to Landenburg:

$$f = \frac{mc\lambda_0^2 g_2}{8\pi^2 e^2 g_1 \tau} = \frac{mc}{\pi e^2 N} \int k(\nu) d\nu \tag{4-3}$$

where the additional constants are the mass of the electron, m; the speed of light, c; and the electronic charge, e. Again, the lifetime of the excited state may be obtained from a measurement of the oscillator strength. However, oscillator strengths and absorption coefficients are sometimes difficult to obtain unambiguously. One must be certain that the spectral line is not broadened by mechanisms other than that of the natural lifetime of the excited state. In the next section we mention some of these other mechanisms of line broadening.

4–3 BROADENING OF OPTICAL RESONANCE LINES

The success of an optical pumping experiment very often hinges on differences in the resonance line profile between the light source and the absorbing species. In order to obtain a high degree of orientation in the m_F energy levels of the ground state of an alkali metal atom one wishes to have maximum intensity of the circularly polarized exciting light at exactly the center of the absorbing gas line shape. For certain hyperfine pumping experiments, one hyperfine component in the exciting light must be filtered out. In general, one has to consider and make use of the various sources of broadening of resonance lines.

An arbitrary breakdown of the contributions to spectral line shapes and broadening is as follows:

   a. Uncertainty broadening due to the natural lifetime of the excited state of the atom;
   b. Doppler broadening due to the thermal motion of the gas;
   c. Lorenz broadening due to collisions with foreign buffer gases;
   d. Holtsmark broadening due to collisions with like atoms;

e. Stark broadening due to collisions with electrons and ions;
f. Zeeman broadening and splitting due to the presence of magnetic fields;
g. Hyperfine splitting.

A number of these contributions to the line width can be controlled by the experimental conditions. In the case of Doppler broadening a theoretical correction for its contribution can sometimes be made.

Under certain conditions where one has a dense gas the Doppler width of a magnetic dipole transition can be narrowed by the collisions between gas particles. This effect was calculated by Dicke (1953; see reprint) who found that when the mean free path of the gas is small compared to the wavelength of the transition, a normal Doppler distribution plus a sharp non-Doppler broadened line results. Very narrow lines are, indeed, found in magnetic resonances of gases and in hyperfine transitions in S-state atoms. This effect is present in solids and is also responsible for the narrow lines found in experiments with the Mössbauer effect. Recently, it has been shown that the collision narrowing also occurs in the optical spectra of gases (Rank, 1963).

Another spectral line narrowing process can occur in a system of atoms that has the upper energy level of the resonance transition more densely populated than the lower. This effect is observed in the emission from lasers and masers.

4—4 SELF-REVERSAL

A common occurrence in the production of resonance radiation by a discharge lamp is the self-reversal of the resonance lines. This usually happens when the lamp is too hot or if there is a high pressure of a foreign gas present in the lamp. A hypothetical self-reversed line profile is illustrated in Figure 4-4. In a situation where the excitation occurs in the central portion of a lamp the resonance light will be absorbed by unexcited atoms surrounding the excitation region. In addition, if the excitation region becomes very hot the resonance lines will be

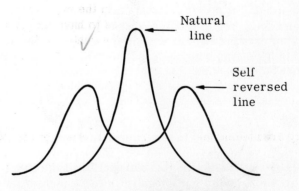

Figure 4-4 Self-reversal.

broadened. Sometimes cooling of the lamp will cause the discharge to be more uniformly distributed. It should be pointed out that only resonance lines, defined as above, will exhibit self-reversal. This fact was used by the early workers in identifying resonance spectral lines.

The production of intense, unreversed, resonance lines for an optical pumping experiment is a matter of considerable concern and has received some attention (Brewer, 1961; Franz, 1963a; Bell, 1961c). The self-reversal problem is quite serious with Rb, Cs, and Hg. If a commercial lamp is used it is helpful to blow air over the discharge bulb; if one makes one's own lamps, care should be taken to assure a clean interior. An inert gas is usually present inside the lamp to support the discharge. If the pressure of this gas is too high, the emitted spectral lines will be broadened. The pressure which gives the best results is a matter of trial and error, although some guides have been established by those who have studied this problem.

5 / Magnetic Interactions: Zeeman and Hyperfine Splitting

5–1 THE HAMILTONIAN

The investigation of the Zeeman and hyperfine structure of an atomic state of an atom by the optical pumping method differs from the atomic beam method mainly in detection techniques. Sometimes, the optical pumping experiment is a more simple approach. However, the analysis of the resulting radiofrequency spectrum proceeds along the same lines as in the atomic beam case.

The Zeeman and hyperfine interactions of an atom in an external magnetic field H_0 are described by the Hamiltonian

$$\mathcal{H} = a\mathbf{I} \cdot \mathbf{J} + g_J \beta \mathbf{J} \cdot \mathbf{H}_0 - g_I \beta_N \mathbf{I} \cdot \mathbf{H}_0 \tag{5-1}$$

where $\mathbf{J}$ is the total electron angular-momentum operator composed of the sum of the electron orbital angular momentum, $\mathbf{L}$, and the electron-spin angular momentum, $\mathbf{S}$. $\mathbf{I}$ is the nuclear-spin angular-momentum operator, g_J and g_I are the electronic and nuclear spectroscopic splitting factors, β and β_N are the Bohr and nuclear magnetons, and a is the hyperfine splitting constant. The evaluation of the energy level structure of the system is simplified for either very weak or very strong external magnetic fields, i.e., if either the Zeeman or the hyperfine terms dominate. When the two types of interaction are comparable, the complete secular equation for the system must be solved.

24

5–2 ENERGY LEVELS IN WEAK, STRONG, AND INTERMEDIATE MAGNETIC FIELDS

In very weak external magnetic fields, I and J are strongly coupled to form $F = I + J$ and the resultant m_F. The energy levels of the system are given in the Fm_F representation by

$$E(F, m_F) = \frac{a}{2}\lfloor F(F + 1) - I(I + 1) - J(J + 1)\rfloor$$

$$-\left[g_J\beta \frac{F(F + 1) + J(J + 1) - I(I + 1)}{2F(F + 1)} \right.$$

$$\left. + g_I\beta_N \frac{F(F + 1) + I(I + 1) - J(J + 1)}{2F(F + 1)} \right] m_F H_0 \qquad (5\text{-}2)$$

Sometimes the term in the energy expression proportional to $g_I\beta_N$ is neglected due to its small size.

In very strong external magnetic fields, I and J are not coupled, and the system is described in terms of the separate magnetic quantum numbers m_J and m_I.

$$E(m_J, m_I) = am_I m_J - g_J\beta m_J H_0 - g_I\beta_N m_I H_0 \qquad (5\text{-}3)$$

In the intermediate case the appropriate secular equation can be solved in either the F, m_F representation or the m_J, m_I representation. A solution for the case of $J = \frac{1}{2}$ (alkali metal atoms) and arbitrary I is given by the Breit-Rabi formula:

$$E(F, m_F) = -\frac{a}{4} - g_I\beta_N m_F H_0$$

$$\pm \frac{a}{4}(2I + 1)\sqrt{1 + \frac{4m_F}{2I + 1}x + x^2} \qquad (5\text{-}4)$$

where

$$x = \frac{2H_0(g_I\beta_N - g_J\beta)}{a(2I + 1)}$$

The (+) sign in Eq. 5-4 is used for $F = I + \frac{1}{2}$, and the (−) sign for $F = I - \frac{1}{2}$.

An example of the energy level structure of an atom with $J = \frac{1}{2}$ and $I = \frac{3}{2}$ and g_I positive is shown in Figure 5-1. This is the level structure one would expect from a Na^{23} atom.

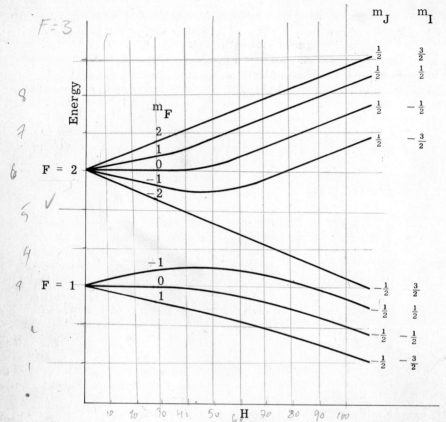

Figure 5-1 Magnetic sublevels of an atom with $J = \frac{1}{2}$ and $I = \frac{3}{2}$ and positive g_I as a function of magnetic field strength, H. Both the F, m_F and the m_J, m_I representations are used to label the energy levels.

If J is greater than $\frac{1}{2}$ or if there are other interactions present, such as the nuclear electric quadrupole interaction, the derivation of the energy levels is complex. The quadrupole coupling interaction will be treated in the next chapter.

5—3 DETERMINATION OF HYPERFINE CONSTANTS, g-FACTORS, AND NUCLEAR SPINS BY OPTICAL PUMPING

As described earlier, optical pumping can be used to produce an orientation or an alignment in the m_F states. It can also be used to populate preferentially one of the hyperfine states. With an oscillator of the appropriate frequency, Zeeman transitions or hyperfine transitions can be induced and can be detected optically. If the frequency of the oscillator is measured with an electronic counter the energy of the transition can be accurately determined. By performing experiments at different applied magnetic fields the unknown parameters in the preceding energy level expressions can be determined. The unknown parameters are usually one or more of the quantities a, g_I, g_J, and I.

The Hamiltonian as written in Eq. 5-1 represents the sum of the hyperfine interaction, the Zeeman interaction of the electronic moment (spin plus orbital), and the Zeeman interaction of the nuclear magnetic moment. The nuclear g-factor, g_I, and spin I are constants for a given nucleus in its ground state. The electronic g-factor, g_J, for a given atomic state characterized by a value of J is usually thought of as a constant quantity given approximately by the Lande formula

$$g_J = 1 + \frac{J(J + 1) + S(S + 1) - L(L + 1)}{2J(J + 1)} \tag{5-5}$$

On the other hand, the hyperfine coupling constant a is dependent upon the electronic wave function of the atom and is subject to any perturbations of the wave function that can occur. For atoms with an odd electron in states of zero orbital angular momentum, e.g., $^2S_{1/2}$ states, the hyperfine interaction is proportional to the amount of electron magnetic moment density at the nucleus. This is usually referred to as the Fermi contact interaction and is given by

$$a\,\mathbf{I} \cdot \mathbf{S} = \frac{16\pi}{3}\,g_J \beta g_I \beta_N\,\mathbf{I} \cdot \mathbf{S}\,\delta(r) \tag{5-6}$$

where the delta-function operator $\delta(r)$ picks out the value of the wave function at the nucleus, r = 0. For an atom with one unpaired s electron described by a wave function ψ_0 the energy levels results from Eq. 5-6 are

$$E(m_I) = \frac{8\pi\beta}{3}\,g_I \beta_N\,|\psi_0(r = 0)|^2\,m_F \tag{5-7}$$

If the unpaired electrons are not s electrons they will not have any electron magnetic moment density at the nucleus. However, there will be an electron orbital magnetic moment which, along with the electron-spin magnetic moment, will produce a direct dipole-dipole interaction with the nucleus. In addition, the unpaired electrons can interact with the filled inner shells of s electrons to produce an unpaired moment density at the nucleus. A rigorous evaluation of this latter "core polarization" effect can be quite complicated, but an approximate formula for the hyperfine coupling constant due to dipolar interactions can be derived in a semiclassical fashion (Ramsey, 1956, p. 74).

$$a = \beta\,\frac{\mu_I}{I}\,\frac{2L(L + 1)\langle\psi_0|1/r^3|\psi_0\rangle}{J(J + 1)}$$

$$\tag{5-8}$$

$$= \frac{hcR_y\,\alpha^2 Z^3 g_I}{n^3(L + \frac{1}{2})J(J + 1)(M/m)}$$

where n is the principal quantum number, R_y is the Rydberg constant $(me^4/4\pi\hbar^3 c)$, α is the fine structure constant, M/m is the proton-electron mass ratio, and Z is the nuclear charge.

As will be seen in a later section, perturbation of the wave function by nearby molecules or atoms can cause a change in the hyperfine constant. These changes yield information about the intermolecular interaction energies between optically pumped species and buffer species.

6 / Electric Interactions: Nuclear Electric Quadrupole and Stark Splitting

6–1 NUCLEAR ELECTRIC QUADRUPOLE COUPLING CONSTANTS

Nuclei with spin angular momentum $I \geq 1$ can possess a nuclear electric quadrupole moment, Q, which is a measure of the departure from spherical symmetry of the nuclear charge distribution. The nuclear electric quadrupole moment can undergo an electrostatic interaction with any surrounding electronic charges that are present, resulting in a quantization of the components of nuclear-spin angular momentum with respect to the surrounding charge distribution. The form of the interaction energy is such that it vanishes if the surrounding distribution of charges has tetrahedral, cubic, or spherical symmetry. Thus, for an alkali metal atom with a nucleus having an electric quadrupole moment, there will be no quadrupole interaction in the ground or S state, but there is the possibility for a finite interaction in some excited non-S states. This interaction energy is usually expressed in terms of a nuclear electric quadrupole coupling constant, e^2qQ, where e is the electronic charge, Q is the nuclear electric quadrupole moment, and q is the electric field gradient at the nucleus. In actual fact the nuclear electric quadrupole moment and the electric field gradient are tensor quantities, but we deal here with scalar quantities which are related to the irreducible components of the nuclear electric quadrupole moment and electric field gradient tensors. Q is a constant quantity for a given nucleus in its ground state, but q is a function of the electronic wave function for the particular atomic state being considered. In a molecule, q at the site of a given nucleus would be a function of the electronic distribution about that nucleus due to nonbonding electrons, bonding electrons, and other nuclear charges.

6—2　ELECTRIC FIELD GRADIENTS IN ATOMS

In an atom where the field gradient arises solely from one electron, q is axially symmetric and can be calculated from

$$q = - \int \psi * \frac{(3 \cos^2 \theta - 1)}{r^3} \psi \, d\tau \qquad (6\text{-}1)$$

where ψ is the electronic wave function defined for the state $m_J = J$. The angular factors in Eq. 6-1 cause $q = 0$ for the $^2S_{1/2}$ and $^2P_{1/2}$ states but do yield a finite value of q in the $^2P_{3/2}$ state.

In order to determine experimentally a nuclear electric quadrupole moment it is not only necessary to know the coupling constant e^2qQ, but also the electric field gradient q. In the alkali metal atoms the quadrupole coupling constant is usually measured in the $^2P_{3/2}$ state. However, the field gradient at the nucleus calculated for a single p-valence electron is not the true field gradient. Besides a small relativistic correction (Casimir, 1936) there is an effect which comes from the filled inner shells of electrons in the atom. A filled inner shell would be expected to make zero contributions to q. However, the nuclear electric quadrupole moment can induce a quadrupole moment in these inner shells of electrons which, in turn, interacts with the field gradient due to the valence electron. The total effect of the inner shells is one of shielding or antishielding (depending upon the sign of the effect) of the field gradient due to a valence electron. This effect has been examined by Sternheimer (1956) who finds that the effective field gradient seen by the nucleus is equal to that given by Eq. 6-1 multiplied by a correction factor $[1 - \gamma(R)]$, where $\gamma(R)$ is called the ''quadrupole antishielding factor.'' The aforementioned quadrupole coupling constant would then be expressed as $[1 - \gamma(R)] e^2qQ$ if q is to retain the definition given in Eq. 6-1. Values of $\gamma(R)$ must be obtained by a calculation and require a knowledge of the atomic wave functions.

6—3　DETERMINATION OF NUCLEAR ELECTRIC
　　　QUADRUPOLE MOMENTS

In the determination of Q from a measurement of the quadrupole coupling constant one must know both q and $[1 - \gamma(R)]$. Any uncertainty in either q or

$\lfloor 1 - \gamma(R) \rfloor$ will be reflected by an uncertainty in Q. In order to test the reliability of a quadrupole moment determination one can measure the coupling constant in two different electronic states of an atom, calculate $\gamma(R)$ and q for each state, and examine the two resulting values of Q for consistency.

The quadrupole coupling constant can be determined in the excited states of atoms by optical pumping methods. The experimental arrangement is essentially that described in Chapter 3 for the case of mercury. The energy level separations in the excited state are determined by observing the polarization of resonance fluorescence when a radio or microwave frequency oscillating field is applied to the optically pumped atoms. A change in polarization of the fluorescence is observed when the applied oscillating field is in resonance with one of the transitions between the sublevels of the excited state of the atom. Early work of this nature was performed on the $^2P_{3/2}$ state of sodium (Sagalyn, 1954). Numerous other elements have been examined by Kopfermann, Bucka, and co-workers at Heidelberg.

6—4 ENERGY LEVELS

With the addition of the nuclear electric quadrupole interaction the Hamiltonian for the atom becomes

$$\mathcal{H} = a\mathbf{I}\cdot\mathbf{J} - g_J\beta\mathbf{J}\cdot\mathbf{H}_0 - g_I\beta_N\mathbf{I}\cdot\mathbf{H}_0$$

$$+ \frac{b3\mathbf{I}\cdot\mathbf{J}(2\mathbf{I}\cdot\mathbf{J} + 1) - I(I + 1)J(J + 1)}{4I(2I - 1)J(2J - 1)} \tag{6-2}$$

where the first three terms on the right have the same definition as given in Eq. 5-1, b is the quadrupole coupling constant, and I and J are the nuclear-spin and total electron angular momentum of the atom, respectively. Often, the terms in Eq. 6-2 can be of comparable magnitude which precludes the use of simple first-order perturbation theory in the derivation of the energy levels of the atom. In such a case the complete secular equation must be solved. On the other hand, when one of the terms is very large or small compared to the others the problem can be treated by perturbation theory. In the case where the hyperfine interaction and quadrupole interactions are comparable and where there are no externally applied magnetic fields the expression for the energy levels becomes (Davis, 1949)

$$E(F) = \frac{aC}{2} + b\frac{3}{8}\left[\frac{C(C+1) - I(I+1)J(J+1)}{I(2I-1)J(2J-1)}\right] \tag{6-3}$$

where $C = F(F+1) - I(I+1) - J(J+1)$. A measurement of the energy level separations would enable one to determine a and b in Eq. 6-3.

A complicating factor that can arise is the broadening of the energy states by the very short lifetime of the excited electronic state of the atom. This lifetime broadening can interfere with the accuracy of the measurement and in some cases prevent the experiment from being performed at all.

6—5 STARK EFFECT

The magnetic sublevels of an atom can also be split by an electric field or Stark effect. The additional term which must be added to the Hamiltonian when an electric field E_z is present is

$$\mathcal{H}_s = e E_z \sum_i z_i \qquad (6\text{-}4)$$

where e is the electronic charge and z_i is the z component of $\mathbf{r}_i$, the position vector of the i-th electron. In the situation where all the other interactions that have been discussed above are either very large or very small compared to $\mathcal{H}_s$, the Stark effect may be treated with perturbation theory. When this is done for atoms where the ℓ degeneracy has been lifted, i.e., for noncentral Coulomb field atoms, the first-order energy correction is zero and the Stark effect appears in second order, the change in energy being dependent only on the absolute value of m_J:

$$\Delta E \left(|m_J| \right) = e^2 E_z \sum_{n,J} \frac{|<0|\Sigma_i z_i|n,J>|^2}{E(0) - E(n,J)} \qquad (6\text{-}5)$$

for an atom whose magnetic sublevels can be described in the m_J representation.

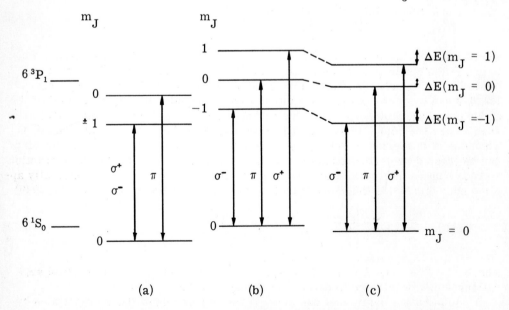

(a)   (b)   (c)

Figure 6-1 (a) Stark splitting of the energy levels of a mercury atom with nuclear spin I = 0. (b) Zeeman splitting. (c) Zeeman splitting plus weak Stark effect.

The summation over n and J represents a sum over all excited states of the atom. When the Stark effect becomes comparable to one of the other interactions that splits magnetic sublevels the complete secular equation must be solved.

Optical pumping has been used to investigate the $6\ ^3P_1$ state of the mercury atom in an electric field (Blamont, 1954, 1956, 1957a,b). The actual experiment was performed in parallel electric and magnetic fields which produce the energy level splitting shown in Figure 6-1. If a magnetic resonance is observed, using the method described for mercury in Section 7-4 in the next chapter, the resonance line will be split into two lines separated by an energy of 2ϵ, where

$$\epsilon = \Delta E\ (m_J = 0) - \Delta E\ (m_J = 1) \tag{6-6}$$

The case where a hyperfine interaction is also present in addition to the Zeeman and Stark effects has also been treated (Blamont, 1957b).

7 / Magnetic Resonance Detection

7—1 THE MAGNETIC RESONANCE CONDITION

Many applications of optical pumping involve the detection of a radio or micro-wave frequency resonance. Measurement of this frequency allows one to deter-mine a hyperfine, quadrupole, Zeeman, or Stark interaction. Consequently, a few words are in order concerning the magnetic resonance condition, methods of de-tection, and the effect of oscillating magnetic fields upon the energy level separa-tions themselves.

With the discovery of nuclear and electron magnetic resonance in bulk material shortly after World War II the subject of magnetic resonances received widespread attention and led to developments in physics and chemistry of far-reaching impor-tance. The development and basic theory of magnetic resonances can be found in numerous places. Three recent books (Abragam, 1961; Pake, 1962; Slichter, 1963) are recommended to the reader as sources. Much of the discussion of nuclear and electron resonance phenomena can be carried over directly to their counterpart in optical pumping phenomena.

In a magnetic resonance experiment one is concerned with the reorientation of a component of angular momentum of a species by allowing it to interact with an oscillating magnetic field. If the frequency of the oscillating magnetic field is in resonance with an energy level separation of the species, transitions between the levels can occur. The probabilities of the transitions will follow the magnetic di-pole selection rules and will be given by the usual result from first-order perturba-tion theory:

$$W_{m \to m'} = \gamma^2 H_1^2 \,|\langle\, m' \,|M_x|\, m \,\rangle|^2 \left| \frac{1 - e^{-i\,\Delta\omega t}}{\Delta\omega} \right|^2 \qquad (7\text{-}1)$$

where $W_{m \to m'}$ is the transition probability per unit time from state m to state m', H_1 is the amplitude of the oscillating magnetic field, γ is the magnetogyric ratio, M_x is the operator corresponding to the x component of angular momentum, and $\Delta\omega$ is given by

$$\Delta\omega = \omega - \omega_0 \qquad (7\text{-}2)$$

where ω is the frequency of H_1 and ω_0 is the frequency corresponding to the energy level separation. The resonance condition is satisfied for $\omega = \omega_0$.

The classical discussion of magnetic resonance starts with the equation of motion of a magnetic moment μ in a magnetic field $\mathbf{H}$. This is obtained by equating the torque exerted on the magnetic moment to the rate of change of angular momentum, $\mathbf{M}$, of the system:

$$\frac{d\mathbf{M}}{dt} = \mathbf{T} = \mu \times \mathbf{H} \qquad (7\text{-}3)$$

The ratio of magnetic moment to angular momentum is the magnetogyric ratio γ which, when substituted into Eq. 7-3, yields

$$\frac{d\mu}{dt} = \mu \times (\gamma\mathbf{H}) \qquad (7\text{-}4)$$

This equation describes the precession of the magnetic moment about the direction of the magnetic field.

In a magnetic resonance experiment the magnetic field $\mathbf{H}$ is composed of a static magnetic field $\mathbf{H}_0$ and an oscillating magnetic field $\mathbf{H}_1(t)$ which is a function of time. Upon introduction of $\mathbf{H}_0$ and $\mathbf{H}_1(t)$, Eq. 7-4 becomes

$$\frac{d\mu}{dt} = \mu \times \gamma[\,\mathbf{H}_0 + \mathbf{H}_1(t)\,] \qquad (7\text{-}5)$$

The magnetic moment now precesses about the resultant field composed of $\mathbf{H}_0$ and $\mathbf{H}_1(t)$. The resultant field is also time-dependent. When the frequency at which $\mathbf{H}_1(t)$ rotates about $\mathbf{H}_0$ is equal to the precessional frequency of the magnetic moment an additional torque is exerted on μ which turns it away from the direction of $\mathbf{H}_0$, and the resonance condition is satisfied. If the frequency of $\mathbf{H}_1(t)$ is different from the Larmor frequency the additional torque will vary with time according to the variation of the relative phases of $\mathbf{H}_1(t)$ and the precession of μ, and the resonance condition is not satisfied.

In order to proceed further with the classical description of magnetic resonance experiments it is useful to transform the equation of motion to a rotating coordinate system that rotates about the direction of H_0 with an angular frequency identical to that of $H_1(t)$. In this way the time dependence of H_1 can be eliminated and future mathematical manipulation simplified. This procedure is described in the references mentioned above.

7-2 OPTICAL DETECTION OF MAGNETIC RESONANCES

The role of optical pumping in magnetic resonance experiments is one of creating a situation which makes the detection of the resonance possible under conditions where other methods would fail or would not give accurate information. One factor that must be considered is the concentration of resonant species. In a conventional nuclear magnetic resonance experiment the sensitivity is limited to samples that have of the order of 10^{19} resonant nuclei per cubic centimeter or more. In electron resonance experiments the lower concentration limit is of the order of 10^{12} spins per cubic centimeter. Of course, these numbers are subject to resonance line-width and apparatus design consideration. In optical pumping experiments one can obtain a very high sensitivity. With improved techniques it would be possible to make measurements on systems with 10^6 species per cubic centimeter. The reason for this increased sensitivity is due to the double resonance nature of the experiment. One uses an optical transition to detect a radiofrequency transition, and the extinction coefficient of an optical resonance absorption is extremely high. Therefore, only a very small concentration of absorbing atoms is needed to detect a change in intensity or polarization of the resonance radiation.

Some of the detection schemes have been mentioned earlier in order to illustrate the principles of optical pumping. These plus some additional ways of studying magnetic resonances are summarized in Table 7-1. The techniques separate into two categories: optically pumped vapors and optically pumped atomic beams. Optical pumping of atomic beams is generally worth while for situations that are definitely not tractable by optical pumping of a vapor contained in an absorption cell. Such cases usually occur if the ground state of the atom being studied has a net electronic orbital angular momentum. An optical pumping experiment in which such an atom is placed in an absorption cell with a buffer gas to prevent wall collisions will generally fail owing to fast spin-relaxation processes.

Table 7-1   Methods of Detection of Magnetic Resonances in Optically Pumped Systems

Vapor cells	Transmitted radiation
	Scattered radiation; change in polarization
	Scattered radiation; change in frequency
	Modulation of a crossed light beam
	Modulation of pumping light
	Spin exchange
Atomic beams	Scattered radiation
	Beam intensity

Fast spin relaxation is encountered for these states because the electron orbital motion is easily perturbed by atomic collisions, and the spin angular momentum, being coupled to the orbital angular momentum, will also be affected strongly by collisions, providing a mechanism for relaxation. Such a resonance experiment must then be performed in a time short compared to the time between collisions of the species. This situation can be obtained in an atomic beam or in the case where the lifetime of the state being studied is very short. An example of a species that has been studied by both beam and vapor-cell methods is the $^2P_{3/2}$ state of Na where the nuclear electric quadrupole interaction was measured (Perl, 1955; Sagalyn, 1954). A brief summary of the methods listed in Table 7-1 follows.

7—3 TRANSMITTED RADIATION THROUGH VAPOR CELLS

This method which is due to Dehmelt (1957a) was described in Chapter 2. It marked a major advance in optical pumping techniques because it is simple and easy to use. Its application has been mainly to alkali metal atoms in their ground electronic state. In this experiment the intensity of circularly polarized radiation passing through a vapor cell is dependent upon the degree of orientation of the atomic species. At resonance the degree of orientation changes and, likewise, the intensity of transmitted light. This change can be detected with a photocell. Both Zeeman and hyperfine transitions can be studied in this way.

7—4 SCATTERED RADIATION FROM VAPOR CELLS; CHANGE IN POLARIZATION

This type of experiment is illustrated by the famous case of mercury also described in Chapter 2. The atoms are illuminated with π resonance radiation to produce pumping in the sublevels of the $^3P_1$ state. The intensity of scattered π radiation is monitored at 90° to the incident beam and is a measure of orientation of angular momentum in the $^3P_1$ state. At resonance $\Delta m = \pm 1$ transitions occur in the $^3P_1$ state resulting in a change in the intensity of the scattered π radiation. Since the early proposals by Kastler (1950, 1951) and the experiments by Brossel and Bitter (1952a; see reprint) this technique has been used for the studies of the mercury isotopes and for the excited states of the alkali metals, helium, zinc, cadmium, and some of the alkaline earth metals.

7—5 SCATTERED RADIATION; CHANGE IN FREQUENCY AND SELECTIVE READSORPTION

In some cases a microwave resonance can be detected by a change in frequency of the scattered light from an atomic system rather than a change in polarization.

The method depends upon the availability of sharp-line light sources and filters which have a narrow band width and uses selective readsoption principles. In one example of this method (Kohler, 1961) use was made of the optical resonance transition in Hg^{198} to excite a transition to the $F = \frac{3}{2}$ level of the $^3P_1$ state of Hg^{201}. The scattered light was passed through a filter cell filled with Hg^{198}. If transitions to the $F = \frac{5}{2}$ or $\frac{1}{2}$ states of Hg^{201} are induced by microwave radiation, the scattered light can pass through the Hg^{198} filter and be detected with a photomultiplier. This method has also been used by Bucka (1958) in an investigation of the $7\ ^2P_{1/2}$ level of cesium and for detection of resonances in solids by optical means (Geschwind, 1959; see reprint).

7–6 CROSSED LIGHT BEAMS

The previous methods described above yielded a measure of the z component of angular momentum, M_Z. This is a measure of the degree of orientation of the species being studied. Radiofrequency resonances can also be detected by

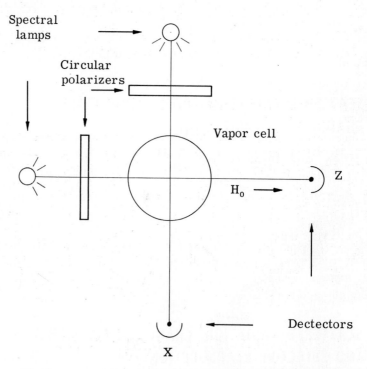

Figure 7-1 Schematic of an experimental arrangement to observe radiofrequency resonances of a vapor in a crossed light beam experiment.

measuring M_x instead of M_z (Bell, 1957). A method for doing this is shown in Figure 7-1 and employs two light beams: a circularly polarized beam in the z direction which optically pumps an alkali metal vapor and which can be used to monitor M_z, and an additional circularly polarized beam in the x direction which is used to monitor M_x. At resonance the x beam is modulated at the Larmor frequency, and the intensity of the modulated signal will depend upon the magnitude of M_x. In addition to monitoring M_x the beam will have two effects: it will tend to produce an orientation in the x direction, and it will produce a relaxation in the z direction. These points have been treated with the Bloch equations by Bell and Bloom (1957) whose experiment was based on a suggestion by Dehmelt (1957b). Other modulation effects have been extensively treated by G. W. Series and co-workers.

7–7 MODULATION OF OPTICAL PUMPING LIGHT

If circularly polarized resonance radiation is applied to a vapor cell at right angles to a magnetic field and if the light intensity is modulated, a change in the total transmitted light intensity can be observed when the modulation frequency is equal to the Larmor frequency of the absorbing species. This method of magnetic resonance detection has been observed and discussed for rubidium, cesium, and helium (Bell, 1961a, b) and also for cadmium (Corney, 1964b, c) and mercury (Dodd, 1963).

7–8 SPIN-EXCHANGE METHOD

The phenomenon of spin exchange will be discussed in Chapter 10. Briefly, spin exchange makes possible the orientation of spin angular momentum of a second species through a coupling interaction with the optically pumped species. Thus, cesium atoms can be oriented if they can collide with oriented rubidium atoms. In a like manner, disorientation can be transmitted by spin exchange and can be optically detected. For example, if one has a vapor cell containing rubidium and cesium with the rubidium being optically pumped, the cesium will be oriented by means of spin exchange. Upon application of a strong radiofrequency field at a cesium resonance the rubidium will be disoriented as well as the cesium, the disorientation being transmitted by spin exchange. One can do radiofrequency spectroscopy experiments on the cesium by detecting changes in the rubidium orientation with an experimental apparatus of the type introduced by Dehmelt (1957a).

7–9 SCATTERED RADIATION FROM ATOMIC BEAMS

Ground-state radiofrequency resonances can also be detected by observation of the scattered resonance radiation from an atomic beam (Hawkins, 1955). One method (Brossel, 1954) uses a beam of sodium atoms which is illuminated by σ^+

resonance radiation in one region to produce an accumulation of sodium atoms in an $m_S = +\frac{1}{2}$ state. In a second region the beam of oriented atoms is irradiated with π light, and the ratio of intensities of σ^+ and σ^- scattered light is measured. This ratio yields the degree of orientation of atoms at that point. If a radiofrequency resonance is excited in between the above two regions, the atomic orientation as measured by the scattered light will change. However, it is more convenient to perform magnetic resonance experiments on the ground states of the alkali metals in vapor-cell experiments rather than beams. Indeed, one can sometimes achieve more narrow magnetic resonance lines in a vapor to which a buffer gas has been added. This effect was predicted by Dicke (1953) and has been observed in numerous experiments.

7—10 DEFLECTION OF OPTICALLY PUMPED ATOMIC BEAMS

Radiofrequency resonances in excited states may also be detected by a combination of atomic beam and optical pumping methods. The nuclear electric equadrupole moment of Na^{23} has been determined by this method. A beam of sodium atoms are first state selected by deflection in a Stern-Gerlach magnet. The beam is then illuminated with optical resonance radiation and sent through a second Stern-Gerlach magnet where the beam is again state selected; the intensity of the beam being a measure of the relative population of the selected state. A radiofrequency field can be applied at the point at which the beam is illuminated, and if transitions between the magnetic sublevels of the excited state are induced during its 10^{-8} sec lifetime the relative population of the selected state will change and can be detected by a change in beam intensity (Perl, 1955). Again, it is possible to make this measurement in a resonance fluorescence experiment.

In experiments where a magnetic resonance transition must be excited during the short lifetime of some excited electronic state, a high flux of radio or microwave frequency photons must be present. This corresponds to a large $H_1(t)$. Otherwise, the excited state will fluoresce before a magnetic resonance transition has occurred. When a magnetic resonance is excited in a ground electronic state the problem is not as serious. However, the mere presence of $H_1(t)$ can perturb the magnetic energy level separations and introduce a small error in some types of experiments (Bloch, 1940). We shall briefly turn our attention to this effect.

7—11 THE BLOCH-SIEGERT SHIFT

In a magnetic resonance experiment transitions between magnetic energy levels are caused by the interaction of the spin system with a magnetic field $H_1(t)$ which oscillates about H_0 at the Larmor frequency. The oscillating magnetic field is composed of two magnetic fields rotating in opposite directions as indicated in Figure 7-2. The spin system interacts with only one of the two rotating fields regardless of whether absorption or stimulated emission is taking place. Which component is effective depends only upon the sign of the g-factor for the spin system involved.

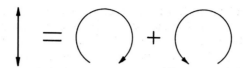

Figure 7-2 Decomposition of a linear
oscillating H_1 into two rotating components.

The remaining rotating component of the oscillating H_1 does not participate
in causing transitions to occur, but it can have an effect upon the experimental
measurement of a resonance frequency. In the early days of atomic beam magnetic resonance there was some concern about this effect. If a resonance frequency were displaced by the presence of this second H_1 component there would
be a corresponding error in the determination of the magnetic moment being
studied.

In 1940, Bloch and Siegert calculated the effect and showed that the experimental resonance frequency is given by

$$\omega = \omega_0 + \frac{(\gamma H_1)^2}{4\omega_0} \qquad (7\text{-}6)$$

where ω_0 is the true Larmor frequency. If H_1 (the magnitude of the radiofrequency field) is small the shift is negligible.

Ramsey (1955) has shown that if H_1 is small and if there is an additional field
of magnitude H_2 rotating about H_0 with frequency ω_2, the resonance will occur
at

$$\omega = \omega_0 + \frac{(\gamma H_2)^2}{2(\omega_0 - \omega_2)} \qquad (7\text{-}7)$$

This general result is identical with the Bloch-Siegert result when $\omega_2 = -\omega_0$.

More recently, an additional small shift in the magnetic energy levels has been
investigated. This displacement is caused by light itself. The effect has been investigated theoretically (Barrat, 1961a, b, c, e) and has been experimentally observed (Cohen-Tannoudji, 1961a, b, c, 1962). It is also discussed in a review by
Kastler (1963a), is referred to as the "lamp shift," and is caused by a reduction of the hyperfine structure of the excited state over that of the ground state.

8 / Phenomenological Description of Oriented Systems

8–1 ORIENTATION AS A BULK MAGNETIZATION

In Chapter 3 expressions were derived for the degree of orientation or alignment of the magnetic moments of a simple system being optically pumped. In the
case of optical orientation it is reasonable to characterize the population differences among the magnetic sublevels of the system by a macroscopic magnetization. In addition, relaxation terms are present in the orientation expressions
that describe the rate at which the atoms regain their normal Boltzmann distribution among the sublevels.

Since the ensemble of atoms can be characterized by a magnetization and by
relaxation it is reasonable that the macroscopic magnetic properties of the system be described by expressions similar to the phenomenological equations of
Bloch (1946) which were formulated to describe the motion of nuclear moments
in the presence of external magnetic fields. The solutions of these equations
would then describe the behavior of the system of optically pumped atoms. The
boundary values for the equations could be specified by a given set of experimental conditions.

In the absence of a pumping process or relaxation, the time variation of the
magnetization per unit volume $\mathbf{M}$ of an ensemble of atoms is given by an equation
similar to Eq. 7-4:

$$\frac{d\mathbf{M}}{dt} = \mathbf{M} \times (\gamma \mathbf{H}) \tag{8-1}$$

where $\mathbf{H}$ is the magnetic field acting on the atoms and γ is the magnetogyric ratio for the magnetic moment of the atom. The magnetogyric ratio is related to the spectroscopic splitting factor, g_F, of the atom, by the relation $\gamma \hbar = g_F \beta$, where β is the Bohr magneton. In the case of nuclear magnetism the Bloch equations are obtained by adding relaxation terms to Eq. 8-1 which then becomes

$$\frac{d\mathbf{M}}{dt} = \gamma \mathbf{M} \times \mathbf{H} - \frac{M_x \mathbf{i} + M_y \mathbf{j}}{T_2} - \frac{M_z - M_0}{T_1} \mathbf{k} \tag{8-2}$$

Here $\mathbf{i}$, $\mathbf{j}$, $\mathbf{k}$ are unit vectors in the laboratory coordinate system, and M_x, M_y, M_z are the components of $\mathbf{M}$ in this coordinate system. M_0 is the z-component value of the magnetization when the ensemble of magnetic moments has achieved a normal Boltzmann distribution. It is assumed that a steady external magnetic field is applied along the $\mathbf{k}$ direction. T_1 and T_2 are the longitudinal and transverse relaxation times, respectively, and describe the rate at which the components of $\mathbf{M}$ relax along their respective directions.

The usual procedure is to solve Eq. 8-2 for M_x, M_y, M_z with particular boundary conditions. These are usually dictated by the experimental conditions and the range of t in which one is interested. $\mathbf{H}$ is generally composed of a steady magnetic field $\mathbf{H}_0$ applied along the $\mathbf{k}$ direction plus a magnetic field $\mathbf{H}_1(t)$ oscillating perpendicular to $\mathbf{k}$ at some frequency ω. The magnitude of $\mathbf{H}_0$ and $\mathbf{H}_1$ plus the frequency ω are experimental variables contained in the expressions for M_x, M_y, and M_z.

8—2 EQUATIONS OF MOTION WITH OPTICAL PUMPING

When optical pumping is also taking place the state populations and, hence, the magnetization are changed from the normal Boltzmann value. This change can be introduced by simply adding the contribution that comes from pumping. If the pumping is such that it changes the total z component of angular momentum of the ensemble of atoms the contributions to be added will be

$$\frac{M_0^P - M_z}{\tau_P} \mathbf{k}$$

where M_0^P is the maximum equilibrium value of M_z while pumping is taking place and τ_P is the "optical pumping time" for this process to occur. It must be noted that M_0^P is a constant determined by three factors: T_1, the transition probabilities for excitation of the atom, and the intensity of light used for the pumping process. Usually M_0^P is much larger than the normal Boltzmann distribution, which enables one to neglect the M_0 term for most problems. Equation 8-2 for the optical pumping case now becomes

$$\frac{dM}{dt} = \gamma M \times H - \frac{M_x i + M_y j}{T_2} - \frac{M_z}{T_1} k + \frac{M_0^P - M_z}{\tau_P} k \qquad (8\text{-}3)$$

As was mentioned in the previous chapter if H is composed of a static field H_0 of magnitude

$$H_0 = H_z = -\frac{\omega_0}{\gamma} \qquad \qquad \mathcal{L}\omega_0 = g\beta M = \hbar\gamma H$$

and a radiofrequency field H_1 of magnitude

$$H_1 = -\frac{\omega_1}{\gamma}$$

rotating at a frequency ω close to ω_0, an effective static magnetic field H_{eff} may be described in a coordinate system which rotates about H_0 at the frequency ω:

$$
\begin{aligned}
H_{eff} &= \left(H_0 + \frac{\omega}{\gamma}\right) k' + H_1 i' \\
&= \frac{(\omega - \omega_0) k' - \omega_1 i'}{\gamma} \qquad\qquad (8\text{-}4) \\
&= \frac{\Delta\omega k' - \omega_1 i'}{\gamma}
\end{aligned}
$$

where the primes indicate that the unit vectors are now taken in the rotating coordinate system. H_{eff} is illustrated in Figure 8-1 for the situation where the rotating coordinate system has the same frequency as does H_1. In such a case it is convenient to transform Eq. 8-3 to the rotating coordinate system:

$$
\begin{aligned}
\frac{dM'}{dt} &= \frac{dM'_x i'}{dt} + \frac{dM'_y j'}{dt} + \frac{dM'_z k'}{dt} \\
&= (M'_x i' + M'_y j' + M_z k) \times (\Delta\omega k - \omega_1 i') \\
&\quad - \frac{M'_x i' + M'_y j'}{T_2} - \frac{M_z k}{T_1} + \frac{M_0^P - M_z}{\tau_P} k \qquad (8\text{-}5)
\end{aligned}
$$

Since the coordinate system rotates about H_0, $k' = k$ and $M'_z = M_z$, which have been taken into account accordingly in Eq. 8-5. The resulting time variations of the components of magnetization in the rotating coordinate system are

$$\frac{dM'_x}{dt} = -\frac{M'_x}{T_2} + \Delta\omega M'_y$$

$$\frac{dM'_y}{dt} = -\Delta\omega M'_x - \frac{M'_y}{T_2} - \omega_1 M_z \qquad\qquad (8\text{-}6)$$

$$\frac{dM_z}{dt} = \omega_1 M'_y - \frac{M_z}{T_1} + \frac{M_0^P - M_z}{\tau_P}$$

Equation 8-6 can be solved for a given set of experimental conditions according to the same procedures that have been used in the nuclear magnetic case. However, it must be pointed out that the usual experimental arrangement sometimes utilizes an H_0 which is a fraction of a gauss. This means that H_1 can easily be comparable to H_0. Under these conditions the validity of the Bloch equations and their solutions must be carefully examined. In these cases T_1 and T_2 become equal, and it would be preferable to modify the Bloch equations such that **M** relaxes toward the instantaneous value of **H** rather than along fixed component directions of **M**. In these circumstances the Bloch equations for nuclear magnetism become (Abragam, 1961)

$$\frac{d\mathbf{M}}{dt} = \gamma \mathbf{M} \times \mathbf{H} - \frac{\mathbf{M} - \chi_0 \mathbf{H}}{T_1} \qquad\qquad (8\text{-}7)$$

where T_1 is equal to T_2, and χ_0 is the spin magnetic susceptibility. The validity of the modified Bloch equation in situations where H_0 is low or even equal to zero has been justified experimentally.

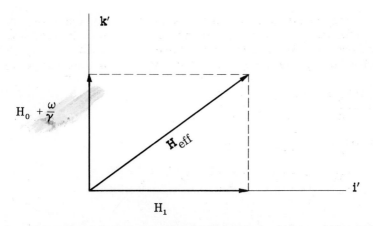

Figure 8-1 Effective magnetic field, H_{eff}, in a
rotating coordinate system.

It seems reasonable that in the optical pumping case the production of magnetization by optical pumping may be simply added to Eq. 8-7 as before to yield

$$\frac{d\mathbf{M}}{dt} = \gamma \mathbf{M} \times \mathbf{H} - \frac{(\mathbf{M} - \chi_0 \mathbf{H})}{T_1} + \frac{\mathbf{M}^P - \mathbf{M}}{\tau_P} \tag{8-8}$$

In actual fact the details of the pumping term must be derived for the particular
type of experiment being performed. If the orientation is along the z direction
defined as along $\mathbf{k}' = \mathbf{k}$ Eq. 8-8 in the rotating coordinate system becomes

$$\frac{dM'_x}{dt} = M'_y \Delta\omega - \frac{M'_x}{T_1} - \frac{\chi_0 \omega_1}{\gamma T_1}$$

$$\frac{dM'_y}{dt} = -M'_x \Delta\omega - \omega_1 M_z - \frac{M'_y}{T'} \tag{8-9}$$

$$\frac{dM_z}{dt} = \omega_1 M'_y - \frac{M_z}{T_1} + \frac{\chi_0 \Delta\omega}{\gamma T_1} + \frac{M_z^P - M_z}{\tau_P}$$

Again, if M_z^P is large, the terms in χ_0 may be neglected. Equation 8-9 can then
be solved with the set of boundary conditions dictated by the specific experimental
conditions.

The case where two light beams are present, one in the z direction and the
other in the x direction, has also been discussed from the phenomenological
point of view by Bell and Bloom (1957) to describe experiments in which a high-
frequency modulation of a second light beam is observed.

A description of optically oriented systems in terms of the density matrix
formalism will not be given here. The reader is referred to the paper by
Cohen-Tannoudji (1962) on this subject.

9 / Energy Level Crossing Experiments

9–1 PRINCIPLE OF THE EXPERIMENT

In certain cases it is possible to make precision measurements of fine and hyperfine level separations without performing a radiofrequency resonance experiment upon the atom under study. This is achieved by what is called a "level crossing experiment." The angular distribution of the resonance fluorescence of the atom under study is observed as a function of the magnitude of some externally applied magnetic field. If two states involved in the resonance fluorescence cross one another at some magnetic field strength, and if both of the states can participate in the absorption of an incoming photon, the angular distribution of resonance fluorescence will be different than that in the noncrossed states.

Such an experiment was first performed on the helium (1s2s) ^{3}P state and resulted in a redetermination of the ^{3}P$_1$ − ^{3}P$_2$ and ^{3}P$_0$ − ^{3}P$_1$ fine structure splittings with a high degree of precision (Colegrove, 1959; Franken, 1961a). The energy levels of the helium states involved in this experiment are shown in Figure 9-1 with the crossing points circled for which the effect exists when the exciting light is unpolarized. The magnetic field at each crossing point can be accurately measured. The fine structure splittings can then be computed. The level crossing phenomenon was discussed by Breit (1933) and more recently by Franken (1961a) and by Rose and Carovillano (1961) who point out that it can be thought of as simply an interference phenomenon between radiation from each of the two states that cross, although it is a one-photon process and not a two-photon process. The amount of interference depends upon the separation between the two states.

47

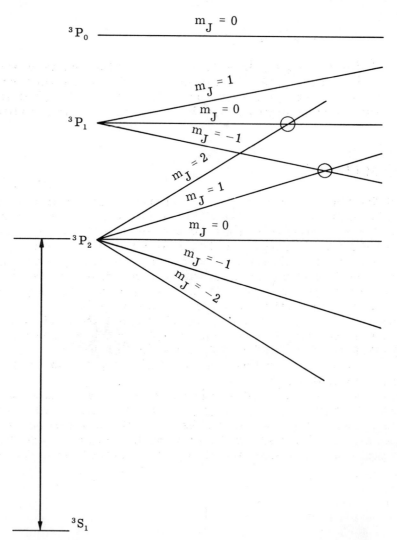

Figure 9-1 Energy level crossing in helium (indicated by circles).

Two extreme cases may be considered to illustrate why the process can be observed: (1) the two states a and b are far apart (resolved), and (2) the two states are exactly crossed. If one examines the rate $R(\mathbf{f},\mathbf{g})$ at which photons of polarization $\mathbf{f}$ are absorbed and photons of polarization $\mathbf{g}$ are emitted in resonance fluorescence, the following proportionalities hold for $R(\mathbf{f},\mathbf{g})$ for the above two cases:

$$R_{\text{resolved}} \sim |f_{ab}g_{ba}|^2 + |f_{ac}g_{ca}|^2 \qquad (9\text{-}1)$$

and

$$R_{crossed} \sim |f_{ab} g_{ba} + f_{ac} g_{ca}|^2$$

where $f_{ab} = \langle a|\mathbf{f} \cdot \mathbf{r}|b \rangle$, $g_{ba} = \langle b|\mathbf{g} \cdot \mathbf{r}|a \rangle$, etc. In order for the level crossing to be an observable process, none of the matrix elements may be equal to zero, otherwise $R_{resolved}$ would be the same as $R_{crossed}$. Therefore, both states must participate in the absorption and re-emission of the resonance radiation being used.

9—2 APPLICATIONS

As might be expected, there are a variety of experimental configurations that might be used, each having its own special consequences. Level crossings with $\Delta m = 0$ or 2 may be observed with unpolarized light whereas $\Delta m = 1$ crossing may be observed with plane polarized light if the direction of polarization is neither parallel nor perpendicular to the externally applied magnetic field. In addition, the line shape of the crossover will be a function of experimental configuration and can vary from a pure Lorenzian to a pure dispersion-type curve depending upon the polarization and scattering angle of the light.

In addition to helium, level crossing techniques have been used to make precision measurements of g_J factors for the (5s5p) $^3P_1$ state of Cd^{111} and Cd^{113} (Thaddeus, 1962) and Cd^{107} and Cd^{109} (Thaddeus, 1963). Level crossings have also been used to measure the hyprefine structure of the (6s6p) $^3P_1$ state of Hg^{199} and Hg^{201} (Hirsch, 1961; Dodd, 1961a, b).

Recently, the same effect has been observed for states which do not actually cross but which come close together, then repel one another. If the two states are coupled by some interaction they will be prevented from crossing one another. The observation of this "anticrossing" can be made, and a theoretical treatment performed in a fashion similar to that for level crossings (Eck, 1963).

10/Spin Exchange

10–1 MAGNETIC RESONANCE DETECTION BY SPIN EXCHANGE

A very important effect that occurs in optical pumping experiments is the ability of two particles to transfer their spin orientation to one another upon making a collision. If one has two species, A and B, present in a vapor cell, pumping can be produced in B by optically pumping species A, the effect being transferred from species A to species B via spin exchange.

As was mentioned in Chapter 7, optical detection of radio frequency resonances in species B can be accomplished by monitoring their effect upon the absorption of resonance radiation by species A; the effect being transferred by spin exchange. This is experimentally a very powerful tool because one can study an atom for which the proper production, filtering, and polarization of resonance radiation is difficult simply by utilizing a second atomic species for which the proper kind of resonance radiation is easily obtainable.

Dehmelt (1958a; see reprint) introduced this technique to study the spin resonance of free electrons. By utilizing spin exchange between free electrons and optically oriented sodium vapor, he was able to obtain a very precise value of the Lande g-factor for the free electron. This is of considerable interest in testing relationships from quantum electrodynamics such as the ratio of the electron-spin magnetic moment, μ_S, to the Bohr magneton, μ_0:

$$\frac{\mu_S}{\mu_0} = 1 + \frac{\alpha}{2\pi} - 2.973 \frac{\alpha^2}{\pi^2} + \cdots \tag{10-1}$$

Potassium (Franken, 1958a), rubidium (Novick, 1958), and cesium (Dehmelt, 1958b) atoms have been oriented by spin exchange with other optically pumped alkali atoms. Also, the hyperfine interaction has been measured in N^{14} (Holloway, 1958) and N^{15} (Anderson, 1959), in P^{31} (Lambert, 1962), and in H, D, and T (Anderson, 1958, 1960b, 1961; Pipkin, 1962) atoms by using spin-exchange techniques.

In addition, nuclear polarization has been achieved by exchange mechanisms. He^3 nuclei can be oriented by spin exchange with optically pumped Rb atoms (Bouchiat, 1960). He^3 nuclei have also been oriented by a metastability exchange with optically pumped ^3S helium atoms (Colegrove, 1963). The orientation of He^+ ions by spin exchange with optically pumped cesium has been achieved by Dehmelt and Major (1962a) in an ingenious experiment where the ions are trapped in a quadrupolar field whose polarity reverses at a high frequency.

Spin exchange is also important in interpreting the details of state population changes in relaxation processes (Anderson, 1961b).

Experimentally, the same procedures are followed as are used in a conventional optical pumping experiment except that two species are placed in the vapor cell—one is optically pumped directly and the other is pumped by spin exchange with the first species. The second species sometimes is produced by an electrical or radiofrequency discharge. This must be done if one wants to examine free electrons or make measurements on atoms whose stable form is a molecule. For example, H atoms must be produced by dissociation of H_2 molecules. The production of the second species could also be the result of a chemical reaction or of decomposition of a parent substance with ultraviolet light or by particles emanating from radioactive materials.

The optical detection of a radiofrequency resonance in the second species is illustrated by Dehmelt's (1958a; see reprint) experiment on free electrons. Sodium atoms in an argon buffer gas are optically pumped by circularly polarized light. Electrons, produced by a series of 1-msec radiofrequency discharges, were oriented by spin-exchange collisions with the oriented sodium atoms. Resonance disorientation of the free electrons was caused by a radiofrequency field applied to the vapor cell, whose frequency was the same as the Larmor frequency of the electrons. This spin disorientation was transferred to the sodium atoms by spin exchange and was detected as a decrease in intensity of circularly polarized sodium resonance radiation passing through the apparatus.

Dehmelt has discussed the interdependence of the orientation of the sodium atoms and the electrons in the above experiment. It serves to illustrate what factors are important in the spin-exchange process. He finds for the equilibrium orientations p and P of electrons and sodium atoms, respectively,

$$p = \frac{f T_e P_I}{f T_e + F \tau_p + 1} \; ; \qquad P = \frac{(f T_e + 1) P_I}{f T_e + F \tau_p + 1} \qquad (10\text{-}2)$$

where f is the frequency of collision of an electron with sodium atoms and F is the frequency of collision of a sodium atom with electrons. f can be expressed $= v\sigma_{ex} N$, where v is the mean relative velocity of the two species, N is the number of sodium atoms per cubic centimeter, and σ_{ex} is the cross section for spin exchange. Likewise, $F = v\sigma_{ex}m$, where m is the number of free electrons per cubic centimeter. T_e in Eq. 10-2 is the electron relaxation time, and P_I is the equilibrium orientation that can be obtained with the light intensity available for the experiment.

When the electrons are disoriented by a radiofrequency field the effect is the same as a shortening of T_e, hence, a decrease in P. From the amount of change in P the spin-exchange cross section σ_{ex} can be estimated. For electron-sodium interactions it is found that $\sigma_{ex} = 2.3 \times 10^{-14}$ cm^2.

10—2 MECHANISM FOR SPIN EXCHANGE

The mechanism for spin exchange has been discussed by Purcell and Field (1956; see reprint), Wittke and Dicke (1956), Glassgold (1963), Bender (1963), and by Balling, Hanson, and Pipkin (1964a, b). Purcell and Field were interested in the effect of spin exchange in establishing the state populations of the hydrogen hyperfine levels and the resulting consequences with respect to 21-cm radio astronomy. Wittke and Dicke were interested in the effects of spin exchange on the relaxation and line width in an experimental redetermination of the hyperfine splitting in the gound state of the hydrogen atom. The spin functions of two colliding hydrogen atoms are represented as being a superposition of singlet and triplet functions. During a collision, a phase shift occurs between the amplitude of the singlet component and the amplitude of the triplet component due to the difference in scattering potential of the two components. The amount of phase shift will depend upon the "hardness" of the collision. It is generally assumed that the phase shift evolve mainly from the singlet state contribution since for this state the potential is attractive and closer distances of approach are involved in producing hard collisions. This means that the centripetal barrier to "hard" collision is lowered. Cross sections for such hard collisions are computed using classical kinematics, and the con tributions from collisions that are not hard can be estimated.

A reappraisal of the treatment of Purcell and Field is given by Glassgold who finds that quantum effects are important and that the cross section will be sensitive to the form of the potential for both the singlet and triplet states. Bender has also examined spin-exchange collisions and has calculated the frequency shift in the hydrogen hyperfine interaction arising from hydrogen-hydrogen spin exchange. This effect must be considered in the operation of a hydrogen maser as a frequency standard. Balling, Hanson, and Pipkin have presented a rather complete treatment of spin exchange by means of a density matrix formalism and have applied it to the electron-rubidium spin-exchange experiment.

One uncertainty inherent in any determination of a spin-exchange cross section is the accuracy of the measurement of the vapor density of the substance or substances participating in spin exchange. If one of the species is produced in a discharge of some kind the problem is particularly acute. In the case of the alkali metals an accurate value of the vapor pressure is needed.

Experimental and theoretical values for σ_{ex} are of the order of 10^{-14} to 10^{-13} cm^2, i.e., they are of the order of the cross sections for changing momentum of the colliding particles.

11/Pressure Shift
of the Hyperfine Interaction

11–1 ORIGIN OF THE PRESSURE SHIFT

Optical pumping makes possible a precision determination of the hyperfine interaction in an atom as discussed earlier. The hyperfine interaction arises mainly from the Fermi contact interaction between the nuclear magnetic moment and the unpaired electron. The Hamiltonian for this scalar interaction is

$$\mathcal{H} = \frac{8\pi}{3} \, g_N g_e \beta_N \beta \, \mathbf{I} \cdot \mathbf{S}_i \, \delta(\mathbf{r}_{iN}) \qquad (11\text{-}1)$$

where g_N and g_e are the nuclear and electronic g-factors, β_N and β are the nuclear and Bohr magnetons, $\mathbf{I}$ is the nuclear-spin angular momentum, $\mathbf{S}_i$ is the spin angular momentum of electron i, and $\delta(\mathbf{r}_{iN})$ is the Dirac delta function which is zero everywhere except at nucleus N.

Upon solving for the energy, the Fermi contact interaction is found to contribute to the hyperfine interaction an amount

$$E(\text{hyperfine}) = \frac{8\pi}{3} \, g_N g_e \beta_N \beta \, m_N m_i \, \psi_n^2(0) \qquad (11\text{-}2)$$

where m_N and m_i are the magnetic quantum numbers describing the z component
54

of angular momentum of the nucleus N and the electron i. $\psi_n^2(0)$ is the wave function of electron i in state n evaluated at the nucleus N. It is assumed here that the interaction is isotropic. We see that, since the hyperfine interaction depends only upon the size of the nuclear magnetic moment and the electron wave function of the atom, it is a constant quantity for an isolated atom.

This presents the possibility of using an optically pumped vapor cell as a frequency standard or "atomic clock" whose base frequency is the hyperfine frequency of the atomic species used. However, it turns out that the hyperfine frequency as measured in such an experiment is dependent upon the pressure of buffer gas present in the vapor cell and upon the temperature of the cell. This is not surprising, as one would expect that during a collision between the atom and a buffer gas particle the wave function of the atom would be highly perturbed and the factor $\psi_n^2(0)$ in Eq. 11-2 would change. When averaged over all types of collisions $\langle \psi_n^2(0) \rangle_{av}$ would be different from $\psi_n^2(0)$ for the isolated atom. This effect is called "the pressure shift of the hyperfine interaction."

In frequency-standard applications one must work in the absence of a buffer gas or with a known pressure of buffer gas in order to correct for the pressure shift. There is also the possibility of using a mixture of buffer gases whose effect upon the wave function and, hence, $\psi_n^2(0)$ would exactly cancel one another.

Although the pressure shift introduces complications in frequency-standard applications, it is in itself an interesting and useful phenomenon. It is a measurable quantity directly related to interatomic interactions, and its interpretation presents another means by which the details of such interactions can be investigated.

11-2 EXPERIMENTAL RESULTS

Table 11-1 shows some representative experimental values of the pressure shift that are available at this time. It is seen that for the rubidium hyperfine interaction very light buffer gases show a positive pressure shift, i.e., an increase in $\langle \psi_n^2(0) \rangle$, while the heavy buffers show a negative pressure shift. Moreover, the variation from one buffer gas to another is smaller for the hyperfine interaction in the hydrogen isotopes than in the alkali metals. In addition, the variation seems to be

Table 11-1 Fractional Pressure Shifts of Hyperfine Frequencies in Various Buffer Gases[a]

Buffer	H[b]	D[b]	T[b]	Na[23] [c]	K[39] (65° C)	Rb[87] (25° C)	Cs[133] (30° C)
He	4.80	—	—	73	93	105.3	174.0
Ne	2.88	3.24	3.24	45	52	57.4	70.7
A	−4.77	−4.52	−5.05	3	− 1	− 7.5	− 27.2
Kr	—	—	—	− 42	−91	− 84.9	−141.4
Xe	—	—	—	− 85	—	—	−261.1
H₂	−0.56	—	—	62	72	96.6	206.7

(continued)

Table 11-1 (continued)

Buffer	H[b]	D[b]	T[b]	Na^{23} [c]	K^{39} (65° C)	Rb^{87} (25° C)	Cs^{133} (30° C)
D_2	—	—	—	—	—	98.0	—
N_2	—	—	—	49	—	76.1	117
CH_4	—	—	—	—	—	− 73.2	—
$n-C_5H_{12}$	—	—	—	—	—	− 409.7	—
$C(CH_4)_4$	—	—	—	—	—	− 420	—
$n-C_7H_{16}$	—	—	—	—	—	− 614.5	—

[a]The pressure shifts, $1/\nu(\partial\nu/\partial P)_T$, are tabulated in units of 10^{-9}/mm Hg. The values are taken from Pipkin (1962), for H, D, and T; Arditi (1958b), and Ramsey (1964b) for Na^{23}; Bender (1958) for Rb^{87}; and Arditi (1958c) and Beaty (1958) for Cs^{133}.
  [b]Pressure measured at 0° C.
  [c]Pressure measured at 295° K.

greater for Cs than for Rb. This is reasonable since one would expect a larger effect upon electrons that are in states of higher principal quantum number and are more easily polarized or distorted by a colliding buffer particle. It would be very interesting to see what the numbers would be for other pumped species such as N and P. Also, it would be valuable to have numbers for other molecular buffer gases, especially those with permanent electric dipole moments.

11–3 THEORETICAL CALCULATIONS OF THE PRESSURE SHIFT

To date, the interpretation of the effect has taken two forms. The first approach, which was used for the alkali metal species, is essentially a parametric one in which empirical data are used to calculate the shift (Margenau, 1959; Herman, 1961; Robinson, 1960). This treatment leads to the result that the change in hyperfine energy for an atom is:

$$\Delta E(\text{hyperfine}) = \Delta E(\text{dispersion})\left(\frac{1}{\overline{E} + I_2} + \frac{2}{I_1}\right)\varepsilon \tag{11-3}$$

where ΔE(hyperfine) is the shift in hyperfine energy, ΔE(dispersion) is the van der Waals energy between the alkali metal atom and the buffer gas particle, and I_1 and I_2 are the ionization energies of the alkali atom and buffer gas particle, respectively. $\overline{E}$ is an average excitation energy of the pumped atom which comes from applying the closure approximation to the second-order energy term arising in the perturbation treatment of the problem. $\overline{E}$ is usually taken as the alkali atom resonance energy or a weighted average of the P states of the alkali atom. ε is the hyperfine energy of the atom in free space and is proportional to $\psi_n^2(0)$.

In order to calculate the fractional pressure shift the expression in Eq. 11-3 must be multiplied by the classical configurational distribution function and integrated over all possible configurations. This gives

$$\left\langle \frac{\Delta \nu}{\nu_0} \right\rangle = \frac{4\pi N}{h\nu_0} \int_0^\infty \Delta E(\text{hyperfine}) \ \exp\left\{ \frac{-V(r)}{kT} \right\} r^2 \ dr \qquad (11\text{-}4)$$

where $\Delta \nu$ is the shift in hyperfine frequency, ν_0 is the true hyperfine frequency, N is the density of buffer particles, and $V(r)$ is the potential energy function between an alkali atom and a buffer gas particle.

One can, for example, assume a Lennard-Jones potential for the interaction, calculate the van der Waals energy, and evaluate the shift from the expression in Eq. 11-4.

A different approach is to evaluate the Fermi contact interaction over the total wave function for the colliding system to obtain the correction to the hyperfine energy. This has been done by Clarke (1962; see reprint) who calculated the first-order perturbation correction to the H-He system. His result is similar to that in Eq. 11-4 except that $\Delta E(\text{hyperfine})/h\nu_0$ is replaced by

$$\frac{\Delta \nu(R)}{\nu_0} = \frac{\langle \psi_{\text{H-He}}(\mathbf{r}_H, \mathbf{r}_{He}, R) | \Sigma_{i=1}^3 \ \mathbf{I}_H \cdot \mathbf{S}_i \ \delta(\mathbf{r}_{iH}) | \psi_{\text{H-He}}(\mathbf{r}_H, \mathbf{r}_{He}, R) \rangle - \nu_0}{\langle \psi_{\text{H-He}}(\mathbf{r}_H, \mathbf{r}_{He}, \infty) | \Sigma_{i=1}^3 \ \mathbf{I}_H \cdot \mathbf{S}_i \ \delta(\mathbf{r}_{iH}) | \psi_{\text{H-He}}(\mathbf{r}_H, \mathbf{r}_{He}, \infty) \rangle}$$

where $\psi_{\text{H-He}}(\mathbf{r}_H, \mathbf{r}_{He}, R)$ is the wave function for the colliding system with internuclear coordinates R and electron coordinates $\mathbf{r}_H$ and $\mathbf{r}_{He}$ associated with H and He. The operator in each matrix element is the Fermi contact interaction and is summed over each of the three electrons of the system.

Clarke also considered the mass-dependent quantum statistical correction and found it to be quite small ($\sim 4\%$), in disagreement with the then available data for the pressure shift of the hydrogen isotopes. However, a subsequent repeat of the experiments show very little mass dependence of the shift (see Table 11-1) in agreement with Clarke's calculation.

For those interested in interatomic and intermolecular interactions, the pressure shift of the hyperfine interaction will continue to be a valuable parameter.

A similar effect should be observed in accurate measurements of the Zeeman splitting. The pressure shift of the g-factor remains to be measured.

12 / Spin-Relaxation Times

12—1 MEASUREMENT OF SPIN-RELAXATION TIMES

The spin-relaxation time has been discussed in the previous pages with respect to the way in which it determines how much orientation or alignment can be achieved in a given experimental situation. It is also one of the factors that determines the width of a radiofrequency resonance. A short spin-relaxation time broadens the resonance line by producing an uncertainty in the energies of the magnetic sublevels used in the experiment. One method of measuring spin-relaxation times is to measure the line width of a Zeeman transition in a very homogeneous magnetic field. The usual interpretation of line widths in terms of relaxation times would then apply. A second method involves the rate of change of intensity of transmitted radiation in a Dehmelt-type experiment upon sudden reversal of the magnetic field Dehmelt, 1957a). Experiments performed with different intensities of pumping radiation yield the spin-relaxation time.

The method which has been most widely used is due to Franzen (1959). A shutter is placed between the lamp and the vapor cell. If the shutter is open, optical pumping is taking place and the atoms eventually attain an equilibrium orientation. When the shutter is closed the atoms are in the dark and will lose their orientation via the spin-relaxation mechanisms present. If the shutter is quickly opened, the transmitted light intensity will be less than in the equilibrium, optically pumped vapor. The magnitude of the decrease in transmitted light intensity is proportional to the fraction of atoms that have undergone relaxation in the dark (Franzen, 1959).

12—2 DIFFUSION COEFFICIENTS
AND SPIN-DISORIENTATION CROSS SECTIONS

Spin relaxation is of interest because its measurement as a function of pressure yields two parameters which are related to interatomic interactions. If the spin-relaxation time of a species is measured at different pressures of some buffer gas present in the vapor cell, the two parameters that may be obtained are the diffusion coefficient of the optically pumped species in the inert buffer gas and the cross section for disorientation of the optically pumped species by the buffer gas atoms. These parameters result from the two processes responsible for relaxation (Franzen, 1959): (1) diffusion of the optically pumped atom through the buffer gas to the walls of the cell where disorientation takes place and (2) interaction with the buffer gas atoms during collisions to produce spin disorientation. A single collision with the glass walls of the cells is assumed to result in disorientation although it may take many collisions with buffer gas atoms before disorientation occurs (about 10^9 collisions for Rb-He). The values of the diffusion coefficients which are obtained in this manner are similar to gaseous diffusion coefficients obtained by other means, e.g., with the use of isotopic tracer techniques. On the other hand, disorientation cross sections turn out to be very unusual quantities. Values of the

Table 12-1 Diffusion Coefficients, D_0 and Spin-Disorientation Cross Sections, σ, for Rubidium Atoms in Various Buffer Gases

Buffer	T($^{\circ}$C)	D_0(cm^2/sec)	σ(cm^2)	Reference
He	50	0.54	6.2×10^{-25}	(Bernheim, 1962)
D_2	35	—	4.3×10^{-24}	(Brewer, 1962)
H_2	70	1.34	3×10^{-24}	(McNeal, 1962; Brewer, 1962)
CH_4	60	0.5	8×10^{-24}	(McNeal, 1962)
C_2H_6	60	0.3	3.8×10^{-23}	(McNeal, 1962)
Ne	47	0.31	5.2×10^{-23}	(Franzen, 1959)
N_2	55	0.33	5.7×10^{-23}	(McNeal, 1962)
C_2H_4	60	0.24	1.3×10^{-22}	(McNeal, 1962)
Ar	47	0.24	3.7×10^{-22}	(Franzen, 1959)
C_6H_{12}	50	0.10	4.5×10^{-22}	(McNeal, 1962)
Kr	47	0.16	5.9×10^{-21}	(Franzen, 1959)
Xe	47	0.13	1.3×10^{-26}	(Franzen, 1959)
C_6H_6	55	—	7×10^{-19}	(McNeal, 1964a)
$(CH_3)_2O$	55	—	3×10^{-18}	(McNeal, 1964a)
$C_4H_8O_2$ (dioxane)	55	—	$\sim 4 \times 10^{-18}$	(McNeal, 1964a)
NH_3	55	—	8×10^{-18}	(McNeal, 1964a)

disorientation cross section for rubidium in various buffer gas species are given in Table 12-1. They vary over an extremely wide range of values: from 6.2×10^{-25} cm² for He to 8×10^{-18} cm² for NH_3. This is a range of seven orders of magnitude. The variation over the rare gases alone covers almost five orders of magnitude.

12–3 THE SPIN-RELAXATION MECHANISM

The mechanism of spin relaxation by collision of Rb with an inert buffer gas atom or molecules has been investigated (Bernheim, 1962) and is thought to arise from a spin-orbit coupling of the rubidium 5s electron with all of the other angular momenta that result from the collision. When one examines in detail the coupling of angular momenta in the colliding pair of atoms, one finds that the interaction Hamiltonian responsible for the spin relaxation is

$$\mathcal{H}_{eff} = \sum_j \gamma_j \mathbf{S}_j \cdot \mathbf{J} \qquad (12\text{-}1)$$

where $\mathbf{J}$ is the total angular momentum (exclusive of spin) of the colliding pair of atoms about their center of mass, and $\mathbf{S}_j$ is the spin of electron j. The coefficients γ_j originate from two effects. One of these arises from the magnetic moment due to motion of the positively charged nuclei about the center of mass of the colliding system; the other effect arises from the electronic orbital motion induced by the collision. The expression for γ_j which is a sum of these two effects is

$$\gamma_j = \frac{eg\beta}{Ic} \left\{ -\sum_K \frac{Z_K}{r_{jK}^3} (\mathbf{r}_j \cdot \mathbf{r}_K - |\mathbf{r}_K|^2) \right.$$
$$\left. + \sum_n \frac{\left\langle 0 \left| \sum_K \left(\frac{Z_K}{m_j r_{jK}^3} \right) \boldsymbol{\ell}_j - \sum_{k>j} \left(\frac{1}{r_{jk}^3} \right) \boldsymbol{\ell}_j \right| n \right\rangle \langle n | \boldsymbol{\ell}_j | 0 \rangle}{E_0 - E_n} \right\} \qquad (12\text{-}2)$$

The quantities e, g, β, I, c, are, respectively, the electronic charge, the electronic g-factor, the Bohr magneton, the moment of inertia of the colliding system of particles about their center of mass, and the velocity of light. In the summations capital subscripts refer to nuclei; lower-case subscripts refer to electrons; all distances r are taken from the center of the mass. Z_K is the atomic number of nucleus K, and ℓ_j is the orbital angular momentum of electron i. The sum over n includes all excited electronic states of the system.

The order of magnitude of γ_j is $(e^2/a_0)\alpha^2 (m/M)$, an energy comparable to the hyperfine interaction. This is about the right interaction energy required to produce the observed transition probability for a spin flip during the time it takes for a collision to occur (Bernheim, 1962).

An interesting empirical relationship was found between the disorientation cross section and atomic number of the buffer atom in rubidium-rare-gas studies. It was found that the disorientation cross section varied approximately as the cube of the atomic number of the buffer used:

$$\alpha = kZ^3 \qquad\qquad (12\text{-}3)$$

reason for using He

This variation is also consistent with Eqs. 12-1 and 12-2 for the rubidium case (Bernheim, 1962), but is not expected to hold for the other alkali metals.

The spin-orbit mechanism has been used actually to calculate disorientation cross sections by Herman (1964) who finds farily good agreement with the measure values despite the approximations involved.

12—4 SPIN DISORIENTATION IN MOLECULAR BUFFER GASES

Molecular buffer gases have also been used in optical pumping experiments, and their disorientation cross sections are quite interesting. Referring to Table 12-1 it will be noted that hydrocarbon vapors have small disorientation cross sections and are, therefore, good buffer gases. On the other hand, molecules with electric dipole moments have very large disorientation cross sections and are poor buffers. In addition, it will be noted that ammonia has an electric dipole moment that is much larger than that of carbon monoxide, and it also has a much larger cross section leading one to suspect a different type of mechanism for relaxation than that found for monatomic or hydrocarbon buffer gases.

McNeal (1962, 1964a) relates the values for the disorientation cross section of atoms and molecules to the number of electrons contained in each buffer atom or molecule. This is a reasonable thing to do for species suspected of producing spin relaxation by the spin-orbit mechanism since γ_j in Eq. 8-2 contains sums over electrons and over nuclear charges. When molecular disorientation cross sections are compared with atomic values it becomes evident that the pumped atom undergoes an interaction with only part of the electrons and nuclei of the buffer molecule. For very large buffer molecules such as cyclohexane, C_6H_{12}, this effect is quite pronounced. This is reasonable since one would expect that the orbital of the unpaired electron would overlap only a part of a molecule whereas it could overlap a major portion of an atom during a collision.

12—5 SPIN DISORIENTATION IN ELECTRIC DIPOLAR BUFFER GASES

The disorientation cross sections of electric dipole-type buffer gases are listed in Table 12-2 with their dipole moments. There is a variation of four orders of magnitude in σ and a little more than one order of magnitude in the dipole moment in going from NH_3 to CO. These values lead one to suppose that for these buffers the mechanism for disorientation must be related to the size of the electric dipole. McNeal (1964a) has investigated this mechanism and finds that the results can be

Table 12-2 The Effect of an Electric Dipole Moment of Buffer Gas Molecules upon the Disorientation Cross Section for Rubidium Atoms[a]

Buffer	$\sigma \, (cm^2)$	μ elect (debyes)
NH_3	8×10^{-18}	1.469
$CH_3 OCH_3$	3×10^{-18}	1.316
CO	1×10^{-22}	0.117

[a] Taken from McNeal (1964a).

explained on the basis of an excitation of the pumped atom to a p state by the electric field of the dipole moment of the colliding buffer molecules. Furthermore, his analysis shows that the transition probability for a spin flip is roughly proportional to the fourth power in the dipole moment. This is consistent with the one order of magnitude variation in dipole moment resulting in four orders of magnitude variation of σ in Table 12-2.

Benzene is an unusual case. It has no electric dipole moment yet its disorientation cross section is more than 1000 times as large as that for cyclohexane — a molecule of roughly the same size and with more electrons than benzene. Obviously, there is an effect here which is different from those discussed above. Benzene has a conjugated π-electron system, and it has unoccupied orbitals that lie lower in energy than any of the other hydrocarbon buffer gases. One explanation for its unusual behavior might be a transient complex formation between a benzene molecule and a rubidium atom arising from a transfer of the rubidium 5s electron to a π-orbital of the benzene (McNeal, 1964a). The pressure shift of the Rb^{87} hyperfine frequency also supports this hypothesis (Brewer, 1964).

Among the more interesting experiments that remain to be performed regarding spin relaxation would be measurements on the hydrogen atom-helium system. The disorientation cross section results for this system would be amenable to accurate theoretical interpretation.

13 / Chemical Applications of Optical Pumping

13-1 ATOMIC STRUCTURE

Recently, chemists have become interested in optical pumping not just because of the role that it plays in such devices as lasers, but because there are a number of chemical problems that can be attacked with optically pumped systems. If we break the interest of the chemist down into several categories we must first mention one area which is of interest to both the physicist and the chemist—that is, atomic structure. Optical pumping experiments yield values for the hyperfine interaction energy, the Zeeman interaction, the electric field gradient at the nucleus, etc. Such information may be obtained for both ground and excited states. These experimental quantities are useful to the theoretical chemist as criteria for testing the accuracy of wave functions for many-electron atoms. In the case where the atom has an unpaired electron in an s orbital, agreement between theoretical and experimental values of the hyperfine interaction is an indication that the wave function is a reasonably accurate description of the electron distribution in the region of the nucleus. For atoms having unpaired p electrons, configuration interaction or an unrestricted orbital method (such as the unrestricted Hartree-Fock method) must be correctly applied to explain not only the magnitude, but even the presence of the hyperfine interaction. An example of the latter type of atom is the nitrogen atom where there are three unpaired electrons in the three 2p orbitals which would give zero hyperfine interaction via the Fermi contact interaction, yet a hyperfine coupling constant of 10.45 Mc/sec is observed for N^{14} (Holloway, 1958; Anderson, 1959).

In the cases where a nuclear electric quadrupole interaction is observed the theoretical chemist is faced with interesting problems. If the nuclear electric quadrupole moment is known from an independent experiment, measurement of the quadrupole interaction yields an experimental value for the electric field-gradient tensor at the nucleus. This value may be compared with a theoretical field gradient which arises from two sources: a contribution from the valence electrons and a contribution from the core electrons. Again, agreement with experiment must require a reasonably good wave function in which the quadrupole polarization of the core has been correctly evaluated.

There are other quantities obtainable from optical pumping experiments that are of interest to the theoretical chemist dealing with atomic structure problems. Among these are values of the Lande g-factor for excited electronic states of atoms such as are obtained from the level crossing experiments, as well as g-factors for ground states.

13—2 INTERMOLECULAR INTERACTIONS

A second area of interest to the chemist is the application of optical pumping to a study of atom-atom or atom-molecule collisions. This can be accomplished by means of the pressure shift of the hyperfine interactions (Clarke, 1962), or with spin-relaxation studies (Bernheim, 1962) as has been mentioned previously. Studies of this nature reveal specific details of the interactions occurring during collision. In addition, any accurate measurement of a magnetic resonance line shape or of a level crossing line shape yields relaxation times which are related to the interactions acting upon the atom under study. Evidence for molecular complex formation between an optically oriented atom and a buffer gas molecule (for example, rubidium and benzene) may be obtained from both relaxation studies (McNeal, 1964a) and pressure shift of the hyperfine interaction studies (Brewer, 1964). Values for the equilibrium constant and activation energy for such a reaction could be obtained. Although only one example of this type of chemical application has been investigated, it is evident that there is the possibility of general utility of optical pumping for certain types of complex reaction equilibria.

13—3 CHEMICAL KINETICS

It has become increasingly evident that in order to untangle the microscopic details of a chemical reaction it is desirable to examine one variable, or state of the system, at a time. The recent work on reactions in crossed molecular beams is a case in point. The reacting molecules can be selected according to a set of translational states which means that their speeds and direction of travel are known in some laboratory coordinate system.

An alternative method of state selection is to create a nonequilibrium distribution in the orientation of spin angular momenta of a reacting mixture. Such a state selection can be obtained in an atomic beam with a Stern-Gerlach magnet or in a vapor by optical pumping. This kind of optical pumping experiment could be useful in certain experiments. For example, consider the simple dimerization equilibirum:

$$2Rb \rightleftharpoons Rb_2$$

If spin orientation of the rubidium atoms is achieved, the above reaction should shift to the left. The reasoning behind this interesting result rests on the fact that the above chemical equilibrium is dependent upon the ability of two rubidium atoms to combine to form a diatomic molecule with some finite probability. If a high degree of spin orientation is achieved, rubidium atoms would collide with one another along triplet potential paths which are most likely antibonding states for alkali metals. Therefore, the probability for bond formation is decreased with a resultant shift in the chemical equilibrium in favor of the monatomic species. A simple statistical argument also predicts a shift in equilibrium. The above conjures up the intriguing possibility of storing hydrogen atoms without recombination by keeping them in the same m state with optical pumping. However, this is unlikely as there will always be some recombination taking place with the release of large amounts of energy which, in turn, can excite processes that facilitate spin relaxation.

Of the more practical possibilities, the use of optically pumped atoms as a probe to measure the concentration of a free radical species has received some attention (McNeal, 1964b). If this is done as a function of time, the kinetics of a free radical reaction can be followed. There are two approaches that can be used in this type of study: one involving the detection of molecular free radicals and the second involving the observation of an atomic by-product of the reaction, e.g., a hydrogen atom. The detection of the molecular free radical could be accomplished by measuring the degree or extent of orientation of the optically pumped species with and without the radical present. When the radical collides with the oriented atom, spin exchange will occur. The spin of the free radical would have a short relaxation time due to coupling with rotational angular momenta and the rapid perturbation of the rotational states via collisions of the free radical with surrounding atoms and molecules. The net effect would result in an apparent decrease in the relaxation time of the pumped atom. Since the spin-exchange cross section between atom and radical is constant and since the relaxation time of the radical can be constant with the right experimental design, the rate of change of apparent relaxation time of the pumped species would be equal to the rate of change of concentration of radical species. This method has the advantage that very small concentrations of radical can be measured, but it also has the disadvantage that it is not specific. If more than one radical species is present a composite effect is observed. If a radiofrequency resonance could be observed in the radical by a spin-exchange experiment similar to those previously described this dilemma could be avoided. Unfortunately, it is unlikely that a radical would remain oriented for a time longer than it takes to produce two spin-exchange collisions with a pumped atom, which would be the minimum time required to observe a radiofrequency resonance. Nevertheless, there are a number of reactions that could be studied by this change in relaxation method that would yield results with a minimum of ambiguity.

If there is an atomic by-product of the reaction, or if an atomic species is a reactant there is the possibility of observing it and following its concentration as a function of time by a direct observation of a magnetic resonance via spin exchange. For example, if hydrogen atoms are produced by photolysis of a hydrocarbon, their rate of disappearance could be measured by observing the decrease in intensity of the 1420-Mc/sec hyperfine transition with time. Additional considerations concerning chemical reactions are discussed by McNeal, Bernheim, Bersohn, and Dorfman (1964b; see reprint).

13—4 MOLECULAR STRUCTURE

In addition to atomic structure, atom-atom and atom-molecule collisions, and chemical reactions, there remains the possibility of investigating molecular structure by direct optical pumping of molecules. At first glance this might seem to be a hopeless dream. As mentioned above, molecules and radical molecules have rotational angular momenta which are perturbed by colliding with the surroundings hindering any orientation of angular momenta. However, optical pumping of the excited states of molecules should be observable without too much difficulty. By observing the polarization of the fluorescence from an excited state one could detect magnetic resonance transitions in the excited states. In an experiment similar to that involving the $^3P_1$ state of mercury one could produce an excess population in one of the sublevels of an excited electronic state of a molecule. Experimental considerations require that the vapor pressure of the molecular species be low enough to prevent relaxation in the excited state before fluorescence. Depending on the sensitivity of the photodetector this could limit the states to be examined to those that give an intense fluorescence. In addition, the exciting light should be as monochromatic as possible in order to make the experiment specific with regard to exactly which rotation-vibration-electronic states are being observed. For magnetic resonance transitions to occur the radio or microwave frequency field must be intense enough to produce the transition during the lifetime of the excited state. Inverted populations have already been detected optically in excited states of molecules (Barger, 1962; Evenson, 1964) although they were produced by a chemical reaction rather than by optical pumping.

Other steps in these directions have been made by Dehmelt and Jefferts (1962b; see reprint) who have considered the possibility of orienting H_2^+ by selective photodissociation of hydrogen molecules. Since H_2^+ is the simplest known molecule its radio frequency spectrum is of considerable interest. The magnetic resonance transitions are to be detected by examining the rate of production of products from a selective photodissociation experiment. During the experiment the ions are trapped in a quadrupolar electric field whose polarity reverses at a high frequency.

Although the methods of optical pumping may not have general utility in their application to chemical problems, these and related techniques can be employed to investigate unique problems of fundamental importance in atomic and molecular structure, atomic and molecular collisions, and chemical reactions and equilibria.

14/Optical Pumping in Solids

14–1 FLUORESCENCE IN SOLIDS

Magnetic resonance has proved to be a very fruitful method for studying the ground electronic states of solid materials and the ground states of ions in solids. However, the extension to excited electronic states is difficult because of the problem of maintaining a high enough concentration of species in the excited state to detect a magnetic resonance absorption directly. A number of experiments have been performed which use optical pumping principles to detect the resonances.

In most cases the performance of a successful optical pumping experiment depends upon the fluorescent properties of a substance. Until this present chapter the discussion has been concerned with the optical pumping of gases. At low pressures the fluorescence of a gas or vapor is not strongly perturbed. However, in a condensed phase, such as a solid or liquid, an atom or molecule cannot be treated as an isolated species; and when light is absorbed a number of processes besides fluorescence can take place, such as predissociation, chemical reaction, conversion of electronic energy to vibrational energy, and energy transfer. Such processes become more probable in condensed phases, and fluorescence will not occur if one of them dominates. In the search for solids that are fluorescent one property which is sometimes helpful is the line width of bands or lines in the absorption spectrum of the solid. A narrow line is an indication that the corresponding electronic transition is not strongly affected by the surroundings. However, this is not a general rule. Narrow bands are neither necessary nor sufficient conditions for fluorescence in solids. If the species in a condensed phase is fluorescent there are several possible ways in which a magnetic resonance can be detected optically.

14–2 OPTICAL DETECTION OF MAGNETIC RESONANCES IN SOLIDS

One method for detecting magnetic resonances in solids is similar to that mentioned in Section 7-5 and involves selective reabsorption of the fluorescence lines from the states between which a magnetic resonance detection is desired. This method is discussed in a series of fine letters which are contained in the collection of reprints (Varsanyi, 1959; Geschwind, 1959; Brossel, 1959; see reprints). Briefly, the method can be illustrated by the experimental arrangement shown in Figure 14-1 and the hypothetical set of energy levels in Figure 14-2.

If the fluorescence from solid I in Figure 14-1 consists of two lines of unequal intensity corresponding to the two transitions in Figure 14-2, and if solid II selectively absorbs one of the two lines, magnetic resonance between the upper two levels can be detected by merely observing the total light transmitted by solid II, the absorber. In certain circumstances (an example is ruby with about 0.05% Cr^{+3}) the self-absorption of the crystal is sufficient to produce the desired result, and a resonance can indeed be observed (Geschwind, 1959; see reprint).

The selective reabsorption method generally will work only at very low temperatures. An alternative method of detection was proposed for higher temperatures where selective reabsorption fails (Brossel, 1959; see reprint). If the two transitions in Figure 14-2 are right and left circularly polarized, the magnetic resonance can be detected by measuring the intensity of either the right or left circularly polarized light in the fluorescence.

The above methods do not require that the separate lines in the fluorescence

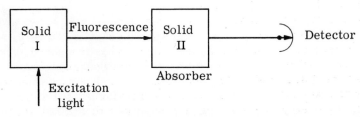

Figure 14-1 Schematic for optical detection of magnetic resonances in solids. The radio or microwave frequency field is applied to solid I. In some cases only a single solid is used, and the self-absorption properties of the solid play the role of solid II.

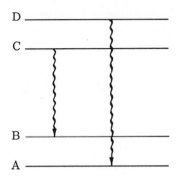

Figure 14-2 Hypothetical set of energy
levels between which fluores-
cence is observed. The transitions must be of unequal
intensity in order to observe
magnetic resonance by selective reabsorption.

be resolvable. If they can be resolved a magnetic resonance can be detected by
measuring the total intensity of one of the fluorescence lines. This method has
also been applied to ruby (Geschwind, 1965).

Recently, photon echoes have been observed in the emission from a laser
(Kurnit, 1964; see reprint). This is an interesting extension of spin echo concepts
to the phase coherence of the oscillating macroscopic electric dipole moment of
the superradiant state of the laser. Future developments in this area should be
very interesting.

14—3 APPLICATION TO MASERS

The discussion above dealt with excited electronic states in solids. The use of
optical pumping to study the ground electronic states in solids is of less interest
because of the relative simplicity with which magnetic resonance absorption is observed directly in the ground state. However, the possibility of optical pumping the
ground state of a solid in order to produce the necessary population inversion for
maser action makes the consideration of the experiment worthwhile. Unfortunately, fast relaxation times and sufficiently intense light sources make the experiment difficult at room temperature (Series, 1958; Margerie, 1964). At liquid helium
temperatures, ruby laser light can be used to depopulate the $m = \frac{1}{2}$ level of the Cr^*
ground state which can then produce maser action between the $m = \frac{3}{2}$ and $m = \frac{1}{2}$
levels at 22.4 kMc (Devor, 1962; Zverev, 1963; Scabo, 1963). The applications of
optical pumping to solid-state masers remain to be more fully investigated.

Bibliography

Prepared with the kind assistance of David Gripshover, Gerald Hurayt, Leslie Kohuth, and Margaret Korte. References to a few related works are also included.

Abragam, A., *Nuclear Magnetism* (Oxford University Press, Oxford, 1961).

Aleksandrov, E. B., and V. A. Khodovoi, "Detection of the K^{40} Isotope Using Optical Alignment of the Atoms," *Opt. Spectr. (USSR) (English Transl.)* **13**, 424 (1962 a).

Aleksandrov, E. B., "Optical Alignment of Rubidium Isotopes," *Opt. Spectr. (USSR) (English Transl.)* **13**, 250 (1962b).

Alley, C. O., "Wall Coatings of Alkyl-Chloro-Silanes for the Inhibition of Spin Relaxation," in *Advances in Quantum Electronics*, J. R. Singer, Ed. (Columbia University Press, New York, 1961), p. 120.

Althoff, K., and H. Krüger, "High Frequency Transitions in the $7 \, ^2P_{3/2}$ Level of the Cs Atom and Determination of the Quadrupole Moment of the Cs^{133} Nucleus," *Naturwiss.* **41**, 368 (1954).

Althoff, K., "High Frequency Transitions in the Excited $7 \, ^2P_{3/2}$ State of Cesium Atoms and the Determination of the Quadrupole Moment of $Cesium^{133}$ Nuclei," *Z. Physik* **141**, 33 (1955).

Anderson, L. W., F. M. Pipkin, and J. C. Baird, Jr., "Optical Polarization of Atomic Hydrogen," *Phys. Rev. Letters* **1**, 229 (1958).

Anderson, L. W., F. M. Pipkin, and J. C. Baird, Jr., "N^{14}-N^{15} Hyperfine Anomaly," *Phys. Rev.* **116**, 87 (1959).

Anderson, L. W., F. M. Pipkin, and J. C. Baird, Jr., "Precision Determination of the Hyperfine Structure of the Ground State of Atomic Hydrogen, Deuterium, and Tritium," *Phys. Rev. Letters* **4**, 69 (1960a).

Anderson, L. W., F. M. Pipkin, and J. C. Baird, Jr., "Hyperfine Structure of Hydrogen, Deuterium, and Tritium," *Phys. Rev.* **120**, 1279 (1960b); *ibid.* **122**, 1962 (1961a).

Anderson, L. W., and A. T. Ramsey, "Effect of Spin Exchange Collisions on the Optical Orientation of Atomic Na," *Phys. Rev.* **124**, 1862 (1961b).

Archambault, Y., J. P. Descoubes, M. Priou, A. Omont, and J. C. Pebay-Peyroula, "Electron Bombardment Study of the Lifetime and Hyperfine Structure of States of Sodium and Cesium," *J. Phys. Radium* **21**, 677 (1960).

Arditi, M., "The Influence of Gas Pressure on the Shift in Frequency and Line Intensity of Hyperfine Transitions in the Ground States of Alkali Metal Atoms," *J. Phys. Radium* **19**, 873 (1958a).

Arditi, M., and T. R. Carver, "Optical Detection of Zero Field Hyperfine Splitting of Na^{23}," *Phys. Rev.* **109**, 1012 (1958b).

Arditi, M., and T. R. Carver, "Frequency Shift of the Zero Field Hyperfine Splitting of Cs^{133} Produced by Various Buffer Gases," *Phys. Rev.* **112**, 449 (1958c).

Arditi, M., and T. R. Carver, "The Principles of the Double Resonance Method Applied to Gas Cell Frequency Standards," *Proc. IEEE*, 190 (1960a).

Arditi, M., "Application of the Principles of Double Resonance to the Realization of Atomic Clocks," *Ann. Phys. (Paris)* **5**, 973 (1960b).

Arditi, M., and T. R. Carver, "Pressure, Light, and Temperature Shifts in Optical Detection of O−O Hyperfine Resonance of Alkali Metals," *Phys. Rev.* **124**, 800 (1961).

Arditi, M., and T. R. Carver, "Hyperfine Relaxation of Optically Pumped Rb^{87} Atoms in Buffer Gases," *Phys. Rev.* **136**, A643 (1964).

Asawa, C. K., and R. A. Satten, "Direct Optical Detection of the Ground State Population Change of Neodynium in Ethylsulfate Crystals," *Phys. Rev.* **127**, 1542 (1962).

Balling, L. C., R. J. Hanson, and F. M. Pipkin, "Frequency Shifts in Spin Exchange Optical Pumping Experiments," *Phys. Rev.* **133**, A607 (1964a).

Balling, L. C., and F. M. Pipkin, "Spin Exchange in a Cesium−Electron System," *Phys. Rev.* **136**, A46 (1964b).

Barger, R. L., H. P. Broida, A. J. Estin, and H. E. Radford, "Optical Detection of Microwave Transitions in Electronically Excited CN Produced by a Chemical Reaction," *Phys. Rev. Letters* **9**, 345 (1962).

Barrat, J., J. Brossel, and A. Kastler, "Optical Production of Atomic Orientation in Saturated Sodium Vapor," *Compt. Rend.* **239**, 1196 (1954).

Barrat, J., "On the Identity of the Coherence Time Measured by Magnetic Resonance and the Magnetic Depolarization of the 202 Isotope of Mercury," *Compt. Rend.* **244**, 2785 (1957).

Barrat, J., and J. Brossel, "Magnetic Resonance in Optically Excited Atomic States: Improvement of the Lines by Double Diffusion of the Light," *Compt. Rend.* **246**, 2744 (1958a).

Barrat, J., "Width of Magnetic Resonance Lines of the $6\,^3P_1$ State of Mercury and Multiple Diffusion of 2537A Photons," *J. Phys. Radium* **19**, 858 (1958b).

Barrat, J., "A Study of Coherent Multiple Diffusion of Optical Resonance Radiation. Application to the $6\,^3P_1$ State of Mercury," *J. Phys. Radium* **20**, 541, 633, 657 (1959).

Barrat, M., and J. C. Pebay-Peyroula, "Magnetic Resonance of Atomic States of Cadmium Excited by Electronic Bombardment," *Compt. Rend.* **251**, 56 (1960).

Barrat, J., and J. Butaux, "Measurement of the Lifetime of the $5\,^3P_1$ State of Cadmium by the Magnetic Resonance Method," *Compt. Rend.* **253**, 2668 (1961a).

Barrat, J., and C. Cohen-Tannoudji, "Study of Optical Pumping in the Density Matrix Formalism," *Compt. Rend.* **252**, 93 (1961b).

Barrat, J., and C. Cohen-Tannoudji, "Study of Optical Pumping in the Formalism of the Density Matrix," *J. Phys. Radium* **22**, 329 (1961c).

Barrat, J., and C. Cohen-Tannoudji, "Broadening and Shift of Magnetic Resonance Lines Caused by Optical Pumping," *Compt. Rend.* **252**, 255 (1961d).

Barrat, J., and C. Cohen-Tannoudji, "Broadening and Shift of Magnetic Resonance Lines Caused by Optical Excitation," *J. Phys. Radium* **22**, 443 (1961e).

Beaty, E. C., P. L. Bender, and A. R. Chi, "Narrow Hyperfine Absorption Lines of Cs^{133} in Various Buffer Gases," *Phys. Rev.* **112**, 450 (1958).

Bell, W. E., and A. L. Bloom, "Optical Detection of Magnetic Resonance in Alkali Metal Vapor," *Phys. Rev.* **107**, 1559 (1957).

Bell, W. E., and A. L. Bloom, "Optically Detected Field Independent Transition in Sodium Vapor," *Phys. Rev.* **109**, 219 (1958).

Bell, W. E., A. L. Bloom, and R. Williams, "Microwave Frequency Standard Employing Optically Pumped Sodium Vapor," *IRE Trans. Microwave Theory Tech.* **7**, 95 (1959).

Bell, W. E., and A. L. Bloom, "Optically Driven Spin Precession," *Phys. Rev. Letters* **6**, 280 (1961a).

Bell, W. E., and A. L. Bloom, "Observation of Forbidden Resonances in Optically Driven Spin Systems," *Phys. Rev. Letters* **6**, 623 (1961b).

Bell, W. E., A. L. Bloom, and J. Lynch, "Alkali Metal Vapor Spectral Lamps," *Rev. Sci. Instr.* **32**, 688 (1961c).

Bender, P. L., E. C. Beaty, and A. R. Chi, "Optical Detection of Narrow Rb^{87} Hyperfine Absorption Lines," *Phys. Rev. Letters* **1**, 311 (1958).

Bender, P. L., "Effect of Hydrogen-Hydrogen Exchange Collisions," *Phys. Rev.* **132**, 2154 (1963).

Bender, P. L., "Interpretation of Frequency Shifts Due to Electron Exchange Collisions," *Phys. Rev.* **134**, A1174 (1964).

Bender, P. L., "Comparison of the Rubidium-87 and Proton Zeeman Transition Frequencies in the Earth's Magnetic Field," *Phys. Rev.* **128**, 2218 (1962).

Bender, P. L., "Optically Pumped Magnetometers and Related Experiments in High Magnetic Fields," in *Quantum Electronics*, P. Grivet and N. Bloembergen, Eds. (Columbia University Press, New York, 1964).

Bernheim, R. A., "Spin Relaxation in Optical Pumping," *J. Chem. Phys.* **36**, 135 (1962).

Bernheim, R. A., and M. W. Korte, "Spin Relaxation of Optically Oriented Potassium Vapor," *J. Chem. Phys.* **42**, 2721 (1965).

Besset, C., J. Horowitz, A. Messiah, and J. Winter, "On the Problem of Reso-
     nances between Several States in an Ensemble of Oriented Atoms," *J. Phys.
     Radium* **15**, 251 (1954).

Bitter, F., "The Optical Detection of Radiofrequency Resonance," *Phys. Rev.* **76**,
     833 (1949).

Bitter, F., and J. Brossel, "An Attempt to Produce Nuclear Orientation in Mer-
     cury Vapor," *Phys. Rev.* **85**, 1051 (1952).

Bitter, F., R. F. Lacey, and B. Richter, "Optically Induced Nuclear Magnetization.
     A Progress Report," *Rev. Mod. Phys.* **25**, 174 (1953).

Bitter, F., "Magnetic Resonance in Radiating or Absorbing Atoms," *Appl. Opt.* **1**,
     1 (1962).

Bjorklund, C., "Stabilized Light Intensity and Small Line Width Using UHF Exci-
     tation," *Arkiv Fysik* **13**, 185 (1958).

Blamont, J. E., and J. Brossel, "Stark Effect of the $6\,^3P_1$ State of Mercury
     Atoms," *Compt. Rend.* **238**, 1487 (1954); *ibid.* **243**, 2038 (1956).

Blamont, J. E., and J. M. Winter, "Transition Probabilities in an Excited Atomic
     System Having Three Unequally Spaced Levels," *Compt. Rend.* **244**, 332
     (1957a).

Blamont, J. E., "Research on the Stark Effect of Mercury Atoms by the Magnetic
     Resonance Method," *Ann. Phys. (Paris)* **2**, 551 (1957b).

Blandin, A., and J. Barrat, "Optical Orientation of Cs Atoms in the Saturated
     Vapor," *Compt. Rend.* **243**, 2041 (1956).

Bloch, F., and A. Siegert, "Magnetic Resonance for Nonrotating Fields," *Phys.
     Rev.* **57**, 522 (1940).

Bloch, F., "Nuclear Induction," *Phys. Rev.* **70**, 460 (1946).

Bloembergen, N., "Solid State Infrared Quantum Counters," *Phys. Rev. Letters* **2**,
     84 (1959).

Bloom, A. L., "Optical Pumping of Alkali Metals in a Foreign Gas at High Pres-
     sure and the Determination of the Spin Distribution," *J. Phys. Radium* **19**,
     881 (1958).

Bloom, A. L., "Spin Relaxation and Line Width in Alkali Metal Vapors," *Phys.
     Rev.* **118**, 664 (1960a).

Bloom, A. L., and J. B. Carr, "Pressure Shifts in the Hyperfine Structure Con-
     stant of Potassium," *Phys. Rev.* **119**, 1946 (1960b).

Bloom, A. L., *Inst. Opt. Univ. Rochester, Tech. Note* **5**, 61 (1961).

Bochmann, K., H. Krüger, and M. Rehmet, "Measurement of the Electric Quad-
     rupole Moment of Zn^{67} Nuclei by Measurement of High Frequency Transi-
     tions in the $4\,^3P_1$ State of Zn^{67} Atoms," *Ann. Physik* **20**, 250 (1957).

Boersch, H., W. Raith, and M. Rehmet, "Determination of the Spin Polarization
     from Transparency Measurements during Optical Pumping with the Na D_1
     Line," *Z. Physik* **163**, 197 (1961).

Bogle, C. S., J. N. Dodd, and W. L. McLean, "Hyperfine Structure Coupling
     Constant of the 6s6p $^3P_1$ Level of ^{199}Hg by Double Resonance," *Proc. Phys.
     Soc. (London)* **B70**, 796 (1957).

Bohr, A., and V. F. Weisskopf, "The Influence of Nuclear Structure on the Hyper-
     fine Structure of Heavy Elements," *Phys. Rev.* **77**, 94 (1950).

BIBLIOGRAPHY

Bohr, A., "Nuclear Magnetic Moments and Atomic Hyperfine Structure," *Phys. Rev.* **81**, 331 (1951).

Bouchiat, M. A., and J. Brossel, "A Study of the Relaxation of Rubidium Atoms on Walls Coated with Silicone Polymers and Paraffins," *Compt. Rend.* **254**, 3828 (1957).

Bouchiat, M. A., T. R. Carver, and C. M. Varnum, "Nuclear Polarization in He³ Gas Induced by Optical Pumping and Dipolar Exchange," *Phys. Rev. Letters* **5**, 373 (1960).

Bouchiat, M. A., and J. Brossel, "A Method of Studying the Relaxation of Optically Oriented Alkali Atoms," *Compt. Rend.* **254**, 3650 (1962).

Bouchiat, M. A., "Magnetic Relaxation of Rubidium Atoms on Paraffin Walls," *J. Phys. Radium* **24**, 379, 611 (1963).

Boutron, F., J. P. Barrat, and J. Brossel, "Magnetic Resonance Measurement of the 'Coherence Time' of the Isotopes ¹⁹⁹Hg and ²⁰¹Hg," *Compt. Rend.* **245**, 2250 (1957).

Breit, G., and A. Ellet, "The Depolarizing Influence of a Rapidly Changing Magnetic Field on the Resonance Radiation," *Phys. Rev.* **25**, 888 (1925).

Breit, G., "Quantum Theory of Dispersion; Parts VI and VII," *Rev. Mod. Phys.* **5**, 91 (1933).

Brewer, R. G., "High Intensity, Low Noise Rb Light Source," *Rev. Sci. Instr.* **32**, 1356 (1961).

Brewer, R. G., "Rb Spin Relaxation Induced by Hydrogen," *J. Chem. Phys.* **37**, 2504 (1962).

Brewer, R. G., "Comparison of Atom Spin Relaxation in the Gas Phase and on a Surface," *J. Chem. Phys.* **38**, 2037 (1963a).

Brewer, R. G., "Study of Atom Wall Collisions by Optical Pumping," *J. Chem. Phys.* **38**, 3015 (1963b).

Brewer, R. G., "Transient Charge Transfer for Gaseous Rubidium—Benzene Collisions," *J. Chem. Phys.* **40**, 1077 (1964).

Brossel, J., and A. Kastler, "The Detection of Magnetic Resonance of Excited Levels: Depolarization Effect of Optical Resonance and Fluorescence Radiations," *Compt. Rend.* **229**, 1213 (1949).

Brossel, J., P. Sagalyn, and F. Bitter, "The Optical Detection of Radiofrequency Resonance," *Phys. Rev.* **79**, 196, 225 (1950).

Brossel, J., and F. Bitter, "A New 'Double Resonance' Method for Investigating Atomic Energy Levels. Application to Hg ³P₁," *Phys. Rev.* **86**, 308 (1952a).

Brossel, J., "Detection of the Magnetic Resonance of Excited Atomic Levels. Structure of the 6 ³P₁ Level of the Mercury Atom," *Ann. Phys. (Paris)* **7**, 622 (1952b).

Brossel, J., A. Kastler, and J. Winter, "Optical Creation of an Inequality of Population between the Zeeman Sublevels of the Ground State of Atoms," *J. Phys. Radium* **13**, 668 (1952c).

Brossel, J., B. Cagnac, and A. Kastler, "Observation of Magnetic Resonance of Several Quanta in a Beam of Sodium Atoms Oriented Optically," *Compt. Rend.* **237**, 984 (1953).

Brossel, J., B. Cagnac, and A. Kastler, "Magnetic Resonance of Optically Oriented Atoms," *J. Phys. Radium* **15**, 6 (1954).

Brossel, J., J. Margerie, and J. Winter, "Bloch-Siegert Effect of Multiple Quantum Resonances," *Compt. Rend.* **241**, 556 (1955a).

Brossel, J., J. L. Mosser, and M. Winter, "Absorption of Sodium by Glass Walls Heated to 120°C," *J. Phys. Radium* **16**, 814 (1955b).

Brossel, J., J. Margerie, and A. Kastler, "Increased Rate of Atomic Orientation of Sodium Vapor in the Presence of Hydrogen," *Compt. Rend.* **241**, 865 (1955c).

Brossel, J., and C. Julienne, "Magnetic Resonance in the $7\,^3S_1$ Level of Mercury," *Compt. Rend.* **242**, 2127 (1956a).

Brossel, J., "Optical Methods of Magnetic Resonance," *Cahiers Phys.* **65**, 59 (1956b).

Brossel, J., "Optical Detection of Nuclear Magnetic Resonance," 15th Holweck Lecture, Physical Society, London.

Brossel, J., S. Geschwind, and A. L. Schawlow, "Optical Detection of Paramagnetic Resonance in Crystals at Low Temperatures," *Phys. Rev. Letters* **3**, 548 (1959).

Brossel, J., "Optical Pumping," in *Advances in Quantum Electronics*, J. R. Singer, Ed. (Columbia University Press, New York, 1961), p. 95.

Brossel, J., "Recent Progress in Optical Pumping," in *Quantum Electronics*, P. Grivet and N. Bloembergen, Eds. (Columbia University Press, New York, 1964), p. 201.

Bucka, H., "A Method of Changing the Hyperfine Structure of the Sodium Ground State," *Z. Physik* **141**, 49 (1955).

Bucka, H., "A New Form of the Double Resonance Method," *Naturwiss.* **43**, 371 (1956).

Bucka, H., "Double Resonance by Excitation with the Hyperfine Components and Detection by Means of Self-absorption," *Z. Physik* **151**, 328 (1958).

Bucka, H., and H. H. Nagel, "On the Lifetime of the $6\,^3P_1$ State in Barium," *Ann. Physik* **8**, 329 (1961a).

Bucka, H., and H. J. Schlüsser, "A Double Resonance Experiment on the $6\,^3P_1$ State of the Even Isotopes of Barium," *Ann. Physik* **7**, 225 (1961b).

Bucka, H., H. Kopfermann, and G. zu Putlitz, "On the Nuclear Electric Quadrupole Moments of the Barium Isotopes Ba^{135} and Ba^{137}," *Z. Physik* **165**, 72 (1961c).

Bucka, H., H. Kopfermann, and G. zu Putlitz, "On the Quadrupole Moment of Strontium-87 Nuclei," *Z. Physik* **168**, 542 (1962a).

Bucka, H., and G. von Oppen, "Hyperfine Structure and Lifetime of the $8\,^2P_{3/2}$ State of Cs," *Ann. Physik* **10**, 119 (1962b).

Bucka, H., and E. W. Otten, "Determination of the g_J-Factor of the 4s4p P_1 Level in the Spectrum of Ca," *Naturwiss.* **49**, 8 (1962c).

Bucka, H., H. Kopfermann, and J. Ney, "Double Resonance Investigation of the Hyperfine Structure of the $5\,^2P_{3/2}$ State of Potassium and the Determination of the Nuclear Electric Quadrupole Moment of K^{40}," *Z. Physik* **167**, 375 (1962d).

Byron, F. W., Jr., M. N. McDermott, and R. Novick, "Spin and Nuclear Moments of 6.7-Hour Cd^{107}," *Phys. Rev.* **132**, 1181 (1963).

Byron, F. W., Jr., M. N. McDermott, and R. Novick, "Self-broadening of Optical
    Double Resonance Line in Cadmium," *Phys. Rev.* **134**, A615 (1964a).
Byron, F. W., Jr., and H. M. Foley, "Theory of Collision Broadening in the Sudden
    Approximation," *Phys. Rev.* **134**, A625 (1964b).
Byron, F. W., Jr., M. N. McDermott, R. Novick, B. W. Perry, and E. B. Soloman,
    "Spin and Nuclear Moments of 245-Day Zn^{65}; Redetermination of the hfs of
    Zn^{67} and $\tau(^3P_1)$ of Zinc," *Phys. Rev.* **134**, A47 (1964c).
Cagnac, B., J. Brossel, and A. Kastler, "Nuclear Magnetic Resonance of ^{204}Hg
    Aligned by Optical Pumping," *Compt. Rend.* **246**, 1827 (1958a).
Cagnac, B., "Optical Detection of Nuclear Magnetic Resonance of Mercury-201,"
    J. Phys. Radium, **19**, 865 (1958b).
Cagnac, B., and J. Brossel, "Nuclear Orientation by Optical Pumping of the
    Isotopes ^{201}Hg and ^{199}Hg and the Measurement of their Magnetic Moments
    by Nuclear Magnetic Resonance," *Compt. Rend.* **249**, 77, 253 (1959a).
Cagnac, B., and J. P. Barrat, "Calculations on the Magnetic Resonance of the
    Ground State of the Odd Isotopes of Mercury in the Presence of Polarized
    Light," *Compt. Rend.* **249**, 534 (1959b).
Cagnac, B., "Nuclear Orientation by Optical Pumping of the Odd Isotopes of
    Mercury," *Ann. Phys. (Paris)* **6**, 467 (1961).
Carver, T. R., "Use of Optical Orientation for Atomic Clocks and Frequency
    Standards," *J. Phys. Radium* **19**, 872 (1958).
Carver, T. R., F. R. Lewis, Jr., R. E. Pollock, and G. Schrank, "Practical Dif-
    ferential Filter for Optical Pumping with Na Light," *Rev. Sci. Instr.* **32**, 861
    (1961).
Casimir, H. B. G., "Interaction between Atomic Nuclei and Electrons," *Teylers
    Tweede Gnootschap* **11**, 36 (1936); (W. H. Freeman, San Francisco, 1963).
Clarke, G. A., "Effects of Helium Buffer Gas Atoms on the Atomic Hydrogen
    Hyperfine Frequency," *J. Chem. Phys.* **36**, 2211 (1962).
Cohen-Tannoudji, C., J. Brossel, and A. Kastler, "The Conservation of Phase
    at the Time of Collision between an Oriented Sodium Atom and an Atom of
    Helium," *Compt. Rend.* **244**, 1027 (1957).
Cohen-Tannoudji, C., "Observation of the Shift of a Magnetic Resonance Line
    Caused by Optical Excitation," *Compt. Rend.* **252**, 394 (1961a).
Cohen-Tannoudji, C., "Partial Conservation of Coherence during the Course of
    the Optical Pumping Cycle," *Compt. Rend.* **253**, 2662 (1961b).
Cohen-Tannoudji, C., "Observation of a Shift of a Magnetic Resonance Line
    Caused by Real Transitions in Optical Resonance," *Compt. Rend.* **253**,
    2899 (1961c).
Cohen-Tannoudji, C., "Quantum Theory of Optical Pumping," in *Advances in
    Quantum Electronics,* J. R. Singer, Ed. (Columbia University Press, New
    York, 1961d), p. 114.
Cohen-Tannoudji, C., "Quantum Theory of the Optical Pumping Cycle," *Ann.
    Phys. (Paris)* **7**, 423, 469 (1962). A basic treatment.
Cohen-Tannoudji, C., "Quadrupole Relaxation of the ^{201}Hg Isotope on Quartz
    Walls," *J. Phys. Radium* **24**, 653 (1963).
Colegrove, F. D., and P. A. Franken, "Optical Pumping of Helium in the $^3S_1$ Meta-
    stable State," *Phys. Rev.* **119**, 680 (1960).

Colegrove, F. D., P. A. Franken, R. R. Lewis, and R. H. Sands, "Novel Method of Spectroscopy with Application to Precision Fine Structure Measurements," *Phys. Rev. Letters* **3**, 420 (1959).

Colegrove, F. D., L. D. Schearer, and G. K. Walters, "Polarization of He³ Gas by Optical Pumping," *Phys. Rev.* **132**, 2561 (1963).

Corney, A., and G. W. Series, "Theory of Resonance Fluorescence Excited by Modulated or Pulsed Light," *Proc. Phys. Soc. (London)* **83**, 207 (1964a).

Corney, A., and G. W. Series, "Double Resonance Excited by Modulated or Pulsed Light," *Proc. Phys. Soc. (London)* **83**, 213 (1964b).

Corney, A., and G. W. Series, "Magnetic Resonance at Nutational Frequency," *Proc. Phys. Soc. (London)* **83**, 331 (1964c).

Davis, L., Jr., B. T. Feld, C. W. Zabel, and J. R. Zacharias, "The Hyperfine Structure and Nuclear Moments of the Stable Chlorine Isotopes," *Phys. Rev.* **76**, 1076 (1949).

Decomps, B., J. C. Pebay-Peyroula, and J. Brossel, "Magnetic Resonance of Atomic States of Helium-4 Excited by Electron Bombardment," *Compt. Rend.* **251**, 941 (1960).

Decomps, B., J. C. Pebay-Peyroula, and J. Brossel, "Magnetic Resonance of Atomic States of Helium-3 Excited by Electronic Bombardment," *Compt. Rend.* **252**, 537 (1961).

Dehmelt, H. G., "Paramagnetic Resonance Reorientation of Atoms and Ions by Electron Impact," *Phys. Rev.* **103**, 1125 (1956).

Dehmelt, H. G., "Slow Spin Relaxation of Optically Polarized Sodium Atoms," *Phys. Rev.* **105**, 1487 (1957a).

Dehmelt, H. G., "Modulation of a Light Beam by Precessing Absorbing Atoms," *Phys. Rev.* **105**, 1924 (1957b).

Dehmelt, H. G., "Spin Resonance of Free Electrons Polarized by Exchange Collisions," *Phys. Rev.* **109**, 381 (1958a).

Dehmelt, H. G., "Resonance of Free Electrons," *J. Phys. Radium* **19**, 866 (1958b).

Dehmelt, H. G., "Realization and Measurement of Long Free Atom Spin State Lifetimes," *Proc. 12th Ann. Symp. Frequency Control, Fort Monmouth,* p. 577 (1958c).

Dehmelt, H. G., and F. G. Major, "Orientation of (He⁴)⁺ Ions by Exchange Collisions with Cesium Atoms," *Phys. Rev. Letters* **8**, 213 (1962a).

Dehmelt, H. G., and K. B. Jefferts, "Alignment of the H₂⁺ Molecular Ion by Selective Photodissociation. I," *Phys. Rev.* **125**, 1318 (1962b).

Dehmelt, H. G., "Absorption Signal from Optically Pumped Sample under Magnetic Field Reversal," *J. Opt. Soc. Am.* **55**, 335 (1965).

Derr, V. E., J. J. Gallagher, R. E. Johnson, and A. P. Sheppard, "Microwave Emission from an Optically Pumped Atomic System," *Phys. Rev. Letters* **5**, 316 (1960).

Descoubes, J. P., and J. C. Pebay-Peyroula, "On the Magnetic Resonance of Atomic States of Mercury Excited by Electron Bombardment," *Compt. Rend.* **247**, 2330 (1958).

Descoubes, J. P., "Fine Structure of the n ³P Levels of ⁴He," *Compt. Rend.* **259**, 327 (1964a).

Descoubes, J. P., "Interpretation of Crossing Experiments of Fine Structure Levels Excited by Electron Bombardment," *Compt. Rend.* **259**, 3733 (1964b).

Devor, D. P., I. J. d'Haenens, and C. K. Asawa, "Microwave Generation in Ruby due to Population Inversion Produced by Optical Absorption," *Phys. Rev. Letters* **8**, 432 (1962).

Diamond, F., J. Legendre, and T. Skalinski, "Optical Detection of Hyperfine Transitions of Atoms of Cesium," *Compt. Rend.* **246**, 90 (1958).

Dicke, R. H., "The Effect of Collisions upon the Doppler Width of Spectral Lines," *Phys. Rev.* **89**, 472 (1953).

Dobrowolski, J. A., "Mica Interference Filters with Transmission Bands of Very Narrow Half-Widths," *J. Opt. Soc. Am.* **49**, 794 (1959).

Dodd, J. N., "A 'Level Crossing' Experiment in Mercury," *Proc. Phys. Soc. (London)* **77**, 669 (1961a).

Dodd, J. N., "The g_J Value of the 6 $^3P_1$ Level in Mercury," *Proc. Phys. Soc. (London)* **78**, 65 (1961b).

Dodd, J. N., and G. W. Series, "Theory of Modulation of Light in a Double Resonance Experiment," *Proc. Roy. Soc. (London)* **A263**, 353 (1961c).

Dodd, J. N., G. W. Series, and M. J. Taylor, "The Modulation of Light in a Double Resonance Experiment," *Proc. Roy. Soc. (London)* **A273**, 41 (1963).

Driscoll, R. L., "Electronic g Factor of Rubidium," *Phys. Rev.* **136**, A54 (1964).

Eck, T. G., L. L. Foldy, and H. Wieder, "Observation of 'Anticrossings' in Optical Resonance Fluorescence," *Phys. Rev. Letters* **10**, 239 (1963).

Evenson, K. M., J. L. Dunn, and H. P. Broida, "Optical Detection of Microwave Transitions between Excited Electronic States of CN and the Identification of the Transitions Involved," *Phys. Rev.* **136**, A1566 (1964).

Fermi, E., and F. Rasetti, "The Effect of an Alternating Magnetic Field on the Polarization of the Resonance Radiation of Mercury Vapor," *Nature* **115**, 764 (1925a).

Fermi, E., and F. Rasetti, "On the Effect of Alternating Magnetic Fields on the Polarization of Resonance Fluorescence," *Z. Physik* **33**, 246 (1925b).

Field, G. B., and R. B. Partridge, "Stimulated Emission of the 3.04 cm Fine Structure Line of Hydrogen in Diffuse Nebulae," *Astrophys. J.* **134**, 959 (1961).

Franken, P. A., R. Sands, and J. Hobart, "Polarization of Free K Atoms by Exchange Collisions with Na," *Phys. Rev. Letters* **1**, 316 (1958a).

Franken, P. A., and F. D. Colegrove, "Alignment of Metastable Helium Atoms by Unpolarized Resonance Radiation," *Phys. Rev. Letters* **1**, 316 (1958b).

Franken, P. A., "Interference Effects in the Resonance Fluorescence of 'Crossed' Excited Atomic States," *Phys. Rev.* **121**, 508 (1961a).

Franken, P. A., A. E. Hill, C. W. Peters, and G. Weinreich, "Generation of Optical Harmonics," *Phys. Rev. Letters* **7**, 118 (1961b).

Franken, P. A., and J. F. Ward, "Optical Harmonics and Nonlinear Phenomena," *Rev. Mod. Phys.* **35**, 23 (1963).

Franz, F. A., "High Intensity Cesium Lamp for Optical Pumping," *Rev. Sci. Instr.* **34**, 589 (1963a).

Franz, F. A., and E. Lüscher, "Spin Relaxation of Optically Pumped Cesium," *Phys. Letters* **7**, 277 (1963b).

Franz, F. A., and E. Lüscher, "Spin Relaxation of Optically Pumped Cesium," *Phys. Rev.* **135**, A582 (1964).

Franzen, W., and A. G. Emslie, "Atomic Orientation by Optical Pumping," *Phys. Rev.* **108**, 1453 (1957).

Franzen, W., "Spin Relaxation of Optically Aligned Rb Vapor," *Phys. Rev.* **115**, 850 (1959).

Franzen, W., and M. Alam, "Magnetic Resonance of Coupled Spins," *Phys. Rev.* **133**, A460 (1964).

Gallagher, A., and A. Lurio, "Optical Detection of Level Crossings in a $J = \frac{1}{2}$ State," *Phys. Rev. Letters* **10**, 25 (1963).

Geschwind, S., R. J. Collins, and A. L. Schawlow, "Optical Detection of Paramagnetic Resonance in an Excited State of Cr^{3+} in Al_2O_3," *Phys. Rev. Letters* **3**, 545 (1959).

Geschwind, S., G. E. Devlin, R. L. Cohen, and S. R. Chinn, "Orbach Relaxation and Hyperfine Structure in the Excited $E(^2E)$ State of Cr^{3+} in Al_2O_3," *Phys. Rev.* **137**, 1087 (1965).

Glassgold, A. E., "Spin Exchange in Collisions between Atoms," *Phys. Rev.* **132**, 2144 (1963).

Goldenberg, H. M., D. Kleppner, and N. F. Ramsey, "Atomic Hydrogen Maser," *Phys. Rev. Letters* **5**, 361 (1960).

Goldenberg, H. M., D. Kleppner, and N. F. Ramsey, "Atomic Beam Resonance Experiments with Stored Beams," *Phys. Rev.* **123**, 530 (1961).

Gozzini, A., "Magnetism of Optically Oriented Atoms," *Compt. Rend.* **255**, 1905 (1962).

Greenhow, R. C., "Optical Pumping in He^3," *Phys. Rev.* **136**, A660 (1964).

Grossetete, F., "Relaxation by Spin Exchange Collisions," *J. Phys. Radium* **25**, 383 (1964a).

Grossetete, F., "Effect of Rubidium-Cesium Exchange Collisions on the Electronic Magnetization of Rubidium," *Compt. Rend.* **258**, 3668 (1964b).

Grossetete, F., "Hyperfine Relaxation of Cesium by Exchange of Collisions with Rubidium," *Compt. Rend.* **259**, 3211 (1964c).

Guiochon, M. A., J. Blamont, and J. Brossel, "On the Coherence of the Phenomeno of Multiple Scattering of Light in Resonance Radiation," *Compt. Rend.* **243**, 1859 (1956); *J. Phys. Radium* **18**, 99 (1957).

Hack, M. N., "Multiple Quantum Transitions of a System of Coupled Angular Momenta," *Phys. Rev.* **104**, 84 (1956).

Hack, M. N., and M. Hamermesh, "Effect of Radiofrequency Resonance on the Natural Line Form," *Nuovo Cimento* **19**, 546 (1961).

Hartmann, F., M. Rambosson, J. Brossel, and A. Kastler, "Effect of Buffers on the Degree of Orientation of Sodium Vapor Produced by Optical Pumping," *Compt. Rend.* **246**, 1522 (1958).

Hawkins, W. B., and R. H. Dicke, "The Polarization of Sodium Atoms," *Phys. Rev.* **91**, 1008 (1953).

Hawkins, W. B., "Alignment of Sodium Atoms," *Phys. Rev.* **96**, 532 (1954).

Hawkins, W. B., "Orientation and Alignment of Na Atoms by Means of Polarized Resonance Radiation," *Phys. Rev.* **98**, 478 (1955).

Hawkins, W. B. "Cesium Transition Probabilities for Optical Pumping," *Phys. Rev.* **123**, 544 (1961).

Herman, R., and H. Margenau, "Frequency Shifts in Hyperfine Splitting of Alkalis; a Correction," *Phys. Rev.* **122**, 1204 (1961).

Herman, R., "Noble Gas Induced Rubidium Spin Disorientation," *Phys. Rev.* **136**, A1576 (1964).

Herman, R., "Theory of Spin Exchange between Optically Pumped Rubidium and Foreign Gas Nuclei," *Phys. Rev.* **137**, A1062 (1965).

Hirsch, H. R., "Hyperfine Structure in the $^3P_1$ Level of the Twenty-four Hour Isomer of Mercury-197," *J. Opt. Soc. Am.* **51**, 1192 (1961).

Holloway, W. W., Jr., and R. Novick, "Detection of the Hyperfine Structure of Atomic Nitrogen by Optical Orientation," *Phys. Rev. Letters* **1**, 367 (1958).

Holloway, W. W., Jr., "On the Calculation of Nuclear Magnetic Moments of $^2S_{1/2}$ Atoms from Hyperfine Structure Data," *Z. Naturforsch.* **17a**, 89 (1962).

Hsu, H., and F. K. Tittle, "Optical Pumping of Microwave Masers," *Proc. IEEE*, 185 (1963).

Ionescu-Pallas, N. J., "Selective Weighting of Zeeman Levels in Alkali-Like Atoms," *Acad. Rep. Populare Romine, Studii Cercetari Fiz.* **11**, 585 (1960).

Jarrett, S. M., "Spin Exchange Cross Section for Rb^{85}-Rb^{87} Collisions," *Phys. Rev.* **133**, A111 (1964).

Karlov, N. V., J. Margerie, Y. Merle-D'Aubigne, "Optical Pumping of F Centers in KBr," *J. Phys. Radium* **24**, 717 (1963).

Kastler, A., "Some Suggestions Concerning the Optical Production and Optical Detection of Inequalities of Population of the Spatially Quantized Levels of Atoms. Application to the Stern-Gerlach Experiment and to Magnetic Resonance," *J. Phys. Radium* **11**, 255 (1950).

Kastler, A., "Optical Methods in the Study of Magnetic Resonance," *Physica* **17**, 191 (1951).

Kastler, A., "Optical Methods of Atomic Orientation and Their Applications," *Proc. Phys. Soc. (London)* **A67**, 853 (1954).

Kastler, A., "Optical Methods of Atomic Orientation and of Magnetic Resonance," *J. Opt. Soc. Am.* **47**, 460 (1957a).

Kastler, A., "Optical Methods of Hertzian Resonance," *Nuovo Cimento, Suppl.* **6**, 1148 (1957b).

Kastler, A., "Orientation of Nuclei by Means of Optical Pumping," *Physikertag. Hauptvortraege Jahrestag. Verbandes Deut. Physik. Ges. 1960,* p. 62.

Kastler, A., "On the Relations between the Experiment of Hanle and Optically Induced Spin Precession. Application to the Study of Excited Levels of Atoms," *Compt. Rend.* **252**, 2396 (1961).

Kastler, A., "Displacement of Energy Levels of Atoms by Light," *J. Opt. Soc. Am.* **53**, 902 (1963a).

Kastler, A., "Recent Developments in Optical Methods of Magnetic Resonance," *Magnetic and Electric Resonance Relaxation* (North-Holland, Amsterdam, 1963b), p. 14.

Kibble, B. P., and G. W. Series, "Further Studies of Modulated Light in a Double Resonance Experiment," *Proc. Roy. Soc. (London)* **A274**, 213 (1963).

Kleppner, D., N. F. Ramsey, and P. Fjelstadt, "Broken Atomic Beam Resonance Experiment," *Phys. Rev. Letters* 1, 232 (1958).

Kleppner, D., H. M. Goldenberg, and N. F. Ramsey, "Theory of the Hydrogen Maser," *Phys. Rev.* 126, 603 (1962).

Kohler, R. H., "Detection of Double Resonance by Frequency Change: Application to Hg^{201}," *Phys. Rev.* 121, 1104 (1961).

Kohler, R., and P. Thaddeus, "g_J of the (5s 5p) $^3P_1$ Level of Cd and the (6s 6p) $^3P_1$ Level of Hg by High-Field Double Resonance," *Phys. Rev.* 134, A1204 (1964).

• Kopfermann, H., "On Optical Pumping in Gases," *Sitzber. Heidelberg. Akad. Wiss. Math. Naturw. Kl. Abhandl.*, 69 (1960).

Krüger, H., "Intensity Ratios in the High-Frequency Spectrum of Excited Atoms Measured by the Double Resonance Method," *Z. Physik* 141, 43 (1955a).

• Krüger, H., and U. Meyer-Berkhout, "Determination of the Electric Quadrupole Moments of Rb^{85} and Rb^{87} by Measurement of the High-Frequency Transitions in the $6\,^2P_{3/2}$ Level of the Rb Atom," *Naturwiss.* 42, 94 (1955b).

Krüger, H., and K. Scheffler, "Double Resonance Experiments on the Excited $4\,^2P_{3/2}$ State of the ^{23}Na Atom," *J. Phys. Radium* 19, 854 (1958).

Kurnit, N. A., I. D. Abella, and S. R. Hartmann, "Observation of a Photon Echo," *Phys. Rev. Letters* 13, 567 (1964).

Lambert, R. H., and F. M. Pipkin, "Hyperfine Structure of Atomic Phosphorous," *Phys. Rev.* 128, 198 (1962).

Landman, A., and R. Novick, "Level Crossing Determination of $\tau\,(^1P_1)$ and g_J ($^3P_1$) in Zinc and the hfs of Zn^{65} and Zn^{67}," *Phys. Rev.* 134, A56 (1964).

Lehmann, J. C., and R. Barbé, "Measurement of the Ratio of the Magnetic Moments of ^{199}Hg and ^{201}Hg," *Compt. Rend.* 257, 3152 (1963).

Lehmann, J. C., and J. Brossel, "On the Production of Nuclear Orientation of ^{67}Zn, ^{111}Cd, and ^{113}Cd by Optical Pumping," *Compt. Rend.* 258, 869 (1964).

Lurio, A., M. Mandel, and R. Novick, "Second Order Hyperfine and Zeeman Corrections for an (sℓ) Configuration," *Phys. Rev.* 126, 1758 (1962).

Lurio, A., and R. Novick, "Lifetime and the hfs of the (5s5p) $^1P_1$ State of Cadmium," *Phys. Rev.* 134, A608 (1964).

McDermott, M. N., and R. Novick, "Large Aperture Polarizers and Retardation Plates for Use in the Far Ultraviolet," *J. Opt. Soc. Am.* 51, 1008 (1961).

McDermott, M. N., and R. Novick, "Optical Double Resonance in Radioactive Atoms: Spin and Nuclear Moments of the Ground State of Cd^{109}," *Phys. Rev.* 131, 707 (1963).

McNeal, R. J., "Disorientation Cross Sections in Optical Pumping," *J. Chem. Phys.* 37, 2726 (1962).

• McNeal, R. J., "Spin Relaxation of Optically Pumped Rubidium Atoms in Molecular Buffer Gases," *J. Chem. Phys.* 40, 1089 (1964a).

McNeal, R. J., R. A. Bernheim, R. Bersohn, and M. Dorfman, "Optical Pumping and Chemical Reactions," *J. Chem. Phys.* 40, 1678 (1964b).

Maiman, T., "Stimulated Optical Emission in Fluorescent Solids. I. Theoretical Considerations. II. Spectroscopy and Stimulated Emission in Ruby," *Phys. Rev.* 123, 1145, 1151 (1961).

Manuel, J., and C. Cohen-Tannoudji, "Optical Detection of Magnetic Resonance by Modulation of the Transverse Paramagnetic Faraday Effect at the Larmor Frequency," *Compt. Rend.* **257**, 413 (1963).

Margenau, H., P. Fontana, and L. Klein, "Frequency Shifts in Hyperfine Splitting of Alkalis Caused by Foreign Gases," *Phys. Rev.* **115**, 87 (1959).

Margerie, J., and J. Brossel, "Transitions by Several Electromagnetic Quanta," *Compt. Rend.* **241**, 373 (1955a).

Margerie, J., J. Brossel, and A. Kastler, "Alignment of Sodium Vapor," *Compt. Rend.* **241**, 474 (1955b).

Margerie, J., "Differences between the Absorption Probabilities for Green Light for the Four Zeeman Sublevels of $^4A_2$ Ground State of Ruby," *Compt. Rend.* **253**, 2055 (1961).

Margerie, J., "Identification of the Components of the $^4A_2 \rightarrow {}^2F_1$ Transition of Ruby," *Compt. Rend.* **255**, 1598 (1962).

Margerie, J., "Measurement of the Coefficients of Optical Absorption in σ^+ and σ^- Light, of Each of the Four Sublevels of the Ground State of Cr^{+3} for the Green $^4A_2 \rightarrow {}^4F_2$ Line of Ruby," *Compt. Rend.* **257**, 2634 (1963).

Margerie, J., "Optical Methods Used in the Study of Paramagnetism of Solids," *Electronic Magnetic Resonance and Solid Dielectrics* (North-Holland, Amsterdam, 1964), p. 69.

May, A. D., "Magnetic Resonance of Atomic Levels of Zinc Excited by Electron Bombardment," *Compt. Rend.* **250**, 3616 (1960a).

May, A. D., "Width of the Magnetic Resonance of the $4\ {}^3P_1$ Level of Zinc Excited by Electron Bombardment," *Compt. Rend.* **251**, 1371 (1960b).

Meyer-Berkhout, U., "Determination of the Electric Quadrupole Moments of Rb^{85} and Rb^{87} Nuclei by Measurement of the High Frequency Transitions in the Excited $6\ {}^2P_{3/2}$ Level of Rb Atoms," *Z. Physik* **141**, 185 (1955).

Mitchell, A. C. G., and M. W. Zemansky, *Resonance Radiation and Excited Atoms* (Cambridge University Press, Cambridge, 1934).

Moos, H. W., and R. H. Sands, "Study of Spin Exchange Collisions in Vapors of Rb^{85}, Rb^{87}, and Cs^{133} by Paramagnetic Resonance," *Phys. Rev.* **135**, A591 (1964).

Nedelec, C., and J. C. Pebay-Peyroula, "Modulation of Light Emitted during the Magnetic Resonance of Atomic Levels Excited by Electron Bombardment," *Compt. Rend.* **254**, 1951 (1962).

Novick, R., and H. E. Peters, "Orientation of Rubidium Atoms by Spin Exchange with Optically Pumped Sodium Atoms," *Phys. Rev. Letters* **1**, 54, 152 (1958).

Omont, A., and J. Brossel, "Optical Anisotropy of a Metal Vapor in the Vicinity of an Absorption Line," *Compt. Rend.* **252**, 710 (1961a).

Omont, A., "Multiple Coherent Diffusion of Optical Resonance Radiation from the $6\ {}^3P_1$ Level of Mercury in Strong Magnetic Fields," *Compt. Rend.* **252**, 861 (1961b).

Omont, A., "Shift of the Magnetic Resonance Line of the $6\ {}^3P_1$ Level of Mercury by Multiple Coherent Diffusion," *Compt. Rend.* **258**, 1193 (1964).

Packard, M. E., and B. E. Swartz, *IRE Trans. Instr.* **11**, 215 (1962).

Pake, G. E., *Paramagnetic Resonance* (W. A. Benjamin, New York, 1962).

Pebay-Peyroula, J. C., J. Brossel, and A. Kastler, "On the Magnetic Resonance of Atomic Levels of Mercury Excited by Electron Bombardment," *Compt. Rend.* **244**, 57 (1957); *ibid.* **245**, 840 (1957).

Pebay-Peyroula, J. C., "Magnetic Resonance of Atomic States Excited by Electron Bombardment," *Arch. Sci. (Geneva)* **11**, 298 (1958).

Pebay-Peyroula, J. C., "Magnetic Resonance of Atomic Levels Excited by Electron Bombardment," *J. Phys. Radium* **20**, 669, 721 (1959).

Perl, M. L., I. I. Rabi, and B. Sentizky, "Nuclear Electric Quadrupole Moment of Na^{23} by the Atomic Beam Resonance Method," *Phys. Rev.* **98**, 611 (1955).

Phillips, G. C., R. R. Perry, P. M. Windham, G. K. Walters, L. D. Schearer, and F. D. Colegrove, "Demonstration of a Polarized He^3 Target for Nuclear Reactions," *Phys. Rev. Letters* **9**, 502 (1962).

Pipkin, F. M., and R. H. Lambert, "Hyperfine Splittings of Hydrogen and Tritium. II," *Phys. Rev.* **127**, 787 (1962).

Pringsheim, P., *Fluorescence and Phosphorescence* (Interscience, New York, 1949).

Pryce, M. H. L., "The Optical Detection of RF Resonances," *Phys. Rev.* **77**, 136 (1950).

Purcell, E. M., and G. B. Field, "Influence of Collisions upon Population of Hyperfine States in Hydrogen," *Astrophys. J.* **124**, 542 (1956).

Rabi, I. I., "Atomic Beam Resonance Method for Excited States," *Phys. Rev.* **87**, 379 (1952).

Raith, W., "On the Determination of Spin Polarization by a Transparency Measurement in Optical Pumping," *Z. Physik* **163**, 467 (1961).

Ramsey, A. T., and L. W. Anderson, "Spin Relaxation in an Optically Oriented Sodium Vapor," *Nuovo Cimento* **32**, 1151 (1964a).

Ramsey, A. T., and L. W. Anderson, "Pressure Shifts of the ^{23}Na Hyperfine Frequency," *Bull. Am. Phys. Soc. Ser. II* **9**, 625 (1964b).

Ramsey, N. F., "Resonance Transitions Induced by Perturbations at Two or More Different Frequencies," *Phys. Rev.* **100**, 1191 (1955).

Ramsey, N. F., *Molecular Beams* (Oxford University Press, Oxford, 1956).

Rank, D. H., and T. A. Wiggins, "Collision Narrowing of Spectral Lines. H$_2$ Quadrupole Spectrum," *J. Chem. Phys.* **39**, 1349 (1963).

Ritter, G. J., and G. W. Series, "Nuclear Electric Quadrupole Moment of Potassium-39," *Proc. Phys. Soc. (London)* **A68**, 450 (1955).

Ritter, G. J., and G. W. Series, "Double Resonance Measurements of Hyperfine Structures in Potassium," *Proc. Roy. Soc. (London)* **A238**. 473 (1957).

Robinson, L. B., "Frequency Shifts in the Hyperfine Spectra of Alkalis Caused by Foreign Gases," *Phys. Rev.* **117**, 1275 (1960).

Rollet, N., J. Brossel, and A. Kastler, "Polarization of the Optical Resonance Radiation of the 198 Isotope of Mercury," *Compt. Rend.* **242**, 240 (1956).

Romestain, R., and J. Margerie, "Structure of the Excited States of F Centers in NaCl, NaBr, and KCl," *Compt. Rend.* **258**, 2525 (1964).

Rose, M. E., and R. L. Carovillano, "Coherence Effects in Resonance Fluorescence," *Phys. Rev.* **122**, 1185 (1961).

Sagalyn, P. L., "The Hyperfine Structure of the 3 $^2P_{1/2}$ State of Na^{23}," *Phys. Rev.* **94**, 885 (1954).

Sagalyn, P. L., and A. C. Melissinos, "Separation and Identification of Overlapping Hyperfine Structure Components: Application to Mercury Resonance Radiation," *Phys. Rev.* **109**, 375 (1958).

Salwen, H., "Resonance Transitions in Molecular Beam Experiments. II. Averages over the Velocity Distribution," *Phys. Rev.* **101**, 621 (1956a).

Salwen, H., "Theory of Multiple Quantum Transitions in the Ground State of K^{40}," *Phys. Rev.* **101**, 623 (1956b).

Scabo, A., "Microwave Maser Action in Ruby at 78° K by Laser Pumping," *Proc. IEEE* **51**, 1037 (1963).

Schawlow, A. L., and C. H. Townes, "Infrared and Optical Masers," *Phys. Rev.* **112**, 1940 (1958).

Schearer, L. D., "Production of Very Stable Magnetic Fields in the Range 0-50 Gauss," *Rev. Sci. Instr.* **23**, 1190 (1961).

Schearer, L. D., F. D. Colegrove, and G. K. Walters, "Large He^3 Nuclear Polarization," *Phys. Rev. Letters* **10**, 108 (1963).

Series, G. W., and W. N. Fox, "Magnetic Resonance of the n = 4 Level of Singly Ionized Helium," *J. Phys. Radium* **19**, 850 (1958a).

Series, G. W., and M. J. Taylor, "Optical Pumping of Paramagnetic Ions in Solids," *J. Phys. Radium* **19**, 901 (1958b).

Series, G. W., "Radiofrequency Spectroscopy of Excited Atoms," *Rept. Progr. Phys.* **26**, 280 (1959).

Series, G. W., "Coherent Scattering by Mercury Vapor," *Inst. Opt. Univ. Rochester, Tech. Note* **5**, 75 (1961).

Skalinski, T., "Optical Orientation of Atoms in a Saturated Cesium Vapor," *Compt. Rend.* **245**, 1908 (1957).

Skalinski, T., "Optical Orientation of Atoms in Cesium Vapor," *J. Phys. Radium* **19**, 890 (1958).

Skillman, T. L., and P. L. Bender, "Measurement of the Earth's Magnetic Field with a Rubidium Vapor Magnetometer," *J. Geophys. Res.* **63**, 513 (1958).

Skinner, H. W. B., "On the Excitation of Polarized Light by Electron Impact," *Proc. Roy. Soc. (London)* **A112**, 642 (1926).

Skinner, H. W. B., and E. T. S. Appleyard, "On the Excitation of Polarized Light by Electron Impact. II. Mercury," *Proc. Roy. Soc. (London)* **A117**, 224 (1928).

Skrotskii, G. V., and T. G. Izyumova, "Optical Orientation of Atoms and Its Applications," *Soviet Phys. —Usp.* **4**, 177 (1961).

Slichter, C. P., *Principles of Magnetic Resonance* (Harper and Row, New York, 1963).

Sternheimer, R. M., "Effect of the Atomic Core on the Nuclear Quadrupole Coupling," *Phys. Rev.* **95**, 736 (1956).

Stroke, H. H., R. J. Blin-Stoyle, and V. Jaccarino, "Configuration Mixing and the Effects of Distributed Nuclear Magnetization on Hyperfine Structure in Odd-A Nuclei," *Phys. Rev.* **123**, 1326 (1961).

Thaddeus, P., and R. Novick, "Optical Delection of Level Crossing in the (5s5p) $^3P_1$ State of Cd^{111} and Cd^{113}," *Phys. Rev.* **126**, 1774 (1962).

Thaddeus, P., and M. N. McDermott, "Level Crossing in the (5s 5p) $^3P_1$ State of Radioactive Cd^{107} and Cd^{109}," *Phys. Rev.* **132**, 1186 (1963).

Theissing, H. H., P. J. Caplan, F. A. Dieter, and N. Rabbiner, "Optical Pumping in Crystals," *Phys. Rev. Letters* **3**, 460 (1959).

Varsanyi, F., D. L. Wood, and A. L. Schawlow, *Phys. Rev. Letters* **3**, 544 (1959).

von Roos, O., "Collision-Induced Splin Flip of Hydrogen Atoms," *Phys. Rev.* **115**, 911 (1959).

Wieder, I., and W. Lamb, "Fine Structure of the 2 ^{3}P and 3 ^{3}P States in Helium," *Phys. Rev.* **107**, 125 (1957).

Winter, J., "Study of Transitions Caused by Several Quanta between Two Atomic Levels," *Compt. Rend.* **241**, 375 (1955a).

Winter, J., "Calculation of the Transition Probabilities between Two Atomic Level When Several Quanta Are Involved," *Compt. Rend.* **241**, 600 (1955b).

Winter, J., and J. Brossel, "Multiple Quantum Transitions between Atomic States," *Arch. Sci. (Geneva)* **9**, 148 (1956).

• Winter, J., "Theoretical and Experimental Study of Multiple Quantum Transitions between the Zeeman Sublevels of an Atom," *J. Phys. Radium* **19**, 802 (1958); *Ann. Phys. (Paris)* **4**, 745 (1959).

Wittke, J. P., and R. H. Dicke, "Redetermination of the Hyperfine Splitting in the Ground State of Atomic Hydrogen," *Phys. Rev.* **103**, 620 (1956).

Wood, R. W., *Researches in Physical Optics, I and II* (Columbia University Press, New York, 1913 and 1919).

Wood, R. W., *Physical Optics* (Macmillan, New York, 1934).

Yatsiv, S., "Multiple Quantum Transitions in Nuclear Magnetic Resonance," *Phys. Rev.* **113**, 1522, 1538 (1959).

Zverev, G. M., A. M. Prokhorov, and A. K. Shevtchenko, "Generation of Millimeter Waves in Ruby by Optical Excitation," *Zh. Eksperim. i Teor. Fiz.* **44**, 1415 (1963).

Reprints

From: *Compt. Rend.* **229**, 1213-1215 (1949)

RÉSONANCE OPTIQUE. — *La détection de la résonance magnétique des niveaux excités : l'effet de dépolarisation des radiations de résonance optique et de fluorescence.* Note de MM. **Jean Brossel** et **Alfred Kastler**, présentée par M. Jean Cabannes.

Les effets de résonance magnétique, détectés par diverses méthodes ([1]), ([2]), ([3]), sont dus à des transitions spectrales entre les sous-niveaux magnétiques du niveau d'énergie fondamental des atomes, transitions induites par une oscillation électromagnétique de haute fréquence. Ces transitions, qui correspondent à l'absorption et à l'émission induite d'un rayonnement dipolaire magnétique, tendent à répartir également les atomes entre les divers sous-niveaux magnétiques, alors que le peuplement de ces sous-niveaux est régi, en abscence de ces transitions, par la formule de Boltzmann.

Dans une récente Note, F. Bitter ([4]) a attiré l'attention sur la possibilité de détecter optiquement le phénomène de résonance magnétique de niveaux atomiques excités. Une des méthodes les plus sensibles pour détecter le phénomène de la résonance magnétique d'un niveau atomique excité nous paraît être l'étude des modifications subies par la polarisation et l'intensité de la lumière de résonance optique issue de ce niveau lorsque les conditions de la résonance magnétique sont réalisées.

([1]) I. Rabi, *Physical Review*, 49, 1936, p. 324; Kellogg et Millman, *Rev. Modern Physics*, 18, 1946, p. 323.

([2]) F. Bloch, *Physical Rev.*, **70**, 1946, p. 460.

([3]) Purcel, Torrey et Pound, *Physical Rev.*, **69**, 1946, p. 37.

([4]) *Physical Rev.*, **76**, 1949, p. 833.

En effet, les états de polarisation remarquables, rectilignes ou circulaires, présentés par les radiations de résonance optique ([5]) sont une conséquence du fait que la radiation excitatrice, lorsque son vecteur électrique a une forme déterminée et une orientation donnée dans l'espace, produit l'*excitation sélective de certains sous-niveaux magnétiques de l'état excité* ([6]). Les transitions induites par la résonance magnétique tendent à détruire cette sélectivité, et si les probabilités de passage de ces transitions atteignent l'ordre de grandeur des probabilités de retour au niveau fondamental par rayonnement, il en résulte une dépolarisation importante de la lumière émise, que des techniques classiques ([5]) permettent de constater et de mesurer. Le rapport de ces deux probabilités dépend d'une part de l'amplitude du champ magnétique oscillant de haute fréquence et, d'autre part, de la durée de vie des niveaux excités qu'on analyse. Pour obtenir un effet important, il y a intérêt à utiliser un champ oscillant intense et à opérer sur des niveaux excités de grande durée de vie.

Considérons l'exemple de la radiation de résonance d'intercombinaison 2537 Å $(6\,^3P_1 - 6\,^1S_0)$ du mercure dont le niveau supérieur $6\,^3P_1$ a une durée de vie $\tau = 10^{-7}$ sec et se décompose dans un champ magnétique en trois sous-niveaux $m = -1$, 0 et $+1$, alors que le niveau fondamental $6\,^1S_0$ est simple.

Soit $Oxyz$ un trièdre trirectangle et considérons en O une cuve à vapeur de mercure éclairée suivant Ox par la radiation excitatrice 2537 Å à travers un prisme de nicol qui laisse passer uniquement le vecteur électrique excitateur Ey, parallèle à Oy. Un champ magnétique constant H_1 est dirigé suivant Oy et l'on observe l'intensité de la radiation de résonance optique rayonnée parallèlement à Oy. Pour les isotopes pairs du mercure l'excitation ne se fait, dans ces conditions, que par la composante Zeeman π et seul le sous-niveau du milieu $m = 0$ de l'état supérieur $6\,^3P_1$ est atteint. La radiation réémise ne contient donc que la composante π invisible suivant Oy. La faible intensité de la lumière de résonance observée dans ces conditions par un observateur placé sur Oy est due uniquement à la présence des isotopes impairs.

Si l'on établit un champ oscillant H_2 de façon à réaliser les conditions de la résonance magnétique du niveau $6\,^3P_1$, des transitions auront lieu de $m = 0$ vers les niveaux $m = \pm 1$ et les composantes σ apparaîtront dans la lumière de résonance optique et produiront un accroissement de l'intensité du rayonnement suivant Oy.

Les isotopes impairs du mercure et leurs propriétés nucléaires se manifesteront par une structure hyperfine, de ces maxima de résonance. Dans l'étude des raies D du sodium par le même procédé il convient de donner la préférence

---

([5]) P. Pringsheim, *Fluoreszenz u. Phosphoreszenz*, 3e édition, 1928, 4e Chapitre; Mitchell A. Zemansky, *Resonance Radiation and Excited Atoms*, 1934, 5e Chapitre.
([6]) A. Kastler, *Physica*, **12**, 1946, p. 619.

à la méthode de polarisation circulaire et d'analyse circulaire de la lumière de résonance qui garantit une haute sélectivité des niveaux magnétiques excités [7]. La méthode préconisée est applicable aux niveaux supérieurs de toutes les radiations de résonance optique et également aux niveaux atteints optiquement par excitation multiple ($7^3 S_1$ de Hg) [6].

Dans le cas d'excitation électronique par des électrons de direction et de vitesse déterminées, l'existence d'une certaine polarisation du rayonnement émis [8] montre que l'excitation électronique, elle aussi, peut favoriser certains sous-niveaux magnétiques de l'état excité et l'on peut en tirer profit pour l'étude de la résonance magnétique de ces niveaux.

La technique que nous préconisons peut donc s'appliquer à l'analyse d'un grand nombre de niveaux excités et peut donner des renseignements sur leur effet Zeeman et sa structure hyperfine.

Mais il convient de remarquer que les bandes de résonance magnétique des niveaux excités sont plus larges que celles du niveau fondamental. Leur largeur dans l'échelle des fréquences est de l'ordre de la largeur naturelle des raies de résonance optique étudiées, soit $\Delta \nu = 1/\tau$, τ étant la durée de vie du niveau excité. Dans le cas du niveau $6^3 P_1$ du mercure ceci correspond à une largeur de bande d'une dizaine d'œrsteds à fréquence constante.

From: *J. Phys. Radium* **11**, 255-265 (1950)

QUELQUES SUGGESTIONS CONCERNANT LA PRODUCTION OPTIQUE ET LA DÉTECTION OPTIQUE D'UNE INÉGALITÉ DE POPULATION DES NIVEAUX DE QUANTIFICATION SPATIALE DES ATOMES. APPLICATION A L'EXPÉRIENCE DE STERN ET GERLACH ET A LA RÉSONANCE MAGNÉTIQUE [1]

Par Alfred KASTLER.

Laboratoire de Physique de l'École Normale Supérieure, Paris.

Sommaire. — 1° En éclairant les atomes d'un gaz ou d'un faisceau atomique par des radiations de résonance orientées (faisceau lumineux ayant une direction déterminée) et convenablement polarisées, il est possible — lorsque ces atomes au niveau fondamental sont paramagnétiques (nombres quantiques $J \neq 0$ ou $F \neq 0$) — d'obtenir un peuplement inégal des divers sous-niveaux m qui caractérisent la quantification spatiale ou magnétique du niveau fondamental. Une évaluation grossière montre qu'avec les moyens d'irradiation actuels, cette dissymétrie de population peut devenir fort importante. Il résulte de l'examen des probabilités de passage des transitions Zeeman π et σ que l'illumination en lumière naturelle ou en lumière polarisée rectilignement permet de concentrer les atomes suivant les cas, soit vers les sous-niveaux m du milieu ($m = 0$), soit, au contraire, vers les sous-niveaux extérieurs ($|m|$ maximum). L'emploi de lumière polarisée circulairement permet de créer une dissymétrie de population entre les niveaux m négatifs et les niveaux m positifs, le sens de cette dissymétrie pouvant être inversé en inversant le sens de polarisation circulaire de la lumière incidente. Cette création de dissymétrie peut s'obtenir soit en l'absence de champ extérieur, soit en présence d'un champ magnétique ou d'un champ électrique. En présence d'un champ extérieur les divers sous-niveaux m (dans le cas d'un champ magnétique) ou $|m|$ (dans le cas d'un champ électrique) sont énergétiquement distincts, et la création d'une dissymétrie de population par le procédé optique correspond à une augmentation ou à une diminution de la « température de spin ».

2° Une dissymétrie de population des sous-niveaux m de l'état fondamental peut être détectée optiquement par l'examen de l'intensité et de la polarisation des radiations de résonance optique. L'emploi de récepteurs photoélectriques et l'utilisation d'une technique de modulation permettent une détection commode et sensible.

3° L'examen optique des diverses branches en lesquelles se divise un pinceau atomique dans l'expérience de Stern et Gerlach permet le contrôle du niveau quantique m des atomes de chacune de ces branches. Cette méthode optique permet d'étendre l'analyse magnétique des atomes dans l'expérience de Stern et Gerlach à l'étude des niveaux excités métastables.

4° Dans les expériences de résonance magnétique, les transitions induites par le champ magnétique oscillant de radiofréquence tendent à détruire l'inégalité de population des niveaux m. L'étude de la résonance magnétique des atomes d'un faisceau atomique peut donc se faire en remplaçant les champs magnétiques non uniformes du dispositif de Rabi, l'un par un producteur optique de dissymétrie qui précède le dispositif de résonance magnétique, l'autre par un détecteur optique de dissymétrie à la sortie du résonateur. La méthode optique permet d'étendre l'étude de la résonance magnétique à des niveaux métastables. Cette méthode permet d'étudier les transitions entre niveaux hyperfins dans un champ nul, les effets Zeeman hyperfins dans des champs faibles et les effets Paschen-Back hyperfins dans des champs forts. Grâce à la connexion entre l'effet Zeeman hyperfin et l'effet Paschen-Back hyperfin on peut ainsi analyser optiquement la résonance nucléaire pure dans des champs qui découplent les vecteurs $\vec{J}$ et $\vec{I}$. Enfin, l'étude de l'effet Stark d'un niveau atomique par la méthode de résonance peut également se faire optiquement. Le procédé d'étude optique d'un faisceau atomique permet l'emploi de faisceaux larges et à contours assez mal définis. L'appareillage à réaliser pour cette étude est donc simple et peu coûteux.

5° La sensibilité de la détection du phénomène de résonance magnétique par les procédés radioélectriques d'induction ou d'absorption est limitée par la faible valeur du facteur $\frac{h\nu}{kT}$ qui régit la dissymétrie naturelle de population des niveaux m. Ceci nécessite l'utilisation de matière sous forte concentration à l'état de solide, de liquide ou de gaz comprimé. En créant par irradiation de la cuve de résonance magnétique une dissymétrie artificielle des niveaux m on peut rendre les gaz ou vapeurs sous faible pression accessibles à ces procédés de détection. Il est intéressant également d'étudier l'action que peut avoir une irradiation sur l'intensité de la résonance magnétique de cristaux contenant des ions paramagnétiques absorbants et fluorescents.

[1] Conférence faite devant la Société française de Physique, le mardi 30 mai 1950.

6° Possibilité d'effets lumino-caloriques et lumino-frigoriques : Dans le cas de vapeurs et de cristaux de sels de terres rares dont les ions possèdent un rendement de fluorescence égal à l'unité, il doit être possible d'obtenir par irradiation une dissymétrie de population des sous-niveaux m du niveau fondamental ou du niveau excité qui correspond, suivant le choix de l'état de polarisation de la lumière incidente, à une augmentation ou à une diminution de la « température de spin ». Celle-ci tend à se mettre en équilibre avec la température du gaz ou du réseau cristallin. Il en résulte, suivant les cas, un effet d'échauffement ou de refroidissement analogue à l'effet magnéto-calorique. Mais alors que dans ce dernier effet on est obligé, pour refroidir un corps, de procéder en deux étapes, aimantation et désaimantation, pour pouvoir évacuer la chaleur produite dans l'aimantation adiabatique, le refroidissement par irradiation peut se poursuivre de manière continue car l'énergie thermique du milieu est évacuée peu à peu par les radiations de fluorescence antistokes. La possibilité d'obtenir de telles radiations dépend de la structure particulière, fine, hyperfine et magnétique des niveaux fondamentaux et excités des atomes ou des ions des terres rares. Mais, même si l'on arrive à réaliser les conditions expérimentales d'un refroidissement par irradiation, cet effet restera une curiosité scientifique plutôt qu'un moyen pratique d'obtention de basses températures.

1. Détection optique des niveaux m dans l'expérience de Stern et Gerlach.

— Dans l'expérience de Stern et Gerlach un pinceau de rayons atomiques de direction OX est soumis à un champ magnétique H transversal, parallèle à OZ et de fort gradient de même direction OZ. Si les atomes sont paramagnétiques, c'est-à-dire s'ils possèdent un moment magnétique non nul

$$\vec{\mu} = \mu_B g \vec{J}$$

(où μ_B est le magnéton de Bohr et g le facteur de Landé), lié à un moment cinétique $\vec{M} = \dfrac{J\vec{h}}{2\pi}$, le pinceau se divise en $2J + 1$ branches caractérisée, chacune, par une valeur déterminée du nombre quantique magnétique ou spatial m, ce nombre pouvant prendre toutes les valeurs différant d'une unité de $+ J$ à $- J$. Si, en outre, les noyaux atomiques possèdent un moment magnétique

$$\vec{\mu}_i = \mu_n g_i \vec{I}$$

(où μ_n est le magnéton nucléaire et g_i le facteur de Landé du noyau) lié à un moment cinétique nucléaire

$$\vec{M}_i = \vec{I} \dfrac{h}{2\pi},$$

chacune de ces branches se subdivise à son tour en $2I + 1$ brins hyperfins, le champ H étant supposé suffisamment intense pour produire l'effet Paschen-Back hyperfin. On peut considérer que le champ H produit la quantification spatiale des atomes et que son gradient effectue le tri des divers sous-niveaux magnétiques m.

En éclairant le pinceau atomique sortant du champ H par une radiation de résonance des atomes, radiation formée de vibrations convenablement orientées et polarisées, il est possible de contrôler optiquement la valeur du nombre m dans chacune des branches. Cette méthode de vérification optique a l'avantage d'être applicable, non seulement aux états fondamentaux des atomes, mais aussi aux états métastables, ce qui permettrait d'étendre l'expérience de Stern et Gerlach à l'analyse magnétique de ces états. Ces états peuvent être produits en proportion importante, soit par bombardement électronique des atomes du pinceau, soit en soumettant ces atomes à une excitation par échelon le long de leur trajet.

Considérons l'exemple d'un pinceau d'atomes de mercure contenant des atomes au niveau métastable 6^3P_2. Éclairons le pinceau à la sortie du champ magnétique par $\lambda\,5461$ Å et observons dans la direction OY l'émission du triplet de fluorescence 4046-4358-5461 Å.

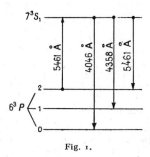

Fig. 1.

La figure 1 montre le diagramme des transitions spectrales qui interviennent, la figure 2 indique la structure magnétique des niveaux

$$6^3P_2 \quad \text{et} \quad 7^3S_1$$

et les transitions Zeeman de la raie

$$5461 \text{ Å } (7^3S_1 - 6^3P_2).$$

Une transition verticale correspond à une composante Zeeman π, une transition oblique à une composante σ. Elle sera de vibrations circulaires droites (σ_+) ou gauches (σ_-) suivant le sens de la pente. Les nombres inscrits sur les traits des transitions représentent les probabilités de passage de Hönl-Kronig [1] des composantes Zeeman. La figure 3 schématise la décomposition du pinceau des atomes Hg 6^3P_2 en cinq branches correspondant aux cinq valeurs du nombre quantique m.

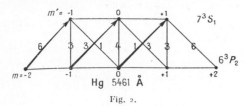

Fig. 2.

Si nous éclairons le pinceau par des rayons lumineux parallèles à OZ contenant des vibrations circulaires droites et correspondant aux transitions d'absorption $\Delta m = +1$ (flèches de la figure 2)

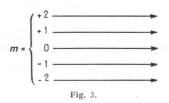

Fig. 3.

seules les trois branches inférieures $m = -2$, -1 et 0 pourront les absorber et s'illumineront. Les rapports de leurs intensités de fluorescence, observées suivant OY pour la raie d'émission 4 358 Å (*fig. 4*),

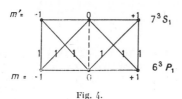

Fig. 4.

seront 6 : 2 : 1. L'inversion du sens de polarisation circulaire de la lumière incidente produira, au contraire, l'illumination des trois branches supérieures $m = +2$, $+1$ et 0 avec le même rapport d'intensité.

Enfin, en éclairant suivant une direction du plan XOY avec des vibrations rectilignes parallèles à OZ (transitions π) on constatera l'illumination des trois branches du milieu -1, 0, $+1$ avec les rapports d'intensités de 4 358 Å : 9 : 8 : 9. En étudiant dans chaque cas les états de polarisation des trois radiations émises par chaque branche du pinceau, on pourra contrôler dans tous leurs détails les prévisions déduites des valeurs des diverses

probabilités de passage. Les indications précédentes ne sont valables que pour les isotopes pairs du mercure dépourvus de spin nucléaire.

2. Production d'une inégalité de population des sous-niveaux m de l'état fondamental par illumination par des radiations de résonance convenablement orientées et polarisées.

L'étude de la polarisation des radiations de résonance et de fluorescence [2] montre que la notion de quantification spatiale conserve son intérêt, même en l'absence de champ extérieur. D'après le postulat de Heisenberg [3] la direction de quantification « fictive » en l'absence de champ doit coïncider avec un axe de symétrie de la vibration lumineuse excitatrice : Si la vibration incidente est polarisée rectilignement, la direction de quantification lui est parallèle et seules les transitions Zeeman π interviendront dans l'absorption. Si la vibration incidente est naturelle (ou polarisée circulairement), il faut quantifier par rapport à un axe perpendiculaire au plan de la vibration et seules les composantes σ (ou σ) seront absorbées. Les états de polarisation des radiations réémises s'interprètent par ce postulat qui conserve sa validité, comme nous l'avons montré [4], dans le cas de l'excitation par échelon, lorsque les vecteurs lumineux incidents sont de direction de quantification concordante. Nous avions aussi attiré l'attention sur le fait que le cas des vecteurs incidents non concordants dans l'excitation par échelon exige une généralisation du postulat de Heisenberg [5]. La solution de ce problème a été donnée par P. Soleillet [6] qui a montré qu'on peut admettre, en l'absence de champ extérieur, une direction de quantification arbitraire à condition de tenir compte d'une certaine cohérence entre les vibrations correspondant aux diverses transitions Zeeman.

L'excitation optique d'un atome par des transitions Zeeman sélectionnées entraîne une sélection des sous-niveaux m' de l'état excité, d'où les atomes retombent à l'état inférieur suivant le jeu des probabilités de passage. Il en résulte, sous l'influence de l'irradiation, une modification de population des sous-niveaux m de cet état. La production et le maintien d'une inégalité de population des niveaux m de l'état fondamental par ce « pompage optique » exige que ni le niveau excité, ni le niveau fondamental ne soient perturbés par les chocs ou par d'autres causes de perturbation. Les études de dépolarisation des radiations de résonance par les chocs [7] ont montré que le niveau excité est très sensible aux chocs et que la section efficace de choc, qui correspond à la perturbation de ses sous-niveaux m, est bien supérieure à la section de choc ordinaire de la théorie cinétique. Les sous-niveaux m de l'état fondamental sont certainement beaucoup moins vulnérables. La section efficace correspondante n'a pas été expérimentalement déterminée mais la possibilité de sa détermination constitue l'une des applications des considérations que nous développons.

Pour réaliser les conditions de production et de maintien d'une inégalité de population des niveaux m il est donc nécessaire d'opérer sur les atomes d'un gaz ou d'une vapeur très raréfiés ou sur un faisceau atomique de faible densité.

Désignons par J' le nombre quantique du niveau supérieur, par J'' celui du niveau inférieur de la transition spectrale envisagée. L'examen des probabilités de passage montre qu'on peut énoncer les règles suivantes :

Une excitation π par vibrations excitatrices polarisées rectilignement concentre les atomes vers les sous-niveaux m du milieu ($\rightarrow m = 0$) lorsque $J' \geqq J''$ et vers les sous-niveaux m extérieurs ($\rightarrow |m| = J$) lorsque $J' < J''$. L'inverse a lieu pour une excitation σ en lumière incidente naturelle.

Une excitation par des vibrations polarisées circulairement permet de concentrer les atomes, soit vers les niveaux $m > 0$ (excitation σ_+), soit, au contraire, vers les niveaux $m < 0$ (excitation σ_-). Nous allons illustrer ces règles par des exemples :

a. Transition $J' = 0 \rightleftharpoons J'' = 1$. — Une excitation π n'agira que sur les atomes au sous-niveau $m = 0$ de l'état inférieur. Des atomes excités,

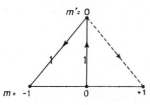

Fig. 5.

un tiers seulement, retournera par émission vers $m = 0$, les deux autres tiers transiteront vers $m = -1$ et $m = +1$. Au bout d'un certain temps, l'état $m = 0$ se sera donc vidé au profit des états $|m| = 1$. L'inverse a lieu lorsqu'on opère par excitation σ.

Une excitation par vibrations circulaires σ_+ videra l'état $m = -1$ au profit des états 0 et $+1$.

Une excitation simultanée en π et σ_+ permettra de concentrer tous les atomes vers $m = +1$.

b. Transition $J' = 1 \rightleftharpoons J'' = 1$. — En consultant le schéma ci-joint, on voit que :

Excitation π concentre $\rightarrow m = 0$,
Excitation σ concentre $\rightarrow |m| = 1$,
Excitation σ_+ concentre $\rightarrow m = +1$.

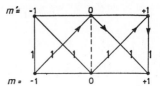

Fig. 6.

c. Transition $J' = 2 \rightleftharpoons J'' = 1$:

$\pi \rightarrow m = 0$,
$\sigma \rightarrow |m| = 1$,
$\sigma_+ \rightarrow m = +1$.

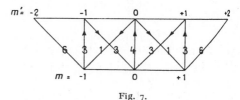

Fig. 7.

Nous allons voir, sur l'exemple de l'atome de sodium que la dissymétrie de population, qu'on peut créer à l'état fondamental, par de tels procédés de « pompage optique », peut devenir fort importante :

L'état fondamental de l'atome Na est un état $3^2S_{\frac{1}{2}}$.

Par absorption du doublet D_1, D_2 l'atome est porté au niveau $3^2P_{\frac{1}{2}, \frac{3}{2}}$.

Voici les schémas de ces deux raies de résonance

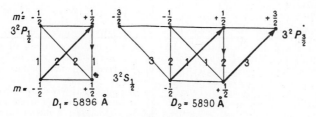

Fig. 8.

Ces schémas ne tiennent pas compte de la structure hyperfine due au spin nucléaire $I = \frac{3}{2}$. Mais il suffit d'un champ magnétique relativement faible, de l'ordre de 500 gauss, pour découpler les vecteurs $\vec{J}$ et $\vec{I}$. Les règles de sélection et de polarisation ne font intervenir alors que le vecteur $\vec{J}$.

Si, dans ces conditions, nous éclairons les atomes avec les raies D_1 et D_2 polarisées circulairement (σ_+) les atomes vont se raréfier à l'état $m = -\frac{1}{2}$ de $3^2S_{\frac{1}{2}}$ pour s'accumuler à l'état $m = +\frac{1}{2}$. Nous allons établir la loi de variation des concentrations en fonction du temps.

Le nombre d'atomes excités pendant le temps Δt est

$$\Delta n'_1 = B_{mm'} \rho_\nu n_m \Delta t,$$

n_m étant le nombre d'atomes au niveau m initial, ρ_ν la densité spectrale du rayonnement incident et $B_{mm'}$ la probabilité d'absorption d'Einstein de la transition Zeeman $m \rightarrow m'$.

Le nombre d'atomes qui retournent à l'état fondamental est

$$-\Delta n'_2 = n'_{m'} \Delta t \sum_m A_{m'm} = \frac{n'_{m'}}{\tau} \Delta t,$$

$A_{m'm}$ étant la probabilité d'émission d'Einstein d'une transition $m' \rightarrow m$ et τ la durée de vie du niveau excité.

A l'état d'équilibre, sous l'influence d'un rayonnement permanent, nous aurons

$$\Delta n'_1 + \Delta n'_2 = 0,$$

d'où

$$\frac{n'_{m'}}{n_m} = \rho_\nu \frac{B_{mm'}}{\sum_m A_{m'm}} = \rho_\nu \frac{c^3}{8\pi h \nu^3} \frac{A_{m'm}}{\sum_m A_{m'm}}.$$

Pour l'excitation au sous-niveau $m' = +\frac{1}{2}$ de l'état excité des atomes provenant du sous-niveau $m = -\frac{1}{2}$ de l'état fondamental, l'expression $\dfrac{A_{m'm}}{\sum_m A_{m'm}}$ est égale à $\frac{2}{3}$ pour D_1 et égale à $\frac{1}{3}$ pour D_2.

La proportion d'atomes excités $\frac{n'_{m'}}{n_m}$ dépend donc essentiellement de ρ_ν, c'est-à-dire de l'intensité du rayonnement incident efficace. Mitchell et Zemansky (référence [2 b], p. 96) estiment que cette proportion peut atteindre 10^{-4} au plus. Mais avec les moyens d'illumination actuels on doit pouvoir dépasser cette valeur, et l'intensité élevée du rayonnement de fluorescence qu'on peut obtenir par excitation

par échelon le confirme. Nous admettrons donc que le facteur $\rho_\nu \dfrac{c^3}{8\pi h \nu^3}$ atteint facilement 10^{-4}.

Le nombre d'atomes $\Delta n''$ qui transite pendant le temps Δt vers le sous-niveau inférieur m'' (différent du niveau initial m) est

$$\Delta n'' = n'_{m'} \Delta t \, A_{m'm''} = n'_{m'} \frac{\Delta t}{\tau} \frac{A_{m'm''}}{\sum_m A_{m'm}},$$

$\dfrac{A_{m'm''}}{\sum_m A_{m'm}}$ pour la transition $m' = +\frac{1}{2} \rightarrow m'' = +\frac{1}{2}$ est égal à $\frac{1}{3}$ pour D_1 et $\frac{2}{3}$ pour D_2.

D'où, finalement pour chacune des raies

$$\Delta n'' = \frac{2}{9} \cdot 10^{-4} n_m \frac{\Delta t}{\tau},$$

$\Delta n''$ représente l'accroissement du nombre d'atomes au niveau $m = +\frac{1}{2}$ de l'état fondamental et est égal à $-\Delta n$, diminution simultanée de ce nombre au niveau $m = -\frac{1}{2}$.

En admettant que les deux raies excitatrices D_1 et D_2 sont de même intensité, le nombre d'atomes de ce niveau baisse donc, sous l'influence de l'irradiation, suivant la relation différentielle

$$\frac{\Delta n}{n} = -\frac{4}{9} \cdot 10^{-4} \frac{\Delta t}{\tau}.$$

Posons

$$\tau' = \frac{9}{4} \cdot 10^4 \tau,$$

$$n_{-\frac{1}{2}} = n_0 \, e^{-\frac{t}{\tau'}},$$

$$n_{+\frac{1}{2}} = n_0 \left(2 - e^{-\frac{t}{\tau'}}\right).$$

Pendant que le nombre d'atomes du niveau $m = -\frac{1}{2}$ décroît exponentiellement, le nombre d'atomes de l'autre niveau $m = +\frac{1}{2}$ tend exponentiellement vers le double du nombre initial.

Au bout d'un temps de l'ordre de τ' le rapport $\dfrac{n_{+\frac{1}{2}}}{n_{-\frac{1}{2}}}$ aura dépassé la valeur 4. La dissymétrie de population sera devenue considérable.

La durée de vie du niveau 3^2P de Na est de l'ordre de $\tau = 10^{-8}$ s. D'où $\tau' \approx 2.10^{-4}$ s. Vers $100°$ C, la vitesse thermique des atomes de sodium est de l'ordre de 500 m : s. Pendant le temps τ' ces atomes parcourent des trajets d'une dizaine de centimètres. Il est donc possible, en irradiant latéralement un faisceau atomique, d'obtenir, après quelques centimètres de parcours, une dissymétrie importante de population des niveaux m de quantification spatiale.

3. Détection optique d'une inégalité de population des niveaux m.

— Les radiations de résonance optique qui servent à créer une dissymétrie de population des sous-niveaux magnétiques m peuvent servir également à détecter cette dissymétrie, car l'intensité et l'état de polarisation de la lumière de résonance optique sont fonction de la population des divers sous-niveaux m. Considérons encore l'exemple du faisceau d'atomes Na qui se

propage suivant OX et que nous éclairons latéralement, parallèlement à OZ avec les raies D_1 et D_4 polarisées circulairement (σ_+). Observons parallèlement à OY l'intensité de la lumière de résonance à travers un polariseur qui ne transmet que les vibrations parallèles à OZ (transitions π). Au fur et à mesure que le long du trajet le nombre d'atomes à l'état $m = -\frac{1}{2}$ diminue, l'intensité de la lumière de résonance baisse. (Si l'on observait sans polariseur on constaterait une augmentation d'intensité pour D_2, une diminution pour D_1).

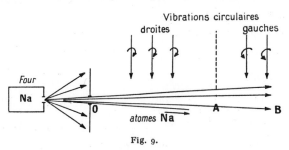

Fig. 9.

Si au delà d'une certaine abscisse A nous inversons le sens de polarisation circulaire de la radiation excitatrice (ce seront maintenant les atomes à l'état $m = +\frac{1}{2}$ qui pourront l'absorber) nous constaterons à cet endroit une augmentation subite de l'intensité de la lumière de résonance optique (vibration π).

Un détecteur optique sensible du facteur de dissymétrie

$$\delta = \frac{n_{+\frac{1}{2}} - n_{-\frac{1}{2}}}{n_{+\frac{1}{2}} + n_{-\frac{1}{2}}}$$

peut être constitué de la manière suivante : le faisceau AB est éclairé suivant OZ à travers un polariseur suivi d'une lame quart d'onde tournante. Tous les quarts de tour le sens de polarisation circulaire de la radiation incidente est ainsi inversé et il en résulte une modulation de l'intensité de la lumière de résonance réémise à angle droit, dont on isole la composante π par un nicol analyseur. Cette lumière de résonance tombe sur la couche sensible d'un multiplicateur d'électrons suivi d'un amplificateur basse fréquence accordé sur la fréquence de modulation.

Si l'on veut mesurer photographiquement le facteur de dissymétrie δ, il vaut mieux éclairer le faisceau atomique à explorer par une vibration rectiligne π et l'observer parallèlement à OZ à travers un analyseur circulaire composé d'une lame quart d'onde suivie d'un wollaston qui fournira

deux images dont le rapport d'intensité est égal au rapport $\dfrac{n_{-\frac{1}{2}}}{n_{+\frac{1}{2}}}$.

On imagine des dispositifs analogues adaptés aux autres cas particuliers.

4. Application à la résonance magnétique d'un faisceau atomique.

— Lorsque des atomes paramagnétiques se trouvent dans un champ magnétique H_0 uniforme et constant dans le temps, les divers états de quantification spatiale m, qui étaient de même énergie E_0 en absence de champ, forment une suite équidistante de niveaux d'énergie

$$E_m = E_0 - mg\Delta,$$

g étant le facteur de Landé et $\Delta = 4,7.10^{-5} H$ (œrsted) l'écart Zeeman normal exprimé en nombres d'ondes au centimètre. Si l'on établit, perpendiculairement au champ H_0 un champ oscillant rectiligne H_1 (qui peut être considéré comme la superposition de deux champs tournant en sens inverse), l'une des composantes circulaires de ce champ produit des transitions énergétiques entre les niveaux m adjacents, transitions dont le nombre passe par un maximum aigu lorsque la fréquence f du champ oscillant (exprimée en cm^{-1}) correspond à l'intervalle $g\Delta$ (en cm^{-1}) entre ces niveaux. On dit qu'il y a résonance magnétique, et les transitions induites entre sous-niveaux m d'un même état atomique correspondent à des transitions spectrales, de fré-

quence radioélectrique, d'un rayonnement dipolaire magnétique (les transitions dipolaires élec-
triques étant interdites par la règle de sélection $\Delta L = \pm\ 1$).

Rabi et ses collaborateurs [8] ont mis au point
une méthode d'étude du phénomène de résonance
magnétique des atomes d'un pinceau atomique dans
le vide. La cellule de résonance magnétique C est
précédée d'un champ magnétique non uniforme H_A
qui joue le rôle de sélecteur des niveaux m. Elle est
suivie d'un champ analogue H_B et d'un récepteur
dont l'ensemble joue le rôle d'analyseur de population des niveaux m.

Dans le dispositif de Rabi la définition géomé-
trique des fentes, la qualité magnétique des matériaux
et l'exécution mécanique de l'appareil doivent être
impeccables. Cet appareil n'a été réalisé qu'en un
seul laboratoire au monde.

Pour beaucoup d'applications, pour l'étude de la
résonance magnétique de particules monoatomiques
notamment, il est possible de remplacer les sélecteurs
et analyseurs magnétiques par les dispositifs optiques
producteurs de dissymétrie et détecteurs de dissymétrie que nous venons de décrire.

Le faisceau atomique sera soumis sur une première
partie de son trajet à l'irradiation qui crée la dissymétrie entre les niveaux m, puis il traversera la
cellule à résonance magnétique pour être soumis
à sa sortie au détecteur optique de dissymétrie.
Lorsque les conditions de la résonance magnétique
sont réalisées, les transitions induites tendent à
produire l'égalité de population des niveaux m,
et le phénomène modulé qu'on enregistre baisse
d'intensité. Il est possible d'utiliser des faisceaux
atomiques larges à contours mal définis. L'appareil
peut être réalisé avec les moyens d'un laboratoire
modeste.

Grâce à la suppression des champs magnétiques
non uniformes, la méthode optique se prête tout
particulièrement à l'étude de la résonance magnétique dans les champs H_0 faibles, c'est-à-dire à
l'analyse des effets Zeeman de structure hyperfine,
par exemple à l'étude de la structure du niveau
fondamental 6^1S_0 des isotopes ^{199}Hg $\left(F = I = \frac{1}{2}\right)$
et ^{201}Hg $\left(F = I = \frac{3}{2}\right)$.

Il sera possible d'appliquer tout le long du trajet
des atomes un champ H_0 constant et de faire ainsi
l'analyse des atomes dans des conditions parfai-
tement définies au point de vue théorique. On
pourra, en particulier, étudier dans un champ nul
les transitions radioélectriques entre les divers
niveaux F hyperfins (par exemple : le niveau fondamental $^2S_{\frac{1}{2}}$ des alcalins); dans le cas de Na :

$$J = \frac{1}{2}, \qquad I = \frac{3}{2},$$
$$F_1 = I - J = 1, \qquad F_2 = I + J = 2.$$

Mais il sera également possible d'étudier la résonance nucléaire pure ($m'_i = m_i \pm 1$) dans un champ
magnétique fort qui découple les vecteurs $\vec{J}$ et $\vec{I}$,
grâce à la connexion entre les niveaux m_F dans les
champs faibles et les niveaux $m_I + m_i$ de l'effet
Paschen-Back hyperfin. Cette étude fournira les
écarts entre niveaux hyperfins F en l'absence de
champ. Le champ magnétique fort devra être limité
à la cellule de résonance magnétique, car autrement
la règle de sélection optique $\Delta m_i = 0$ empêcherait
la détection optique des transitions nucléaires.

La méthode optique permet également l'étude de
l'effet Stark par la méthode de résonance radioélectrique, en associant dans la cellule de résonance
un champ électrique constant, séparant énergétiquement les niveaux m, à un champ magnétique
oscillant. On emploiera de la lumière naturelle ou
polarisée rectilignement et l'on tirera parti des
règles énoncées précédemment.

Enfin, ici aussi, la méthode optique aura l'avantage de permettre l'analyse de niveaux métastables.

Nous allons, de nouveau, considérer le cas du
niveau 6^3P_2 de Hg (isotopes pairs).

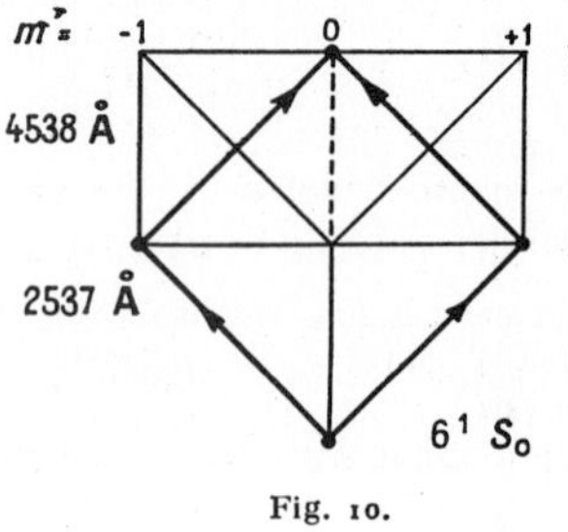

Fig. 10.

L'irradiation d'un faisceau d'atomes de mercure,
parallèlement aux lignes de force d'un champ
magnétique constant, par les radiations 2 537 Å
et 4 358 Å (vibrations naturelles) permettra
d'atteindre le seul sous-niveau $m = 0$ de l'état 7^3S_1,
d'où la moitié des atomes environ (les $5/11^e$ exac-
tement) transitera vers l'état 6^3P_2, mais seuls les
sous-niveaux du milieu $m = -1$, 0, $+1$ seront
peuplés dans la proportion $3 : 4 : 3$ (fig. 2).

La détection se fera en éclairant le faisceau
par 5 461 Å (vibrations naturelles σ) et en étudiant
les radiations 4 046-4 358 Å émises à angle droit,
à travers un analyseur tournant modulant le
rapport $\dfrac{I_\pi}{I_\sigma}$.

En l'absence de perturbation, l'éclairement
par 5 461 Å (excitation σ) redonnera $\frac{9}{1}$ fois plus
d'atomes au niveau $m = 0$ de 7^3S_1, qu'aux deux
niveaux $m = \pm 1$ réunis.

Il en résulte pour la raie 4 046 émise, un rapport de polarisation $\frac{I_\pi}{I_\sigma} = \frac{9}{2}$ et pour la raie 4 358 un rapport $\frac{I_\pi}{I_\sigma} = \frac{1}{11}$. Pour obtenir une modulation concordante de l'ensemble de ces deux raies, il suffit de placer devant l'analyseur tournant une lame de mica d'axes inclinés à 45°, onde pour l'une et demi-onde pour l'autre radiation.

Lorsque la résonance magnétique réalise l'égalité complète de population des niveaux m de l'état 6^3P_2, l'excitation de ce niveau par 5 461 Å fournira pour la raie 4 046 Å le rapport de polarisation $\frac{I_\pi}{I_\sigma} = \frac{6}{7}$ et pour 4 358 Å le rapport $\frac{I_\pi}{I_\sigma} = \frac{14}{13}$.

La modulation sera légèrement inversée. Elle sera donc sensiblement annulée si l'égalité de population n'est pas tout à fait réalisée.

5. Application à l'étude de la résonance magnétique par les procédés de détection radio-électriques.

— La sensibilité des méthodes d'étude de la relaxation paramagnétique [9] et de la résonance magnétique électronique [10] ou nucléaire par les procédés de détection radioélectriques d'induction [11] ou d'absorption [12] est limitée par la faible inégalité de population entre les divers sous-niveaux magnétiques. Cette inégalité est conditionnée par le facteur $\frac{h\nu}{kT}$ qui, pour les fréquences radioélectriques et à des températures qui ne sont pas extrêmement basses, n'est que de l'ordre de 10^{-6} à 10^{-5}. Dans ces conditions, l'absorption du rayonnement radioélectrique est presque compensée par l'émission induite d'Einstein, et sous l'influence même de cette absorption les populations des niveaux m s'égalisent et la compensation devient totale : il y a effet de saturation. Comme dans le domaine radioélectrique l'émission spontanée est négligeable, l'équilibre thermique initial ne peut être restitué que s'il existe des mécanismes de transfert d'énergie ou de « relaxation » : chocs dans le cas des gaz ou liquides, interaction avec les ondes thermo-élastiques du réseau dans le cas des solides. La faiblesse de l'effet à déceler d'une part, la nécessité d'une relaxation d'autre part, imposent donc l'étude de la matière à l'état condensé et dans ces conditions la finesse de la bande de résonance est conditionnée essentiellement par les mécanismes d'interaction.

Purcell et ses collaborateurs ont néanmoins réussi, en travaillant à la limite de sensibilité des procédés de détection, à déceler la résonance nucléaire des protons dans l'hydrogène gazeux à 10 atm [13], et Roberts, Beers et Hill [11] ont pu mettre en évidence, sur la vapeur de cæsium sous la pression de 10^{-2} mm de mercure, la transition radioélectrique entre les deux niveaux hyperfins $F = I - \frac{1}{2}$ et $F' = I + \frac{1}{2}$ de l'état fondamental

$$6\,^2S_{\frac{1}{2}}\ (\Delta\nu = 0,30\ \text{cm}^{-1} = 9192,6\ \text{Mc:s})$$

et ont pu analyser l'effet Zeeman de cette transition.

En augmentant artificiellement la dissymétrie de population par irradiation optique, on peut accroître énormément la sensibilité des procédés de détection radioélectriques, et des gaz et vapeurs sous très faible pression peuvent ainsi devenir accessibles à ces méthodes. D'ailleurs, comme nous l'avons déjà vu plus haut, l'efficacité de l'intervention optique est conditionnée par l'emploi de très faibles pressions (10^{-7} mm pour la vapeur de sodium, 10^{-4} mm pour la vapeur de mercure), car à des pressions plus élevées la perturbation par les chocs du niveau excité devient notable [7]. A d'aussi faibles pressions, la largeur des bandes de résonance dépend essentiellement de la durée de transit des atomes d'une paroi à l'autre du récipient, durée de l'ordre de 10^{-4} s. Pour des fréquences de résonance de l'ordre de 100 Mc:s, la largeur relative des bandes sera alors

$$\frac{\Delta\nu}{\nu} \leq \frac{10^4}{10^8} = 10^{-4}.$$

Par l'irradiation on pourra augmenter la sensibilité de la détection par un facteur de l'ordre de 10^5.

La probabilité des transitions dipolaires magnétiques [12 b] :

$$W_{m \to m-1} = \frac{1}{4}\,\gamma^2 H_1^2\, g(\nu)\, (F+m)(F-m+1)$$

dépend du rapport gyromagnétique γ et du facteur de forme $g(\gamma)$ qui est pratiquement égal à l'inverse de la largeur $\Delta\nu$ de la bande de résonance. La comparaison avec le cas du gaz hydrogène comprimé [13] montre que la résonance nucléaire pure du niveau $6\,^1S_0$ des atomes de mercure ^{199}Hg et ^{201}Hg ne peut pas être décelée radioélectriquement dans la vapeur de mercure, mais que la résonance électronique du niveau $3\,^2S_{\frac{1}{2}}$ de la vapeur de sodium doit être décelable, surtout si l'on module l'état de polarisation circulaire de la lumière incidente afin de favoriser tour à tour l'absorption et l'émission induite. Il convient de rechercher également si la résonance magnétique des ions paramagnétiques dans un cristal ne peut pas être renforcée par une irradiation appropriée. Lorsque les ions sont fluorescents et que le temps de relaxation est grand, un tel effet est probable.

6. Possibilité d'un effet lumino-calorique et lumino-frigorique.

— Lorsque les sous-niveaux m de l'état fondamental d'atomes ou d'ions paramagnétiques sont énergétiquement séparés par un champ extérieur ou un champ cristallin, la population de ces divers sous-niveaux m est régie, à une température donnée, par la formule de Boltzmann :

$$\frac{n_{m_1}}{n_{m_2}} = e^{-\frac{W_{m_1} - W_{m_2}}{kT}} = e^{-\frac{\Delta W}{kT}}.$$

Quand on modifie la valeur du champ (ΔW) la formule n'est plus satisfaite, et une nouvelle répartition d'équilibre des populations s'établit, sous l'influence des chocs dans le cas d'un gaz, sous l'influence des échanges d'énergie avec les vibrations du réseau dans le cas d'un cristal. Lorsqu'on augmente ΔW, en augmentant le champ magnétique H qui sépare les niveaux m, des atomes passent du niveau supérieur m_1 au niveau inférieur m_2 en cédant leur énergie au réseau. La température du cristal augmente. L'inverse a lieu lorsqu'on diminue le champ H. Ainsi s'expliquent, à l'échelle moléculaire, l'échauffement par aimantation adiabatique et le refroidissement par désaimantation adiabatique [15]. Pour refroidir une substance par désaimantation adiabatique on est obligé de procéder en deux étapes, car il faut l'aimanter d'abord et éliminer la chaleur d'aimantation par conduction avant de pouvoir la refroidir par désaimantation.

Aux effets magnéto-calorique et magnéto-frigorique on peut faire correspondre des effets luminocalorique et lumino-frigorique. Nous avons vu, en effet, qu'il est possible de modifier par irradiation la population relative des divers niveaux m (dans un champ constant). En modifiant ainsi le rapport $\frac{n_{m_1}}{n_{m_2}}$ on altère la « température de spin » des atomes ou des ions, et par un choix judicieux de la fréquence et de l'état de polarisation des radiations lumineuses incidentes on peut soit augmenter, soit diminuer à volonté la « température de spin ». Cette température de spin cherche à se mettre en équilibre avec la température des autres degrés de liberté du milieu (translations et rotations du gaz ou vibrations du réseau), et ces échanges d'énergie entraînent un échauffement ou un refroidissement correspondant à l'ensemble des degrés de liberté du milieu.

L'irradiation peut se poursuivre d'une manière continue, et si le système est bien isolé thermiquement, il peut en résulter un échauffement ou un refroidissement continu. En diminuant le champ extérieur et l'intervalle d'énergie ΔW au fur et à mesure que le refroidissement optique se poursuit, on peut évacuer ainsi des quanta d'énergie de plus en plus petits et atteindre théoriquement le zéro absolu.

Considérons le modèle d'un atome ou d'un ion paramagnétique placé dans un champ magnétique et dont les niveaux inférieurs et supérieurs sont tous les deux caractérisés par le nombre quantique $J = \frac{1}{2}$. Chacun de ces niveaux sera dédoublé par le champ en $m = +\frac{1}{2}$ et $m = -\frac{1}{2}$,

le niveau $m = +\frac{1}{2}$ étant situé au-dessus du niveau $m = -\frac{1}{2}$ (le facteur de Landé g étant supposé positif). La figure 11 a montre le schéma des transitions Zeeman et la figure 11 b l'aspect des composantes de la raie dans l'échelle des fréquences.

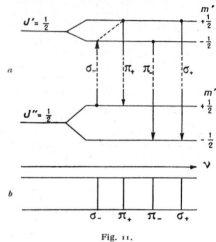

Fig. 11.

Si nous éclairons les atomes par de la lumière excitatrice polarisée circulairement σ_+, nous faisons passer des atomes du niveau $m'' = -\frac{1}{2}$ au niveau excité $m' = +\frac{1}{2}$ et nous aurons émission de la raie de résonance σ_+ de même fréquence ν que la lumière incidente et de la raie π_+ de fréquence plus basse $\nu - \Delta\nu$ que nous pouvons considérer comme une raie de fluorescence stokes. La population du niveau $m'' = -\frac{1}{2}$ baisse au profit de la population du niveau $m'' = +\frac{1}{2}$. La « température de spin » des atomes augmente, et cette énergie thermique se communiquera aux autres degrés de liberté du milieu sous l'influence des chocs. Si le niveau supérieur est lui aussi perturbé par les chocs, cette perturbation ne peut consister qu'en un passage de $m' = +\frac{1}{2}$ à $m' = -\frac{1}{2}$ et de nouvelles composantes stokes π_- et σ_- apparaîtront dans l'émission.

Supposons, au contraire, que la lumière incidente soit polarisée circulairement en sens inverse. Seule la transition σ (celle qui a la fréquence la plus faible du groupe de composantes Zeeman) sera cette fois-ci absorbée, ce qui portera les atomes du niveau $m'' = +\frac{1}{2}$ au niveau excité $m' = -\frac{1}{2}$. La lumière émise contiendra, à côté de la raie de résonance σ_- de fréquence ν', la raie de fluorescence antistokes π_- de fréquence $\nu' + \Delta\nu$. (Si le niveau supérieur est perturbé lui aussi par des chocs, les raies antistokes π_+ et σ_+ seront émises à leur tour.)

La population du niveau $m'' = +\frac{1}{2}$ baissera au profit de la population du niveau $m'' = -\frac{1}{2}$. La « température de spin » des atomes baissera et se mettra, grâce aux chocs, en équilibre avec la température des autres degrés de liberté du milieu. Ceci aura pour effet de ramener des atomes de l'état $m'' = -\frac{1}{2}$ à l'état $m'' = +\frac{1}{2}$ où ils pourront réabsorber la lumière incidente, et le cycle des opérations recommencera. Ainsi, par un cycle continu, l'énergie thermique des divers degrés de liberté du milieu sera évacuée par les radiations de fluorescence antistokes, l'émission de chaque photon antistokes de fréquence $\nu' + \Delta\nu$ assurant l'éva-cuation de l'énergie $h\Delta\nu$ du milieu, et ceci jusqu'à épuisement de l'énergie thermique du milieu. En définitive, lorsqu'en irradiant un milieu il est possible d'obtenir l'émission, à côté de la radiation excitatrice, de radiations de fluorescence stokes sans émission simultanée de radiations antistokes, le milieu s'échauffera. Si, au contraire, les conditions sont telles qu'à côté de la radiation excitatrice le milieu ne puisse émettre que des radiations anti-stokes, sa température peut diminuer, *si le rendement de fluorescence est égal à l'unité.*

Exemples d'application. — Le rendement de résonance optique est voisin de l'unité pour les gaz et les vapeurs. Considérons l'exemple de la vapeur de sodium. Le schéma que nous avons discuté $\left(J'' = \frac{1}{2},\ J' = \frac{1}{2}\right)$ convient pour la raie D_1, mais le cas de la raie $D_2\left(J'' = \frac{1}{2},\ J' = \frac{1}{2}\right)$, conduit aux mêmes conclusions : l'irradiation par σ_- ne fournit que des raies de fluorescence antistokes, l'irradiation par σ_+ que des raies de fluorescence stokes.

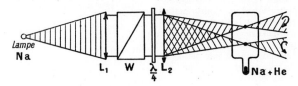

Lampe
Na

L_1 W $\frac{\lambda}{4}$ L_2 Na + He

Fig. 12.

En éclairant la vapeur de sodium placée dans un champ magnétique à travers un wollaston W suivi d'une lame quart d'onde, on peut exciter les atomes de deux régions de la vapeur par des vibrations circulaires inverses et il doit être possible de constater une différence de température entre les deux régions éclairées de la cuve de résonance. Il convient de mélanger à la vapeur de sodium sous très faible pression (10^{-5} à 10^{-6} mm Hg) un gaz inerte (hélium ou argon) sous une pression d'environ 0,1 mm Hg qui réduira le libre parcours moyen des atomes Na et qui jouera le rôle de réservoir thermique. On sait qu'un gaz inerte sous faible pression ne produit pas de chocs extinctifs et ne réduit pas le rendement de la résonance optique.

On peut remarquer que dans le cas particulier de la vapeur de sodium un autre effet, plus ample, doit conduire à un résultat bien plus efficace :

Lorsqu'on éclaire la vapeur par l'une des composantes D_1 ou D_2 seule, en présence d'un gaz étranger, les deux raies D_1 et D_2 sont émises à la fois par suite des transferts d'énergie par choc [16]. Une région de la cuve de résonance éclairée par D_1 va donc se refroidir, une région éclairée par D_2 va s'échauffer et l'écart de température entre les deux régions peut devenir important. L'écart $\Delta\nu$ entre les niveaux $^2P_{\frac{1}{2}}$ et $^2P_{\frac{3}{2}}$

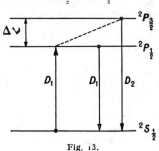

$\Delta\nu$ $^2P_{\frac{3}{2}}$

$^2P_{\frac{1}{2}}$

D_1 D_1 D_2

$^2S_{\frac{1}{2}}$

Fig. 13.

est $\Delta\nu = 17$ cm^{-1} et correspond, d'après la relation

$$hc\,\Delta\nu = k\,\Delta T$$

à une différence de température

$$\Delta T = \frac{hc}{k}\,\Delta\nu = 1,432 \times 17 = 24°.$$

Un atome de sodium qui a absorbé la raie D_1 et qui, après un choc avec un atome d'hélium réémet la raie D_2, a donc produit un refroidissement de 24° par atome. Nous avons vu plus haut qu'il est possible, avec une irradiation modérée, d'exciter un atome de Na tous les 10^{-4} s. Si la cuve de résonance contient 10^4 atomes d'hélium ou d'argon pour 1 atome de sodium, le refroidissement de l'ensemble du gaz sera d'une vingtaine de degrés par seconde. L'écart de température entre la région éclairée par D_1 et la région éclairée par D_2 peut donc devenir notable et doit être facilement mesurable.

Cas des cristaux paramagnétiques des terres rares. — Les ions des terres rares, dans les cristaux de leurs sels, possèdent des raies d'absorption et de fluorescence très fines, surtout à basse température. Elles correspondent à des transitions à l'intérieur de la couche électronique $4f$, protégée vers l'extérieur par les électrons des couches remplies $5s$ et $5p$ [17]. Ces ions possèdent donc à l'intérieur du cristal une certaine autonomie qui permet de les assimiler aux atomes d'un gaz. Les champs cristallins produisent dans les divers cristaux des décompositions des niveaux spectraux analogues à des effets Stark et l'application d'un champ magnétique produit des effets Zeeman remarquables [18]. Ce sont les différences d'énergie entre les niveaux Zeeman des états fondamentaux de ces ions qui sont utilisées dans le refroidissement par désaimantation adiabatique. Un refroidissement par effet lumino-frigorique ne peut être efficace que si le rendement de fluorescence de ces ions est élevé et s'il est possible de trouver des cas où seules des radiations antistokes sont émises à côté de la radiation excitatrice. A côté des fréquences correspondant aux transitions électroniques pures des ions, le cristal peut émettre et absorber des radiations de combinaison comme l'ont montré Ehrenfest et Tomaschek [19] pour l'émission et H. Ewald [20] pour l'absorption. Les fréquences de ces radiations diffèrent des fréquences électroniques par l'addition ou la soustraction des fréquences de vibration du réseau ou des anions du réseau. Notre raisonnement suppose que la probabilité de ces processus d'effet Raman reste faible par rapport à la probabilité des processus électroniques pures. Le rendement de fluorescence des sels purs d'ions de terres rares est faible [17 d] mais pour les ions très dilués dans un sel isomorphe le rendement de fluorescence à basse température doit s'approcher de l'unité. Il convient de remarquer qu'un tel effet lumino-frigorique reste une simple curiosité scientifique et ne peut guère être utilisé pour refroidir pratiquement une substance, car, d'une part, l'effet est faible et lent, et, d'autre part, la nécessité d'évacuer les radiations réémises par le milieu ne permet pas d'entourer la substance de parois réfléchissantes. Cependant, en employant une double paroi semi-argentée constituant un filtre interférentiel translucide aux radiations de résonance, on pourrait évacuer celles-ci tout en empêchant les radiations infrarouges de pénétrer à l'intérieur du vase Dewar. Il ne paraît donc pas impossible d'obtenir à basse température un refroidissement par irradiation provoquant la réémission antistokes si le rendement de fluorescence du cristal irradié est voisin de l'unité.

Manuscrit reçu le 23 février 1950.

BIBLIOGRAPHIE.

[1] HöNL. — *Z. Physik*, 1925, **31**, 340; *Ann. Physik*, 1926, **79**, 288. — KRONIG. — *Z. Physik*, 1925, **31**, 885.

[2] *a.* PRINGSHEIM P. — Fluoreszenz und Phosphoreszenz, 3e édition, 1928, 4e Chapitre.
b. MITCHELL et ZEMANSKY. — Resonance Radiation and Excited Atoms, 1934, 5e Chapitre.
c. PRINGSHEIM P. — Fluorescence and Phosphorescence, New-York, 1949.

[3] HEISENBERG W. — *Z. Physik.*, 1926, **31**, 617.

[4] KASTLER A. — *Ann. Phys.*, 1936, **6**, 663; *Physica*, 1946, **12**, 619.

[5] KASTLER A. — *Acta Physica Polonica*, 1936, **5**, 59.

[6] SOLEILLET P. — *J. Phys.*, 1936, **7**, 77, 118, 173.

[7] PRINGSHEIM P. — Réf. [2 *a*], p. 131-132; réf. [2 *c*], p. 102.

[8] RABI I. I., MILLMAN S. et KUSCH P. — *Phys. Rev.*, 1939, **55**, 526. — KELLOGG et MILLMAN. — *Rev. Mod. Phys.*, 1946, **18**, 323.

[9] GORTER C. J. — *Physica*, 1936, **3**, 503 et 1006; Paramagnetic Relaxation, édit. Elsevier, 1947.

[10] ZAVOISKY E. — *J. Phys. U.R.S.S.*, 1945, **9**, 211 et, 1946, **10**, 197. — CUMMEROW, HALLIDAY et MOORE. — *Phys. Rev.*, 1946, **70**, 433 et 1947, **72**, 1233. — BAGGULEY, GRIFFITHS et PRYCE. — *Nature*, 1948, **162**, 538-539. — WEIDNER et WEISS a. AL. — *Phys. Rev.*, 1948, **74**, 1478 et 1949, **76**, 1727. — ARNOLD a. KIP. — *Phys. Rev.*, 1949, **75**, 1199.

[11] BLOCH F. — *Phys. Rev.*, 1946, **70**, 460. — BLOCH F., HANSEN W. W. et PACKARD M. — *Phys. Rev.*, 1946, **70**, 474.

[12] *a.* PURCELL, TORREY et POUND. — *Phys. Rev.*, 1946, **69**, 37.
b. BLOEMBERGEN, PURCELL et POUND. — *Phys. Rev.*, 1948, **73**, 679.

[13] PURCELL, POUND et BLOEMBERGEN. — *Phys. Rev.*, 1946, **70**, 986.

[14] ROBERTS, BEERS et HILL. — *Phys. Rev.*, 1946, **70**, 112.

[15] HERZBERG G. — Atomic Spectra a. Atomic Structure, New-York, 1944, p. 211.

[16] PRINGSHEIM P. — Réf. [2 *c*], p. 97.

[17] *a.* JOOS G. — *Ergebn. exakt. Naturw.*, 1940, **18**, 78.
b. TOMASCHEK R. — *Ergebn. exakt. Naturw.*, 1941, **20**, 268.
c. FREED S. — *Rev. Mod. Phys.*, 1942, **14**, 105.
d. HELLWIGE K. H. — *Naturwissensch.*, 1947, **34**, 225.
e. TOMASCHEK R. et DEUTSCHBEIN O. — *Physik. Z.*, 1932, **33**, 878 et 1933, **34**, 374; *Z. Physik.*, 1933, **82**, 309.
f. PRINGSHEIM P. — Réf. [2 *c*], Chapitre VI.

[18] BECQUEREL J. — *J. Phys.*, 1929, **10**, 313 ou *Z. Physik.*, 1929, **58**, 205.

[19] TOMASCHEK R. — *Z. Elektrochemie*, 1930, **36**, 737. — EHRENFEST P. — Gedenkboek Kammerling-Onnes, p. 362.

[20] EWALD H. — *Ann. Physik.*, 1939, **34**, 209.

Optical Methods of Atomic Orientation and of Magnetic Resonance*

ALFRED KASTLER

Laboratoire de Physique, Ecole Normale Supérieure, Paris, France

(Received May 21, 1956)

In the optical excitation of atoms with polarized light, producing excited atoms, only some of the Zeeman sublevels of the excited state are actually reached, so that large differences of population can be built up between Zeeman sublevels or between hyperfine structure (hfs) levels. This property can be used to detect radio-frequency resonance in optically excited atomic states. These resonances produce a characteristic change in intensity or in the degree of polarization of the light re-emitted. Zeeman intervals, Stark effects, and hfs intervals can be measured in this manner. (The Stark constant of the 6^3P_1 level of Hg and the electric quadrupole moments of the alkali atoms have been obtained in this way.)

The technique of "optical pumping" gives a way to concentrate atoms in some of the Zeeman sublevels of one of the hfs levels of the ground state.

Atomic orientation has been obtained with the Na atom, in an atomic beam and in the vapor in equilibrium with the metal. The orientation effects have been studied by detection of radio-frequency resonance signals in the ground state. Orientation can be increased many times by adding a variable pressure of a foreign gas to the pure Na vapor. Because of the coupling between nuclear spin and electron spin, nuclear orientation is produced at the same time as atomic orientation.

THE starting point of all research on optical detection of radio-frequency resonance was a paper by Professor Francis Bitter in The Physical Review 1949.[1] He showed the importance of studying optically excited states of atoms to obtain information on nuclear properties. For instance: the ground state of alkali atoms is a $^2S_{\frac{1}{2}}$ state, with $J=\frac{1}{2}$. Radio-frequency measurements on this state can give no information on the electric quadrupole moment of the nucleus. To obtain such information, states with J number greater than $\frac{1}{2}$ are needed, such as the optically excited $^2P_{\frac{3}{2}}$ state. The hyperfine structure of optically excited states can be studied by conventional optical methods as interferometric analysis of optical lines, but the precision of radio-frequency methods is much higher.

Radio-frequency resonances of optically excited states can be detected by the double resonance method proposed by Brossel and the author[2] and first applied to the 6^3P_1 state of the mercury atom by Brossel and Bitter.[3] This case is a simple one and quite adequate to explain the principle of the method. We start with the experiment on optical resonance of mercury vapor. Let us consider a coordinate system $Oxyz$ (Fig. 1) and a cell of mercury vapor at its origin. H_0 is a permanent magnetic field parallel to the z axis and causing a Zeeman splitting of paramagnetic atomic states

The vapor is illuminated by mercury resonance radiation λ 2537 A raising the atoms from the ground state 6^1S_0 to the excited triplet state 6^3P_1. If the incident light is polarized with its electric vector $E_z//oz$, only the π Zeeman component of this radiation is excited and all excited atoms are in the Zeeman sublevel $m=0$ (Fig. 2). Alternatively in using circularly polarized light in the plane xoy, the $m=+1$ or the $m=-1$ level can be selected. Such a selection is equivalent to an orientation in space of the magnetic moments of the atoms.[4] Atoms in the $m=-1$ state are pointing

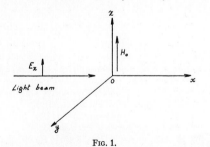

FIG. 1.

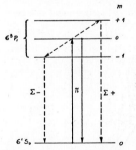

FIG. 2. Zeeman structure of the mercury resonance line 2537 A.

* Presented at the Fourth Congress of the International Commission of Optics, held in Cambridge-Boston, Massachusetts, March 28–April 3, 1956. Published with financial assistance from UNESCO and the International Union of Pure and Applied Physics.

[1] F. Bitter, Phys. Rev. **76**, 833 (1949). M. H. L. Pryce, Phys. Rev. **77**, 136 (1950).

[2] J. Brossel and A. Kastler, Compt. rend. **229**, 1213 (1949).

[3] J. Brossel and F. Bitter, Phys. Rev. **86**, 311 (1952). J. Brossel, Ann. phys. **7**, 622 (1952).

[4] The polarization of resonance radiation of atoms is analyzed in the following books. A. G. Mitchell and N. W. Zemansky *Resonance Radiation and Excited Atoms* (Cambridge University Press, New York, 1934); P. Pringsheim, *Fluorescence and Phosphorescence* (Interscience Publishers, Inc., New York, 1949).

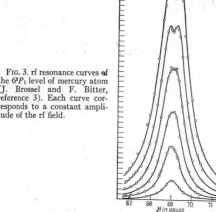

FIG. 3. rf resonance curves of the 6^3P_1 level of mercury atom (J. Brossel and F. Bitter, reference 3). Each curve corresponds to a constant amplitude of the rf field.

sequences. From the position of the resonance in the H scale, the g factor of the level is determined, the width of the lines for very low radio-field amplitude is a measure of the natural breadth of the level, e.g., its lifetime. The results are $g=1.484$, $\tau=1.55.10^{-7}$ sec.†
Figure 4 shows analogous curves obtained for the 7^3S_1 level of mercury (with a much shorter lifetime. The resonance curve is much broader than for the 6^3P_1 level, as expected). This study is actually being continued by Miss C. Julienne.

If a static electric field E_0 is superimposed on the magnetic field H_0 and parallel to it, the Stark effect of the level can be studied. This is actually done for the 6^3P_1 level of mercury by Blamont.[5] In presence of an electric field the two intervals $m=0\rightarrow+1$ and $m=0 \rightarrow-1$ are no longer equal and as a result the resonance curve is split. Figure 5 shows this splitting for a field

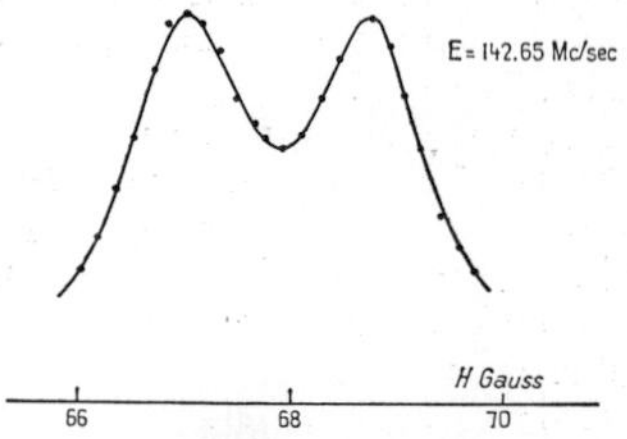

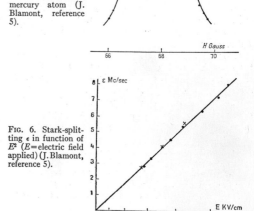

FIG. 5. Stark effect of the 6^3P_1 level of mercury atom (J. Blamont, reference 5).

FIG. 6. Stark-splitting ϵ in function of E^2 ($E=$electric field applied) (J. Blamont, reference 5).

with their moments in the direction of the field H_0; atoms in the $m=+1$ state are pointing with their moments in the opposite direction. If we define a temperature of the optically excited atoms by the Boltzmann relation, applied to the m sublevels, we can say that polarized light is able to produce extreme temperatures: $0°K$ in the first case, a negative absolute temperature in the second one.

Coming back to the selection in the $m=0$ level by π radiation, we note that the emitted resonance light also contains only π radiation, completely polarized when emitted in the xy plane, with intensity zero in the z direction. If now a radio-frequency field perpendicular to H_0 is applied, the frequency of which corresponds to the Zeeman interval, transitions to the $m=-1$ and $m=+1$ states are induced and the σ components will appear in the emitted light. The intensity and polarization of the emitted light are changed and this gives a way to detect radio-frequency resonance. Figure 3 shows resonance curves obtained by Brossel and Bitter in this manner. We do not have space here to discuss the shape of the resonance curves but we will say that the Rabi-Majorana formula is verified in all its conse-

of 29.0 kv/cm. Blamont could show that this splitting corresponds to a pure quadratic Stark effect, as shown in Fig. 6. The Stark constant is determined to be 20 Mc/sec/100 kv cm⁻¹. Note that one of the maxima corresponds to absorption of the radio-frequency energy, the other to induced emission. The optical detection method does not differentiate between them and does not give the sign of the Stark splitting. However, this sign can be deduced from the study of the odd mercury isotopes having nonzero nuclear moments and showing hyperfine structure.

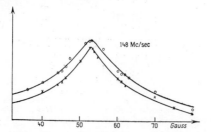

FIG. 4. rf resonance curves of the 7^3S_1 level of mercury atom [J. Brossel and C. Julienne, Compt. rend. 242, 2127 (1956)].

† Note added in proof.—Experiments made at different vapor densities showed that τ depends on the density and reaches an asymptotic value of $1.20\cdot10^{-7}$ sec at very low density. See Guiochon, Blamant, and Brossel, Compt. rend. 243, 1958 (1956).
[5] J. E. Blamont, Compt. rend. 238, 1487 (1954); 242, 2038 (1956).

It can be shown that not only Zeeman transitions ($\Delta F=0$, $\Delta m_F=\pm1$) change the intensity and the polarization of the emitted light, but that hyperfine transitions ($\Delta F=1$) in the excited state change it also and can be detected in this manner.

The double resonance method has been applied to the hyperfine structure analysis of the $^2P_{\frac{3}{2}}$ states of alkali atoms. In this manner the electric quadrupole moments of these nuclei could be determined. The levels studied hitherto are: the $3^2P_{\frac{3}{2}}$ level of Na^{23} studied by Sagalyn at M.I.T.[6]; the $5^2P_{\frac{3}{2}}$ level of K^{39} studied by Ritter and Series at Oxford[7]; the $6^2P_{\frac{3}{2}}$ level of Rb^{85} and Rb^{87} studied by Meyer-Berkhout[8]; and the $7^2P_{\frac{3}{2}}$ level of Cs^{133} studied by Althoff[9]. The last two elements were studied in Professor Kopfermann's institute at Heidelberg.

Professor Rabi has combined the method of optical excitation with his original beam deflection technique. He has studied in this way Na and Rb atoms and is studying Cs and K.[10]

The results are in agreement.

The quadrupole moments measured in this way are[‡]: $Q_{Na}=(+0.11\pm0.01)0.10^{-24}$ cm²; $Q_K=(+0.11\pm0.035)\times0.10^{-24}$ cm²; $Q_{Rb}^{85}=(+0.29_5\pm0.02)0.10^{-24}$ cm²; $Q_{Rb}^{87}=(+0.14_3\pm0.01)0.10^{-24}$ cm²; $Q_{Cs}=-(0.003\pm0.002)\times0.10^{-24}$ cm².

Figure 7 shows the hyperfine structure intervals of the state $7^2P_{\frac{3}{2}}$ of Cs and Fig. 8 is a typical record for this state, showing the 3 radio-frequency resonances corresponding to the 3 hyperfine intervals.

The second part of this paper is devoted to the development of the method of optical pumping to produce orientation of atoms by light in the ground state.[11] This orientation can be used to produce and detect radio-frequency transitions. The principle of the method may be illustrated for the case of Na atoms, disregarding first the effect of nuclear moment. Figure 9 shows the Zeeman diagram of the two resonance lines D_1 and D_2, the different m levels are shown

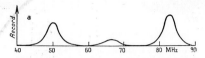

FIG. 8. Resonance curves corresponding to the hfs intervals of $7^2P_{\frac{3}{2}}$ of Cs^{133} (K. Althoff, reference 9).

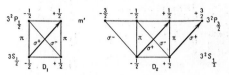

FIG. 9. Zeeman structure of the D_1 and D_2 lines of Na atom (A. Kastler, reference 26).

separated on a horizontal scale. On this diagram π transitions are vertical, σ^+ transitions and σ^- transitions can be easily distinguished by their slope.

Suppose we illuminate the atoms of an atomic beam of sodium with the circularly polarized yellow light of a sodium lamp. Only the Zeeman components σ^+ (the heavy arrows) are exciting the atoms, and in the excited states only $m>0$ states will be reached. From there the atoms fall back to the ground state, corresponding to the transition probabilities of spontaneous emission. Some of them fall back to the state from which they came. Others will transit to the $m=+\frac{1}{2}$ state. If this process is repeated several times, all atoms of the ground state will leave the $m=-\frac{1}{2}$ level and will accumulate in the $m=+\frac{1}{2}$ level. We have produced optical pumping. This change of population can be detected optically: Take a Na beam (Fig. 10) and orient the atoms in the A region by illumination with σ^+ light. In the B region the atoms are illuminated again with π light and we measure the ratio of the intensities $I\sigma^+$ and $I\sigma^-$ emitted (by analyzers of circularly polarized light: quarterwave plate + polaroid). This ratio

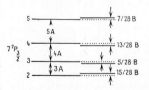

FIG. 7. Hyperfine structure of the $7^2P_{\frac{3}{2}}$ level of Cs^{133} ($i=7/2$). A ⊤-magnetic coupling constant, B ⊥-electric quadrupole coupling constant (K. Althoff, reference 9).

[6] P. L. Sagalyn, Phys. Rev. 94, 885 (1954).
[7] G. J. Ritter and G. W. Series, Proc. Phys. Soc. (London) 68, 450 (1955); Proc. Roy. Soc. (London) A238, 473 (1957).
[8] U. Meyer-Berkhout, Z. Physik 141, 185 (1955).
[9] K. Althoff, Z. Physik 141, 33 (1955).
[10] Perl, Rabi, and Senitzky, Phys. Rev. 98, 611 (1955); Senitzky, Rabi, and Perl, Phys. Rev. 98, 611 (1956); 103, 315 (1956); 104, 553 (1956).
[‡] Rabi's result included. The plus sign has to be confirmed by a method indicated by Bogle, Dodd, and Purser. Boggle, Dodd, and Purser, Phys. Rev. 101, 246 (1956).
[11] A. Kastler, J. phys. radium 11, 255 (1950); Physica 17, 191 (1951).

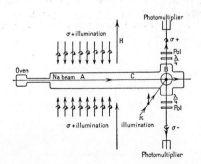

FIG. 10. Production and detection of atomic orientation in a beam of Na atoms (A. Kastler, reference 26).

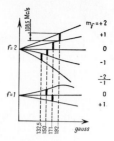

Fig. 11. hfs structure and Zeeman effect of the ground state of Na²³. Field values of resonances calculated according to the Breit-Rabi formula for a frequency of 108.5 Mc/sec (Brossel, Cagnac, and Kastler, reference 14).

levels.[13] These curves were obtained by Brossel and Cagnac. An increase in the radio-frequency amplitude produces double-quanta resonances.[14] They were independently recognized by Kusch,[15] using the Rabi method.

An interesting modification of the optical pumping technique has been applied to the case of Na by Bucka.[16] He uses the Doppler effect in illuminating a beam of Na atoms to obtain a selection of hyperfine levels in the ground state.

The method of optical pumping was applied by Bitter *et al.*[17] to produce nuclear orientation of mercury atoms Hg¹⁹⁹, actually with negative results probably because of lack of light intensity. The diagram in this case for the two hyperfine components of 2537 A is just the same as that shown for the lines D_1 and D_2 of sodium.

gives the degree of orientation. We define

$$\rho = (I\sigma^+ - I\sigma^-)/(I\sigma^+ + I\sigma^-).$$

ρ values up to 30% can be obtained in this manner.[12]

For the study of radio-frequency resonances which disorient the oriented atoms, we use the intermediate C region where in presence of a permanent field H_0 a radio-frequency field H_1 is applied. In fact there is a nuclear spin $i = \frac{3}{2}$ and the ground state of Na²³ shows hyperfine structure. Figure 11 shows the magnetic splitting of the levels $F=2$ and $F=1$ and the four distinct resonances expected separated by the Back-Goudsmit effect. It can be shown that illumination with σ^+ light in the A region concentrates the atoms in the $m_F = +2$ Zeeman level of the $F=2$ state and that illumination with σ^- light concentrates them in the $m_F = -2$ Zeeman level of the $F=2$ state. Figure 12 shows resonance curves obtained, one with σ^+ pumping concentrating the atoms in the $m_F = 2$ level, the other with σ^- pumping concentrating the atoms in the $m_F = -2$ level. The intensities of the four resonances indicate the difference in population of the involved

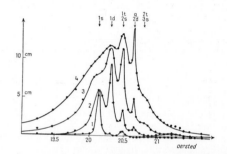

Fig. 13. rf resonance curves obtained in Na vapor (J. P. Barrat, reference 18). Orientation with σ^- light, at 14.48 Mc/sec, oven temperature 118°C. rf field intensities in arbitrary units given in column 2:

curve 1:	0.7	$1s - 2s - 3s$	mono-quantum resonances
curve 2:	3.3	$1d - 2d -$	two-quantum resonances
curve 3:	8.0	$1t - 2t -$	three-quantum resonances
curve 4:	15.0	$q -$	four-quantum resonance.

We tried to orient atoms by optical pumping in Na vapor. In this case the pumping region and detection region are not separated in space. The incident light is σ^+ light traveling parallel to field H_0. For detection the light emitted at 90° is analyzed, and I_π and I_σ intensities are compared and matched. Figure 13 shows resonance curves obtained by Barrat with increasing radio-frequency amplitudes. Two-three-four quantum transitions are easily obtained.[18] Note that for this type of multiple quanta transitions an n-quantum transition

[13] Brossel, Cagnac, and Kastler, J. phys. radium **15**, 6 (1954).

[14] Brossel, Cagnac, and Kastler, Compt. rend. **237**, 984 (1953). Besset, Horowitz, Messiah, and Winter, J. phys. radium **15**, 251 (1954). H. Salwen, Phys. Rev. **99**, 1274 (1955). M. N. Hack, Phys. Rev. **104**, 84 (1956).

[15] P. Kusch, Phys. Rev. **93**, 1022 (1954); **101**, 627 (1956). See also reference 9 and W. W. Hugues and J. S. Geiger, Phys. Rev. **99**, 1842 (1955); Christinsen, Hamilton, Lemonick, Pipkin, Reynolds, and Stroke, Phys. Rev. **101**, 1389 (1956).

[16] H. Bucka, Z. Physik **141**, 49 (1955).

[17] F. Bitter and J. Brossel, Phys. Rev. **85**, 1051 (1952). Bitter, Lacey, and Richter, Revs. Modern Phys. **25**, 174 (1953).

[18] Barrat, Brossel, and Kastler, Compt. rend. **239**, 1196 (1954).

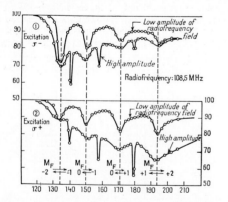

Fig. 12. Resonance curves of the ground state of Na²³ (Brossel, Cagnac, and Kastler, reference 18). σ^- excitation (light circularly polarized in the opposite direction of the coil-current producing H_0 field). σ^+ excitation (light circularly polarized in the same direction as the coil-current producing H_0 field).

[12] Brossel, Kastler, and Winter, J. phys. radium **13**, 668 (1952).

corresponds to a jump $\Delta m = n$ of the magnetic quantum number of the levels. Each electromagnetic quantum involved is circularly polarized in the same direction contributing one unity (h) of angular momentum. Margerie, illuminating the vapor with nonpolarized light, demonstrated effects of alignment of the atomic axis.[19] Analogous effects were obtained at Princeton University by Professor Dicke and his collaborators Dr. Hawkins and Dr. Bender.[20]

Radio-frequency resonances on vapors are suitable for studying the effect of foreign gases on atomic orientation. Depolarizing effects of foreign gases on resonance radiations are well known. They are interpreted as collision-induced mixing of the m levels of the optically excited state.§ Foreign gas molecules can have two different effects on atomic orientation in the ground state:

(a) A disorientation effect by collisions, similar to the one observed in the excited state.

(b) A "buffer" effect, that is a protection of oriented atoms against collisions with the walls.

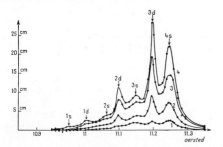

Fig. 14. Atomic orientation in presence of hydrogen gas (Margerie, Brossel, and Kastler, reference 21). Resonance curves of ground state of Na^{23}. Orientation with σ^+ light. Oven temperature: 90°C. rf frequency 7.77 Mc/sec, of constant intensity for the 4 curves.

H_2 pressures for curves	1	2	3	4
	0.00	0.084	0.154	0.38 mm Hg.

Abscissas: magnetic field H_0 ordinate: galvanometer deflection.

In the absence of a foreign gas the atoms fly from wall to wall; the time between two wall collisions is of the order of 10^{-4} sec. If the atoms conserve their orientation in collisions with foreign gas molecules, then the incident light can orient them during a long time before they reach the walls and in this way an enhancement of orientation may be obtained in adding a foreign gas. We have observed an enhancement of this type in a sodium vapor vessel where accidentally the vacuum was bad, and we decided to make a systematic study of the action of foreign gases.

The effect of hydrogen and deuterium at pressures up to 1 mm Hg was studied. The effect of helium is actually

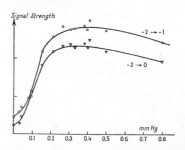

Fig. 15. Signal strength in function of hydrogen pressure for the two resonances m_F: $-2 \to -1$ and $-2 \to 0$. Pressure unit: 10^{-1} mm Hg. (Brossel, Margerie, and Kastler, reference 21.)

being studied. The vessel can be filled easily with pure hydrogen and pure deuterium and the gas pressure can be varied through a heated palladium valve. Figure 14 shows the effect of H_2 at different pressures. A considerable enhancement of the resonances, hence of atomic orientation, is obtained. The factor of amplification depends on the type of resonances observed. Factors up to 10 and 15 have been obtained.[21]

Figure 15 shows the variation of the amplification factor as a function of hydrogen pressure. The curves go through a maximum at about 0.3 mm Hg which is followed by a slow decrease. This decreasing effect is probably due to disorientation in the excited state. Analogous results have been obtained in Professor Dicke's laboratory by Dr. Bender.[22]

Dr. Bender has made a theoretical study of disorienting collisions. It appears that an S state with spherical symmetry is much less sensitive to collisions than a P state with orbital anisotropy. Deuterium and helium give analogous results with higher amplification factors. Replacing H_2 by D_2 multiplies the amplification factor by about 1.4. Replacing H_2 by He multiplies it by about a factor 2.[23] Other experiments have shown that in their ground state $^2S_{\frac{1}{2}}$ atoms are remarkably insensitive to collision perturbations. We may mention the "collision

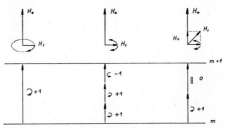

Fig. 16. Conservation of momentum in multiple quantum transitions.

[19] Margerie, Brossel, and Kastler, Compt. rend. 241, 474 (1955).
[20] W. B. Hawkins and R. H. Dicke, Phys. Rev. 91, 1008 (1953); W. B. Hawkins, Phys. Rev. 98, 478 (1955).
§ See reference 4.

[21] Brossel, Margerie, and Kastler, Compt. rend. 241, 865 (1955).
[22] Bender, thesis, Princeton University (1956).
[23] C. Cohen-Tannoudji, Compt. rend. 244, 1027 (1957).

narrowing" effect predicted by Dicke[24] and observed by Wittke and Dicke[25] in studying the hyperfine transition in atomic hydrogen which is colliding with hydrogen molecules. Atomic orientation by light and its conservation in collisions may give rise to important applications: orientation of radioactive nuclei, production of polarized electrons, application of oriented atoms to the construction of a maser.[26]

Another type of multiple quanta transitions has been observed on the ground state of optically oriented sodium atoms. The experiment was performed at very low fields with a frequency of about 1 Mc/sec. The Back-Goudsmit effect is very small then and all the Zeemen intervals are practically the same. A single resonance line is to be expected, as in the case of an atomic

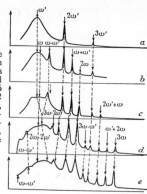

Fig. 18. Resonance curves obtained with two rf frequencies (Brossel, Winter, and Margerie). $\omega = 1.206$ Mc/sec and $\omega' = 0.942$ Mc/sec. Curves a, b, c, d, e: ω' constant intensity, ω increasing intensity. (Brossel, Margerie, and Winter, reference 28.)

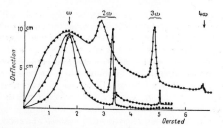

FIG. 17. Resonance curves obtained for rf frequency of 1.206 Mc/sec [J. Margerie and J. Brossel, Compt. rend. **241**, 373 (1955)]. rf field intensities in arbitrary units:

curve 1: 1.57;   curve 2: 3.8;   curve 3: 9.1.

system with 2 energy states only (m) and $(m+1)$. If the rf field H_1 (perpendicular to H_0) keeps a constant amplitude and rotates with angular velocity ω around H_0, it will induce in the atomic system transitions $\Delta m = +1$ (for $\omega > 0$ and $\Delta m = -1$ for $\omega < 0$); the rf photon carries one unit of angular momentum and transfers it to the atom. In this case only a one-quantum transition is possible. If the rf field H_1 perpendicular to H_0

is linear, two types of quanta are present, carrying $+1$ and -1 unit of angular momentum, so that a $\Delta m = +1$ atomic transition can be produced by adsorption *of an odd number of quanta* $[(+1)+(+1)+(-1)]$ as long as conservation of energy is also satisfied. If the rf field H_1 is not perpendicular to H_0, its component along H_0 carries no angular momentum so that conservation of energy and angular momentum can be satisfied by absorption of any number of quanta. Figure 16 illustrates the above cases.

The experiment suggested by J. M. Winter[27] was made on oriented Na vapor (Fig. 17). One, two, three, and four quanta resonances were observed whenever $\omega_0 = p\omega$.[2] A striking feature of these resonances is their shift with increasing rf amplitude. This shift is analogous to the Bloch-Siegert displacement. When two rf fields ω and ω' are applied simultaneously, one observes, besides the resonances $p\omega = \omega_0$ and $q\omega' = \omega_0$, the beat frequencies $p\omega + q\omega' = \omega_0$, p and q being any positive or negative integers.[28]

Figure 18 shows what happens when a fixed amplitude at frequency ω' being set, an increasing amplitude at frequency ω' is added. Resonances $\omega + \omega'$, $2\omega + \omega'$, $\omega + 2\omega'$, $2\omega - \omega'$, $3\omega - \omega'$, etc., appear in succession.

[24] R. H. Dicke, Phys. Rev. **89**, 472 (1953).
[25] J. P. Wittke and R. H. Dicke, Phys. Rev. **96**, 530 (1954). J. P. Wittke, thesis, Princeton University (1954).
[26] A. Kastler, Holweck Lecture, Proc. Phys. Soc. (London) **A67**, 853 (1954).

[27] J. M. Winter, Compt. rend. **241**, 375 and 600 (1955).
[28] Brossel, Margerie, and Winter, Compt. rend. **241**, 556 (1955).

From: *Phys. Rev.* 86, 308-316 (1952)   107

A New "Double Resonance" Method for Investigating Atomic Energy Levels. Application to Hg $^3P_1$*

JEAN BROSSEL† AND FRANCIS BITTER

Research Laboratory of Electronics, Massachusetts Institute of Technology, Cambridge, Massachusetts

(Received December 17, 1951)

Excitation of atoms in a vapor by polarized light produces unequal population of the magnetic sublevels of the excited state. The emitted optical resonance radiation is therefore partly polarized. The application of radiofrequency or microwave fields at a magnetic resonance frequency will induce transitions between sublevels of the excited state. The degree of polarization of the emitted optical resonance radiation is altered when the magnetic resonance condition is fulfilled. As suggested by Brossel and Kastler, this effect may be used to reveal the structure of the energy level. A detailed theory applicable to, and experiments on the $^3P_1$ state of all the isotopes of mercury are reported. The results obtained indicate that double resonance phenomena constitute a valuable new tool for investigating the structure of atomic energy levels. The mean life of the $^3P_1$ state is shown by observations on the resonance line widths to be 1.55×10^{-7} sec for all the isotopes. The g-factor of the $^3P_1$ state for isotopes with zero spin, measured in terms of the proton g-factor, is 1.4838 ± 0.0004.

INTRODUCTION

THE only means available at present for investigating the internal structure of nuclei involves accurate determinations of nuclear moments and hyperfine structures.[1] These determinations have previously been made by magnetic resonance experiments on the ground state of atoms or molecules in a beam or on diamagnetic liquids. In such experiments magnetic dipole transitions are induced by an oscillating magnetic field. If, in the sample being investigated, there is an initial inequality in the population of the magnetic sublevels of any given state, the net effect of the transitions induced by the oscillating magnetic field is to change this inequality and therefore to modify any property depending on it. In an atomic or molecular beam experiment the number of particles having a given trajectory through the apparatus is altered. In a nuclear resonance experiment, the degree of magnetization of the core of a coil, and therefore its impedance, is altered. A further possibility, having the great advantage of extending observations to the excited states of atoms, is to detect magnetic resonance in an energy level by observing changes in the optical radiation involving transitions from or to that level.[2]

The present paper gives an analysis and a detailed description of effects first observed in 1950,[3] based on suggestions put forward by Brossel and Kastler.[4] Excitation of a level by optical resonance radiation with polarized light provides the initial inequality of population in the Zeeman pattern of the excited state. The degree of polarization of the light spontaneously re-emitted depends on this initial inequality and changes when it is altered by magnetic resonance absorption. This is the physical basis of the observations reported below.

Changes in frequency of the optical resonance radiation caused by magnetic resonance among the sublevels of either the upper or lower of the energy levels involved in the radiation process have also been predicted.[2] Such changes have been observed by Autler and Townes[5] in a somewhat analogous case in molecular spectra but are much too small to be significant for the atomic spectra discussed in the following.

GENERAL DISCUSSION OF EFFECTS IN MERCURY VAPOR

Mercury was the element studied experimentally. Naturally occurring mercury was used for the investigation of isotopes with even mass number and zero nuclear spin. Samples enriched in Hg^{199} and Hg^{201} were supplied by the Atomic Energy Commission for the investigation of these isotopes. Isotopic abundances of the samples used are shown in Table I.

The level studied was the $^3P_1$ excited state reached by excitation with the intercombination line $^1S_0 - {}^3P_1$, having a wavelength 2537A. A diagram of the transitions involved and of the hyperfine structure of the line is shown in Fig. 1. The ground state is a diamagnetic $^1S_0$ state. The optical transition probabilities have been computed using the formulas of Hill[6] and Inglis[7] and are shown in Fig. 2 for the weak field case of no decoupling of the nuclear and electronic angular momenta. In this diagram the vertical arrows correspond

* This work has been supported in part by the Signal Corps, the Air Materiel Command, and ONR.
† Joint fellow of Spectroscopy Laboratory and Laboratory for Nuclear Science and Engineering.
[1] A. Bohr, Phys. Rev. **73**, 1109 (1948); F. Bitter, Phys. Rev. **76**, 150 (1949); A. Bohr and F. Weisskopf, Phys. Rev. **77**, 94 (1950).
[2] F. Bitter, Phys. Rev. **76**, 833 (1949); M. L. Pryce, Phys. Rev. **77**, 136 (1950).
[3] Brossel, Sagalyn, and Bitter, Phys. Rev. **79**, 196, 225 (1950). Attention is also called to the pioneering work of E. Fermi and F. Rasetti [Nature **115**, 764 (1925); and Z. Physik **33**, 246 (1925)], who first observed the depolarization of the resonance radiation of mercury by radiofrequency magnetic fields.
[4] J. Brossel and A. Kastler, Compt. rend. **229**, 1213 (1949).

[5] S. H. Autler and C. H. Townes, Phys. Rev. **78**, 340 (1950).
[6] E. H. Hill, Proc. Nat. Acad. Sci. **15**, 779 (1929).
[7] D. Inglis, Z. Phys. **84**, 466 (1933).

to transitions with $\Delta m_F = 0$, or plane polarized π-radiation in absorption or emission with the electric vector parallel to the applied field, and diagonal arrows correspond to transitions with $\Delta m_F = \pm 1$ or circularly polarized σ-radiation.

For isotopes with even mass number [shown in Fig. 2(a)] π-excitation leads to the middle upper state only, and in the absence of perturbations, the re-emitted radiation contains this π-component only. The experiment then consists of the application of a radiofrequency field which transfers atoms to the states with $m = \pm 1$ when the magnetic resonance condition $\omega = \gamma H_z$ is fulfilled. Here ω is the frequency of the oscillating field, H_z is the constant magnetic field, and γ is the gyromagnetic ratio of the state in question, namely, the $^3P_1$ state. When the resonance condition is fulfilled, the intensity of the π-component diminishes, and that of the σ-component increases. These changes were observed and used to detect resonance.

Collisions involving excited atoms will modify the aforementioned simple description, since atoms can then be reoriented not only by the absorption of rf energy, but also as a result of inelastic collisions. According to previous work,[8] the vapor pressure of mercury at $-15°C$ is low enough so that the effect of such collisions is negligible, but this is not true at $0°C$, the temperature used in the experiments to be described. At this temperature a considerable fraction of the atoms excited to the level with $m = 0$ are transferred by collisions to the levels with $m = \pm 1$, and the re-emitted light is partly depolarized even in the absence of an oscillating field. This depolarization of resonance radiation as a result of inelastic collisions will reduce the magnitude of the signal to be expected when an oscillating field is applied, and will shorten the mean life of an atom in any given excited level. No experimental investigation of these effects was undertaken. It is simply assumed that magnetic relaxation phenomena may affect the two quantities just mentioned, but may otherwise be neglected.

The effects to be expected have been analyzed in considerable detail.[9] A summary of results will be given here. The problem concerns the reorientation of a magnetic dipole with fixed total angular momentum. This situation was analyzed in a very general way by

TABLE I. Isotopic abundances of the samples of mercury used.

	Percent of isotopes with even mass number	Percent 199	Percent 201
Natural Hg	69.80	17.0	13.2
Enriched Hg199	32.27	62.5	5.23
Enriched Hg201	37.3	4.76	57.9

[8] V. von Keussler, Ann. Physik **82**, 793 (1927).
[9] F. Bitter and J. Brossel, Technical Report No. 176, Research Laboratory of Electronics, M.I.T. (hereafter called simply Technical Report No. 176).

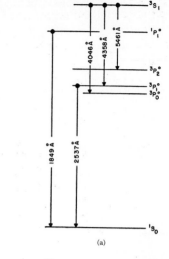

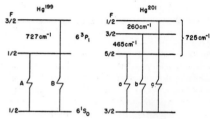

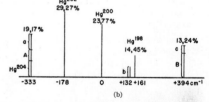

FIG. 1. (a) The low-lying energy levels of mercury; (b) the hyperfine structure of the resonance line.

Majorana[10] and by Rabi,[11] who derived the expressions for the required transition probabilities. An angular momentum F in one of its substates m_F is in a rotating field H_1 at right angles to a constant field H_z. Under these conditions the probability of transitions to another state m_F' is considered. For simplicity we shall write the magnetic quantum numbers without the subscript F. Modifications caused by use of linearly oscillating rather than rotating fields have been considered by Bloch and Siegert.[12] These modifications are negligible

[10] E. Majorana, Nuovo cimento **9**, 43 (1932).
[11] I. I. Rabi, Phys. Rev. **51**, 652 (1932).
[12] F. Bloch and A. Siegert, Phys. Rev. **57**, 522 (1940).

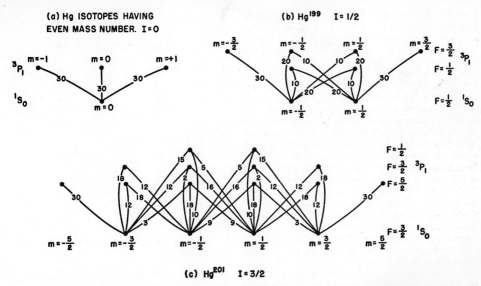

FIG. 2. Transition probabilities for the components of the resonance line of mercury (a) for isotopes and even mass number, (b) for Hg[199] with $I=1/2$, and (c) for Hg[201] with $I=3/2$.

for most purposes. We shall return to their discussion further on. For rotating fields Majorana and Rabi derive an expression for the probability that a system of total angular momentum F, known to be in a state m at time $t=0$, shall be in a state m' at some later time t. We designate this transition probability by $P(F, m, m', t)$. It is rigorously derived from the Schroedinger time dependent equation and is not arrived at by perturbation theory. It is therefore valid for large amplitudes of the rotating field and for large values of the time.

Let ω be the frequency, in radians per second, of the rotating field H_1. The gyromagnetic ratio is $\gamma = ge/2Mc$. The Larmor frequency ω_0 in the constant field H_z is given by $\omega_0 = \gamma H_z$. The Landé g-factors for the various isotopes of mercury in the $^3P_1$ state in question are given in Table II. The values listed have only a limited validity, since g_J is computed on the assumption of L-S coupling which is surely not rigorously valid for the $^3P_1$ state of mercury. If it were, transitions to the ground state, which is a singlet state, would be forbidden, whereas in fact, the life of the metastable triplet state is of the order of 10^{-7} sec.

We now define an angle, α, by the relation

$$\sin^2\frac{\alpha}{2} = \frac{(\omega/\gamma H_1)^2}{1+[1+(H_z/H_1)]^2} \cdot \frac{(\gamma H_1)^2}{(\gamma H_1)^2+(\omega-\omega_0)^2}$$
$$\cdot \sin^2\frac{1}{2}[(\gamma H_1)^2+(\omega-\omega_0)^2]^{\frac{1}{2}}t. \quad (1)$$

This is a periodic function of the time. The amplitude of this periodic function is shown in Fig. 3. From an

inspection of this illustration it is clear that for $H_z/H_1 \gtrsim 10$ the function plotted has a maximum near $\omega = \omega_0$, and Eq. (1) may be written, to a good approximation,

$$\sin^2\frac{\alpha}{2} = \frac{(\gamma H_1)^2}{(\gamma H_1)^2+(\omega-\omega_0)^2}$$
$$\times \sin^2\frac{1}{2}[(\gamma H_1)^2+(\omega-\omega_0)^2]^{\frac{1}{2}}t. \quad (2)$$

In terms of this angle α the required transition probabilities given by the Majorana formula are

$$P(F, m, m', t)$$
$$= (\cos\tfrac{1}{2}\alpha)^{4F}(F+m)!(F+m')!(F-m)!(F-m')!$$
$$\times\left[\sum_{n=0}^{2F}\frac{(-1)^n(\tan\tfrac{1}{2}\alpha)^{2n-m+m'}}{n!(n-m+m')!(F+m-n)!(F-m'-n)!}\right]^2 \quad (3)$$

The simplest case is for $F=1/2$. The aforementioned formula then reduces to

$$P(\tfrac{1}{2}, \tfrac{1}{2}, -\tfrac{1}{2}, t) = \sin^2\left(\frac{\alpha}{2}\right) = \frac{(\gamma H_1)^2}{(\gamma H_1)^2+(\omega-\omega_0)^2}$$
$$\times\sin^2\frac{1}{2}[(\gamma H_1)^2+(\omega-\omega_0)^2]^{\frac{1}{2}}t.$$

Transitions induced by the oscillating field will take place with appreciable probability in a radiating vapor if the above transition probability has an appreciable value within the lifetime of the excited state. For example, for lifetimes of the order of 10^{-7} sec we must have γH_1, of the order of 10^7 sec^{-1}, or since $\gamma \sim 10^7$, we must have rotating fields of the order of a gauss.

Effects caused by transitions induced by the rotating magnetic field must now be combined with effects caused by transitions involving optical resonance radiation. We shall describe here procedures to be followed in making the calculations and leave the discussion of specific formulas to later parts of this paper where they will be compared with experimental results.

Let n be the number of optical quanta absorbed per second involving transitions from some one particular magnetic sublevel of the ground state, designated by m_g, to one particular magnetic sublevel of the excited state, designated by the two quantum numbers F and m. The number of atoms excited in an interval of time dt at the time $t=0$ is then ndt. If T_e is the mean life of atoms in the excited state, the number of atoms remaining in the excited state after a time t has elapsed is $ndte^{-t/T_e}$. If the excited atoms were in a rotating magnetic field during the entire time interval t, the number in a sublevel m' of the excited state at the time t is $nP(F, m, m', t)e^{-t/T_e}dt$.

We wish to compute the total number of excited atoms in a vapor in the sublevel m'. We have just derived the number which had been in the excited state for a time between t and $t+dt$. Evidently, the total number may be arrived at by integrating

$$N_{m'} = \int_0^{\infty} nP(F, m, m', t)e^{-t/T_e}dt. \qquad (4)$$

In this expression the excitation rate is obtained from the steady state condition $n = N_m/T_e$, where $N_m \sim A_{m,m_g}N_{m_g}I_0$. The coefficient A_{m,m_g} is the transition probability between an excited sublevel m and a ground state sublevel m_g shown in Fig. 2. N_{m_g} is the number of atoms in the ground state sublevel in question, and I_0 is the intensity of the light used to produce the excitation. The only one of these quantities requiring further discussion is N_{m_g}. For practically realizable intensities of illumination the fraction of the atoms in

TABLE II. The Landé g-factors for the $^3P_1$ state of the isotopes of mercury computed from the relation

$$g_F = g_J \frac{F(F+1)+J(J+1)-I(I+1)}{2F(F+1)}$$
$$- g_I \frac{F(F+1)+I(I+1)-J(J+1)}{2F(F+1)}$$
$$g_J = 1 + \frac{2J(J+1)+S(S+1)-L(L+1)}{2J(J+1)}.$$

Isotopes with even mass number	F 1	g_F 3/2
Hg^{199} {3/2		$1-1.81\times10^{-4}$
{1/2		$2+1.81\times10^{-4}$
Hg^{201} {5/2		$\frac{3}{5}+1.19\times10^{-4}$
{3/2		$\frac{3}{5}+1.46\times10^{-4}$
{1/2		$-1+3.31\times10^{-4}$

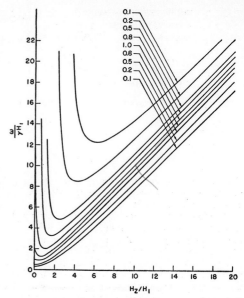

Fig. 3. A contour plot of
$(\omega/\gamma H_1)^2/1 + [1+(H_z/H_1)]^2 \cdot (\gamma H_1)^2/[(\gamma H_1)^2 + (\omega-\omega_0)^2]$.

a vapor which are in an excited state at any instant is very small and may be neglected in comparison with the number in the ground state. Normally thermal relaxation processes insure that the various magnetic sublevels of the ground state are equally populated. The use of polarized resonance radiation may upset this thermal equilibrium, particularly when circularly polarized radiation is used. Such effects are not important in the experiments discussed here, and we shall therefore neglect them in this discussion. For isotopes with even mass number N_{m_g} is simply the total number of such atoms present. For Hg^{199} with a spin of $\frac{1}{2}$ there are two ground-state sublevels, and $N_{m_g}=N_{199}/2$. For Hg^{201} with a spin of $\frac{3}{2}$ there are four sublevels, and $N_{m_g}=N_{201}/4$.

The intensity of the light radiated by atoms which have been excited from m_g to m, transferred from m to m', and which finally decay from m' to m_g' is proportional to

$$N_{m'}A_{m',m_g'}.$$

$N_{m'}$ is given by Eq. (4), and the transition probability A is that shown in Fig. 2. The dependence of the state of polarization of the resonance radiation on the magnitude and frequency of the rotating magnetic field may then be obtained by summing over the various levels involved. In general, in a vapor containing a mixture of isotopes, several optical frequencies will be absorbed and some assumption must be made regarding the structure of the resonance line used [see Fig. 1(b)].

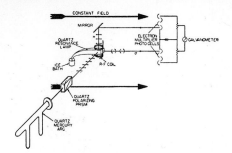

Fig. 4. Diagram of the apparatus.

The simplest assumption is that of "broad line" excitation, and this was used in the detailed calculations of Technical Report No. 176.

The aforementioned transitions refer exclusively to changes in the magnetic quantum number of a rigid rotator with a given total angular momentum F. Observations involving such transitions may be used to determine the gyromagnetic ratio of an atom in a particular state. High frequency magnetic fields may also be used to induce transitions resulting in the reorientation of the nucleus in the field of the electrons. Observations on such transitions give information on the hyperfine structure of a level and may be used to compute nuclear moments. Such transitions, however, are not reported in this paper.

EXPERIMENTAL ARRANGEMENTS

The apparatus used is illustrated in Fig. 4. Light from a low pressure mercury lamp made by Hanovia, operated at 150 ma and cooled with an air blast, is collimated by a quartz lens and polarized by a Glaze-brook prism cemented with glycerine. This light is allowed to fall on one of the five mutually perpendicular faces of a fused quartz resonance lamp. The liquid mercury in the tail of the lamp was kept at a temperature of 0°C. The light incident on the lamp was polarized with its electric vector parallel to the constant field H_z. In other words, only the π-component was used for excitation in these experiments. A magnetic field of a few hundred gauss is produced by Helmholtz coils. The σ-component of the resonance radiation may be observed in the direction of this constant field, and both σ- and π-components may be observed at right angles to this field. Around the lamp are a few turns of water-cooled copper tubing forming part of a tuned radiofrequency circuit inductively coupled to a generator capable of supplying up to 100 watts. At maximum rf power the resonance lamp lights up if it is not very well evacuated or if traces of mercury have deposited on the windows of the lamp. The axis of the rf coils is at right angles to the constant field.

In the first experiments attempted, changes were observed in the intensity of the σ-component of the resonance radiation in the direction of the constant field. The intensity of the light emitted by the mercury arc lamp was found to be constant to only about 3 percent, so that small changes in intensity were difficult to measure against this fluctuating background. The sensitivity of the apparatus was greatly improved by the introduction of an optical bridge.[13] Two photomultiplier tubes are used. One of these receives the σ-component in the direction of the field, and the other receives the π-component or the π- and σ-components emitted at right angles to the field. The resistors shown in the illustration are so adjusted that under normal operation no current flows in the galvanometer. This was found to eliminate fluctuations in the galvanometer deflection resulting from fluctuations in the brightness of the light source. When magnetic resonance increases the intensity of the σ-component at the expense of the π-component, the balance of the bridge is upset, and the resulting galvanometer deflection measures directly the quantity desired. The response is linear. Galvanometers with sensitivities up to 10^{-11} amp/mm and periods from 10 to 40 seconds were used. The fluctuation in zero of the galvanometer was about that to be expected due to the IP28 phototubes, but some of this noise may have been caused by spontaneous fluctuations of the polarization of the resonance radiation. Without the optical bridge the random movements of the galvanometer were about 30 times as large.

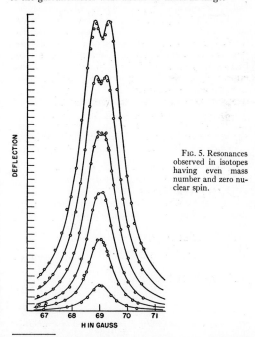

Fig. 5. Resonances observed in isotopes having even mass number and zero nuclear spin.

[13] O. Oldenberg and H. P. Broida, J. Opt. Soc. Am. **40**, 381 (1950).

No measurements were made of the absolute magnitude of the oscillating field. Relative measurements were made by means of a crest voltmeter in an auxiliary inductively coupled circuit and are considered reliable to about 1 percent.

Magnet currents were measured with a Leeds and Northrup Type K_2 potentiometer, with the auxiliary shunt kept at 0°C. Two magnets were used. The first, having a uniformity of only about one part in 10^3 over the volume of the resonance lamp, was used for the determination of line shape and of the mean life of the $^3P_1$ state. The second was uniform to better than one part in 10^4 over the region occupied by the lamp and was used in the determination of the gyromagnetic ratio. This magnet was calibrated by means of proton resonances at 1.6, 0.812, 0.530, and 0.350 Mc/sec. The local earth's field was evaluated by making resonance measurements with the magnet current flowing in both senses through the magnet.

OBSERVATIONS ON ISOTOPES WITH EVEN MASS NUMBER

With the aforementioned apparatus operated at frequencies from 50 to 150 Mc/sec, resonance curves such as are plotted in Fig. 5 are obtained. They show, at one given frequency, galvanometer deflections as a function of the applied constant field for various rf amplitudes. Increasing the rf amplitude produces a stronger and wider line and also produces characteristic changes in the line shape. All of these features, as we shall see, are accounted for by Eq. 4. In Technical Report No. 176 it is shown that for the case in question involving integrals containing $P(1, 0, 1, t)$, the galvanometer deflection should be proportional to a quantity which we call B:

$$B = \frac{I_0}{2} \frac{(\gamma H_1)^2}{(\gamma H_1)^2 + (\omega - \omega_0)^2} \left[\frac{(\gamma H_1)^2}{(1/T_e)^2 + 4(\gamma H_1)^2 + (\omega - \omega_0)^2} \right.$$
$$\left. + \frac{(\omega - \omega_0)^2}{(1/T_e)^2 + (\gamma H_1)^2 + (\omega - \omega_0)^2} \right]. \quad (5)$$

This represents a bell-shaped curve for values of $\gamma H_1 \ll 1/T_e$, but for $\gamma H_1 \gg 1/T_e$ the curve has two maxima. The separation between these maxima is $\sqrt{2}H_1$, and the ratio of the intensity at maximum to that at resonance is, in the limit for large rf power, 4/3.

A detailed check of Eq. (5) was undertaken. One finds for the intensity at resonance

$$B_r = k \frac{(\gamma H_1)^2}{4(\gamma H_1)^2 + (1/T_e)^2}, \quad (6)$$

where k is an arbitrary constant. In order to check this equation the quantity H_1^2/B_r was plotted as a function of H_1^2 in arbitrary units. The result is shown in Fig. 6(a). It is clear that this aspect of the theory is well borne

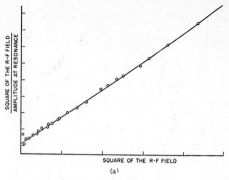

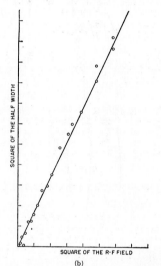

Fig. 6. (a) A plot of Eq. (6); (b) a plot of Eq. (7).

out by the experiments. In the absence of an absolute determination of H_1, however, it is not possible to deduce T_e from this relation. Another procedure was adopted to determine this quantity. From Eq. (6) it is possible to compute the width of the resonance line $\Delta\omega$ when the amplitude is half its value at resonance, as a function of H_1. For our purposes the complete expression is not important. The first two terms in a power series expansion are

$$\Delta\omega^2 = (4/T_e^2)[1 + 5.8(\gamma H_1 T_e)^2]. \quad (7)$$

The form of this expression is also experimentally verified for the range of rf amplitudes used, as is shown in Fig. 6(b) where the experimental data are plotted in arbitrary units. It is possible, however, to plot this data using the correct units. The half-width of the resonance curve in frequency units may be obtained from the observed half-width in gauss and the known

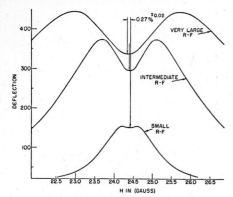

Fig. 7. Experimental verification of the expected shift of the resonant frequency with rf amplitude.

gyromagnetic ratio. The value of $(\gamma H_1 T_e)^2$ for any arbitrary setting of the rf amplitude may be obtained as follows. Calling the ordinate of Fig. 6(a) y, we may write

$$y = \frac{H_1^2}{B_r} = [4(\gamma H_1 T_e)^2 + 1]/k\gamma^2 T_e^2, \qquad (8)$$

and for the value of y when $H_1 = 0$,

$$y_0 = 1/k\gamma^2 T_e^2. \qquad (9)$$

Combining (8) and (9), we have the measurable dimensionless quantity

$$(y - y_0)/y_0 = 4(\gamma H_1 T_e)^2, \qquad (10)$$

which may be used in plotting Eq. (7). By means of this procedure the value of the numerical coefficient 5.8 was verified, and the mean life of the excited state was obtained by extrapolation to zero amplitude of the rf field. This was done at frequencies of 50, 100, 120, and 144 Mc/sec. The same value was obtained from all these measurements with a total spread of 1 percent. The value obtained in this way for the mean life of the $^3P_1$ state of the even isotopes of Hg is 1.55×10^{-7} sec.[14] The true value may be somewhat longer because the broadening of the line as a result of collisions and field inhomogeneities was not explicitly taken into account. The above value is about 30 percent longer than the previously accepted value, obtained, not too consistently, by conventional optical methods. As we shall report further on, the same value was found for Hg[199] and Hg[201] within the experimental error.

The line shape itself, as given by Eq. (5), was then checked in the following way. T_e was given the above value. H_1 was obtained from experimental determinations of $\gamma H_1 T_e$ as aforementioned. The arbitrary constant determining the magnitude of the galvanometer

deflection was chosen so that the greatest deflection at resonance coincided with the observed value. The parameters I_0, T_e, and H_1 being determined, a complete plot of Eq. (5) was made. This is shown in the solid curves of Fig. 5. In these curves the parameter $\gamma H_1 T_e$ assumes values up to 0.7. The experimental points corresponding to these curves are also plotted. The agreement seems to be entirely satisfactory and leaves little doubt as to the adequacy of the above theoretical discussion. Observations made at different frequencies proved that the resonant frequency is a linear function of the magnetic field to within one part in 5000.

At 50 Mc a slight shift in the resonance frequency with rf amplitude was observed at large rf amplitudes, as predicted by Bloch and Siegert,[12] when a linearly oscillating rather than a rotating field is used. As shown in Fig. 7, at high rf fields the resonant field for a given frequency is smaller than at low rf fields. The shift is predicted to be proportional to $(H_1/H_z)^2$. This dependence was roughly verified, but the magnitude of the observed shifts was 30 percent greater than the predicted shift. This discrepancy is not considered significant because the equivalent rotating field H_1 was arrived at only indirectly and because the oscillating field was certainly not completely linear, but somewhat elliptical.

The Landé g-factor for the $^3P_1$ state of the isotopes with zero spin was determined by measuring both the frequency and the field required to establish the resonance condition illustrated in Fig. 5. Frequency determinations were made with a Signal Corps BC 221 frequency meter and are considered reliable to one part in 10,000. The field was measured in terms of a proton resonance, so the computation takes the form

$$g = g_{\text{proton}} \times \frac{m}{M} \times \frac{\omega_{\text{Hg}}}{\omega_{\text{proton}}}. \qquad (11)$$

Using 5.58501 for the gyromagnetic ratio of the proton[15] and 1836.12 for the ratio of the mass of the proton to

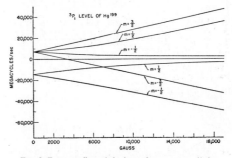

Fig. 8. Zeeman effect of the hyperfine structure of the $^3P_1$ level of Hg[199].

[14] J. Brossel, Phys. Rev. 83, 210 (1951).

[15] Sommer, Thomas, and Hipple, Phys. Rev. 82, 697 (1951).

that of the electron,[15] we find for the desired g-factor

$$g = 1.4838 + 0.0004. \qquad (12)$$

EXPERIMENTS ON Hg[199] AND Hg[201]

The 199 isotope with a nuclear spin of $1/2$ has two hyperfine structure levels in the $^3P_1$ state with $F=1/2$ and $F=3/2$, as shown in Fig. 8. The use of π-excitation does not lead to any inequality of population of levels with $m=\pm 1/2$ [see Fig. 2(b)]. For this reason excitation to $F=1/2$ and magnetic resonance in this level produces no changes in polarization of the resonance radiation. Magnetic resonance in this level can therefore not be observed. However, magnetic resonance in the level with $F=3/2$ was observed and studied in some detail.

At 144 Mc the decoupling of I and J is sufficient to make the three frequencies $(-3/2 \rightarrow -1/2)$, $(-1/2 \rightarrow 1/2)$, and $(1/2 \rightarrow 3/2)$ slightly different. The Zeeman effect of this case was computed following Inglis[7] and is shown in Fig. 8. The line corresponding to the transition $(-1/2 \rightarrow 1/2)$ is not observable with π-excitation because the levels in question are equally populated. The other two transitions are displaced with respect to each other by an amount, in frequency units, equal to (Zeeman separation)^2/hfs separation, or $(150 \times 10^6)^2/2 \times 10^{10}$. This separation is only a small fraction of the line width, and therefore the two components were not resolved in the fields used.

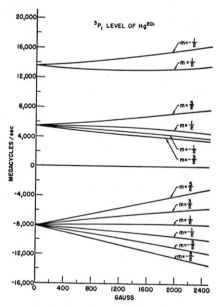

FIG. 9. The Zeeman effect of the hyperfine structure of the $^3P_1$ level of Hg[201].

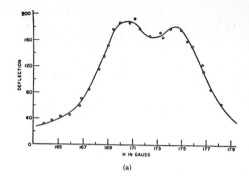

(a)

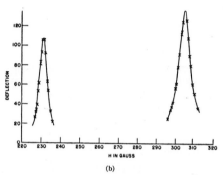

(b)

FIG. 10. Resonances observed at 144 Mc in the $^3P_1$ state of Hg[201] (a) for the level $F=5/2$ and (b) for the level $F=3/2$.

Estimates of the mean life of the excited state of this isotope were made by computing $\gamma H_1 T_e$ for both the even and 199 isotopes [see Eq. (10)]. The ratio of the two values obtained for a fixed value of H_1 should give the ratio of the γ's if the mean life is the same for both isotopes. This was found to be the case at 50, 100, and 144 Mc to within 2 percent.

For the isotope Hg[201] with a spin of $3/2$, resonances were observed in the levels $F=5/2$ and $F=3/2$. Because of the small g-values, high rf field intensities are needed. These resonances are much less marked than those previously described, being only about 5 times the noise level. At frequencies above 50 Mc the decoupling of I and J is considerable, as may be seen from the inequality in spacing of the Zeeman levels in Fig. 9. At 50 Mc very broad resonances were observed for both the $F=3/2$ and $F=5/2$ levels. At 144 Mc the $F=5/2$ resonance shown in Fig. 10(a) was observed. This resonance consists of four unresolved components corresponding to the transitions $(5/2 \rightarrow 3/2)$, $(3/2 \rightarrow 1/2)$, $(-1/2 \rightarrow -3/2)$, and $(-3/2 \rightarrow -5/2)$. The resonances in the $F=3/2$ level consist of two well-resolved lines corresponding to the transitions $(3/2 \rightarrow 1/2)$ and $(-1/2 \rightarrow -3/2)$. The width of these lines agrees to within 2 percent with that found for the isotopes of even mass number, again indicating that all isotopes have the same mean life in the excited state.

SUMMARY

1. An effective method has been demonstrated for extending rf absorption measurements to the excited states of atoms.

2. The g-factor and the level widths for the $^3P_1$ state of mercury have been studied. These levels could be examined in sufficient detail to establish their center to within 2 percent of the level widths.

3. The method can be extended to measurements of the hyperfine structure.

4. Other promising fields of observation include the Stark effect, the quenching and depolarization of resonance radiation, and in general, problems related to magnetic relaxation phenomena in vapors.

From: *Phys. Rev.* **98**, 478-486 (1955)

Orientation and Alignment of Sodium Atoms by Means of Polarized Resonance Radiation*

WILLIAM BRUCE HAWKINS†

Palmer Physical Laboratory, Princeton University, Princeton, New Jersey

(Received December 17, 1954)

Sodium atoms have been oriented by means of circularly polarized resonance radiation. The amount of orientation agrees with that calculated from the intensity of the light source used. The polarization of the light scattered from the sodium sample varies in the expected manner when the light intensity and applied magnetic field are varied. Illumination with unpolarized resonance radiation is shown to result in alignment of the sodium atoms. The largest degree of orientation achieved corresponds to an average value for the nuclear, electronic, and total angular momenta of $\bar{M}_I=0.180=0.120I$, $\bar{M}_S=0.035=0.070S$, $\bar{M}_F=0.216$ $=0.108F$, respectively.

INTRODUCTION

KASTLER[1] has proposed that atoms could be oriented by means of circularly polarized resonance radiation. I shall use the word orientation to denote a state in which an ensemble of atoms has an average atomic or nuclear magnetic moment not equal to zero; I prefer this to the more commonly used word polarization in order to avoid confusion with light polarization. I shall retain the common usage of the word alignment to denote a condition in which, while the ensemble average magnetic moment is zero, atomic states with $|M_F|=F$ are more probable than those with $M_F=0$. A substantial quantity of oriented atoms could be used as a source of oriented nuclei for such experiments as the study of angular distribution of radioactive decay products, as a source of polarized electrons, or as a means of enhancing the signal in nuclear magnetic resonance experiments.

Bitter and Brossel[2] have unsuccessfully attempted to induce orientation in mercury by this method. More recently, Brossel, Kastler, and Winter[3] have achieved a positive result with sodium, while Bitter, Lacey, and Richter[4] also report failure with mercury. The present experiment using sodium has already been briefly described.[5,6] Brossel, Cagnac, and Kastler[7] have induced radio-frequency transitions between the Zeeman sublevels of oriented sodium atoms. They observe transitions involving two rf photons corresponding to a change $\Delta M_F=2$ in the axial angular momentum as well as the usual single-photon $\Delta M_F=1$ transitions. An excellent review of the whole subject has been given by Kastler in his recent Holweck lecture.[8]

* This research was supported by the U. S. Atomic Energy Commission and the Higgins Scientific Trust Fund. It has also been described in a dissertation submitted to Princeton University in partial fulfillment of the requirements for the PhD degree.
† National Science Foundation Predoctoral Fellow 1953–54. Present address: Physikalisches Institut der E. T. H., Gloriastrasse 35, Zürich, Switzerland.
[1] A. Kastler, J. phys. et radium **11**, 255 (1950).
[2] F. Bitter and J. Brossel, Phys. Rev. **85**, 1051 (1952).
[3] Brossel, Kastler, and Winter, J. phys. et radium **13**, 668 (1952).
[4] Bitter, Lacey, and Richter, Revs. Modern Phys. **25**, 174 (1953).
[5] W. B. Hawkins and R. H. Dicke, Phys. Rev. **91**, 1008 (1953).
[6] W. B. Hawkins, Phys. Rev. **96**, 532 (1954).
[7] Brossel, Cagnac, and Kastler, J. phys. et radium **15**, 6 (1954).
[8] A. Kastler, Proc. Phys. Soc. (London) **A67**, 853 (1954).

THEORY OF ORIENTATION

General

The simplest atomic system which can be oriented by means of circularly polarized resonance radiation is one having a ground state of total angular momentum $F=\frac{1}{2}$ and an optical first excited state having $F=\frac{3}{2}$. If such an atom is in the ground state sublevel with axial angular momentum $M_F=+\frac{1}{2}$ and absorbs a circularly polarized photon with axial angular momentum $+1$, it will go into the $M_F=+\frac{3}{2}$ substate of the excited level. By virtue of the electric dipole selection rules which are assumed for the transition, this excited atom must return to the substate $M_F=+\frac{1}{2}$ when it radiates. An atom originally in the $M_F=-\frac{1}{2}$ ground state absorbing such a photon can return to either ground state sublevel when it radiates. Thus the result of the scattering of this kind of light by an ensemble of such atoms is that all atoms originally in the $M_F=+\frac{1}{2}$ state will return there, while some of those with $M_F=-\frac{1}{2}$ will be transferred to the $M_F=+\frac{1}{2}$ state by the scattering process. The ensemble has been partially oriented.

More complicated atoms having larger angular momenta or hyperfine structure behave in essentially the same way, the ground-state sublevel of largest (or smallest if the sense of the light polarization be reversed) magnetic quantum number gaining atoms at the expense of the others. Figure 1 shows how the orientation process works for one of the hyperfine transitions in Na^{23} together with the complete energy

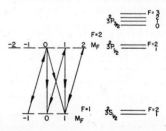

FIG. 1. Na^{23} energy level diagram with a sample of the transitions involved in orientation, in this case transitions via the $3\,^2P_{\frac{1}{2}}$, $F=2$ states.

level diagram. Although the magnetic quantum number can change by at most two units during a single scattering process, the scattering of further photons will increase the orientation if the partially oriented ensemble remains undisturbed. However, its members may be disturbed between photon-scattering events by collisions with other atoms or by the presence of magnetic fields.

A magnetic field perpendicular to the axis of quantization defined by the direction of the incident light will cause a mixing of all the M_F states for a particular F. Although the resulting state is not one of thermal equilibrium, it may be treated as such for present purposes. A field of about 10^{-3} gauss is sufficient for thorough mixing in a time of the order of 10^{-4} second, the time of observation in this experiment. However, the situation is quite different if in addition to this transverse component a larger axial field component is present, for a field nearly parallel to the axis of quantization mixes the states only slightly. The angle between the axis and whatever magnetic field is present is more important than the size of the field, provided that it is not large enough to seriously alter the atomic wave functions. The fields normally applied in this experiment did not appear to be large enough to cause significant alteration. Such changes in wave functions, while rendering the calculations for zero field invalid, do not interfere with the basis process of "optical pumping." Their avoidance is thus a matter of convenience in the interpretation rather than an essential of the experiment.

Collisions with other atoms of suitable kinds can result in disorientation either by electron exchange or by mutual spin-flipping. This source of disturbance can be eliminated by keeping the sodium mean free path large compared to the dimensions of the apparatus, which is equivalent in this experiment to keeping the pressure below 10^{-2} mm of Hg. The normal pressure was 10^{-6} to 10^{-4} mm of Hg.

Sodium Resonance Fluorescence

The electronic ground state of sodium is a $3\,^2S_{\frac{1}{2}}$ state which combines with the nuclear spin of the stable isotope, $I = \frac{3}{2}$, in two hyperfine states having $F = 1$ and 2. The first excited state is a doublet having term values $3\,^2P_{\frac{1}{2}}$ and $3\,^2P_{\frac{3}{2}}$, the lower of which $(J = \frac{1}{2})$ has the same hyperfine structure as the ground state, while the upper has four hyperfine states with F ranging from 0 to 3 (see Fig. 1).

Since the smallest hyperfine splitting is only 2.6 times the natural level breadth, the treatment of resonance fluorescence given in Heitler[9] must be extended to include the effect of the overlapping of levels. The derivation is very similar to Heitler's, and only the result will be given. The probability of an atom being in a given final state (at $t = \infty$ when absorption is known to have taken place) is

$$|b_{\mathrm{m}}(\infty)|^2 = \frac{4\pi^2 \rho_\omega{}^2}{\Gamma \hbar^4} \sum_{n,n'} \frac{H_{mn}H_{n0}H_{mn'}{}^* H_{n'0}{}^*}{\gamma - i\omega_{nn'}}, \quad (1)$$

where ρ_ω is the density of radiation oscillators at the resonance frequency, $1/\Gamma$ is the lifetime of the initial state, $1/\gamma$ that of the intermediate state, and $\omega_{nn'}$ the energy difference between the two indicated intermediate states. The index 0 refers to the initial state, n and n' to intermediate states, and m to the final state. This result has been averaged over the frequency distributions of the emitted and absorbed photons, assuming a continuous spectrum incident. This assumption is justified for a light source emitting lines much broader than the absorption Doppler breadth such as the one used in this experiment.

The matrix elements H_{mn} and H_{n0} for the emission and absorption processes may be obtained from the formulas in Condon and Shortley,[10] page 63, although a unitary transformation must be applied to obtain the values in the desired representation having the quantum numbers I, J, F, and M_F. The matrix of this unitary transformation may be constructed from the tables in Condon and Shortley, page 76. Applying this transformation, one obtains the matrix elements of electron momentum in the desired representation. The elements H_{mn} and H_{n0} of the Hamiltonian are derived from these by taking the inner product of the electron momentum and the vector potential of the radiation field in the dipole wave approximation, care being taken to appropriately restrict the polarization of the incident wave.

It may be seen from Eq. (1) that a pair of intermediate levels will contribute an interference term whose ratio to the direct transition terms is $2/(\omega_{nn'}{}^2 + \gamma^2)$. The natural line breadth γ is[11] 6.1×10^7 radians/sec, while the total hyperfine splittings used in the calculations are[12] 1.5×10^9 radians/sec for the $3\,^2P_{\frac{3}{2}}$ state and 9.4×10^8 radians/sec for the $3\,^2P_{\frac{1}{2}}$ state. Applying the Landé interval rule, it is found that only the levels $F = 0$ and $F = 1$ of the latter state $(\omega_{01} = 2.6\gamma)$ are close enough to contribute interference terms as large as 10 percent of the direct transition terms. More recent measurements[13] give a smaller total splitting in the $3\,^2P_{\frac{1}{2}}$ state, as well as a small deviation from the interval rule, but the difference does not significantly affect the results of the present calculations.

The transition probabilities also depend on the intensity ratio in the light source of the two fine structure components of the sodium D-line. The source used yielded equal peak intensities of the two

[9] W. Heitler, *The Quantum Theory of Radiation* (Oxford University Press, London, 1944), second edition, pp. 137–142.

[10] E. U. Condon and G. H. Shortley, *Theory of Atomic Spectra* (Cambridge University Press, London, 1951).
[11] L. Larrick, Phys. Rev. **46**, 581 (1934).
[12] L. P. Granath and C. M. Van Atta, Phys. Rev. **44**, 935 (1933).
[13] P. Sagalyn, Phys. Rev. **94**, 885 (1954).

TABLE I. Probabilities of transitions induced by resonance radiation between substates of the sodium $3\,^2P_{\frac{1}{2}}$ ground state complex for equal incident fluxes of the two D-line components. Column one gives the quantum numbers F and M_F of the initial states; the other columns are headed by the quantum numbers F and M_F of the final states. The probabilities are so normalized that each initial state has a total absorption probability of one.

Initial F, M_F	1,−1	1,0	1,1	Final F, M_F 2,−2	2,−1	2,0	2,1	2,2
1,−1	0.343	0.167	0.268	0	0.085	0.056	0.082	0
1, 0	0	0.312	0.299	0	0	0.140	0.085	0.164
1, 1	0	0	0.500	0	0	0	0.167	0.333
2,−2	0.169	0.164	0	0.321	0.193	0.154	0	0
2,−1	0.085	0.167	0.082	0	0.229	0.207	0.229	0
2, 0	0	0.140	0.138	0	0	0.292	0.276	0.154
2, 1	0	0	0.167	0	0	0	0.500	0.333
2, 2	0	0	0	0	0	0	0	1.000

lines; and therefore, because of the difference in statistical weights of the two levels, the total absorption probability leading to the $3\,^2P_{\frac{3}{2}}$ state is twice that for the $3\,^2P_{\frac{1}{2}}$ level. This having been taken into account, Table I gives the total relative probabilities of resonance fluorescence between given initial and final states via all possible intermediate states. The columns are labeled by the quantum numbers of the final states, and the rows by those of the initial states. Both initial and final states are all members of the $3\,^2S_{\frac{1}{2}}$ ground state complex. The total absorption probabilities of all the initial states are the same, which is only true for equal intensities in the source of the two components of the doublet.

Table I may be regarded as a matrix operator. The vector on which it operates has components proportional to the occupation probabilities of the various initial states for whatever ensemble of atoms is under consideration. Similarly, the vector resulting from the operation gives the occupation probabilities for the same ensemble after each of its members has scattered one and only one photon. The initial ensemble is normally taken as being in thermal equilibrium, and by n applications of the operator one may find the occupation probabilities of an ensemble each of whose members has scattered exactly n photons.

One may simplify the computation of the polarization of the scattered light by observing that each element in the matrix operator just described corresponds to a definite polarization component, σ or π, in the scattered radiation. Summing the elements of like polarization in each row of the matrix produces a pair of vectors whose components are labeled by the quantum numbers of initial states. The inner product of one of these vectors with the occupation vector of an ensemble is proportional to the amount of the corresponding polarization emitted when each member of that ensemble scatters one photon. For example, applying this process to an ensemble whose members have each scattered two photons, one can compute the polarization emitted when a third photon is scattered.

Table II gives the state occupation probability distributions of ensembles whose members have each scattered a definite number, n, of photons. It also gives the expectation values for these ensembles of the observables M_F, M_I, and M_S, the axial projections of the total, nuclear, and electronic angular momenta, as well as the polarization ratio $R_n = (\sigma - \pi)/(\sigma + \pi)$ of the light scattered at 90° to the axis of quantization. π radiation has its electric vector parallel to the axis, σ, perpendicular, both being plane polarized at this scattering angle.

Of course, no physically realizable ensemble is composed of members all of which have scattered the same number of photons. However, the expectation value of an observable for a physical ensemble may be computed by taking a weighted average of the expectation values for the several such idealized ensembles. The value of the observable for the ith ensemble is weighted by the probability P_i of an atom in the physical ensemble scattering i photons.

To compute P_i, consider a beam of sodium atoms passing through an illuminated region such that each atom scatters on the average N photons in the L cm of illuminated beam. The probability of absorbing a photon in any interval of path dl is $(N/L)dl$, and the probability of not absorbing any photon at all is

$$P_0 = (1 - N\,dl/L)^{L/dl} = e^{-N}, \qquad (2)$$

of absorbing one and only one photon is

$$P_1 = \int_0^L \frac{N}{L} e^{-N} dl = N e^{-N}, \qquad (3)$$

and of absorbing exactly i photons is

$$P_i = N^i e^{-N}/i!. \qquad (4)$$

EXPERIMENTAL PROCEDURE

The apparatus consisted of a source of sodium resonance radiation, a sodium sample in the form of a

TABLE II. Expectation values of various quantities for ensembles each of whose members has scattered n photons. R_n is the polarization ratio of photons scattered at 90° for the nth scattering process.

n	$M_F = 1$	F=1 0	−1	2	1	F=2 0	−1	−2	M_F	M_I	M_S	R_n
				Occupation numbers								
1	0.182	0.119	0.075	0.247	0.168	0.106	0.063	0.040	0.626	0.523	0.103	0.070
2	0.194	0.082	0.038	0.399	0.174	0.071	0.029	0.012	1.075	0.884	0.191	0.173
3	0.173	0.049	0.018	0.546	0.156	0.042	0.012	0.004	1.384	1.116	0.268	0.313

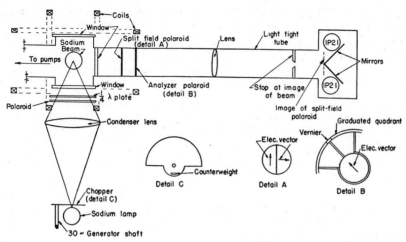

FIG. 2. Optical system used to orient sodium and to detect the orientation when produced.

beam, coils to control the magnetic field seen by the sample, and equipment to detect the polarization of the light scattered by the sample. A view of the optical system is shown in Fig. 2.

A Phillips sodium spectral lamp No. 93122E was used, together with a sheet of polaroid and a quarter wave plate, to produce circularly polarized sodium resonance radiation. A lens formed an image of the lamp at the beam position, and the light was interrupted at 30 cycles per second by a semicircular metal segment on the shaft of a small motor generator. The 30-cycle/sec output from the generator was used as the reference signal for the lock-in amplifier that formed part of the polarization detector.

A sodium beam was used as a simple means of insuring relative freedom from foreign gas contamination. The beam source was a stainless steel oven heated to 100°–200°C by 60-cycle/sec ac. The beam was collimated into a cone of 9° half-angle and caught by a liquid nitrogen trap after leaving the illuminated region. The beam chamber was evacuated by an oil diffusion pump provided with a solid CO_2 cooled trap to intercept oil vapor. With both traps cold, a vacuum of between 10^{-4} and 10^{-6} mm of Hg could be obtained, depending on the beam source conditions.

In the early stages of the experiment, the magnetic field applied was quite inhomogeneous, especially the axial component (that parallel to the direction of the incident light), since it was supplied by two solenoids separated axially by a distance equal to their diameter, the diameter being no larger than the region in which the sodium was observed. When it was found that this inhomogeneity increased the difficulty of interpreting the data, the first set of coils was replaced by three mutually perpendicular Helmholtz pairs, each producing a field of 4 gauss/ampere within the accuracy of

mounting them to fulfill the Helmholtz condition. No refined technique of mounting them was used, neither the field calibration nor the homogeneity being sufficiently critical to the experiment to require it. The smallest of the three pairs had a radius of 11.4 cm and the largest 19.0, while the length of sodium beam observed was 3.8 cm.

The polarization ratio $(\sigma-\pi)/(\sigma+\pi)$ of the light scattered by the sodium beam was determined by an optical bridge whose parts are indicated in Fig. 2. All observations were made at a scattering angle of 90°. The light passed through a polaroid filter consisting of two semicircular segments each transmitting only σ or only π radiation. At 90° to the axis of quantization, each component is plane polarized with their planes of polarization perpendicular to each other. Each half of this split-field polaroid was imaged by a lens on one of two 1P21 photomultiplier tubes. Between the split-field polaroid and the lens was a rotatable polaroid (hereafter called the analyzer) provided with a graduated quadrant and vernier. Its function was to produce known changes in the intensity ratio of the two light polarization components and thus calibrate the detector. It was normally set at 45° in order to transmit equal amounts of the two components. All this equipment was enclosed in a light-tight tube. To reduce stray light to a minimum, the detector was placed opposite the vacuum pumping lead; and a stop was placed at the image of the beam (see Fig. 2) to intercept light scattered from the edges of the observation window.

Since the incident light was modulated at 30 cycles/sec, ac detection could be used. The output of one 1P21 was inverted in phase and added to that of the other, the combined signal being fed into a 30-cycle/sec lock-in amplifier. The output of this amplifier appeared on an Esterline-Angus recording milliammeter. The system thus formed an optical bridge giving a null signal for equal outputs from the two photomultiplier tubes. Since the gains of the two 1P21's could not be depended on to be the same, absolute light polarization ratios could not be measured. All polarization measurements were therefore referred to a standard condition, that in which sodium orientation was destroyed by application of a magnetic field perpendicular to the axis. The field of the earth was found to serve this purpose excellently. With unoriented sodium, the bridge was approximately balanced by adjusting the applied voltage, and thus the gain, of one photomultiplier. The difference between the resulting signal and that for any other sodium sample condition was reduced to a light polarization difference by comparing it with the signal change produced by rotating the analyzer polaroid a known amount.

RESULTS AND DISCUSSION

The sodium lamp used was compared with a white lamp of known intensity by means of visual observation with a flicker photometer (average of 92 comparisons) and found to emit 2.72×10^{16} photons/(cm^2 sec steradian) perpendicular to its surface. If an image of this source is formed by a lens, it can be shown that the photon flux through the image is simply $I\Omega$, where I is the surface intensity of the source as given above and Ω is the solid angle subtended by the lens at the image. For a given lens, the maximum solid angle is determined by the requirement that the image of the light source be at least as big as the region occupied by the sodium beam. In practice, the solid angle was limited not by the lens, but by the window admitting light to the vacuum system, which subtended an angle at the sodium beam of $\pi/16$ steradian; since the polaroid had a transmission of 0.365, the total photon flux at the beam was therefore 1.95×10^{15} photons/cm^2 sec.

To determine the intensity ratio and line widths of the two fine structure components, the light source was photographed through a Lummer-Gehrcke plate (crossed with a prism), for the loan of which I am indebted to Professor A. G. Shenstone. The density of the photographic images was measured with a recording densitometer owned by the R. C. A. laboratory in Penn's Neck, New Jersey. I am grateful to Dr. Hillier of that laboratory for permission to use the instrument and to Dr. H. Halma for making the measurements with it. The two components of the doublet were found to have approximately the same peak intensities; their widths were 10^{10} cycles/sec for the component radiated by atoms in the $3\,^2P_{\frac{1}{2}}$ level and 1.4×10^{10} cycles/sec for the $3\,^2P_{\frac{3}{2}}$ component. This equality of peak intensities, together with the extreme breadth (20 times Doppler breadth), suggests that the source is so self-reversed as to be effectively a blackbody at the center of the lines. This is quite reasonable since we shall see that approximately 10^{10} atoms cm^{-2} completely absorb all light at the resonance frequency. For a thickness of 1 cm, this

corresponds to a pressure of 2.5×10^{-7} mm of Hg, and the sodium partial pressure in the lamp was certainly much higher than this. From these observations, the common peak flux per unit frequency at the sodium beam is

$$I_0 = 1.29 \times 10^4 \text{ photons/cm}^2 \text{ radian}$$

for each component.

In sodium the transition to the first excited state complex accounts for 0.975 of all the radiation absorbed by atoms in the ground state (see Condon and Shortley,[10] p. 149). For present purposes the oscillator strength of the line may therefore be taken as one, and the number of photons absorbed per atom is thus given by the formula (Heitler,[9] p. 108) for a classical oscillator,

$$n = 2\pi^2 r_0 c I_0, \qquad (5)$$

where r_0 is the classical radius of the electron. Thus for the given light flux,

$$n = 2.14 \times 10^3 \text{ photons/sec atom.}$$

A sodium beam source temperature of 200°C corresponds to a velocity of 4.8×10^4 cm/sec. Since the illuminated length of beam was 3.8 cm, each atom might be expected to absorb on the average 0.17 photon.

Clearly the number of sodium atoms which can be oriented is no larger than that number which absorbs all the incident light. A larger sample will result in multiple scattering of photons and a lower orientation per atom. For a sodium sample (not necessarily a beam) at a temperature in the neighborhood of 200°C, the Doppler breadth of the absorbed line is approximately 2×10^9 radians/sec. The total number of photons which can be absorbed is roughly equal to the line breadth times the peak intensity, or 2.4×10^{13} photons/cm^2 sec. Since each atom absorbs 2.1×10^3 photons/sec, 10^{10} atoms/cm^2 will absorb all photons in the usable range. Other considerations, based on the tendency of a gas to radiate coherently,[14] thus reradiating photons of the same polarization as those absorbed, limit the sample to about one-fifth this number.

Although the fact is obscured by the method of derivation, the sample size is independent of the light intensity; for as the intensity increases, each atom absorbs more photons. In other words, the absorption cross section is independent of the light intensity.

This limitation of the sample size is naturally a serious limitation on any experiments it is desired to perform with atoms or nuclei oriented by this technique. As an example, if it were desired to study the angular distribution of radioactive emissions, an isotope with a half-life of one year would produce 130 counts/min in a perfectly efficient counter subtending a solid angle of $4\pi \times 10^{-2}$ steradian if the radiation were isotropic. Again, the hyperfine structure resonance of

[14] R. H. Dicke, Phys. Rev. **93**, 99 (1954).

Na[23] could be observed with a signal-to-noise ratio of about 500 assuming an orientation of 10 percent. The signal-to-noise ratio varies as the square of the amount of orientation.

It was found that the sodium source temperature (and beam density) could be allowed to vary over wide limits without changing the experimental results. This is interpreted to mean that the density was at all times well below the allowable maximum. No attempt was made to observe the actual source temperature beyond rough estimates.

Since the rate of light absorption is now known, the probability of an atom scattering any given number of photons i may be computed from Eq. (4). The average polarization of the light scattered is given by

$$\bar{R} = \sum_{i=1}^{\infty} R_i \sum_{j=i}^{\infty} P_j \bigg/ \sum_{i=1}^{\infty} iP_i, \qquad (6)$$

where the R_i are taken from Table II. For the given absorption probability, P_3 is only 5 percent of P_2, and all higher P_i's may be neglected. The average polarization is then

$$\bar{R} = 0.0789.$$

When orientation is destroyed by application of a transverse magnetic field, the polarization of the scattered light is not quite equal to R_1, as one would expect if true thermal equilibrium were produced. It can be shown that a slight degree of *alignment* remains and that the average scattered polarization in this case is

$$\bar{R} = 0.0710,$$

while the value of R_1 is 0.0700. The change in light polarization expected upon destruction of orientation by a transverse field is therefore

$$\Delta \bar{R}_{\text{th}} = 0.0079.$$

Twenty-one observations of this change were made over a period of five months, and their average was

$$\Delta \bar{R}_{\text{obs}} = 0.0097.$$

The largest and smallest values observed were

$$\Delta \bar{R}_{\text{min}} = 0.0058,$$
$$\Delta \bar{R}_{\text{max}} = 0.0129.$$

Since the intensity of illumination may easily be affected by changes in position of the light source, line voltage changes, and other effects not under experimental control, this variation is not considered alarming.

The agreement with the predicted value of ΔR is considered good in view of the uncertainties involved in the use of the flicker photometer and the photographic measurement of the line width, especially since the latter was not done with as much skill as might be desirable.

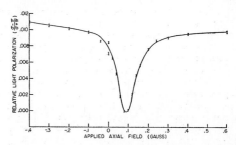

FIG. 3. Polarization ratio of the scattered resonance radiation as a function of the applied axial field component, incident light circularly polarized.

Although the transverse components of the ambient magnetic field were compensated as well as possible, one could not hope to reduce them below the 10^{-3} gauss necessary to avoid disturbing the sodium orientation. In addition, no attempt was made to compensate ac fields. Thus one might expect that orientation would disappear for insufficiently large values of the axial field. This was indeed the case, and a representative curve of light polarization *versus* applied axial field is shown in Fig. 3. The minimum is displaced from zero by the presence of a terrestrial component of 0.1 gauss in the axial direction. It should be stressed that ideally the incident light is sufficient to define the axis of quantization, and it is only necessary to apply a field to overcome the disturbing effects of fields already present.

When the measurements are extended to axial fields of several gauss, the polarization at first increases for one field direction and decreases for the other as the absolute value of the field is increased. In both directions it eventually goes through a minimum and then increases steadily. This is believed to be the result of the alteration of atomic wave functions by the magnetic field. The asymmetry is a result of the asymmetry of the light polarization and disappears for unpolarized light although the changes in polarization with increasing field remain.

The measurements of $\Delta \bar{R}$ discussed above were all taken from curves similar to Fig. 3. at about -0.2 gauss applied where the axial field is sufficiently large to allow orientation to proceed undisturbed but not large enough to change the wave functions appreciably.

The vacuum system was later modified to increase by a factor of 2.5 the illuminated solid angle seen by the sodium beam. The change in light polarization upon destruction of orientation then became $\Delta \bar{R} = 0.0175$, an increase by a factor of 1.8. This could reasonably be expected to be less than the increase in solid angle because the additional light is all moving at an angle to the axis and is therefore less effective in producing orientation.

This polarization change of 1.75 percent corresponds theoretically to an effective average of 0.365 photon

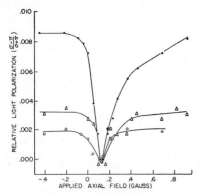

FIG. 4. Polarization ratio of the scattered resonance radiation as a function of incident intensity of circularly polarized radiation. Incident light intensities in ratio 1.00:0.39:0.17 for upper, middle, and lower curves, respectively.

scattered by each atom. For this probability of photon scattering, the ensemble averages of the expectation values of nuclear, total, and electronic angular momenta are, respectively,

$$\bar{M}_I = 0.180 = 0.120I,$$
$$\bar{M}_F = 0.216 = 0.108F,$$
$$\bar{M}_S = 0.035 = 0.070S.$$

In the case of F, the fractional figure is given relative to the larger F value of the two hyperfine states, for if orientation were complete, all atoms would be in the state $F=2$.

In order to obtain an experimental check on the polarization of the first photon scattered by an unoriented atom, the absolute polarization of light scattered by sodium atoms in the earth's magnetic field was measured. An attempt was made to do this by using the electronic detector already described and a modified scheme of analyzing polaroids, but the results were not self-consistent. Visual methods were therefore used. A Babinet compensator followed by a Nichol prism shows dark bands crossing the field of view if the polarization ratio of the light incident on the arrangement is greater than about 0.01. A glass plate between the light source and the Babinet compensator may be used to introduce an opposite polarization by rotating it in a plane containing the electric vector of the observed polarization. The polarization of the light may be calculated from the angle at which the bands disappear.[15] The angle observed was 34.2±1.5° (average of ten measurements) when a glass plate of refractive index 1.52 was used. The index was not known exactly and limits of ±0.02 were assigned which account for about one-quarter of the error quoted below for the

15 R. W. Wood, *Physical Optics* (Macmillan Company, New York, 1934), third edition, pp. 341–343.

polarization. The resulting polarization ratio is

$$R = 0.049 \pm 0.008,$$

which differs from the predicted value of 0.071 by 2.8 times the probable error. An error of this size has a probability of 6 percent, viewed as a random deviation.

To explain this result by an error in the measurement of relative intensities of the two components emitted by the source would require the assumption that the $3\,^2P_{\frac{3}{2}}$ component had only one-half the intensity of the other. Not only does this large an error in the photometric measurement seem highly unlikely, but it contradicts the very plausible assumption of blackbody emission at the line centers. An incorrect value for the hyperfine splittings would not affect the polarization by such a large amount, for the predicted polarization is decreased by wider separation of the levels, and with levels completely separated the polarization is only decreased to 0.069. Moreover, the more recent values of the splitting lead to a smaller level separation than the value used.

The intensity of the incident light was varied by means of neutral density filters. By a simple algebraic manipulation of the probabilities P_i of Eq. (4), it can be shown that if P_3 is neglected, the polarization of the scattered light is proportional to $N/(N+1)$ where N is the average number of photons scattered per atom. Since N is small compared to 1 ($N \leqslant 0.2$ in Table III), the polarization can be considered proportional to the light intensity. Figure 4 shows a sample set of curves taken with two filters of different density and without any filter. The asymmetry in these curves was a result of the inhomogeneity of the field produced by the first set of coils used. Table III gives the change in light polarization when orientation is destroyed for two sets of observations similar to those in Fig. 4. The light intensities were determined from the size of the signal produced by rotating the analyzer polaroid a known amount and agree with the filter densities given by the manufacturer. The variation is seen to be linear as expected.

Representative data are given in Fig. 5 and Fig. 6 showing the effect of varying a transverse component of the magnetic field keeping the axial component fixed. The axial components are different for the two figures. The solid curves are theoretical curves computed by assuming that many cycles of Larmor precession occur between successive photon scattering events for any one atom. Since these events are random, only time

TABLE III. Change in scattered light polarization ($\Delta\bar{R}$) when orientation is destroyed as a function of incident light intensity.

Light intensity (arbitrary units)	$\Delta\bar{R}$ (arbitrary units)	
	run 1	run 2
1.00	1.00	1.00
0.39	0.36±0.1	0.38±0.1
0.17	0.20±0.1	0.18±0.1

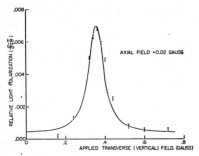

FIG. 5. Polarization ratio of the scattered resonance radiation as a function of one applied transverse field component; the solid curve is computed theoretically.

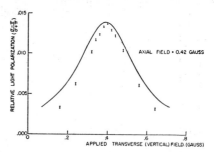

FIG. 6. Polarization ratio of the scattered resonance radiation as a function of one applied transverse field component; the solid curve is computed theoretically.

average results are required. Time-average projection operators of the z-component of angular momentum in a rotating coordinate system were derived. These were used to find the time-average occupation probabilities of the precessing atoms in eigenstates of M_F referred to stationary axes. The calculation is straightforward but too lengthy to be reproduced here. It results in the following expression for the polarization of the second-scattered photon (R_2) as a function of the angle between the magnetic field and the axis of quantization defined by the incident light:

$$R_2(\theta) = \frac{9.8 \times 10^{-4} \cos^8\theta - 0.115 \cos^6\theta + 4.14 \cos^4\theta + 4.58 \cos^2\theta + 7.0}{-10.8 \times 10^{-4} \cos^8\theta + 3.86 \times 10^{-2} \cos^6\theta - 1.28 \cos^4\theta - 1.50 \cos^2\theta + 93.4}. \quad (7)$$

This reduces to the correct value of R_2 for $\theta = 0$.

The data shown in the figures are typical in that the agreement with theory is good for small axial fields and not for larger ones, the experimental points always falling below the theoretical curve. The only adjustable parameter is the value of the polarization at the maximum of the curve. The disagreement may well be a result of the alteration of atomic wave functions by the larger total fields.

When the incident radiation is unpolarized, the curve of scattered light polarization versus axial magnetic field is similar to Fig. 3 in every respect except the light polarization scale. The total change in light polarization is only $\Delta \bar{R} = 0.0048$. This may be explained by considering the incident light as composed of equal parts of the two senses of circular polarization. Table II shows that scattering of a circularly polarized photon reduces the population in the $M_F = 0$ states independently of its sense of rotation. Consequently, scattering of unpolarized light will increase the populations of the states with $|M_F| = F$ relative to those with $M_F = 0$. The atomic ensemble is then in a condition of partial alignment. Among the atoms which scatter two photons there are some which scatter two with the same sense of rotation and contribute to the alignment of the

ensemble as well as others which scatter photons of opposite senses and do not contribute significantly. Since the effect of unpolarized resonance radiation on a completely aligned ensemble is to reduce the alignment, the process does not proceed to complete alignment for very large light intensity but rather reaches an equilibrium partial alignment. This possibility of alignment by unpolarized light was briefly mentioned by Kastler in the article already cited.[1]

Table IV gives the probability of an atom being in various angular momentum states after scattering one to four photons, as well as the values at equilibrium ($n = \infty$). These were computed by a straightforward application of Table I considered as a matrix operator. Although the approach to equilibrium is rapid, the equilibrium alignment is small. However, the difference in population of corresponding magnetic substates of the two hyperfine levels is still many times that resulting from the energy separation in thermal equilibrium at room temperature.

Combining the photon polarizations in Table IV with the figure (obtained from the degree of orientation for the same amount of polarized light) of 0.365 photon absorbed per atom, the total change in light polarization expected upon destruction of alignment is calculated to be $\Delta \bar{R} = 0.0034$, compared to an observed value of 0.0048. This indicates that the incident light may not have been completely unpolarized.

There is no reason to believe that the effect should be confined to sodium, since the argument for the produc-

TABLE IV. Occupation probabilities for ensembles each of whose members has scattered n photons of unpolarized light, including the equilibrium state ($n = \infty$). P_1 and P_2 are the probabilities of atoms being in states with F equal to 1 and 2. R_n is the polarization ratio of photons scattered at 90° in the nth scattering process.

n	$F = 1$		$F = 2$			P_1	P_2	R_n
	$M_F = \pm 1$	0	± 2	± 1	0			
1	0.128	0.119	0.144	0.115	0.106	0.375	0.624	0.0700
2	0.128	0.116	0.154	0.110	0.100	0.372	0.628	0.0905
3	0.126	0.115	0.161	0.108	0.099	0.367	0.637	0.0997
4	0.126	0.115	0.162	0.108	0.099	0.367	0.639	0.1049
∞	0.125	0.115	0.163	0.106	0.098	0.365	0.636	$\cdots$

tion of alignment, like that for orientation, is quite general. The argument applies, however, only when the light is incident from a restricted part of a sphere, for isotropic unpolarized light defines no axis with respect to which alignment can occur.

I wish to express my gratitude to Dr. R. H. Dicke, without whose inspiration and invaluable counsel this research could not have been undertaken or completed. I am also indebted to Dr. D. R. Hamilton for assistance in the early part of the work.

From: *Phys. Rev.* 108, 1453-1458 (1957)   125

Atomic Orientation by Optical Pumping*

W. Franzen and A. G. Emslie
Arthur D. Little, Incorporated, Cambridge, Massachusetts
(Received July 16, 1957)

A variation of the usual method of atomic orientation of alkali metal vapors by optical pumping is proposed. This variation consists of employing a single circularly polarized D_1 line as pumping radiation, instead of a mixture of the two D lines. Under these conditions, one magnetic substate of the ground state is transparent to the pumping radiation. It is shown that for a sufficiently intense light source and relatively weak relaxation, the entire population of the vapor will tend to be pumped into this single state, resulting in nearly one-hundred percent atomic orientation. The pumping process is analyzed in detail for sodium vapor illuminated with $3P_{\frac{1}{2}}-3S_{\frac{1}{2}}$ radiation, and the time dependence of the populations of the eight magnetic sublevels of the ground state is computed. It is shown that in the steady state, the light absorption by the vapor is linear rather than exponential with distance. A simple method of measuring relaxation times based on this observation is suggested. The conditions under which the imprisonment of resonance radiation limits the size of the oriented sample are discussed, and it is suggested that the proposed technique will allow the alignment of larger samples than is possible by the usual method of optical pumping.

INTRODUCTION

THE orientation of alkali metal atoms by optical pumping with circularly polarized resonance radiation has recently attracted wide attention.[1-9] The usual method consists of illuminating the vapor with circularly polarized resonance radiation consisting of a mixture of two D lines. Under these conditions, only a limited degree of orientation can be achieved, and the size of the vapor sample that can be aligned is small, as discussed by Hawkins.[5]

It has recently been demonstrated by Dehmelt[8] that it is possible to attain relaxation times of the order of 0.2 sec for optically pumped sodium vapor diffusing through an argon buffer gas atmosphere. Argon-sodium collisions are therefore relatively ineffective as far as disturbing the spin alignment of the sodium atom in its ground state is concerned. The influence of buffer gas collisions on the optical excited state has been investigated by Wood,[10-13] Lochte-Holtgreven,[14] Seiwert,[15] and Bender.[7] A review of this subject is to be found in Pringsheim's book.[16] In the earlier experiments in this field, sodium vapor in an argon buffer gas atmosphere was illuminated with resonance light consisting of one of the two D lines. It was found that when the partial pressure of the buffer gas is increased to a few millimeters of mercury, the relative intensity of the two D lines in the scattered resonance radiation tends toward the equilibrium ratio $1:2$, regardless of which of the two lines is used for excitation. Lochte-Holtgreven[14] obtained a cross section of 1.0×10^{-14} cm^2 for the transfer of sodium atoms from the $3P_{\frac{1}{2}}$ to the $3P_{\frac{3}{2}}$ state in sodium-argon collisions, and a cross section of 0.6×10^{-14} cm^2 for the inverse process at a temperature of 443°K. These cross sections are of the order of gas-kinetic collision cross sections. One would therefore expect substantially complete mixing of the magnetic sublevels of the excited P states when the buffer gas pressure is raised to such a point that the mean time between collisions approaches the lifetime of the excited state $(1.6 \times 10^{-8}$ sec).[17-20]

Dehmelt[8] has pointed out that it is possible to obtain partial orientation of sodium vapor with optical pumping even when there is complete reorientation in the excited state, i.e., complete mixing of the magnetic sublevels in this state, provided there is some difference in the peak intensities of the two D lines emitted by the light source.

We would like to go a step further to suggest that it is possible to approach one-hundred percent orientation of alkali metal atoms by illuminating them with circularly polarized resonance radiation containing only one of the two D lines, namely the one corresponding to an optical transition of the type $nP_{\frac{1}{2}}-mS_{\frac{1}{2}}$. This is true even when $n > m$, that is, when higher members of the principal series of the alkali spectra are employed. Furthermore, the orientation mechanism should be effective regardless of the degree of reorientation that

* This work was supported by the U. S. Army Signal Corps.
[1] A. Kastler, J. phys. radium **11**, 255 (1950).
[2] Brossel, Kastler, and Winter, J. phys. radium **13**, 668 (1952).
[3] Brossel, Cagnac, and Kastler, J. phys. radium **15**, 6 (1954).
[4] A. Kastler, Proc. Phys. Soc. (London) **A67**, 853 (1954).
[5] W. B. Hawkins, Phys. Rev. **98**, 478 (1955).
[6] A. Blandin and J. P. Barrat, Compt. rend. **243**, 2041 (1956).
[7] P. L. Bender, Ph.D. thesis, Department of Physics, Princeton University, 1956 (unpublished).
[8] H. G. Dehmelt, Phys. Rev. **105**, 1487 (1957).
[9] T. Carver and R. H. Dicke, Proceedings of the Eleventh Annual Symposium on Frequency Control, Signal Corps Engineering Laboratories, Fort Monmouth, New Jersey, May, 1957.
[10] R. W. Wood and L. Dunoyer, Phil. Mag. **27**, 1018 (1914).
[11] R. W. Wood and L. Dunoyer, Compt. rend. **158**, 1490 (1914).
[12] R. W. Wood and L. Dunoyer, Radium **11**, 119 (1914).
[13] R. W. Wood and F. L. Mahler, Phys. Rev. **11**, 70 (1918).
[14] W. Lochte-Holtgreven, Z. Physik **47**, 362 (1928).
[15] R. Seiwert, Ann. Physik **18**, 54 (1956).
[16] P. Pringsheim, *Fluorescence and Phosphorescence* (Interscience Publishers, Inc., New York, 1949), pp. 96–102.

[17] A. C. G. Mitchell and M. W. Zemansky, *Resonance Radiation and Excited Atoms* (Cambridge University Press, Cambridge, 1934), p. 36.
[18] R. Minkowski, Z. Physik **36**, 839 (1926).
[19] W. Schuetz, Z. Physik **45**, 30 (1927).
[20] M. Weingeroff, Z. Physik **67**, 679 (1931).

may take place in the excited state, or any intermediate excited state, as will be demonstrated.

Consider the case where the direction of rotation of the magnetic vector of the circularly polarized resonance radiation used for pumping is such that the selection rule $\Delta m_F = +1$ applies relative to an axis of quantization defined by a weak longitudinal magnetic field as described by Hawkins.[5] For a nuclear spin I, the two hyperfine states in the ground state have spins $I - \frac{1}{2}$ and $I + \frac{1}{2}$, respectively. The highest m_F value in the ground state is therefore $m_F = I + \frac{1}{2}$. An identical situation prevails in any of the $P_{\frac{1}{2}}$ excited states for which the two hyperfine states also have $F = I - \frac{1}{2}$ and $F = I + \frac{1}{2}$, the highest m_F value being $m_F = I + \frac{1}{2}$. It is clear that the $m_F = I + \frac{1}{2}$ substate of the ground state cannot undergo transitions subject to the selection rule $\Delta m_F = +1$ since no state having m_F larger than $I + \frac{1}{2}$ is available in the $P_{\frac{1}{2}}$ excited state.

On the other hand, all the other $4I+1$ substates of the ground state hyperfine doublet are able to absorb the circularly polarized resonance radiation. A certain proportion of the excited atoms thus produced will decay into the nonabsorbing $m_F = I + \frac{1}{2}$ sublevel, where they will remain for a time of the order of the relaxation time, undisturbed by the pumping radiation. If the pumping radiation is sufficiently intense and the relaxation time is sufficiently long, the entire population will be thrown into the single nonabsorbing $m_F = I + \frac{1}{2}$ sublevel of the ground state, as we intend to show. This condition corresponds to complete orientation of the alkali atoms, with the coupled nuclear and electron spins both aligned in the direction of the applied magnetic field.

In any actual experimental situation, the relaxation time of course cannot be made indefinitely long, as assumed above. The amount of orientation that can be achieved depends then on the quantity $\rho = 1/\beta_0 T$, where $1/T$ is the relaxation probability per atom per unit time, and β_0 is the average light absorption probability per atom per unit time when the occupation probabilities of the magnetic substates of the ground state are assumed to be equal. The smaller the value of ρ, the nearer the approach of the system to one-hundred percent orientation. This situation is analyzed in detail below.

ANALYSIS OF PUMPING PROCESS

To make the subsequent discussion quite definite, we shall analyze the pumping process as applied specifically to sodium optically pumped with circularly polarized $3P_{\frac{1}{2}} - 3S_{\frac{1}{2}}$ resonance radiation. The choice of this particular case, however, does not restrict the general validity of the method of analysis which can be applied equally well to any of the other alkali metals, or to optical pumping with one of the higher members of the principal series.

Normal sodium consists of a single isotope having a nuclear spin of $\frac{3}{2}$. The hyperfine doublet in the ground

state therefore has $F=1$ and $F=2$, with a total of eight sublevels: $(1, -1)$, $(1, 0)$, $(1, +1)$; $(2, -2)$, $(2, -1)$, $(2, 0)$, $(2, +1)$, $(2, +2)$. The numbers in the parentheses indicate F and m_F, respectively. We shall distinguish these sublevels by using subscripts 1 through 8, in the order stated. Let b_{ij} be the probability per unit time that an atom in the substate i of the ground state has undergone a transition to a substate j of the ground state by absorption and re-emission of a photon. Similarly, we denote by w_{ij} the probability per unit time for the corresponding transition induced by relaxation. The occupation probability $p_k(t)$ of the kth state can be obtained by a solution of the eight simultaneous differential equations

$$\dot{p}_k = -\sum_{j=1}^{8}{}' (b_{kj} + w_{kj}) p_k + \sum_{i=1}^{8}{}' (b_{ik} + w_{ik}) p_i;$$

$$k = 1, 2, \cdots 8. \quad (1)$$

Only seven of these equations are independent in view of the relation $\sum_k p_k = 1$. The dot denotes differentiation with respect to time, and the prime is used to indicate that the terms $j = k$ and $i = k$ are to be omitted in the summations.

The omission of the diagonal terms corresponds to the fact that a transition in which an atom in state k absorbs a photon and then returns to the same state does not affect the occupation probability of that state. However, such a transition does contribute to the absorption coefficient of the vapor for the incident resonance radiation. Thus the probability per unit time that an atom in state k will absorb a photon is given by $\sum_j b_{kj}$ and the probability per unit time that any atom will absorb a photon is $\beta = \sum_k \sum_j b_{kj} p_k$. If we assume that the occupation probabilities are all equal at thermal equilibrium (in other words, if we neglect the small differences in the occupation probabilities at sodium vapor temperatures), the average light absorption probability per atom per unit time is

$$\beta_0 = \frac{1}{8} \sum_k \sum_i b_{kj} = \int_0^\infty I_\nu \sigma_\nu d\nu, \quad (2)$$

where I_ν is the spectral density of the incident light in

TABLE I. Relative absorption probabilities $(1/\beta_0) \sum_j b_{kj}$ per unit time of the eight magnetic substates of the ground state of the sodium atom for circularly polarized resonance radiation containing the $3P_{\frac{1}{2}} - 3S_{\frac{1}{2}}$ line only.

(F, m_F)	k	$(1/\beta_0) \sum_j b_{kj}$
$(1, -1)$	1	$\frac{1}{2}$
$(1, 0)$	2	1
$(1, +1)$	3	$\frac{3}{2}$
$(2, -2)$	4	2
$(2, -1)$	5	$\frac{3}{2}$
$(2, 0)$	6	1
$(2, +1)$	7	$\frac{1}{2}$
$(2, +2)$	8	0

TABLE II. Array of coefficients B_{ik} to be used in the simultaneous differential equations (5) for sodium optically pumped with circularly polarized D_1 radiation. No reorientation in the excited state.

(F, m_F)		$(1, -1)$	$(1, 0)$	$(1, 1)$	$(2, -2)$	$(2, -1)$	$(2, 0)$	$(2, 1)$	$(2, 2)$
	i	1	2	3	4	5	6	7	8
(F, m_F)	k								
$(1, -1)$	1	$-8\rho - 11/3$	0	0	2	1	0	0	0
$(1, 0)$	2	$2/3$	$-8\rho - 19/3$	0	2	2	$5/3$	0	0
$(1, 1)$	3	$1/3$	$5/3$	$-8\rho - 6$	0	1	$5/3$	2	0
$(2, -2)$	4	0	0	0	$-8\rho - 28/3$	0	0	0	0
$(2, -1)$	5	1	0	0	$10/3$	$-8\rho - 9$	0	0	0
$(2, 0)$	6	$2/3$	$5/3$	0	2	2	$-8\rho - 19/3$	0	0
$(2, 1)$	7	1	1	2	0	3	1	$-8\rho - 10/3$	0
$(2, 2)$	8	0	2	4	0	0	2	$4/3$	-8ρ

photons per cm² per sec per unit frequency range, and σ_ν is the cross section for absorption of a photon of frequency ν by a sodium atom when the eight sublevels in the ground state are equally populated. If we take the oscillator strength of the circularly polarized D_1 line as $\frac{1}{6}$, we can employ the dispersion theory relation[17,21]

$$\int_0^\infty \sigma_\nu d\nu = \frac{1}{6}\pi c r_0 = 4.40 \times 10^{-3} \text{ cm}^2/\text{sec},$$

where $r_0 = e^2/mc^2$ is the classical radius of the electron and c is the velocity of light, to obtain $\beta_0 = 4.40 \times 10^{-3} I_0$ for the layer of sodium vapor first struck by the incident resonance radiation. We have assumed here that the light source emits a spectral line that is considerably broader than the width at half-maximum of the Doppler-broadened absorption line,[22] so that we can set $I_\nu = I_0 = $ constant at the center of the line.

The relative absorption probabilities $(1/\beta_0)\sum_j b_{kj}$ of the eight substates $k = 1, 2, \cdots, 8$, for the circularly polarized D_1 line are listed in Table I.[23,24] We note in the first place that the absorption probability of the eighth state $(F = 2, m_F = +2)$ is zero. This is due to the fact that the transition $3S_{\frac{1}{2}} - 3P_{\frac{1}{2}}$ is forbidden for this state by the selection rule $\Delta m_F = +1$. Secondly, we observe that the average absorption probability per atom for a condition where the p_k's are unequal is given by

$$\beta = \beta_0[\tfrac{1}{2}p_1 + p_2 + \tfrac{3}{2}p_3 + 2p_4 + \tfrac{3}{2}p_5 + p_6 + \tfrac{1}{2}p_7]. \quad (3)$$

It should be emphasized that these statements are valid

regardless of the amount of reorientation of the sodium atom in its excited state.

The simplest assumption that one can make with regard to the relaxation probabilities w_{ij} occurring in Eq. (1) is that all the w's are equal to each other. This implies that in an individual relaxation event, such as an electron exchange collision between two sodium atoms,[25,26] or a wall collision, an atom in a given substate has an equal probability for making a transition to any of the other seven substates. If we set $w = 1/8T$ for all the w's in Eq. (1), then the differential equation satisfied by p_k when no pumping radiation is present is

$$\dot{p}_k = -(1/T)(p_k - \tfrac{1}{8}), \quad (4)$$

so that T has the significance of a spin-lattice relaxation time in the usual sense.[27]

The actual values of the individual transition probabilities b_{ij} of course do depend on the amount of reorientation in the excited state. Two extreme situations can be analyzed simply, namely the case of no reorientation in the excited state, and the case of complete reorientation in the excited state. Any actual physical system would be expected to be intermediate between these two extremes.

In view of (4), the system of Eqs. (1) can be written in the form

$$\dot{p}_k = \left(\frac{\beta_0}{8}\right) \sum_{i=1}^8 B_{ik}p_i + \frac{1}{8T}; \quad k = 1, 2, \cdots, 8. \quad (5)$$

The coefficients B_{ik} are related to the transition probabilities defined previously by $B_{ik} = (8/\beta_0)b_{ik}$ for $i \neq k$, and $B_{kk} = -(8/\beta_0)[(1/T) + \sum_j' b_{kj}]$, where the prime again denotes omission of the term $j = k$ in the summation. Normalization of the transition probabilities computed by Hawkins[24] leads to the array of coefficients B_{ik} shown in Table II for the case of no reorientation in the excited state.

For the case of complete reorientation in the excited

[21] W. Heitler, *The Quantum Theory of Radiation* (Oxford University Press New York, 1954), third edition, p. 180.

[22] For sodium vapor at 400°K, the Doppler width at half-maximum is $\Delta\nu_D = 1500$ Mc/sec, while a sodium spectral lamp under typical operating conditions emits a D_1 line of width 10^4 Mc/sec. (See reference 5.) These figures are to be compared with a zero-field hyperfine splitting in the ground state of 1770 Mc/sec and a natural width of 10 Mc/sec. The Lorentz width is negligible at moderate buffer gas pressures.

[23] E. U. Condon and G. H. Shortley, *The Theory of Atomic Spectra* (Cambridge University Press, Cambridge, 1935), Chaps. IX and XII.

[24] W. B. Hawkins, Ph.D. thesis, Department of Physics, Princeton University, May, 1954 (unpublished), Appendix D.

[25] J. P. Wittke and R. H. Dicke, Phys. Rev. **103**, 620 (1956).
[26] E. M. Purcell and G. B. Field, Astrophys. J. **124**, 542 (1956).
[27] E. R. Andrews, *Nuclear Magnetic Resonance* (Cambridge University Press, Cambridge, 1954), p. 15.

TABLE III. Array of coefficients B_{ik} to be used in the simultaneous differential Eqs. (5) for sodium optically pumped with circularly polarized D_1 radiation. Complete reorientation in the excited state.

(F, m_F)		$(1, -1)$	$(1, 0)$	$(1, 1)$	$(2, -2)$	$(2, -1)$	$(2, 0)$	$(2, 1)$	$(2, 2)$
	i	1	2	3	4	5	6	7	8
(F, m_F)	k								
$(1, -1)$	1	$-8\rho-3.5$	1	1.5	2	1.5	1	0.5	0
$(1, 0)$	2	0.5	$-8\rho-7$	1.5	2	1.5	1	0.5	0
$(1, 1)$	3	0.5	1	$-8\rho-10.5$	2	1.5	1	0.5	0
$(2, -2)$	4	0.5	1	1.5	$-8\rho-14$	1.5	1	0.5	0
$(2, -1)$	5	0.5	1	1.5	2	$-8\rho-10.5$	1	0.5	0
$(2, 0)$	6	0.5	1	1.5	2	1.5	$-8\rho-7$	0.5	0
$(2, 1)$	7	0.5	1	1.5	2	1.5	1	$-8\rho-3.5$	0
$(2, 2)$	8	0.5	1	1.5	2	1.5	1	0.5	-8ρ

state, we assume with Dehmelt[8] that the rates at which atoms return to the eight magnetic sublevels of the ground state are equal. Using the same normalization procedure applied above, we then get the array of coefficients shown in Table III.

Figure 1 displays graphically solutions of the two sets of simultaneous differential equations (5) that have been obtained by use of an electronic computer for the case $\rho=1/\beta_0T=0.01$. We note the approach of the system to a steady state in which most of the population is in the single substate 8 ($F=2$, $m_F=+2$). It is also interesting to observe the rapid decrease of the absorption probability $\beta=\beta_0(\frac{1}{2}p_1+p_2+\frac{3}{2}p_3+2p_4 +\frac{3}{2}p_5+p_6+\frac{1}{2}p_7)$ as the steady state is approached.

Of considerable practical interest are analytical solutions of the two sets of equations for the steady state when $\rho=1/\beta_0T$ is small. In that case, the steady-state occupation probabilities of the eight states have the approximate values listed in Table IV. We note that the light absorption probability β per unit time per atom approaches the value $7\rho\beta_0=7/T$ in the case of complete reorientation in the excited state, and the value $3.63/T$ in the case of no reorientation in the excited state. Remarkably enough, the probability of

light absorption per atom becomes independent of light intensity in the steady state. This follows from the fact that the number of atoms in the seven absorbing states in the steady state is inversely proportional to light intensity. (These statements are valid only when ρ is small compared to unity, i.e., when the light source is sufficiently intense and the relaxation time is long.)

In the practical case where some reorientation in the excited state takes place, the absorption probability β can be written

$$\beta=\left(\frac{1}{N}\right)\frac{\partial}{\partial z}\left[\int_0^\infty I_\nu(z)d\nu\right]=-\frac{\eta}{T},$$

where η is a dimensionless constant having a value somewhere between 3.63 and 7.00, N is the number of sodium atoms per cm³, and z is a distance measured from the front of the vapor sample cell in the direction of light propagation. The integrated light intensity therefore decreases linearly with z in accordance with

$$\int_0^\infty I_\nu(0)d\nu-\int_0^\infty I_\nu(z)d\nu=\left(\frac{N\eta}{T}\right)z. \qquad (6)$$

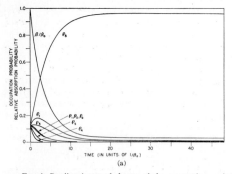

(a)

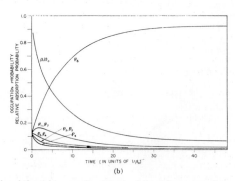

(b)

FIG. 1. Predicted rate of change of the occupation probabilities of the eight magnetic sublevels of the sodium atom when illuminated with circularly polarized D_1 radiation. The curves represent solutions of the simultaneous equations (5) obtained by means of an electronic computer for the case $\rho=1/\beta_0T=0.01$. The curve labeled β/β_0 shows the relative light absorption probability per atom per unit time as a function of time. The time $t=0$ corresponds to the instant at which the pumping radiation is suddenly turned on. (a) No reorientation in the excited state of the sodium atom. (b) Complete reorientation in the excited state.

TABLE IV. Steady-state occupation probabilities of the eight magnetic sublevels of the ground state of the sodium atom optically pumped with circularly polarized D_1 radiation. The occupation probabilities are expressed in terms of $\rho = 1/\beta_0 T$ which is assumed to be small compared to unity. The last column gives the steady-state value of the ratio β/β_0 of the average absorption probability per atom per unit time to its value at thermal equilibrium.

	p_1	p_2	p_3	p_4	p_5	p_6	p_7	p_8	β/β_0
No reorientation	0.384ρ	0.398ρ	0.941ρ	0.107ρ	0.194ρ	0.398ρ	1.45ρ	$1-3.87\rho$	3.63ρ
Complete reorientation	2ρ	ρ	$\frac{2}{3}\rho$	$\frac{1}{2}\rho$	$\frac{2}{3}\rho$	ρ	2ρ	$1-7.89\rho$	7ρ

The amount of light absorbed by the vapor is thus inversely proportional to the relaxation time T. This observation suggests a convenient method for measuring relaxation times. Evidently, in the steady state the number of photons $N\eta/T$ which are removed from unit area of the incident light beam in unit distance traveled through the vapor just suffices to counteract the effect of relaxation. For a sodium vapor pressure of 7.6×10^{-6} mm Hg, $\eta=7$ (complete reorientation), and $T=0.2$ sec (Dehmelt's longest observed relaxation time[8]), we have $N\eta/T=6.4\times10^{12}$ photons/cm³-sec. The condition that $\rho=1/\beta_0 T$ be small compared to unity requires that $\beta_0=4.40\times10^{-3}I_0\gg1/T$. For $T=0.2$ sec, this leads to $I_0\gg1000$ photons/cm² sec sec⁻¹ as a condition on the spectral density per unit frequency range at the center of the emitted D_1 line.

RELAXATION PROCESSES

The relaxation of a partially oriented alkali metal vapor in a buffer gas would be expected to take place by electron exchange between colliding alkali atoms, as discussed by Dicke[25] and Purcell,[26] by collisions with buffer gas atoms, and by collisions with the cell walls. The frequency of electron exchange collisions is a function of the alkali vapor pressure. The rates at which the other two types of relaxation events take place is affected by the pressure of the buffer gas, but in an opposite manner for the two cases. An increase in pressure results in an enhanced collision rate with the buffer gas atoms, but it also serves to reduce the diffusion rate of the alkali atoms to the walls. An optimum buffer gas pressure should therefore exist at which the relaxation rate of the oriented alkali atoms is a minimum.

In the case of optical pumping with a single D_1 line, this optimum pressure can be chosen more or less without regard to the effect of disorienting collisions between excited alkali atoms and buffer gas atoms. We have shown that for sodium vapor optically pumped with $3P_{\frac{1}{2}}-3S_{\frac{1}{2}}$ radiation, the pumping rate and the degree of orientation that can be achieved in the steady state, are at the most decreased by a factor of two as the buffer gas pressure is increased from a small value (practically no disorientation collisions) to a large value (complete disorientation in the excited state). On the other hand, in the ordinary method of optical pumping, that is, when a mixture of the two D lines of approximately equal peak intensity is employed, the pumping efficiency goes to zero as the buffer gas pressure is increased, as has been shown by Bender.[7] It is therefore necessary to use a value for the buffer gas pressure which is considerably lower than the optimum value discussed above in order to keep the frequency of disorienting collisions between excited alkali atoms and buffer gas atoms to a minimum. Furthermore, a large gas container must be used in order to achieve a reasonably long diffusion time to the walls. Neither of these restrictions apply to the method of pumping proposed here.

The different effect of excited state collisions on the pumping process for the two methods can be explained as follows for the case of sodium. When the intensity of the two circularly-polarized D lines is equal, as would be true for the broad self-reversed lines from a high-intensity spectral lamp, the absorption probabilities of the magnetic substates of the ground state are also equal. The rate at which the absorption of resonance radiation transfers a given atom from the ground state to the excited states is therefore the same for all the substates of the ground state. The pumping process then depends in an essential manner on the preservation, in the excited state, of the change in the z component of the angular momentum brought about by the absorption of the circularly polarized quantum. When the substates of the excited states are completely mixed by collisions with buffer gas atoms, the information contributed by the absorption process is lost, and the pumping efficiency goes to zero.

On the other hand, when a single circularly polarized D_1 line is employed, the absorption probabilities of the substates are unequal. In particular, one of the substates has zero absorption probability. For this reason, a redistribution of the populations of the hyperfine states of the ground state will take place even when the excited substates are completely mixed by collision. The pumping process then depends not so much on the change in magnetic quantum number brought about by the absorption of the circularly polarized quantum, but more on the operation of selection rules on the absorption.

IMPRISONMENT OF RESONANCE RADIATION

In the usual method of optical pumping, the partially oriented vapor remains highly absorbent to the incident radiation and therefore constitutes a strong source of unpolarized scattered resonance radiation. This scattered resonance radiation has a depolarizing effect which makes it impossible to partially orient more than a very small number of atoms.

On the other hand, when the D_1 line alone is used, the absorption probability of the nearly completely oriented vapor decreases to a small value, as we have shown. The vapor therefore represents a comparatively weak source of scattered light. Under these circumstances, it should be possible to extend the aligned sample in the direction of propagation of the collimated pumping radiation, provided its dimensions are kept small in a transverse direction. Thus, a photon of the nearly isotropically emitted scattered light will have a much smaller probability of absorption before escaping from the system than would be the case for the pumping radiation.

In our analysis of the pumping process, the influence of the scattered resonance radiation on the establishment of the steady state has not been taken into account. This influence will depend on the geometry of the sample cell. If the reabsorption probability can be made small enough, we can regard the scattered photons as contributing simply to an effective shortening of the relaxation time. The use of the separated D_1 line gives us considerable freedom of choice as far as the geometry of the sample cell is concerned, as we saw in the previous section, so that this condition can always be fulfilled in a practical case.

The influence of cooperative reradiation, as discussed by Dicke,[28,29] also has not been considered. In view of the present state of knowledge of this subject, it is not clear to what extent this effect will limit the total number of atoms that can be aligned by optical pumping techniques.

ACKNOWLEDGMENTS

We have derived much inspiration from several illuminating discussions with Professor F. M. Pipkin of Harvard University. We would like to thank Professors N. F. Ramsey and M. W. P. Strandberg, and Dr. W. B. Hawkins for a number of helpful comments, Mr. James Daly for his help in setting up the electronic computer, and Mr. Chester Hwang for his enthusiastic cooperation in the later stages of this work.

Note added in proof.—At the meeting of the American Physical Society in Boulder, Colorado, on September 6, 1957, Dr. H. G. Dehmelt independently described the principles of an optical pumping experiment using a single circularly polarized D_1 line.

[28] R. H. Dicke, Phys. Rev. **93**, 99 (1954).
[29] R. B. Griffiths and R. H. Dicke, Rev. Sci. Instr. **28**, 646 (1957).

OPTICAL MOSSBAUER EFFECT

The Effect of Collisions upon the Doppler Width of Spectral Lines

R. H. DICKE
Palmer Physical Laboratory, Princeton University, Princeton, New Jersey
(Received September 17, 1952)

Quantum mechanically the Doppler effect results from the recoil momentum changing the translational energy of the radiating atom. The assumption that the recoil momentum is given to the radiating atom is shown to be incorrect if collisions are taking place. If the collisions do not cause broadening by affecting the internal state of the radiator, they result in a substantial narrowing of the Doppler broadened line.

QUANTUM mechanically, the Doppler effect results from the recoil momentum given to the radiating system by the emitted photon.[1] This recoil momentum implies a change in the kinetic energy of the radiating atom which is in turn mirrored by a corresponding change in the photon's energy. This change in the photon's energy is proportional to the component of the atom's velocity in the direction of emission of the photon and leads to the normal expression for the Doppler effect. Since for gas pressures commonly encountered the fraction of the time that an atom is in collision is negligibly small, it might seem reasonable to assume that the recoil momentum is absorbed by the single radiating atom or molecule rather than by an atomic aggregate. In this case the Doppler breadth

would, within limits, be pressure-independent. Actually, under certain circumstances, this assumption is far from correct. Collisions which do not affect the internal state of the radiating system have a large effect upon the Doppler breadth.

The effect of collisions upon the Doppler effect is best illustrated with a simple example treated first classically and then quantum mechanically. Assume that the radiating atom, but not the radiation, is confined to a one-dimensional well of width a, and that it moves back and forth between the two walls with a speed v. The wave emitted by the atom is frequency modulated with the various harmonics of the oscillation frequency of the atom in the square well. For negligible collision and radiation damping, the spectral distribution of the emitted radiation is obtained from a Fourier series. A set of equally spaced sharp lines is obtained. They occur at the non-Doppler shifted frequency plus or minus-integral multiples of the oscillation frequency of the atom in the square well. The intensity distribution of these lines is shown for several values of a/λ in Fig. 1.

In the quantum-mechanical description of this example, the radiating system possesses two types of energy, internal and external. The external energy is the quantized energy of the atomic center-of-mass moving in the one-dimensional square well. In a transition in which a photon is absorbed or emitted, both the internal and external quantum numbers may change. The frequency of the emitted photon is

$$\nu_{nm} = \nu + (h/8Ma^2)(n^2 - m^2).$$

Here ν is the frequency of the non-Doppler shifted line, M is the mass of the radiator, and n, m are integers. A calculation of the transition probabilities gives results for the intensities which are for large n and m essentially the same as the classical results (Fig. 1).

The introduction of a Maxwellian distribution in v in the case of the classical calculation leads to a continuous distribution very similar to a normal Doppler distribution plus a sharp non-Doppler broadened line (see Fig. 2). The fraction of the energy radiated in the sharp line is

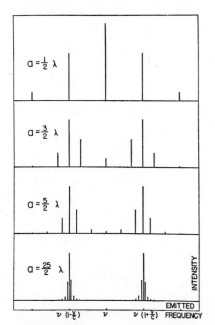

FIG. 1. Spectral distribution of radiation emitted by an atom confined to a one-dimensional box of width a.

$$\frac{\sin^2(\pi a/\lambda)}{(\pi a/\lambda)^2}.$$

[1] E. Fermi, Revs. Modern Phys. 4, 105 (1932).

The sharp line has its origin in the fact that, for a non-integral value of $\pi a/\lambda$, the normal unshifted frequency is emitted by all atoms independent of their speed. Since for $a \geq \frac{1}{2}\lambda$ the dominant noncentral lines in Fig. 1 are always close to the normal Doppler shifted frequencies, the broad distribution has a line contour nearly identical with the normal Doppler line. For $a < \frac{1}{2}\lambda$, the distribution increases in breadth but becomes much weaker.

For the quantum-mechanical treatment, a Maxwell-Boltzmann distribution among the various energy levels leads to a fine complex of lines having frequencies ν_{nm}. If the zero-point energy of oscillation of the atom in the well is very small compared with kT, the degenerate frequency $\nu = \nu_{nn}$ is usually the most intense single frequency emitted. For a small amount of collision or natural broadening, the complex of lines becomes a continuous distribution (Fig. 2) essentially identical with that given by the classical calculation. Note that although the atom is in contact with the walls of the cavity only an infinitesimal part of the time, the probability of the photon's momentum being given to the walls rather than to the atom is finite, being

$$\frac{\sin^2(\pi a/\lambda)}{(\pi a/\lambda)^2}.$$

For a gas confined to a large volume but with a mean free path small compared with a wavelength, the shape of a Doppler broadened line has been calculated treating the radiation classically and using a statistical procedure. In this treatment the phase of the radiation emitted as a function of the time is given by the position of the radiator as a function of the time. The probability distribution of position given by diffusion theory is used to calculate the mean intensity as a function of frequency. Substantially the same result is obtained also quantum mechanically, using a method similar to Foley's.[2] This quantum-mechanical calculation is valid only if the recoil energy of the radiator is small compared with kT. Assuming that the Doppler

[1] H. M. Foley, Phys. Rev. **69**, 616 (1946).

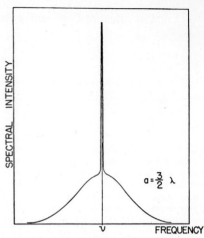

Fig. 2. Doppler broadened line of a gas in a one-dimensional box.

effect is the only appreciable source of the line breadth, it is found that the line has a Lorentz rather than Gaussian shape. The line contour is given by

$$I(\alpha) = I_0 \frac{2\pi D/\lambda^2}{(\alpha - \nu)^2 + (2\pi D/\lambda^2)^2}.$$

The width of the line at half-intensity is, in cycles per second, $4\pi D/\lambda^2$. Here D is the self-diffusion constant of the gas. This line width is roughly $2.8L/\lambda$ times that of a normal Doppler broadened line (L is the mean free path). Therefore, under those conditions for which the calculation is valid, the line breadth which is wholly Doppler is greatly reduced.

Because of the requirement that the gas collisions should not influence the internal state of the radiator, the above results are ordinarily valid only for certain magnetic dipole transitions. Nuclear magnetic resonance absorption, paramagnetic resonance absorption, and S-state hyperfine transitions are examples of transitions which are but weakly affected by collisions.

From: *Phys. Rev.* **105**, 1924-1925 (1957)

Modulation of a Light Beam by Precessing Absorbing Atoms

H. G. Dehmelt

University of Washington, Seattle, Washington
(Received January 7, 1957)

RECENT experiments[1,2] have demonstrated that the orientation of atoms (and molecules) can be effectively monitored by observing the transmission of a beam of polarized optical resonance radiation. This note will serve to point out that the monitoring technique can be extended to faster motions like the precession in a magnetic field where the result is a high-frequency modulation of the transmitted light beam. For simplicity we will assume a ground state angular momentum $J=\frac{1}{2}$ and complete polarization. Then the state for which the vector $\langle \mathbf{M} \rangle$ formed from the expectation values of the angular momentum components, $\langle M_x \rangle$, $\langle M_y \rangle$, and $\langle M_z \rangle$, points in the direction (ϑ, φ) can be described by

$$\Psi_{\vartheta, \varphi} = \cos(\vartheta/2) e^{-i\varphi/2}(+) + \sin(\vartheta/2) e^{i\varphi/2}(-),$$

where $(+)$ and $(-)$ denote the two eigenstates with $m_z = +\frac{1}{2}$ and $m_z = -\frac{1}{2}$. Now for the simplest case of an optical transition $J=\frac{1}{2} \rightarrow J'=\frac{1}{2}$ under the influence of circularly polarized light incident parallel to the z axis for which the selection rule $\Delta m_z = +1$ applies, only the fraction of Ψ in the $(-)$ state will contribute to the absorption. This fraction is given by

$$f = \sin^2(\vartheta/2) = \tfrac{1}{2}[1 - \cos\vartheta],$$

where ϑ is the angle between the angular momentum vector and the beam. This result must be independent of the special choice of coordinate system and eigenstates. Consequently it must hold quite generally that

$$f = \tfrac{1}{2}[1 - (\mathbf{m} \cdot \mathbf{p})],$$

where $\mathbf{m}$ and $\mathbf{p}$ are unit vectors in the direction of the angular momentum vector $\langle \mathbf{M} \rangle$ and the beam direction. In the important case that $\langle \mathbf{M} \rangle$ precesses around a magnetic field in the z direction with a circular frequency ω forming an angle ϑ against it while the direction of the light beam is parallel to the x axis one obtains

$$f_x = \tfrac{1}{2}[1 - \sin\vartheta \, \cos\omega t]$$

indicating a sinusoidal variation at the frequency ω of the absorption. Similar expressions are to be expected for optical transitions involving higher J, J' values when the ground state is executing a precessing motion. Further examples of precessing motions which could be used for modulation purposes are found in the ones caused by crystalline electric fields or the ones due to electric and magnetic interaction with the atomic nucleus.

One example of experimentally realizing the precession of the momentum vector $\langle \mathbf{M} \rangle$ essential in the proposed modulation scheme is discussed in the following: Sodium atoms contained in a spherical absorption cell are subjected to an intense beam of circularly polarized resonance light, "z beam," and a static magnetic field of the order of one gauss, both in the z direction. This creates a polarization of the atomic momenta by optical pumping,[3] the vector $\langle \mathbf{M} \rangle$, of absolute value M_0, pointing in the z direction. The time dependence of $\langle \mathbf{M} \rangle$ now is governed by the Bloch equations[4] for the angular momentum components,

$$\dot{M}_x - \gamma(M_y H_z - M_z H_y) + (1/T_2)M_x = 0,$$
$$\dot{M}_y - \gamma(M_z H_x - M_x H_z) + (1/T_2)M_y = 0,$$
$$\dot{M}_z - \gamma(M_x H_y - M_y H_x) + (1/\tau)M_z = (1/\tau)M_0.$$

Here and in the following the angular brackets to indicate expectation values have been omitted. The polarization decay time τ depends on the light intensity, being of the order of 0.01–0.1 sec in practical cases.[2] The phase memory time is denoted by T_2 as usual. Experimentally it can be made to approach τ. Under these conditions all the methods discussed by Bloch,[4] Hahn,[5] and Packard and Varian[6] can be used to create a precessing angular momentum component, the most common one being the application of a rf field perpendicular to the z axis whose frequency fulfills the resonance condition. For the two hfs substates of sodium this frequency turns out to be very nearly equal to 700 (kc/sec)/gauss, the Back-Goudsmit effect being negligible. A second (weaker) beam of circularly polarized resonance light, "x beam," applied in the x direction, will then exhibit the modulation at the precession frequency after passing through the cell since the absorption coefficient K_x of the partially polarized sodium vapor will vary according to

$$K_x = K[1 - a(M_x/M_0)].$$

Here K is the absorption coefficient for the unpolarized vapor while a is a dimensionless constant depending on the degree of polarization attained and also on nuclear effects. The absorption of the z beam on the other hand, as determined by

$$K_z = K[1 - a(M_z/M_0)],$$

provides a measure of M_z. Under favorable conditions[2]

rf fields of the order of microgauss can be made to modulate intense light beams.

Very strong and narrow resonance signals have been obtained by observing the variation of the transmitted z beam. By feeding the rf field from the (amplified) photocurrent generated by the modulated x beam an atomic oscillator can be constructed. Further experiments along the above lines are under way in collaboration with Dr. A. Bloom and Dr. E. Bell and with Mr. E. S. Ensberg.

[1] H. G. Dehmelt, Phys. Rev. **103**, 1125 (1956).
[2] H. G. Dehmelt, Phys. Rev. **105**, 1487 (1957).
[3] A. Kastler, J. phys. radium **11**, 255 (1950).
[4] F. Bloch, Phys. Rev. **70**, 1 (1946).
[5] E. L. Hahn, Phys. Rev. **80**, 580 (1950).
[6] M. E. Packard and R. Varian, Phys. Rev. **93**, 941 (1954).

From: *Phys. Rev.* 107, 1559-1565 (1957)

Optical Detection of Magnetic Resonance in Alkali Metal Vapor

WILLIAM E. BELL AND ARNOLD L. BLOOM
Varian Associates, Palo Alto, California
(Received June 10, 1957)

This paper discusses two types of rf magnetic resonance experiments involving optical pumping in alkali vapor which have recently been suggested by Dehmelt. These experiments are, respectively, observation of a change of intensity at resonance of the transmitted pumping light, and observation of high-frequency intensity modulation in a second light beam (the "cross beam") incident at an angle to the first. The method of pumping used here is reviewed, together with some of the special assumptions on which it is based. The function of the light in monitoring population differences is treated as a separate matter from the pumping function; it is shown that the observed changes in transmitted light intensity can be correlated in a simple way with other observables of a spin system, and this leads to a simple explanation of the high-frequency modulation effects. A system of spin-$\frac{1}{2}$ particles subject to optical pumping and monitoring is then treated phenomenologically. The resulting equations have the same form as Bloch's equations except that (1) the time constants must include effects of the incident light, and (2) there is an additional term due to the cross beam which, however, is shown to have no effect on the shape of the resonance.

The apparatus is described, together with experimental conditions under which signals have been observed. Possible applications of the technique include magnetic-field measurements, and studies of atomic constants of alkali metal isotopes.

I. INTRODUCTION

IN a recent paper, Dehmelt[1] described an optical pumping experiment which demonstrated a thermal relaxation time of about 0.2 second for the magnetic moments of sodium atoms in relatively high-pressure argon buffer gas, together with a means of detecting the pumping process with very high signal-to-noise ratio. The detection method was that of monitoring the transmitted light, whose intensity depends upon deviations from the population equilibrium established by the pumping process. Although this paper described only a reorientation process, it was suggested that the method could be applied to magnetic resonance, and in fact this was actually done soon afterwards.[2] More recently, Dehmelt has suggested[3] a novel method for detecting magnetic resonance by the Larmor frequency modulation of a light beam placed at right angles to the magnetic field, an effect which has also been demonstrated recently.[4] The purpose of this paper is to discuss the demonstration experiments of both magnetic resonance phenomena, together with some phenomenological theory capable of predicting with reasonable accuracy the signal intensities and conditions under which signals can be expected. In the concluding remarks a number of possible applications of this experiment is discussed. Many of these applications involve considerable refinement of the apparatus, in particular the development of a light-filtering system and production of a magnetic field whose homogeneity is considerably greater than has ever before been required in experiments of this type. Rather than wait until the apparatus was developed to this point, we felt it to be desirable to publish the work that has been performed up to now.

II. PUMPING PROCESS

Fairly complete descriptions and histories of optical pumping as applicable to these experiments have been given previously by Kastler,[5] Hawkins[6] and by Dehmelt,[1] and the process will be briefly summarized here. The pumping process employs circularly polarized light transmitted along the direction of a magnetic field, producing transitions $\Delta m = +1$, for example, for which the transition probabilities from the various Zeeman sublevels of the ground state are different for some levels than for others. Because of the presence of the relatively high-pressure buffer gas, the optically excited atoms have extremely short relaxation times for disorientation within the Zeeman sublevels of the excited states themselves, and therefore it is likely that considerable disorientation and loss of phase memory occurs for these excited atoms before they are able to re-emit their optical energy and return to the ground state.[7] This allows one to make the simplifying assumption that all sublevels of the ground state have an equal probability of being repopulated by the returning atoms. The pumping process can then be described entirely in terms of transition probabilities for optical excitation from the various ground-state sublevels, and, because the lifetime in the optically excited state is short, can be treated macroscopically in terms of an equivalent relaxation process between ground-state sublevels. Dehmelt[1] has indeed shown experimentally the exponential approach to equilibrium characteristic of such processes. In this way we hope to sidestep a problem mentioned by Sagalyn,[8] namely, that the picture of an atom "jumping" between quantum levels is rather naive and a rigorous treatment of optical double-resonance

[1] H. G. Dehmelt, Phys. Rev. **105**, 1487 (1957).
[2] H. G. Dehmelt (private communication).
[3] H. G. Dehmelt, Phys. Rev. **105**, 1924 (1957).
[4] W. Bell and A. Bloom, Bull. Am. Phys. Soc. Ser. II, **2**, 226 (1957).

[5] A. Kastler, Proc. Phys. Soc. (London) **A67**, 853 (1954), J. Opt. Soc. Am. **47**, 460 (1957).
[6] W. B. Hawkins, Phys. Rev. **98**, 478 (1955).
[7] P. L. Bender, thesis, Princeton University, 1956 (unpublished).
[8] P. Sagalyn, Phys. Rev. **94**, 885 (1954).

TABLE I. Unnormalized relative transition probabilities ($\Delta m = +1$) for D_1 and D_2 light (or their equivalents in the other alkali metals). The pumping rate P_i for any level is obtained by weighting the intensities of the D_1 and D_2 components by the coefficients given below.

F	m	D_1 $(^2S_{\frac{1}{2}} \rightarrow ^2P_{\frac{1}{2}})$	D_2 $(^2S_{\frac{1}{2}} \rightarrow ^2P_{\frac{3}{2}})$
2	2	0	6
	1	1	5
	0	2	4
	−1	3	3
	−2	4	2
1	1	3	3
	0	2	4
	−1	1	5
$\frac{1}{2}$	$\frac{1}{2}$	0	3
	$-\frac{1}{2}$	2	1

problems has not yet been developed. By treating the optical pumping as a relaxation process, we can avoid the use of any specific model. We merely assert that if a rigorous theory were available it could be used to obtain a time-dependent perturbation solution of the wave equation, perhaps similar to that of Wangsness and Bloch[9] for thermal processes, which would include terms linear in time (relaxation terms) and higher order terms which we have reason to believe are very small. There may also exist relatively large secular terms, giving rise to shifts in resonant frequencies, but we need not be concerned about them here.

The relative transition probabilities for optical excitation from the various F, m sublevels of the $S_{\frac{1}{2}}$ ground state to the $P_{\frac{1}{2}}$ and $P_{\frac{3}{2}}$ excited states can be calculated by a straightforward application of the matrix elements for electric dipole excitation ($\Delta m = +1$) and the Wigner coefficients $(IJm_Im_J | IJFm)$.[10] They have been calculated by Dehmelt[1] for the case $I = \frac{3}{2}$ and are presented here in a somewhat different form in Table I. Table I also lists the case for $I = 0$, or for nuclear spin uncoupled from electron spin, which is applicable in strong magnetic fields. If P_i is the pumping rate out of the ith level, and a_i is the population of this level then the net pumping process can be described by the following system of equations:

$$da_i/dt = -a_iP_i + n^{-1}\sum a_jP_j, \qquad (1)$$

$$\sum a_i = A_0, \qquad (2)$$

where n is the number of levels in the $S_{\frac{1}{2}}$ ground state, A_0 is the total population of the sample, and the summation term in Eq. (1) is based on the previously expressed assumption that re-emission from the optically excited state is the same to all sublevels of the ground state. From Eqs. (1) and (2) we arrive at the following result for the equilibrium population difference, without

thermal relaxation, between any two states:

$$a_i - a_j = A_0(P_i^{-1} - P_j^{-1})/\sum(P_i^{-1}). \qquad (3)$$

This expression, which is somewhat more general than a similar expression given by Dehmelt, is applicable to any situation where the P_i are known for each of the ground-state sublevels and applies not only for cases of D_1 and D_2 radiation or its equivalent, but for any other radiation which might be present to excite optical transitions. It can also be applied to include the effect of incompletely circularly polarized light and the effect of trapped resonance radiation which is necessarily unpolarized.

It is evident from an inspection of Eq. (3) and Table I that the end result of pumping with pure circularly polarized D_1 light is to place the entire population A_0 in the state $F = 2$, $m = 2$, except for the effect of thermal relaxation processes. This is true not only in the case of weak magnetic fields but also in strong magnetic fields where I and J are nearly decoupled. In that case the optical pumping process acts directly only on the electronic angular momentum; however, it is interesting to examine the indirect effect on the nuclear moment. This is most easily accomplished by a "circuit diagram" of the type suggested by Bloch[11] for a study of the Overhauser effect. Figure 1 shows the circuit based on the assumption that the chief relaxation mechanism available to the nucleus is the spin-flip exchange generated by the hyperfine coupling with the surrounding electron, and that this relaxation mechanism is strong compared to direct nuclear interactions with extra-atomic surroundings. The "battery" across each pair of electronic levels corresponds to the optical pumping process. It is evident that the effect of the hyperfine relaxation process is to place all the "batteries" in series resulting in an overwhelming alignment in the upper energy state.

Although the condition of nearly 100% population in the $F = 2$, $m = 2$ level may be highly desirable for certain types of experiments, the actual condition using unfiltered light from the usual alkali metal vapor discharge is that the intensities of both lines are very nearly equal.[6] Let us use Q to denote the fractional intensity difference between the two lines:

$$Q = [\mathcal{I}(D_2) - \mathcal{I}(D_1)]/\mathcal{I}(D_2),$$

where $\mathcal{I} = $ intensity. If $|Q| \ll 1$, then it can be calculated from Table I and Eq. (3) that the population difference (in weak fields) between any two adjacent levels is about the same for all such combinations and is approximately equal to $QA_0/48$. This indicates that we are actually observing a rather small net population difference, and the fact that signal-to-noise ratios are as high as they are at the present time gives considerable promise for those experiments where an appreciably

[9] R. K. Wangsness and F. Bloch, Phys. Rev. **89**, 728 (1953).
[10] E. U. Condon and G. H. Shortley, *Theory of Atomic Spectra* (Cambridge University Press, New York, 1935).

[11] F. Bloch, Phys. Rev. **102**, 104 (1956).

large population difference (10% or greater) can be achieved.

III. MONITORING PROCESS

Let us now consider the other function of the light—that of monitoring the orientation of the sample. If we observe the intensity of the transmitted light beam relative to a constant input, we can observe the removal of energy from the incident beam. This effect we shall call the "signal" and denote by the symbol S. If we omit the purely geometrical factors which are constant for a given experimental setup, then

$$S = \sum a_i P_i, \qquad (4)$$

a statement which is true regardless of any assumptions which one might make regarding the role of the light in a pumping process. The form of Eq. (4) suggests the trace of an operator product and, indeed, if the a_i are the diagonal elements of a spin density matrix, ρ, then (4) is true even if ρ has nonvanishing off-diagonal elements. However, we can generalize even further and define, for any kind of incident light, a "monitoring operator" P such that

$$S = \langle P \rangle = \mathrm{Tr}(P\rho), \qquad (5)$$

and if the nature of the light is completely specified so that the components of P are known, then S becomes an observable of the system ρ. Fano[12] has shown that, for a system described in terms of n states, there are n^2 independent operators including the identity operator. Any monitoring operator, therefore, can be expressed in terms of the identity operator plus familiar observables such as the multipoles and, furthermore, must satisfy the same transformation relationships as these observables.* (The identity operator must be included because $\mathrm{Tr}\,P \geq 0$ by definition.) Dehmelt has shown[3] that for pure circularly polarized D_1 light incident on a hypothetical sodium atom of spin $\frac{1}{2}$, the monitoring operator has the form $(1 - \mathbf{p} \cdot \boldsymbol{\sigma})$, where $\mathbf{p}$ is the direction defined by the polarization of the light, and the components of $\boldsymbol{\sigma}$ are the Pauli spin operators. Here the corresponding signal is related directly to the magnetic dipole moment of the sample in the direction of the light beam. However, the method is quite general and one can easily devise experiments where the signal gives information about quadrupole or higher moments of the system.[2,13]

In our experiments we have a primary light beam

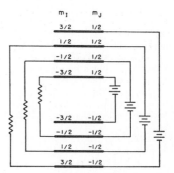

FIG. 1. "Circuit diagram" to describe optical pumping in strong magnetic fields.

(the z beam), which performs the optical pumping and whose signal gives information about the z component of magnetic moment, M_z. There may be another light beam—the cross beam or x beam—whose signal is related to M_x in exactly the same way that the z beam signal is related to M_z. If there is Larmor precession about the z axis then the x beam will be modulated at the corresponding frequency. This signal will depend directly on M_x and not on dM_x/dt as is the case when the magnetic moment is coupled rf-wise to a detecting coil or cavity; there is therefore no frequency dependence of the type usually encountered in magnetic resonance.

Although the x beam is intended for monitoring purposes only, we must inquire about any pumping effects it may have. There are two such effects. First of all, it attempts to set up an orientation in the x direction. This effect is obviously very small unless the x beam is of such intensity that it can produce essentially complete orientation in a fraction of a Larmor cycle. Secondly it acts somewhat to the detriment of the pumping process generated by the z beam. In the representation in which the Hamiltonian is diagonal, the x-beam monitoring operator has large off-diagonal elements and acts equally on pairs of levels. This tends to equalize the populations of the ground state sublevels while shortening their over-all lifetimes. These points are illustrated in the phenomenological description which follows.

IV. PHENOMENOLOGICAL EQUATIONS

We shall describe the behavior of the spin system in terms of phenomenological equations for a system of particles of spin $\frac{1}{2}$, with the hope that it will be a fairly good approximation for the resonance behavior of the more complex system which actually exists. In general, this approximation can be expected to hold under operating conditions such that only population differences between the two levels directly concerned in the resonance need be considered.

---

[12] U. Fano, Revs. Modern Phys. **29**, 74 (1957).

* *Note added in proof.*—This statement is true if the line width of the incident light is broad compared to the level splittings. More generally, however, it is valid only if the light contains frequency and polarization components corresponding to *all* the optical transitions implied by the transformed monitoring operator.

[13] Strictly speaking, optical monitoring gives direct information only about population of spin states, and indirect information about electromagnetic moments only if the moments are already known to be associated with the spin. Thus, for example, the strength of the signal bears no direct relationship to the magnitude of the magnetic moment of the atom.

The phenomenological behavior can be thought of as being composed of two parts—the magnetic and thermal relaxation parts common to all spin systems, and the part due to optical pumping. For the magnetic and thermal description we shall use Bloch's equations[14] with the Boltzmann population factor set equal to one, since its effect is obviously small compared to effects of optical pumping. For the optical effects consider only two Zeeman levels, α and β; then Eqs. (1) and (2) can be rewritten in the following form for the z light alone:

$$(dM_z/dt)_{\text{pumping}} = (\mathfrak{M}_0 - M_z)P_z, \qquad (6a)$$

where[15]

$$P_z = \tfrac{1}{2}(P_\alpha + P_\beta),$$

$$M_z = a_\alpha - a_\beta, \qquad (6b)$$

$$\mathfrak{M}_0 = A_0(P_\beta - P_\alpha)/(P_\beta + P_\alpha).$$

A similar relation holds for the x beam alone:

$$(dM_x/dt)_{\text{pumping}} = (\mathfrak{M}_0' - M_x)P_x. \qquad (6c)$$

(If the two light beams have the same spectral quality, then $\mathfrak{M}_0 = \mathfrak{M}_0'$ and P_x/P_z is merely the ratio of intensities of the two beams.) In addition we need equations describing the effect of the j light on M_i, where $i \neq j$:

$$dM_i/dt + M_i P_j = 0. \qquad (6d)$$

By combining the Bloch equations with Eqs. (6) we arrive at our phenomenological equations of motion of the macroscopic moment:

$$dM_x/dt + \gamma[\mathbf{H} \times \mathbf{M}]_x + M_x/S_2 = M_0'/S_2, \qquad (7a)$$

$$dM_y/dt + \gamma[\mathbf{H} \times \mathbf{M}]_y + M_y/S_2 = 0, \qquad (7b)$$

$$dM_z/dt + \gamma[\mathbf{H} \times \mathbf{M}]_z + M_z/S_1 = M_0/S_1, \qquad (7c)$$

where we define

$$S_1 = (P_x + P_z + T_1^{-1})^{-1},$$

$$S_2 = (P_x + P_z + T_2^{-1})^{-1},$$

$$M_0' = \mathfrak{M}_0' P_x S_2, \quad M_0 = \mathfrak{M}_0 P_z S_1. \qquad (8)$$

We can neglect the term on the right-hand side of Eq. (7a) (this will be justified later), and in that case Eqs. (7) become identical to the Bloch equations if we substitute S_1, S_2 for T_1, T_2 of Bloch's equations. The observed signals in the phototubes are given by expressions like Eq. (4) which, when rewritten using the definitions of (6) and (8), become

$$S_x = A_0 P_x - \mathfrak{M}_0' M_x P_x / A_0, \qquad (9a)$$

$$S_z = A_0 P_z - \mathfrak{M}_0 M_z P_z / A_0. \qquad (9b)$$

On substituting into Eq. (7) and setting the derivatives

equal to zero, we obtain the slow-passage signals:

$$S_x = A_0 P_x - \frac{\gamma H_1 S_2 [1 + (S_2 \Delta \omega)^2]^{\frac{1}{2}} M_0 P_x \mathfrak{M}_0' / A_0}{1 + (S_2 \Delta \omega)^2 + \gamma^2 H_1^2 S_1 S_2}$$
$$\times \cos(\omega t + \varphi), \qquad (10a)$$

$$S_z = A_0 P_z - \frac{[1 + (S_2 \Delta \omega)^2] M_0 P_z \mathfrak{M}_0 / A_0}{1 + (S_2 \Delta \omega)^2 + \gamma^2 H_1^2 S_1 S_2}, \qquad (10b)$$

where H_1 is a rotating rf field and all other terms not defined elsewhere are as defined originally by Bloch.[14] The phase term φ can also be determined from Bloch's original equations.

Equations (8) and (10) clearly indicate the competition between the pumping action of the z light and the degrading effects of the thermal relaxation and the x beam. They also show the way in which the optical pumping broadens the line. If we vary the intensity of the x beam, and hence P_z, keeping all other quantities constant, the maximum high-frequency signal $|S_z - A_0 P_z|$ occurs when

$$P_z^2 = (P_x + T_1^{-1})(P_z + T_2^{-1}). \qquad (11)$$

In practice, where P_z is large compared to the thermal relaxation rates, this indicates that both light beams should have about the same amplitude. In that case the observed z-beam signal has twice the width and half the amplitude that would be expected from the signal observed when the z beam is used alone.

We now return to the question of the term on the right-hand side of Eq. (7a), and show why we have been justified in neglecting it.[16] Let us specialize Eq. (7) to the case of a dc magnetic field $H_z = H_0$ and an alternating rf field $H_x = 2H_1 \cos \omega t$. The "x beam" may lie anywhere in the xy plane although we shall continue to denote it by the subscript x. Let us define $F = M_x + iM_y$, then the phenomenological equations become

$$dF/dt + i\gamma H_0 F + F/S_2 - i\gamma H_1 M_z(e^{i\omega t} + e^{-i\omega t})$$
$$= M_0' e^{i\epsilon}/S_2, \qquad (12a)$$

$$dM_z/dt + M_z/S_1 - \tfrac{1}{2} i\gamma H_1(F - F^*)(e^{i\omega t} + e^{-i\omega t})$$
$$= M_0/S_1, \qquad (12b)$$

where the phase term $e^{i\epsilon}$ indicates the direction of the x beam. We now analyze F and M_z in terms of Fourier coefficients,

$$F = \sum_{n=-\infty}^{\infty} f_n e^{in\omega t}, \quad M_z = \sum_{n=-\infty}^{\infty} m_n e^{in\omega t}. \qquad (13)$$

If we substitute Eq. (13) into (12) we can equate those terms with like values of $e^{in\omega t}$, since the equalities must hold at all times. As a result we obtain recursion

[14] F. Bloch, Phys. Rev. **70**, 460 (1946).
[15] We use symbols like M_z which normally represent magnetic moment only for the sake of familiarity, since here they really represent population differences only. See reference 13.

[16] The following treatment is similar to one suggested by E. T. Jaynes (unpublished work).

formulas of the following form:

$$(in\omega + S_2^{-1} + i\gamma H_0)f_n - i\gamma H_1(m_{n-1} + m_{n+1})$$
$$= M_0' S_2^{-1}\delta_{n0}e^{i\epsilon}, \quad (14a)$$

$$(in\omega + S_1^{-1})m_n - \tfrac{1}{2}i\gamma H_1(f_{n+1} + f_{n-1} - f_{-n+1}^* - f_{-n-1}^*)$$
$$= M_0 S_1^{-1}\delta_{n0}. \quad (14b)$$

Similar, but somewhat simpler equations are obtained if a rotating rf field is used instead of the alternating one.

For our purposes, the most interesting point about Eqs. (14) is that the second inhomogeneous term, $P_zM_0\delta_{n0}$, defines the terms m_{even} and f_{odd} but not their converses. The first inhomogeneous term $P_xM_0\delta_{n0}e^{i\epsilon}$, on the other hand, defines the terms m_{odd} and f_{even}. There is no mechanism within the framework of these equations whereby the two sets of terms can interact. Thus the first inhomogeneous term can produce signals in the modulation of the x beam with frequency components 0, $2\omega_0$, $4\omega_0$, etc., but cannot affect the term at the Larmor frequency itself. Therefore, if the output of the phototube monitoring the x beam is tuned so as to accept only frequencies of the order of ω_0 and not other frequencies, then the perturbation of the x beam cannot change the shape of the resonance in any way. Similar considerations hold for observing the z-beam signal at low frequencies. On the other hand, if one were to attempt detection under conditions of very weak external magnetic fields, then it might be difficult to filter out the unwanted terms and some perturbation in the detected signals might be observed.

V. EXPERIMENTS

A block diagram of the relatively simple experimental apparatus is shown in Fig. 2. The part of the apparatus which employs the beam parallel to H_0, together with associated sweep or field-reversal coils (not shown in the figure), is similar to that used by Dehmelt.[1] The cross beam and its associated electronic apparatus is the new part of the experiment. Although the word "sodium" is used in the figure, identical experiments have been performed with potassium and presumably could also be done in rubidium and cesium. It is possible to observe signals in the cross beam if this beam is originally unpolarized but an analyzer is placed in front of the photocell so that the photocell sees only one component of circular polarization. This occurs because each component of circular polarization in the unpolarized cross beam is modulated merely by the presence of a precessing orientation, although the modulations are 180° out of phase and therefore cannot be detected in the unpolarized light beam. Detection of the precession by this method is not as useful as by that using polarized light, since the unused component of polarization depumps the sample.

It has been pointed out by Dehmelt[2] and can be seen from the analysis of Secs. II and III, that the two beams in the cross-beam experiment could be replaced

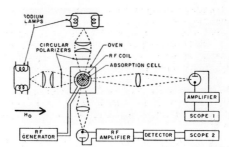

FIG. 2. Schematic diagram of apparatus. Sweep coils, coaxial with H_0, are not shown.

by a single beam oriented at about 45° to the dc magnetic field. Such an arrangement would have a reduced signal-to-noise ratio and the experiment has not been attempted.

The samples used in these experiments were made from one-liter Pyrex flasks which, in some cases, were glazed with a thin layer of fused potassium fluoborate (KBF_4) to keep the alkali metal from discoloring the glass.[17] The flasks were sealed off with the metal deposited as a thin layer in the neck and with spectroscopic-grade argon at a pressure (at room temperature) of about 30 mm Hg. The optimum operating temperatures for the absorption cells appeared to be about 140°C for sodium and 65°C for potassium. In both cases these correspond to equilibrium vapor pressures of about 2×10^{-6} mm Hg for the metals concerned. The mean free path of a photon at the center of the optical resonance is, according to a calculation by Hawkins,[6] about 0.1 cm at these pressures. The actual mean free path appeared to be about 15 cm. The reasons for the discrepancy are not entirely clear but probably include the following as contributing factors: (1) broadening of the absorption line by the buffer gas, over and above the usual Doppler broadening, thus reducing the absorption cross section per atom; (2) a relatively small evaporating surface area of the metal; and (3) the possible existence of part of the vapor in diatomic form. No differences in behavior have been observed between glazed or unglazed cells, nor have any aging effects been observed.

One of the advantages of the cross-beam method of detecting magnetic resonance in alkali vapor is the fact that the observed signal is at the Larmor frequency (in this case 360 kc/sec) and not at dc or a relatively low sweep frequency where the photocell detection is subject to interference from microphonics and extraneous sources of variable light. We have been able to observe the cross-beam signal not only in the presence of light from 60-cycle fluorescent lamps, which completely obliterates the z-beam signal, but we have even detected the signal when the discharge lamps themselves were excited from 60-cycle ac. Figure 3 shows

---

[17] This process was kindly suggested by Mr. P. E. Dittman of Corning Glass Works.

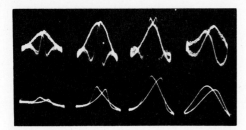

FIG. 3. Oscilloscope traces of resonance signals from cross beam (above) and z beam (below) as a function of rf field intensity (increasing left to right). The light beam geometries were such that $P_x \approx P_z \approx 10^{-2}$ sec.

typical oscilloscope signals employing a 60-cycle sweep modulation, from both the x-beam and z-beam signals. The first two sets of traces indicate that, as the rf level is increased, the cross-beam signal increases at a rate faster than the z-beam signal. This is to be expected from the form of Bloch's equations, which predict a quadratic dependence of $(M_0 - M_z)$ and a linear dependence of $M_{x,y}$ on weak rf. There is an indication of structure in the pictures third from the left, corresponding to "optimum" rf. The actual hyperfine structure to be expected from sodium if line widths were infinitely narrow is shown in Fig. 4. Although field homogeneity is not yet sufficient to resolve individual lines there is a definite indication that there is resolution of the two over-all structures corresponding to $F=2$ and $F=1$. This is further substantiated by the fact that this type of structure is not observed in the potassium samples, where the hyperfine structure does not split itself into two groups this way. These observations, together with measurements of resonance position as a function of frequency, indicate that the line width of the observed resonances is of the order of 1000 cps. It is believed that this width is caused almost entirely by field inhomogeneity. The principal contributors to the inhomogeneity are the ferromagnetic components of the lamps and the photocells, which in

the present optical system are necessarily close to the absorption cell.

Of particular interest in Fig. 3 is the signal-to-noise ratio which can be obtained even under conditions of unfiltered light. The z-beam signals, shown on the bottom, were taken with no band-width limiting in the photocell amplifier or oscilloscope except for the natural band width of the amplifier itself, which was about 30 kc/sec. The x-beam traces, showing a somewhat poorer signal-to-noise ratio, were taken through a band pass of about 1000 cps following the diode detector. The reasons for the poorer signal-to-noise ratio in the cross beam are probably the following: (1) smaller effective volume of the absorption cell (the intersection of the two beams), and (2) a poor impedance match between the photocell and its load, which consisted of a tuned circuit whose resonant impedance was about 2000 ohms. On the basis of impedance matching alone it is calculated that the cross-beam signal-to-noise ratio should be reduced a factor of 10 from that of the z beam, which is in reasonable agreement with experiment.

An interesting variant of the cross-beam experiment is produced by connecting the output of the rf amplifier of the cross-beam photocell to the rf coil itself. This provides an oscillator whose frequency of oscillation is determined by the peak of the resonance curve, presumably in this case some average of the Larmor frequencies of the hyperfine lines. It can be easily demonstrated in the laboratory that the oscillation frequency of this system is determined by and follows variations in the magnetic field.

VI. POSSIBLE APPLICATIONS

The most obvious application of this experimental method is to the precise measurements of weak magnetic fields. An interesting factor in its usefulness is the fact that the intensity of the observed optical signals is independent of the value of the magnetic field, provided only that the field is small compared to the hyperfine structure constant so that optical transition probabilities are approximately constant as a function of magnetic field, and not so small as to be comparable to the line width. The existing apparatus has been used quite satisfactorily for this purpose and it is believed that one can do even better by proper design and filtering of the light. Considerable improvement can also be achieved as magnetic-field homogeneity over the sample is brought under control. When the line structure is well resolved it will be possible to make an accurate measurement of g factors of the various alkali metals by comparing the resonant frequencies of the metals between themselves and with protons in the same magnetic field. Because the resonance frequency depends on the g factor to first order in weak fields, and because the lines are so narrow, it is believed that the g factors can be measured to an order of magnitude greater accuracy than has been possible up to now. The

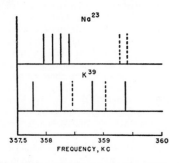

FIG. 4. Theoretical resonance spectrum for Na and K in a field H_0 of 0.513 gauss. Solid lines are $F=2$; dashed lines are $F=1$.

hyperfine splittings will also give information regarding the hyperfine structure constant and magnetic moments of the nuclei; however, it is not likely that these measurements can be made to any greater accuracy than by existing methods.

VII. ACKNOWLEDGMENTS

We are indebted to Professor Dehmelt for suggesting this work and for his assistance, and to Mr. H. R. Lawler for constructing most of the apparatus. The absorption cells were prepared by Mr. E. Hodges.

Theory of modulation of light in a double resonance experiment

By J. N. Dodd†

Department of Physics, University of Otago, Dunedin, New Zealand,

and G. W. Series

Clarendon Laboratory, University of Oxford

(*Communicated by H. G. Kuhn, F.R.S.—Received* 3 *December* 1960—
Revised 8 *May* 1961)

A theory is formulated to describe the modulation which has been observed in fluorescent light from atoms subjected simultaneously to optical and radio-frequency radiation. The optical field stimulates one or more of a set of excited states of the atom, between which the radio-frequency field establishes coherence. This coherence is manifest in the fluorescent radiation. Interference between radiations of different frequency leads to modulation. General expressions are given for the intensity of the fluorescent light as a function of time. The Zeeman structure of the transition $(6^3P_1 - 6^1S_0)$, $\lambda 2537$ Å, in mercury is studied in detail. Modulation at frequencies, 1, 2, 3 and 4 times that of the radio-frequency field, ω_0, is predicted, and resonant effects at static magnetic fields, 0, $\frac{1}{2}$, 1, $\frac{3}{2}$, 2 and 3 times H_0, the field for which ω_0 is the Larmor frequency. Resonances at fields other than H_0 are due to excitation with light of mixed polarization. Most of the predicted effects have been found experimentally.

A 'frequency diagram' is introduced and discussed, to represent the combined effects of static and radio-frequency magnetic fields. To each excited state belong a set of r frequencies, where r is the number of states linked by the radio-frequency perturbation. The 9 levels are drawn, as functions of H, for the states $m_J = 0, \pm 1$, of $^3P_1$. The resonances at fields other than H_0 may be associated with intersections of frequency levels belonging to different m_J.

1. Introduction

It has been shown experimentally that the fluorescent light in a double resonance experiment is strongly modulated (Dodd, Fox, Series & Taylor 1959). A theory of the phenomenon is presented in this paper.

In a double resonance experiment, free atoms are subjected simultaneously to optical and radio-frequency radiations, both of which are near to resonant frequencies of the atoms. The first experiment of this type (Brossel & Bitter 1952) was performed with mercury vapour situated in a uniform magnetic field. Optical radiation at 2537 Å excited the atoms from the ground state, $^1S_0$, to the state $m = 0$ of the level $^3P_1$, from which transitions to $m = \pm 1$ were induced by a radio-frequency field at the Larmor frequency. The transitions were detected by the changes which they brought about in the polarization and spatial distribution of the fluorescent light.

A complete description of the response of the atoms to the electromagnetic fields cannot, however, be given simply in terms of populations of states, but must take account of the fact that the occupation probabilities are not independent. The phases of the probability amplitudes are related to the phase of the radio-frequency field,

† On leave at the Clarendon Laboratory, Oxford, 1959.

and hence to one another. In the fluorescent light, the coherence between the excited states is manifest as interference between optical radiations of different frequencies. It is this interference, giving rise to modulation, which was detected in the experiments of Dodd *et al.*

In this paper, and in that of Barrat which follows, the problem is formulated in terms of probability amplitudes. Related phenomena have been interpreted in other ways. Under similar conditions of irradiation of an atomic vapour with optical and radio-frequency fields, Bell & Bloom (1957) detected modulation in the absorbed light. Following Dehmelt's suggestion (1957) they used a phenomenological model, based on the Bloch equations, to interpret their experiments. We believe that the two sets of experiments are the emission and absorption counterparts of each other, and that both can be legitimately described either by the quantum-mechanical or by the phenomenological model

In the following sections we calculate the intensity of light scattered by a single atom, and assume that there is no coherence between light scattered by different atoms. This is justifiable only to the extent that we are concerned with laterally scattered radiation whose wavelength is very much smaller than the mean distance between neighbouring atoms. We assume also that there is no multiple scattering. The assumption that different atoms radiate incoherently allows us to ignore the dependence of phase on the position of the scattering centre. The size of the sample is small compared with the wavelength at radio-frequencies.

The calculations in this paper have been carried through with particular reference to the transition $(6^3P_1 - 6^1S_0)$, $\lambda 2537\,\text{Å}$ in mercury, where the radio-frequency mixing is taking place between the Zeeman states of the upper level. This is a particularly simple case in that the three excited states are equally spaced in energy and are damped at the same rate, and in that there is only one ground state. The principles of the calculation could be applied to other situations: for example, the radio-frequency transitions could be between multiplet or hyperfine states. When radio-frequency mixing in the ground states is to be studied, some assumption concerning phase memory would have to be made, equivalent to that of introducing radiative damping into the excited state.

2. Formulation of the problem

Consider an atom in a uniform magnetic field **H**. Of the possible eigenstates we shall be concerned only with a non-degenerate ground state $|g\rangle$ and a set of excited states $|m\rangle$ which belong to a particular level of angular momentum **J**. It is supposed that the states $|m\rangle$, and no others, are accessible from $|g\rangle$ by optical excitation, owing to the limited spectral range of the light. The $|m\rangle$ are connected with one another by the radio-frequency perturbation.

In order to avoid unnecessary complication, the particular value $J = 0$ is chosen for $|g\rangle$. Since this restriction may readily be lifted, we prefer not to impose on the excited states the restrictions on J which electric dipole transitions from $|g\rangle$ would require.

(i) *The states and the Hamiltonians*

The state of the atom, $|t\rangle$, at any time t satisfies the equation

$$i\hbar\, d|t\rangle/dt = \mathscr{H}|t\rangle, \tag{1}$$

where the Hamiltonian $\mathscr{H}$ may be written, to describe the type of experiment we are considering,

$$\mathscr{H} = \mathscr{H}_0 + \gamma \mathbf{J}.\mathbf{H} + \mathscr{H}_D + \mathscr{H}_{\text{r.f.}} + \mathscr{H}_{\text{opt.}}. \tag{2}$$

The first two terms on the right describe the interactions within the atom and the effect of the field $\mathbf{H}$; γ is the gyromagnetic ratio.

The third term describes the radiative damping of the excited states. We assume that the matrix of $\mathscr{H}_D$ is diagonal, with elements $-\frac{1}{2}i\hbar\Gamma$ for the states $|m\rangle$, and zero for $|g\rangle$.

The fourth and fifth terms describe the radio-frequency and optical perturbations, respectively. These are formulated semi-classically, and discussed in detail below.

The state of the atom may be expressed as a superposition of states independent of time by the expansion

$$|t\rangle = \sum_m a_m(t)\,|m\rangle + a_g(t)\,|g\rangle. \tag{3}$$

Explicit forms for the a_m and a_g are found by solving the equation of motion, given that the atom is initially in the state $|g\rangle$.

(ii) *Method of solution*

Since the optical excitation is weak ($a_g \approx 1$ at all times), we can treat $\mathscr{H}_{\text{opt.}}$ as a small perturbation and write $\mathscr{H} = \mathscr{H}^* + \mathscr{H}_{\text{opt.}}$, where

$$\mathscr{H}^* = \mathscr{H}_0 + \gamma \mathbf{J}.\mathbf{H} + \mathscr{H}_D + \mathscr{H}_{\text{r.f.}}.$$

Let $|\,\rangle$ symbolize a state of the system at time t which would evolve from the state $|t_0\rangle$ under the influence of $\mathscr{H}^*$ only. The equation of motion of this state is

$$i\hbar\, d|\,\rangle/dt = \mathscr{H}^*|\,\rangle, \tag{4}$$

with the condition $|\,\rangle = |t_0\rangle$ when $t = t_0$. The transformation from $|t_0\rangle$ to $|\,\rangle$ may conveniently be expressed by defining an operator $U(t, t_0)$ as follows:

$$U(t, t_0)\,|t_0\rangle = |\,\rangle. \tag{5}$$

It is then readily verified that $|t\rangle$, the solution of (1) may be written

$$|t\rangle = U(t, 0)|0\rangle + \frac{1}{i\hbar}\int_0^t dt_0\, U(t, t_0)\,\mathscr{H}_{\text{opt.}}(t_0)\, U(t_0, 0)\,|0\rangle \tag{6}$$

$$+ \text{ terms of second order in } \mathscr{H}_{\text{opt.}}.$$

With the use of explicit expressions for $\mathscr{H}_{\text{opt.}}$ and U which are to be obtained in section (3), equation (6) may be expanded in the form of equation (3), thereby obtaining the coefficients $a_m(t) \equiv \langle m|t\rangle$. The precise value of $a_g(t)$ is not of particular interest, provided it does not depart greatly from unity.

It remains to calculate the intensity of the fluorescent light as a function of time. This is proportional to the modulus squared of the matrix element of the electric dipole operator $\mathbf{P}$ between the states $|t\rangle$ and $|g\rangle$. The result, and its justification by a Correspondence argument, is given in §4.

3. Solution of the Equation of Motion

(i) *The operator* $\mathscr{H}_{\text{opt}}$.

Let the electric field of the incident light at time t be $\mathbf{E}_i(t) = E_i(t)\,\mathbf{e}_i^0$, where $\mathbf{e}_i^0$ is a unit vector representing the direction of polarization. We shall see in due course that $E_i(t)$ need not be completely specified: the significant quantity is the real correlation function $\langle E_i(t)\,E_i(t+\tau)\rangle$. This will ultimately be chosen to represent a steady beam of light of spectral width greater than any of the frequency differences with which we are concerned, in the neighbourhood of the excitation frequencies of the states $|m\rangle$.

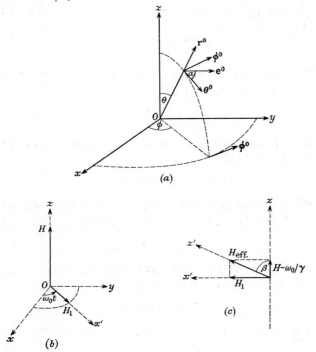

FIGURE 1. The notation.

The operator $\mathscr{H}_{\text{opt}}$. we consider only in the first approximation, in which it is the scalar product $\mathbf{E}_i.\mathbf{P}$, where $\mathbf{P}$ is the electric dipole operator. We shall write

$$\mathscr{H}_{\text{opt}}. = E_i(t)\,\mathbf{e}_i^0.\mathbf{P} \equiv E_i(t)\,F. \tag{7}$$

The only matrix elements of F which do not vanish are those between the excited states $|m\rangle$ and the ground state $|g\rangle$; we write them as $F_m \equiv \langle m|\,F\,|g\rangle$.

For later reference we expand $\mathbf{e}^0$. Let the direction of the light be specified by θ, ϕ (figure 1(a)), and let the electric vector make an angle α with the unit vector associated with θ. Then

$$\begin{aligned}
\mathbf{e}^0 = \; &\mathbf{i}(\cos\theta\cos\phi\cos\alpha - \sin\phi\sin\alpha) \\
&+ \mathbf{j}(\cos\theta\sin\phi\cos\alpha + \cos\phi\sin\alpha) \\
&+ \mathbf{k}(-\sin\theta\cos\alpha).
\end{aligned} \tag{8}$$

(ii) The operator U

Through equations (4) and (5), U is related to

$$\mathscr{H}^* = \mathscr{H}_0 + \gamma \mathbf{J}.\mathbf{H} + \mathscr{H}_D + \mathscr{H}_{\text{r.f.}}.$$

We are interested in the effect of a radio-frequency field of amplitude H_1 rotating with angular velocity ω_0 in a plane perpendicular to $\mathbf{H}$, the z-direction (figure 1(b)). The perturbation operator is

$$\mathscr{H}_{\text{r.f.}} = \gamma\mathbf{J}.\{(H_1\cos\omega_0 t)\,\mathbf{i} + (H_1\sin\omega_0 t)\mathbf{j}\}. \tag{9}$$

With this form for $\mathscr{H}_{\text{r.f.}}$, the Hamiltonian $\mathscr{H}^*$ may be written (Salwen 1955, for example)

$$\mathscr{H}^* = \exp\{(-\mathrm{i}J_z\omega_0 t/\hbar)\}\,\mathscr{H}_1\{\exp(\mathrm{i}J_z\omega_0 t/\hbar)\}, \tag{10}$$

where

$$\mathscr{H}_1 = \mathscr{H}_0 + \mathscr{H}_D + \gamma H J_z + \gamma H_1 J_x. \tag{11}$$

It is convenient to make a unitary transformation T to a co-ordinate system $Ox'y'z$ rotating about Oz with angular velocity ω_0. This transforms $\mathscr{H}^*$ to $\mathscr{H}_1$, and $|\rangle$ into $|'\rangle = \exp(\mathrm{i}J_z\omega_0 t/\hbar)|\rangle$. The equation of motion (4) now becomes (Rabi, Ramsey & Schwinger 1954)

$$\mathrm{i}\hbar\,\mathrm{d}|'\rangle/\mathrm{d}t = (\mathscr{H}_1 - \omega_0 J_z)\,|'\rangle = \mathscr{H}'|'\rangle, \tag{12}$$

where

$$\mathscr{H}' = \mathscr{H}_0 + \mathscr{H}_D + \delta J_z + b J_x, \tag{13}$$

in which

$$\delta = \omega - \omega_0, \quad \omega = \gamma H \quad \text{and} \quad b = \gamma H_1.$$

The Hamiltonian $\mathscr{H}'$ is now independent of time, and the equation of motion (12) may readily be solved giving

$$|'\rangle = \exp\{(\mathscr{H}'/\mathrm{i}\hbar)(t - t_0)\,|'t_0\rangle\}, \tag{14}$$

where the state $|'\rangle$ at $t = t_0$ is written $|'t_0\rangle$.

By applying the inverse transformation, T^{-1}, to $|'\rangle$ and $|'t_0\rangle$, we find the relation between $|\rangle$ and $|t_0\rangle$, which, by comparison with equation (5), yields

$$U(t, t_0) = \exp(-\mathrm{i}J_z\omega_0 t/\hbar)\exp\{(\mathscr{H}'/\mathrm{i}\hbar)(t - t_0)\}\exp(\mathrm{i}J_z\omega_0 t_0/\hbar). \tag{15}$$

In the evaluation of the intensity of fluorescent radiation, we shall need the matrix elements $U_{mn} \equiv \langle m|\,U\,|n\rangle$ taken between any two of the excited states $|m\rangle$ and $|n\rangle$ (the letter n is used for possible values of m to avoid difficulties in notation created by the use of subscripts and primes). The U_{mn} are obtained from the eigenstates and eigenvalues of J_z and $\mathscr{H}'$.

The eigenstates of J_z are $|g\rangle$ and $|m\rangle$, with eigenvalues 0 and $m\hbar$, respectively.

The eigenstates of $\mathcal{H}'$ are most easily expressed in terms of a co-ordinate system produced by a rotation of Oz about Oy' by an angle $\beta = \tan^{-1}(b/\delta)$ (figure 1(c)). $\mathcal{H}'$ may then be written $\mathcal{H}_0 + \mathcal{H}_D + pJ_{z'}$ where $p = (\delta^2 + b^2)^{\frac{1}{2}}$. As the field H increases from zero, through the resonant field $H_0 = \omega_0/\gamma$, to infinity, the angle β passes from the value π, through $\frac{1}{2}\pi$ to zero. The eigenvalues of $\mathcal{H}'$ are

$$0 \quad \text{and} \quad \hbar\lambda_\mu = \hbar(k_0 - \tfrac{1}{2}i\Gamma + \mu p),$$

corresponding respectively to the eigenstates $|\gamma\rangle$ and $|\mu\rangle$ of the atom in $H_{\text{eff.}}$, the effective field in the rotating co-ordinate system. The states $|m\rangle$ and $|\mu\rangle$, $|g\rangle$ and $|\gamma\rangle$ are related by the linear transformations

$$|\mu\rangle = \sum_m \langle m|\mu\rangle |m\rangle = \sum_m \mathcal{D}^J(0,\beta,0)_{m\mu}|m\rangle; \quad |\gamma\rangle = |g\rangle, \tag{16}$$

where the $\mathcal{D}^J(0,\beta,0)_{m\mu}$ are elements of the rotation matrix (Rose 1957, for example). Using these results we obtain

$$\begin{aligned}
U_{mn}(t,t_0) &= \langle m|\exp(-iJ_z\omega_0 t/\hbar)\exp(\mathcal{H}'/i\hbar)(t-t_0)\exp(iJ_z\omega_0 t_0/\hbar)|n\rangle \\
&= \exp(-im\omega_0 t)\exp(in\omega_0 t_0)\sum_\mu \langle m|\mu\rangle\langle\mu|\exp(\mathcal{H}'/i\hbar)(t-t_0)|n\rangle \\
&= \exp(-im\omega_0 t)\exp(in\omega_0 t_0)\sum_{\mu,\nu}\langle m|\mu\rangle\langle\mu|\exp(\mathcal{H}'/i\hbar)(t-t_0)|\nu\rangle\langle\nu|n\rangle \\
&= \exp(-im\omega_0 t)\exp(in\omega_0 t_0)\sum_\mu \langle m|\mu\rangle\langle\mu|n\rangle\exp\{-i\lambda_\mu(t-t_0)\}, \tag{17}
\end{aligned}$$

since the $|\mu\rangle$ are eigenstates of $\mathcal{H}'$.

(iii) Expansion of the state $|t\rangle$

We are now in a position to find the coefficients $a_m(t)$ of equation (3). From equation (6) we find, by forming the bracket product with $|m\rangle$,

$$a_m(t) \equiv \langle m|t\rangle = \langle m|U(t,0)|0\rangle + (1/i\hbar)\int_0^t dt_0\langle m|U(t,t_0)\mathcal{H}_{\text{opt.}}(t_0)U(t_0,0)|0\rangle, \tag{18}$$

in which $|0\rangle$, the state at $t = 0$, is simply $|g\rangle$. Since $|g\rangle$ is an eigenstate of J_z with eigenvalue 0, and since $|\gamma\rangle = |g\rangle$ is an eigenstate of $\mathcal{H}'$ with eigenvalue 0, $|g\rangle$ is also an eigenstate of U with eigenvalue 1 for all t. Hence the first term on the right of equation (18) is $\langle m|g\rangle = 0$, and the second term reduces to

$$(1/i\hbar)\int_0^t dt_0\langle m|U(t,t_0)\mathcal{H}_{\text{opt.}}(t_0)|g\rangle.$$

With the use of equation (7) this becomes

$$-(1/i\hbar)\int_0^t dt_0 E_i(t_0)\sum_n F_n\langle m|U(t,t_0)|n\rangle. \tag{19}$$

Finally, from (17), (19) and (3) we have

$$\begin{aligned}
|t\rangle = a_g|g\rangle \mp (1/i\hbar)\int_0^t dt_0 E_i(t_0)\sum_{m\mu n}\langle m|\mu\rangle\langle\mu|n\rangle F_n \\
\times \exp(-im\omega_0 t)\exp\{-i\lambda_\mu(t-t_0)\}\exp(in\omega_0 t_0)|m\rangle. \tag{20}
\end{aligned}$$

The physical meaning of the second term on the right is simply the following: the coefficient $(1/i\hbar) E_i(t_0) F_n dt_0$ represents the probability amplitude of the state $|n\rangle$ when the optical perturbation acts on an atom in state $|g\rangle$ (which is approximately the state $|t_0\rangle$) for a time dt_0 at t_0; the coefficient

$$\sum_{\mu} \langle m|\mu\rangle \langle \mu|n\rangle \exp(-im\omega_0 t) \exp\{-i\lambda_\mu(t-t_0)\} \exp(in\omega_0 t_0)$$

represents the probability amplitude of the state $|m\rangle$ at time t when the radio-frequency and damping perturbations have acted for a time $(t-t_0)$ on an atom which, at time t_0, was in the state $|n\rangle$; (this coefficient, in a different form, and without the radiative damping, was derived by Majorana (1932) (see also Ramsey 1956, appendix E)); the combined coefficients, summed over the m, μ and n, and integrated over t_0, represent the net effect of optical, radio-frequency and damping perturbations in an approximation in which the excitation rate is weak compared with the rate of spontaneous decay, that is to say, the probability of finding the atom in the ground state is always very much greater than the probability of finding it excited ($a_g \approx 1$).

4. The fluorescent radiation

(i) *Calculation of the intensity I*

The energy flux per unit area of radiation in an electromagnetic field specified by the complex vectors $\mathbf{E}$, $\mathbf{H}$, is given by

$$\mathbf{S}_{\text{av.}} = c(\mathbf{E} \wedge \mathbf{H}^* + \mathbf{E}^* \wedge \mathbf{H})/16\pi.$$

Using $\mathbf{H} = \mathbf{r}^0 \wedge \mathbf{E}$ for electromagnetic waves propagated in the direction of the unit vector $\mathbf{r}^0$, one obtains

$$\mathbf{S}_{\text{av.}} = I\mathbf{r}^0 = c(\mathbf{E}^* . \mathbf{E}/8\pi) \mathbf{r}^0. \tag{21}$$

The radiation field $\mathbf{E}(r, \theta, \phi, t)$, to first approximation, is related to the matrix element $\langle g| P |t\rangle$ by

$$\mathbf{E} = (2k^2/rc^2) \langle g| \mathbf{P} - (\mathbf{r}^0 . \mathbf{P}) \mathbf{r}^0 |t\rangle. \tag{22}$$

Its component in the direction $\mathbf{e}^0$, which lies in the plane normal to $\mathbf{r}^0$ (see figure 1(a)) is

$$\mathbf{e}^0 . \mathbf{E} = (2k^2/rc^2) \langle g| \mathbf{e}^0 . \mathbf{P} |t\rangle. \tag{23}$$

Equation (22) may be derived by a Correspondence argument (see, for example, Condon & Shortley 1951, pp. 89, 90) when the states concerned are pure states of a time-independent Hamiltonian. Its application when $|t\rangle$ is expressed as a linear superposition of such states may be justified from the superposition theorem for electric fields.

The expression for I thus depends on the form of the matrix elements $\langle g| \mathbf{e}^0 . \mathbf{P} |t\rangle$, which, are, by equation (20)

$$\langle g|\mathbf{e}^0.\mathbf{P}|t\rangle = (1/i\hbar) \int_0^t dt_0 E_i(t_0) \sum_{m\mu n} G_m^* \langle m|\mu\rangle \langle \mu|n\rangle F_n$$
$$\times \exp(-im\omega_0 t) \exp\{-i\lambda_\mu(t-t_0)\} \exp(in\omega_0 t_0), \quad (24)$$

in which we have introduced $G_m^* = \langle g|\mathbf{e}^0.\mathbf{P}|m\rangle$. By this definition F_m and G_m are defined identically except for the direction of the polarization vector.

Combining equations (21), (23) and (24) we arrive at the following expression for the intensity of light at time t, plane polarized in the direction e^0, due to the scattering from one atom:

$$I = \frac{k_0^4}{2\pi c^3 \hbar^2 r^2} \int_0^t dt_0 E_i(t_0) \sum_{m\mu n} G_m^* \langle m|\mu\rangle \langle \mu|n\rangle F_n \exp\left(-im\omega_0 t\right)$$
$$\times \exp\{-i\lambda_\mu(t-t_0)\} \exp\left(in\omega_0 t_0\right)$$
$$\times \int_0^t dt_0' E_i(t_0') \sum_{m'\mu'n'} F_{n'}^* \langle n'|\mu'\rangle \langle \mu'|m'\rangle G_{m'} \exp\left(im'\omega_0 t\right) \exp\{i\lambda_{\mu'}^*(t-t_0')\}$$
$$\times \exp\left(-in'\omega_0 t_0'\right), \tag{25}$$

in which k_0 is an average optical frequency. For laterally scattered radiation from N atoms the expression is to be multiplied by N and $(1/r^2)$ replaced by a mean value, $(1/r_0^2)$.

The dependence on t, t_0 and t_0' of the terms in equation (25) is of the form

$$\exp\{-i(m-m'-n+n')\omega_0 t\} \int_0^t dt_0 \exp\{-(\Gamma+ix)(t-t_0)\} \int_0^t dt_0' E_i(t_0) E_i(t_0')$$
$$\times \exp\{-(\tfrac{1}{2}\Gamma - ik')(t_0 - t_0')\} \tag{26}$$

in which
$$k' = k_0 + \mu'p + n'\omega_0 \quad \text{and} \quad x = (\mu-\mu')p + (n-n')\omega_0. \tag{27}$$

In order to evaluate the double integral it is not necessary to specify the field $E_i(t_0)$ itself, nor even the product $\Phi(t_0, \tau) = E_i(t_0) E_i(t_0+\tau)$, where $\tau = (t_0 - t_0')$. It is sufficient to know the average value $\langle \Phi(t_0, \tau)\rangle$, taken with fixed τ over a time, centred on t_0, which covers many periods of the optical frequency k'. To see this, notice that the only term in (26), apart from Φ, which oscillates rapidly, is $\exp -(\tfrac{1}{2}\Gamma - ik')\tau$. Now fix τ, and integrate over a range of t_0 large compared with $1/k'$ but small compared with $(\Gamma^2 + x^2)^{\frac{1}{2}}$. The only quantity which changes appreciably during this time is Φ. The value of (26) is therefore unchanged if we substitute for Φ the mean value

$$\langle \Phi(t_0, \tau)\rangle = \frac{1}{2T_0} \int_{t_0-T_0}^{t_0+T_0} \Phi(t, \tau)\, dt.$$

The advantage of introducing $\langle \Phi\rangle$ is that it is closely related to a quantity which can actually be measured, the power spectrum of the incident light.

Several cases now can be distinguished:

(i) The intensity of the exciting light is independent of time, as in the ordinary double resonance experiment. In this case $\langle \Phi\rangle$ is the auto-correlation function for stationary fields. It is a function of τ only, not of t_0, and is related to the power spectrum $\rho(k)$:

$$\langle E_i(t_0) E_i(t_0')\rangle = \langle \Phi(\tau)\rangle = \frac{8\pi}{c} \int_{-\infty}^{+\infty} dk\, \rho(k) \exp\left(-ik\tau\right), \tag{28}$$

(see, for example, Born & Wolf 1959, p. 501; the factor $\exp(-2\pi i\nu t)$ in their equation (27) should read $\exp -2\pi i\nu\tau$).

(ii) The exciting light is modulated or pulsed. In this case $\langle \Phi\rangle$ is a function of t_0 as well as of τ. We shall not pursue the analysis of this case, but refer to it again at the end of § 6.

Returning to case (i) and inserting (28) into (26), we find that the integral over t_0' may be expressed

$$\frac{8\pi}{c}\int_{t_0-t}^{t_0} d\tau \exp\left(-\tfrac{1}{2}\Gamma\tau\right)\int_{-\infty}^{+\infty} dk\, \rho(k)\exp\left\{-i(k-k')\tau\right\}. \tag{29}$$

Again, we distinguish cases for which $\rho(k)$ has different forms:

(a) Monochromatic light of angular frequency k'. In this case the form of $\rho(k)$ is $R\delta(k-k')$, the double integral (29) becomes $(16\pi R/c\Gamma)\exp\tfrac{1}{2}\Gamma(t-t_0)$ for $t_0 \gg 1/\Gamma$, and (26) reduces to

$$\frac{16\pi R}{c\Gamma}\frac{1}{(\tfrac{1}{2}\Gamma+ix)}\exp\left\{-i(m-m'-n+n')\,\omega_0 t\right\}. \tag{30}$$

(b) White light. In this case $\rho(k) = \rho_0$, independent of k, the integral over k in (29) becomes $\rho_0\,\delta(\tau)$, the value of (29), $8\pi\rho_0/c$, and (26) reduces to

$$\frac{8\pi\rho_0}{c}\frac{1}{(\Gamma+ix)}\exp\left\{-i(m-m'-n+n')\,\omega_0 t\right\}. \tag{31}$$

(c) Quasi-monochromatic light of mean angular frequency k' and spectral width $\Delta \gg \Gamma$, such as was used in the experiments. In this case $\rho(k)$ might take the form, for example, $\rho_0\exp\left\{-(k-k')^2/\Delta^2\right\}$. More important than the exact form of $\rho(k)$, provided it is a slowly varying function, is the time $\tau_\Delta \approx 1/\Delta$ over which coherence persists in the optical field, for if τ_Δ is much less than the lifetime of the atoms, then we find the same result as for white light, as may readily be shown:

Choose a time τ_0 such that $1/\Delta \ll \tau_0 \ll 1/\Gamma$. Now the integral over k in (29) behaves like $\rho_0\,\delta(k-k')$ except in the region $|\tau| < \tau_0$. Inside this region we may, to a good approximation, replace $\exp-\tfrac{1}{2}\Gamma\tau$ by unity. The expression (29) thus has the value, in this case,

$$\frac{8\pi}{c}\int_{t_0-t}^{t_0} d\tau \int_{-\infty}^{+\infty} dk\,\rho(k)\exp\left\{-i(k-k')\tau\right\} = \frac{8\pi}{c}\int_{-\infty}^{+\infty} dk\,\rho(k)\int_{t_0-t}^{t_0} d\tau\exp\left\{-i(k-k')\tau\right\}$$

$$= \frac{8\pi}{c}\int_{-\infty}^{+\infty} dk\,\rho(k)\,\delta(k-k') = \frac{8\pi}{c}\rho(k')$$

from which the expression (26) again reduces to (31), the result obtained for white light.

If the spectral range of the light not only greatly exceeds Γ, but also spans all possible values of k' in equation (27), equation (25) becomes, for N atoms,

$$\left\|\, I = \frac{4Nk_0^4}{\Gamma c^4\hbar^2 r_0^2}\rho(k_0)\sum_{\substack{m\mu n \\ m'\mu'n'}}\mathscr{F}_{nn'}\langle m|\mu\rangle\langle\mu|n\rangle\langle n'|\mu'\rangle\langle\mu'|m'\rangle\mathscr{G}_{mm'}\frac{\Gamma}{\Gamma+ix}\right.$$
$$\left. \times \exp\left\{-i(m-m'-n+n')\,\omega_0 t\right\},\,\right\| \tag{32}$$

where m, μ, n, m', μ', n' take the values $-J, -J+1, \ldots +J$. We have introduced the notation $\mathscr{F}_{nn'} = F_n F_n^*$, $\mathscr{G}_{mm'} = G_m^* G_{m'}$, where F and G, it will be recalled, refer to excitation by, and the observation of, plane polarized light

$$F_n = \langle n|e_i^0.\mathbf{P}|g\rangle, \quad G_m = \langle m|e^0.\mathbf{P}|g\rangle.$$

For convenience, we here repeat the definitions of the other symbols

$$\langle m|\mu\rangle = \mathscr{D}^J(0,\beta,0)_{m\mu}; \quad x = (\mu-\mu')p+(n-n')\omega_0; \quad p = (\delta^2+b^2)^{\frac{1}{2}};$$

$$b = \gamma H_1; \quad \delta = \omega-\omega_0; \quad \omega = \gamma H; \quad \beta = \tan^{-1}(b/\delta);$$

and $\rho(k_0)$ is the energy flux of the incident light per unit area, per unit spectral range.

The elements $\mathscr{F}_{nn'}$, and $\mathscr{G}_{mm'}$ form what may be termed the excitation and emission matrices, respectively. They may be generalized to unpolarized light, and to polarized light other than plane. Thus, for unpolarized light, the matrix element $\mathscr{F}_{nn'}^u$ may be formed by adding to $(F_n F_n^*)$ the element formed by using the polarization vector perpendicular to e_i^0. Introducing the unit vectors $\mathbf{r}^0$, $\boldsymbol{\theta}^0$ and $\boldsymbol{\phi}^0$ (figure 1 (a)), we define

$$\mathbf{F}_n = \langle n|\,\mathbf{P}-(\mathbf{r}^0.\,\mathbf{P})\,\mathbf{r}^0|g\rangle = \langle n|(\boldsymbol{\theta}^0.\,\mathbf{P})\,\boldsymbol{\theta}^0+(\boldsymbol{\phi}^0.\,\mathbf{P})\boldsymbol{\phi}^0|g\rangle. \tag{33a}$$

Then we have for unpolarized light,

$$\mathscr{F}_{nn'}^u = \mathbf{F}_n.\mathbf{F}_n^*, \tag{33b}$$

and for circularly polarized light

$$\mathscr{F}_{nn'}^c = F_n^c F_{n'}^{*c}, \tag{33c}$$

in which $F_n^c = \frac{1}{2}(\boldsymbol{\theta}^0 \pm i\boldsymbol{\phi}^0).\mathbf{F}_n$.

Explicit forms for $\mathscr{F}_{nn'}$ and $\mathscr{G}_{mm'}$ in a particular case are given in §5.

(ii) Discussion of the result, equation (32)

Consider first the case when the polarization of the exciting light allows excitation to only one state $|n\rangle$ of the excited level, so that $n' = n$. The result (32) shows that the light intensity is modulated at frequencies $|m-m'|\,\omega_0$. The angular dependence of the emitted light is contained in the elements $\mathscr{G}_{mm'}$ of the emission matrix. The rotation matrix elements give the variation of intensity with field and frequency. They all show some type of resonant behaviour near $\delta = 0$, i.e. when $H = H_0 = \omega_0/\gamma$. The term $\Gamma/(\Gamma+ix)$, which reduces to $\Gamma/\{\Gamma+i(\mu-\mu')p\}$, also shows resonant behaviour near $\delta = 0$ unless $\mu = \mu'$, in which case it is independent of H. The terms of zero-frequency $(m = m')$ sum to give the well known Brossel–Bitter resonance (Brossel & Bitter 1952).

The more general case when more than one of the $|n\rangle$ are simultaneously excited shows additional features which have been observed in the experiments, namely, modulation at frequencies higher than the maximum value of $|m-m'|\,\omega_0$, and resonance effects at frequencies other than H_0. The possible modulation frequencies are now $|m-m'-n+n'|\,\omega_0$. The extra resonance effects are seen in the behaviour of the term $\Gamma/(\Gamma+ix)$ when $x = 0$, i.e. when $(\mu-\mu')p = (n'-n)\omega_0$. In the case of the $^3P_1-{}^1S_0$ transition, modulation up to the fourth harmonic is present, and resonances occur when $H = 0$, $\frac{1}{2}H_0$, $\frac{3}{2}H_0$, $2H_0$ and $3H_0$. Not all of these may be strong enough to be easily observable.

5. Application to the transition $6^3P_1 - 6^1S_0$ in mercury

Atoms in the ground level 6^1S_0 are excited by light of wavelength 2537 Å to the level 6^3P_1, whose states $|m_J = 0, \pm 1\rangle$ are connected by the radio-frequency field. The expression (32) for the intensity of the fluorescent light is most readily understood by separate attention to the three parts of the process.

(i a) Excitation

The coefficients F_n for the case of incident light passing through a linear polarizer specified by the unit vector e_i^0 are given by $F_n = e_i^0 . \langle n| \mathbf{P} |g\rangle$. Using the matrix elements for $\langle n| \mathbf{P} |g\rangle$ given by Condon & Shortley (1951, p. 53), and equation (8) we obtain

$$F_{\pm 1} = 2^{-\frac{1}{2}} P(\cos \alpha_i \cos \theta_i \mp i \sin \alpha_i) \exp(\mp i\phi_i), \Big\}$$
$$F_0 = -P(\cos \alpha_i \sin \theta_i), \qquad \qquad \Big\} \tag{34}$$

where $P = \langle 1 \vdots P \vdots 0 \rangle$.

For the particular case of light incident along the x-axis, polarized so that the electric vector makes an angle α_i with the direction of the field, the excitation matrix becomes

$$\mathscr{F}_{nn'} = |P|^2 \begin{pmatrix} \frac{1}{2}\sin^2\alpha_i & -2^{-\frac{1}{2}}i\sin\alpha_i\cos\alpha_i & \frac{1}{2}\sin^2\alpha_i \\ 2^{-\frac{1}{2}}i\sin\alpha_i\cos\alpha_i & \cos^2\alpha_i & 2^{-\frac{1}{2}}i\sin\alpha_i\cos\alpha_i \\ \frac{1}{2}\sin^2\alpha_i & -2^{-\frac{1}{2}}i\sin\alpha_i\cos\alpha_i & \frac{1}{2}\sin^2\alpha_i \end{pmatrix}. \tag{35a}$$

For the case of unpolarized light, a matrix obtained by replacing α_i by $\alpha_i + \frac{1}{2}\pi$ must be added to the above. The excitation matrix is then

$$\mathscr{F}_{nn'}^u = |P|^2 \begin{pmatrix} \frac{1}{2} & 0 & \frac{1}{2} \\ 0 & 1 & 0 \\ \frac{1}{2} & 0 & \frac{1}{2} \end{pmatrix}. \tag{35b}$$

(i b) The mixing of states

The effect of the radio-frequency magnetic field in producing a coherent mixture of the states $|m\rangle$ is contained in the products

$$\langle m|\mu\rangle \langle \mu|n\rangle \langle n'|\mu'\rangle \langle \mu'|m'\rangle.$$

The rotation matrix elements, for $J = 1$, are

$$\langle m|\mu\rangle = \begin{pmatrix} \cos^2\frac{1}{2}\beta & -\sqrt{2}\sin\frac{1}{2}\beta\cos\frac{1}{2}\beta & \sin^2\frac{1}{2}\beta \\ \sqrt{2}\sin\frac{1}{2}\beta\cos\frac{1}{2}\beta & \cos^2\frac{1}{2}\beta - \sin^2\frac{1}{2}\beta & -\sqrt{2}\sin\frac{1}{2}\beta\cos\frac{1}{2}\beta \\ \sin^2\frac{1}{2}\beta & \sqrt{2}\sin\frac{1}{2}\beta\cos\frac{1}{2}\beta & \cos^2\frac{1}{2}\beta \end{pmatrix} \tag{36}$$

in which β is defined in §3 (figure 1 (c)). The elements $\langle \mu|m\rangle$ are obtained by transposition of rows and columns.

The variation of these matrix elements, and of the factor $\Gamma/(\Gamma + ix)$, with H, gives rise to resonances in the steady and modulated components of the fluorescent radiation.

(ic) *Emission*

The angular distribution of the fluorescent light is determined by the emission matrix $\mathscr{G}_{mm'}$. If no analyzer is used, $\mathscr{G}^u_{mm'} = \mathbf{G}^*_m . \mathbf{G}_{m'}$ with

$$G_{\pm 1} = \mp 2^{-\frac{1}{2}} P(\boldsymbol{\theta}^0 \cos\theta \mp i\boldsymbol{\phi}^0) \, \mathrm{e}^{\mp i\phi}, \\ G_0 = -P\boldsymbol{\theta}^0 \sin\theta. \tag{37}$$

For observation in the direction θ, ϕ the emission matrix becomes

$$\mathscr{G}^u_{mm'} = |P|^2 \begin{pmatrix} \frac{1}{2}(\cos^2\theta + 1) & 2^{-\frac{1}{2}}\sin\theta\cos\theta\,\mathrm{e}^{i\phi} & \frac{1}{2}\sin^2\theta\,\mathrm{e}^{i2\phi} \\ 2^{-\frac{1}{2}}\sin\theta\cos\theta\,\mathrm{e}^{-i\phi} & \sin^2\theta & -2^{-\frac{1}{2}}\sin\theta\cos\theta\,\mathrm{e}^{i\phi} \\ \frac{1}{2}\sin^2\theta\,\mathrm{e}^{-i2\phi} & -2^{-\frac{1}{2}}\sin\theta\cos\theta\,\mathrm{e}^{-i\phi} & \frac{1}{2}(\cos^2\theta + 1) \end{pmatrix}. \tag{38}$$

If an analyzer is used to select the electric vector at angle α, the elements of the emission matrix are $\mathscr{G}_{mm'} = G^*_m G_{m'}$, where the $G_m = \mathbf{e}^0 . \mathbf{G}_m$ are given by equations like (34).

(ii) *Excitation to a single state*

The terms of equation (32) will be evaluated for the particular case of excitation to the state $|0\rangle$ exclusively (light incident along the x-axis, $\alpha_i = 0$). Writing I_0 for the accumulation of constants, we find

$$I = I_0 \frac{N}{\Gamma} [\sin^2\theta + (\cos^2\theta - \tfrac{1}{2}\sin^2\theta)\, 2A \\ - \sin\theta\cos\theta\,\{B\cos(\omega_0 t - \phi) + C\sin(\omega_0 t - \phi)\} \\ - \sin^2\theta\,\{D\cos(2\omega_0 t - 2\phi) + E\sin(2\omega_0 t - 2\phi)\}] \tag{39}$$

in which

$$A = \frac{b^2(4\delta^2 + b^2 + \Gamma^2)}{(\delta^2 + b^2 + \Gamma^2)(4\delta^2 + 4b^2 + \Gamma^2)},$$

$$B = \frac{2b\delta(4\delta^2 - 2b^2 + \Gamma^2)}{(\delta^2 + b^2 + \Gamma^2)(4\delta^2 + 4b^2 + \Gamma^2)},$$

$$C = \frac{2b\Gamma(4\delta^2 + b^2 + \Gamma^2)}{(\delta^2 + b^2 + \Gamma^2)(4\delta^2 + 4b^2 + \Gamma^2)},$$

$$D = \frac{b^2(2\delta^2 - b^2 - \Gamma^2)}{(\delta^2 + b^2 + \Gamma^2)(4\delta^2 + 4b^2 + \Gamma^2)},$$

$$E = \frac{3b^2\Gamma\delta}{(\delta^2 + b^2 + \Gamma^2)(4\delta^2 + 4b^2 + \Gamma^2)}.$$

The quantity A determines the variation of the unmodulated component of the fluorescent light as one alters H (or ω_0); this displays a reasonance when

$$\delta = \omega - \omega_0 = 0,$$

i.e. at $H = H_0$. The variation is exactly that described by Brossel & Bitter (1952).

The intensity is also modulated at the first and second harmonics of the applied radio-frequency, the variation of amplitude and phase of the modulations being described by the quantities B, C and D, E, respectively. The quantities B and C bear a striking resemblance to the solutions of the Bloch equations, which lends support to the belief that the modulation may also be described by the phenomenological approach of Bell & Bloom (1957). It is to be noticed that the phase of the modulations (with respect to that of the oscillating field) varies as one goes through resonance, and is a function of the azimuth angle ϕ.

The variations have received experimental confirmation in work which has been briefly reported (Dodd *et al.* 1959) and which is to be more fully described in a later paper. In particular, the variations with angle of observation, and of polarizer and analyzer have been confirmed.

(iii) *Excitation to a mixture of states*

As a further example we show how, and under what conditions, resonances can occur near the fields $H = \frac{1}{2}H_0$ and $\frac{3}{2}H_0$.

The general expression for the intensity (equation (32)) is a formidable one, but it is possible to extract from the summations those terms which have a resonance in a certain region of magnetic field. Resonances occur when the quantity $x = (\mu - \mu')p + (n - n')\omega_0$ in the equation passes through zero. For the particular terms in which $n - n' = +1$, $\mu - \mu' = -2$, and $n - n' = -1$, $\mu - \mu' = +2$, this leads to the condition $2p = \omega_0$ for resonance. Expressed in terms of fields the condition is

$$H = H_0 \pm \tfrac{1}{2}H_0(1 - 4H_1^2/H_0^2)^{\frac{1}{2}}. \tag{40}$$

If H_1 is not too large this gives $H \approx \frac{1}{2}H_0$ and $H \approx \frac{3}{2}H_0$ for the resonances. As H_1 approaches the value $\frac{1}{2}H_0$, both resonances move towards H_0.

The frequencies of modulation of the intensity at these resonances are the possible values of $|m - m' - n + n'|\omega_0$. Since $m - m'$ can take all values from zero to ± 2 (and recalling that we have selected those terms for which $n - n' = \pm 1$) we find terms in unmodulated, fundamental, second- and third-harmonic components of the intensity. The strengths of the resonances of these various components are not all the same; they depend on some power of H_1/H_0. The strongest resonances predicted (for small H_1) are those of the unmodulated and fundamental components which occur near $\frac{1}{2}H_0$. These have been observed. Resonances near $\frac{1}{2}H_0$ and $\frac{3}{2}H_0$ have also been observed in the light modulated at the second and third harmonics. The third harmonic resonance at $\frac{3}{2}H_0$ is stronger than that at $\frac{1}{2}H_0$ as predicted by the theory.

A necessary condition for the production of these resonances at $\frac{1}{2}H_0$ and $\frac{3}{2}H_0$ is the excitation of a mixture of states $|n\rangle$ between which n differs by unity. For light incident along the x-axis, this implies that plane polarized light must be polarized obliquely to the magnetic field. This accords with the appearance of the factor $\sin \alpha_i \cos \alpha_i$ which is common to all the terms at present under consideration. The necessity of oblique polarization has been confirmed by experiment.

Among the other terms in equation (32) are some which give rise to resonances at zero field, at $2H_0$ and at $3H_0$. Modulations up to the fourth harmonic are found at these fields. Systematic experimental study of the higher modulations has not yet been undertaken.

6. Frequency Diagram

In the course of these studies we have found it useful to develop a frequency diagram for the excited state $J = 1$ to represent its structure under the simultaneous application of a steady field along Oz and rotating field in the xy plane. A diagram of this type for $J = \frac{1}{2}$ was drawn by Pryce (1950). The frequency diagram is simply a generalization, for the case when the Hamiltonian function is time-dependent, of the normal term diagram. To each state, in the normal case, there corresponds one and only one frequency. When the Hamiltonian is periodic in time there may be more than one. The representation of radiation damping by broadened energy levels is a familiar example of this generalized term diagram.

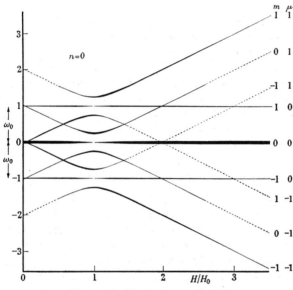

FIGURE 2. The frequency diagram.

The terms in equation (20) which represent the excited state contain, after separating the factor $\exp\{-i(k_0 - \frac{1}{2}i\Gamma)\}$, oscillating terms of frequency $(m\omega_0 \pm \mu p)$. For example, when $n = 0$ the probability amplitudes of the states $|1\rangle$, $|0\rangle$, and $|-1\rangle$ are in the ratio

$$[2sc^3 \exp\{-i(\omega_0 + p)\,t'\}\quad -2sc(c^2 - s^2)\exp(-i\omega_0 t')$$
$$-2s^3c\exp\{-i(\omega_0 - p)\,t'\}]\exp(-i\omega_0 t_0)$$

$$:[2s^2c^2\exp(-ipt')\qquad +(c^2 - s^2)^2$$
$$+2s^2c^2\exp\{-i(-p)\,t'\}]$$

$$:[2s^3c\exp\{-i(-\omega_0 + p)\,t'\} + 2sc(c^2 - s^2)\exp\{-i(-\omega_0)\,t'\}$$
$$-2sc^3\exp\{-i(-\omega_0 - p)\,t'\}]\exp\{-i(-\omega_0)t_0\}$$

in which $s = \sin\frac{1}{2}\beta$, $c = \cos\frac{1}{2}\beta$ and $t' = t - t_0$. The frequency diagram associated with the excited level is shown in figure 2.

The interpretation of the diagram is facilitated by recalling how the expansion was obtained. The states $|m\rangle$ were defined with reference to a laboratory co-ordinate system in which a steady magnetic field **H** is applied along Oz. The frequencies of the $|m\rangle$, $(k_0 +)m\gamma H$, are shown in figure 3 (a) as functions of H.

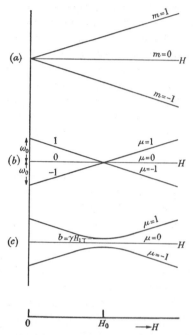

FIGURE 3. Precessional frequencies, f, as functions of H. (a) Laboratory co-ordinate system. $f = m\gamma H$ about **H**. (b) Rotating co-ordinate system. No radio-frequency field. $f = \mu\gamma|H - H_0|$ about $\mathbf{H_{eff.}}$. (c) Rotating co-ordinate system. Radio-frequency field applied. $f = \mu\gamma[(H - H_0)^2 + H_1^2]^{\frac{1}{2}}$ about $\mathbf{H_{eff.}}$.

The transformation was then made to a co-ordinate system rotating about Oz with angular velocity ω_0, in which system the frequencies of the $|m\rangle$ are decreased by $m\omega_0$. In anticipation of the subsequent addition of the field $\mathbf{H_1}$, it was found convenient to quantize with reference to an axis Oz', parallel to the effective field in the rotating system. The quantum numbers μ label the states with reference to Oz'. Before $\mathbf{H_1}$ is added the effective field is always either parallel or anti-parallel to Oz, according as H is greater or less than ω_0/γ. The state $|\mu = 1\rangle$ always has a higher frequency than $|\mu = 0\rangle$ or $|\mu = -1\rangle$ and lies above them in figure 3 (b) for all values of H.

The field $\mathbf{H_1}$ was then added. In the rotating system $\mathbf{H_1}$ is steady, along Ox'. The effective field, $[(\mathbf{H} - \omega_0/\gamma) + \mathbf{H_1}]$ now makes an angle β with Oz. The Larmor precessional frequencies, μp, about $\mathbf{H_{eff.}}$, are shown in figure 3 (c). p is often termed the 'flipping frequency'.

Since the $|\mu\rangle$ are linear superpositions of the $|m\rangle$ each of the $|m\rangle$ is fractionally associated with each level in figure 3 (c). Thus, in the return to the laboratory system, when the frequency of each state $|m\rangle$ is increased by $m\omega_0$, the diagram of figure 2 is obtained, in which the number of frequency levels is $(2J+1)^2$.

The thicknesses of the levels in figure 2 indicate the relative magnitudes of the coefficients of each frequency term in the expansion. The magnitudes used are those appropriate to $n = 0$. While they give some representation of relative probabilities, they are neither probability amplitudes nor true probabilities. Within a given $|m\rangle$, the coefficients give relative probabilities for the three frequencies μp. The sum of these probabilities is the relative probability amplitude of the state $|m\rangle$.

Transitions induced by the rotating magnetic field must be interpreted on the diagram in the following manner: absorption or emission of a radio-frequency photon corresponds to a change of frequency by ω_0, i.e. a jump between two parallel curves. In this transition m changes by ± 1, but μ remains unchanged (as it must, since it labels the eigenstates in the rotating co-ordinate system, in which the Hamiltonian is independent of time).

Use of the diagram

One can see immediately from the diagram that the Brossel–Bitter 'double resonance' curve is double-peaked. The thicknesses of the levels which represent the states $|m = \pm 1\rangle$ are greatest in the region of H_0, but have their maxima, at two values of the field slightly higher and lower than H_0. As H_1 is reduced the curves for $\mu = \pm 1$ approach their asymptotes as in figure 3 (b), and the positions of maximum thickness move closer to the centre. Not indicated in figure 2 is the natural width of the levels due to radiative decay. Thus, when H_1 becomes small, the resolution of the double peak is lost in the natural width of the resonance. Figure 2 is drawn for a ratio $H_1/H_0 = \frac{1}{4}$, which is higher than is used for most experiments of the double resonance type, but corresponds to the conditions used in the experiments of Dodd *et. al.* (1959).

Questions concerning the coherence between different states, and possibilities of light modulation, may also be answered by reference to the diagram. Let us suppose that the exciting light is steady, and of wide spectral range. In a Fourier expansion of the amplitude of the light vector, the phases of the components $\mathbf{E}(k)$ will be random, corresponding to the random positions and motion of the radiating atoms in the source. Hence the optical perturbation will excite incoherently states which are at different levels in the frequency diagram (the word 'state' here is not used in its ordinary sense). The radio-frequency perturbation, however, links states of different m but the same μ. Thus, if the optical perturbation excites $(m, \mu) = (0, 0)$, then the radio-frequency perturbation will establish coherence between $(1, 0)$, $(0, 0)$ and $(-1, 0)$, whatever the value of the field H. The frequency differences which are found between the coherent levels (ω_0 and $2\omega_0$ in this case) are found as modulation frequencies in the fluorescent radiation. The depth of modulation will depend on those parameters (H, H_1, etc.) which govern the relative 'weights' of the coherent states.

Light of the particular polarization which excited $(0, 0)$ will excite $(0, 1)$ and $(0, -1)$ also, but since the frequencies associated with these states are different, they are excited by different components of the optical field, and therefore incoherent with respect to the states $\mu = 0$. Frequency differences between incoherent levels do not appear in the modulation of the fluorescent radiation.

An important exception to the rule that levels of different μ are incoherent occurs when such levels intersect, for then they may be excited by the same component of the optical field. In this case, provided the excitation has taken place from some common initial level, coherence obtains between the intersecting levels and all others of the same values of μ. The consequences of this coherence were examined analytically in §5 (iii). The diagram allows similar conclusions to be drawn more directly. Consider, for example, the relative positions of the levels when $H \approx \frac{1}{2}H_0$. Coherence obtains between $(0, 1)$ and $(1, -1)$ because of the intersection when they are both excited from the same ground level. Further, by virtue of the radio-frequency perturbation, all other levels which have $\mu = 1$ or -1 are coherent with the intersecting pair. Only the levels $\mu = 0$ remain incoherent. The possible frequency differences between the coherent levels are 0, ω_0, $2\omega_0$, $3\omega_0$; consequently the fluorescent light is modulated at these frequencies. The phenomenon is confined to the region of intersection since the coherence between $(0, 1)$ and $(1, -1)$ is lost as one moves away.

One can immediately see, from a study of figure 2, at what fields are to be found the resonances associated with intersections, and at what frequencies the light will be modulated. In addition to the intersections near $\frac{1}{2}H_0$ which we have discussed, there exist intersections near $\frac{3}{2}H_0$ with possibilities for modulation up to, but not exceeding the third harmonic, and further intersections near the fields 0, $2H_0$ and $3H_0$. The possibilities for modulation here include the fourth harmonic.

The association of intersections in the frequency diagram with abnormal intensities in the fluorescent light relates this work with that of Hanle (1924, 1925) on the polarization of resonance radiation in low fields, and with that of Colegrove, Franken, Lewis & Sands (1959) on intensity changes in the region of intersecting energy levels. All these phenomena are completely described by equation (32), with ω (i.e. H) taking small positive and negative values in the neighbourhood of $\omega = 0$, and with H_1 and $\omega_0 = 0$. It is to be noticed that the half-intensity widths of the resonances which are associated with intersecting levels both in modulated and in unmodulated light, are determined by the natural widths of the levels. This contrasts with the resonances which occur at H_0 for which the half-intensity widths are determined by the magnitude of the radio-frequency field if that is sufficiently strong. These predictions are borne out by the experiments.

Finally, it is to be noticed that further possibilities for coherence arise if the exciting radiation is modulated or pulsed, for coherence then resides in the optical perturbation itself. The consequences of this can be deduced qualitatively from a frequency diagram such as figure 2 if a radio-frequency field (or other periodic perturbation of sharp frequency) is acting on the scattering material, or from an ordinary term diagram if there is no such field.

We have been stimulated in the development of these calculations by daily contact with the experimental work, most of which has been carried out by Dr M. J. Taylor. On the theoretical side, we are deeply grateful to Professor J. P. Barrat for allowing us to study his work before publication, to Professor W. E. Lamb and Dr R. J. Blin-Stoyle for criticism of early drafts of this paper, and to a referee for his constructive suggestions, in particular for his suggestion of the use of the operator U. We owe to Professor Barrat the suggestion that resonances at fields other than H_0 may be due to coherent excitation into states of different polarization.

REFERENCES

Bell, W. & Bloom, A. 1957 *Phys. Rev.* **107**, 1559.
Born, M. & Wolf, E. 1959 *Principles of optics.* London: Pergamon Press.
Brossel, J. & Bitter, F. 1952 *Phys. Rev.* **86**, 308.
Colegrove, F. D., Franken, P. A., Lewis, R. R. & Sands, R. H. 1959 *Phys. Rev. Lett.* **3**, 420.
Condon, E. U. & Shortley, G. H. 1951 *The theory of atomic spectra.* Cambridge University Press.
Dehmelt, H. G. 1957 *Phys. Rev.* **105**, 1924.
Dodd, J. N., Fox, W. N., Series, G. W. & Taylor, M. J. 1959 *Proc. Phys. Soc.* **74**, 789.
Hanle, W. 1924 *Z. Phys.* **30**, 93.
Hanle, W. 1925 *Egebn. exakt. Naturw.* **4**, 214.
Majorana, E. 1932 *Nuovo Cim.* **9**, 43.
Pryce, M. H. L. 1950 *Phys. Rev.* **77**, 136.
Rabi, I. I., Ramsey, N. F. & Schwinger, J. 1954 *Rev. Mod. Phys.* **26**, 167.
Ramsey, N. F. 1956 *Molecular beams.* Oxford University Press.
Rose, M. E. 1957 *Elementary theory of angular momentum.* New York: John Wiley and Sons, Inc.
Salwen, H. 1955 *Phys. Rev.* **99**, 1274.

ERRATA

pages 145 147.		Equations (7), (19), and (20). Insert minus sign before $E_i(t)$.
page 149.	line 16.	Replace $(t_0 + \tau)$ by $(t_0 - \tau)$.
	21.	Replace $(\Gamma^2 + x^2)^{1/2}$ by $1/(\Gamma^2 + x^2)^{1/2}$.
page 150.	line 10.	Change $\rho_0 \delta(\tau)$ to $2\pi \rho_0 \delta(\tau)$.
	line 10.	Change $8\pi\rho_0/c$ to $2\pi 8\pi\rho_0/c$.
		equation (31) Multiply this by 2π.
	line 19.	Replace $\delta(k - k')$ by $\delta(\tau)$.
	line 22.	Replace 8π by $16\pi^2$ twice.
		equation (32). Replace 4 by 8π.
page 152.	line 9.	Change (1951, p. 53) to (1951, p. 63).
		equation (34). Insert $\mp$ on the right-hand side of the top equation.
page 156.	line 4.	Replace $(k_0 +)m\gamma H$ by $(k_0 + m\gamma H)$.

Supplementary notes (May, 1965)

A. The argument that follows equation (27) on page 149 is not strictly valid. It purports to relate the 'instantaneous' intensity, I(t) (equation (25), derived from (21)), to $\langle \Phi(t_0, \tau) \rangle$, the average of the quadratic function $E_i(t_0)E_i(t_0 - \tau)$ of the incident light. The conclusion, while not valid for I(t) itself, is nevertheless valid for

$$\langle I(t) \rangle = \frac{1}{2T_0} \int_{t-T_0}^{t+T_0} I(s)ds,$$

provided that $\langle \Phi(t_0, \tau) \rangle$ is constant over time intervals of the order of T_0. $\langle I(t) \rangle$ should replace I in equation (32).

B. Case (ii) at the bottom of page 149 has now been studied:
Aleksandrov, E. B. 1963, 1964 *Opt. i Spektroskopiya* **14**, 436; **17**, 957.
Corney, A. and Series, G. W. 1964 *Proc. Phys. Soc.* **83**, 207, 213, 331.
Dodd, J. N., Kaul, R. D. and Warrington, D. M. 1964 *Proc. Phys. Soc.* **84**, 176.
Konstantinov, O. V. and Perel', V. I. 1963 *Soviet Phys. JETP* **45**, 279.
Skalinski, T. and Rosinski, K. 1965 *J. Appl. Math. Phys.* **16**, 15.

C. For monochromatic light of frequency $k \neq k'$, equation (30) on page 150 becomes

$$\frac{8\pi R}{c} \left(\frac{1}{\Gamma + ix} \right) \left[\frac{1}{\frac{1}{2}\Gamma + i(k - k')} + \frac{1}{\frac{1}{2}\Gamma - i(k - k' - x)} \right]$$

$$\times \exp\{-i(m - m' - n + n')\omega_0 t\}.$$

From: *Phys. Rev.* **121**, 508–512 (1961)   161

Interference Effects in the Resonance Fluorescence of "Crossed" Excited Atomic States*

P. A. Franken†

The Harrison M. Randall Laboratory of Physics, The University of Michigan, Ann Arbor, Michigan

(Received September 12, 1960)

The recent spectroscopic method developed by Colegrove, Franken, Lewis, and Sands exploits interference effects which occur in the resonance fluorescence of atoms exhibiting pairs of "crossed" excited states. Some of the theoretical features of the technique are discussed in terms of the formalism developed by Breit from which the salient features of the observed lineshapes can be readily deduced. Alternative derivations of the Breit formula are given together with a discussion of the nature and representation of the requisite resonance radiation.

INTRODUCTION

A SPECTROSCOPIC method which exploits interference effects in the resonance scattering from "crossed" excited atomic states has recently been developed[1] and applied to the measurement of helium $2\,^3P$ fine structure[1] and the hyperfine structure of the $^3P_1$ state of Hg^{199}.[2] It is the purpose of this report to discuss some of the theoretical features of the technique with particular attention to lineshape problems and the nature of the requisite resonance radiation.

I. A BRIEF DESCRIPTION OF THE METHOD AND RELATED PHENOMENA

Consider an atom (Fig. 1) having one or more ground-state Zeeman levels a and a group of excited states containing, among others not shown, the two levels b and c which are split in zero magnetic field due to fine or hyperfine interactions and which "cross" at some particular field. It is assumed that these excited states are connected to the ground state by an allowed electric dipole transition so that the phenomenon of resonance fluorescence can occur.

A vapor of these atoms is placed in a cell situated in the apparatus shown in Fig. 2. A spectroscopic lamp projects a beam of the necessary resonance radiation through the cell which is situated in a homogeneous and variable magnetic field. A photodetector is placed as shown and can be monitored by a cathode-ray oscilloscope (CRO).

If the magnetic field is now set at that value where the two levels b and c cross, it is found that more light is received by the detector as shown in the CRO insert of Fig. 2. (A decrease can also be observed depending on the atom, the light polarization if any, and the geometry.) The "width" of this effect is comparable to the natural linewidth of the excited states.

The gist of the phenomenon is discussed in reference 1 and will be summarized at this point. We are inter-

ested in writing the expression for the rate $R(\mathbf{f},\mathbf{g})$ at which photons of polarization $\mathbf{f}$ are absorbed and photons of polarization $\mathbf{g}$ are re-emitted by the atoms in the resonance fluorescence process. Assuming that the resonance radiation from the lamp is sufficiently broad, the expression for R when the levels b and c are completely resolved is given by

$$R_{\text{resolved}} \sim |f_{ab}g_{ba}|^2 + |f_{ac}g_{ca}|^2, \tag{1a}$$

where $f_{ab} = (a|\mathbf{f}\cdot\mathbf{r}|b)$, $g_{ba} = (b|\mathbf{g}\cdot\mathbf{r}|a)$, etc. The expression for R when the levels b and c are completely unresolved (crossed) is given by

$$R_{\text{crossed}} \sim |f_{ab}g_{ba} + f_{ac}g_{ca}|^2. \tag{1b}$$

The expressions (1a) and (1b) are identical if any of the matrix elements vanish, i.e., the interference effect vanishes unless the two levels are able to "share" photons of polarization $\mathbf{f}$ and $\mathbf{g}$. This is analogous to the classical phenomenon of double-slit interference patterns where it is said that the same photon can be shared by both slits. Furthermore, it is found that the total

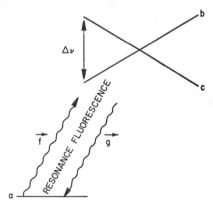

FIG. 1. Energy level diagram. The excited states b and c, among others not shown, are separated in zero magnetic field by the amount $\Delta\nu$ due to fine or hyperfine structure interactions and cross at some specific value of the field. In the resonance fluorescence process, photons of polarization $\mathbf{f}$ are absorbed and those of polarization $\mathbf{g}$ are re-emitted.

* This work was supported in part by the U. S. Atomic Energy Commission and the Alfred P. Sloan Foundation.

† Alfred P. Sloan Foundation Fellow.

[1] F. D. Colegrove, P. A. Franken, R. R. Lewis, and R. H. Sands, Phys. Rev. Letters **3**, 420 (1959).

[2] H. R. Hirsch, Bull. Am. Phys. Soc. **5**, 274 (1960).

absorption cross section for the resonance radiation is independent of whether the levels are crossed; the only effect of the crossing is to modify the angular distribution of the re-emitted radiation. The double-slit analogy is simply that the same amount of light (number of photons per second) goes through the slits whether they are close together or well resolved; the only effect produced when the slits are close (apart from possible geometric factors) is the modification of the distribution of light intensity on the display screen.

The interference phenomenon exhibited in this experiment on atoms is intimately related to the effects produced by degeneracy in the intermediate state of a gamma-gamma cascade in which angular correlation is studied.[3] Similar interference effects also play a predominant role in the "light beat" experiments of Series et al.[4] in which a radio-frequency modulation of the resonance fluorescence can be observed upon the application of specific radio-frequency magnetic fields to the absorbing atoms.

The exploitation of this phenomenon for the precision spectroscopy of excited atomic states[1,2] rests upon the fact that the magnetic field at which pairs of levels cross can be determined accurately and hence the zero-field splittings can be estimated, provided the field dependence of the levels is known. As a spectroscopic method the technique is analogous to the double-resonance method of Brossel et al.[5] in which changes in the angular distribution of resonance fluorescence are achieved by "mixing" two excited states together by the action of a radio-frequency magnetic field that satisfies the resonance condition for the energy separation. In the present method no radio-frequency field is required because the energy separation at crossing is zero and the "mixing" becomes simply an intimate part of the radiation process itself.

Finally, it should be noted that the interference phenomenon of the present method has already been

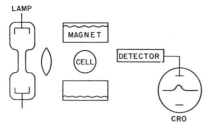

FIG. 2. Schematic diagram of the apparatus discussed in the text.

[3] See, for example, L. C. Biedenharn and M. E. Rose, Revs. Modern Phys. 25, 729 (1953).
[4] J. N. Dodd, W. N. Fox, G. W. Series, and M. J. Taylor, Proc. Phys. Soc. (London) 74, 789 (1959). The theory of these effects will be submitted shortly to Proc. Phys. Soc. by Dodd and Series. [G. W. Series (private communication)].
[5] J. Brossel and A. Kastler, Compt. rend. 229, 1213 (1949); and J. Brossel and F. Bitter, Phys. Rev. 86, 308 (1952).

studied in much detail for the case of zero or low magnetic fields where the several Zeeman levels in a typical excited state become degenerate, i.e., a special case of crossing. This zero-field crossing gives rise to changes in the polarization and angular dependence of the resonance fluorescence and is usually referred to as the Hanle effect.[6]

II. THE BREIT FORMULA

The expressions for R given in Eqs. 1(a) and 1(b) suffice for the calculation of many experimental parameters such as the magnitude of the interference effect, its directional sensitivity, polarization conditions for optimum sensitivity, etc.[7] However, these equations do not give any information about the interference other than at its extremes; i.e., at complete crossing and at complete separation of the excited states. The in-between region requires a more detailed treatment of the resonance fluorescence process that yields information about the lineshape as well as Eqs. (1) in appropriate limits.

A. Discussion of the Pulse Excitation

Breit[8] has derived an expression for the resonance fluorescence under pulse excitation for atoms exhibiting partial or complete degeneracy in the excited states. (A simple derivation of this formula is given in Appendix 1.) Consider a lamp containing atoms (called source atoms) of the same type as the atoms in the cell (called sample atoms). At $t=t_0$ a source atom is an excited state and the sample atom is in the ground state. The sample atoms will be assumed to have a decay rate, when excited, of Γ sec^{-1} (mean lifetime of $1/\Gamma$ seconds). The source atoms are assumed to have a decay rate of γ sec^{-1}. The pulse excitation process is realized if γ is allowed to become very large. That is, the source atom decays so abruptly that it emits light having a very broad range of spectral frequencies and the excitation of the sample atom occurs in a time very short compared with times characteristic of the fluorescence process. Most importantly, this type of excitation has the distinct characteristic of coherent excitation of the sample atom; i.e., if the light emitted from the source atom has a polarization such that two levels of the sample atom can be excited, then these levels are excited coherently with this one pulse even if the levels are completely resolved.

A more realistic model for a lamp does not exhibit

[6] See, for example, A. C. G. Mitchell and M. W. Zemansky, Resonance radiation and excited atoms (Cambridge University Press, New York, 1934), Chap. V.
[7] While preparing this manuscript the author has learned that M. E. Rose and R. Carovillano have prepared a more general formulation of the angular dependence of the interference effects and performed a detailed analysis of the interference effects to be expected in atomic hydrogen. This material will be published shortly [M. E. Rose and R. R. Lewis (private communication)].
[8] G. Breit, Revs. Modern Phys. 5, 91 (1933); see particularly pp. 117–125.

this pulse characteristic. Specifically, the lamp contains atoms having decay rates comparable to the decay rate of the sample atoms and the broad frequency spectrum of the lamp comes about because the emitting atoms exhibit a broad range of Doppler shifts. For this case two resolved excited states of the sample atom would not be excited coherently; i.e., these two excited states could not be excited with the photon emitted from one of the source atoms since that light could no longer have Fourier components available for both excitations. These two states could be excited coherently only if they were separated by less than approximately γ sec^{-1} or Γ sec^{-1}, whichever is larger. We might thus expect that the range in the excited state separation in which interference effects would be appreciable might be sensitive to the magnitude of the source-atom decay rate γ, and that therefore the Breit formula would only be an approximation to actual experimental conditions.

In order to examine this possibility we have generalized the calculation to include arbitrary decay rates in the source atoms, which calculation includes Breit's pulse limit, and find that the interference effects in the resonance fluorescence are actually independent of the decay rate. (This more general calculation is described in Appendix II.) It can be argued that this result could be anticipated from the fact that the density matrix describing weak radiation fields is independent of whether sharp wave packets at random times (pulses) or a spread of monochromatic waves of random phases are supposed.[9]

It is important to note, however, that for the situation of strong radiation fields (i.e., classical fields) one can construct experiments that do distinguish between these two models. The essential feature of the strong field is that there are enough photons present in particular modes to permit the simultaneous specification of phase and amplitude as, for example, in the case of a microwave cavity. In the present experiment, as in all experiments dealing with conventional sources, the light beam contains much less than one photon per mode in the appropriate frequency interval and must therefore be considered as a weak field.[10] The derivation of the Breit formula given in Appendix II does treat the radiation field calssically but nevertheless yields the correct weak-field result.

B. The Application of Breit's Formula to the Crossed-Level Technique

The Breit formula treats the general case of an atom having one or more ground-state levels m, m', etc., and a group of excited states μ, μ', etc., which may exhibit partial or complete degeneracy (crossings). The expression gives the rate $R(\mathbf{f},\mathbf{g})$ at which photons of polarization $\mathbf{f}$ are absorbed and photons of polarization $\mathbf{g}$ are re-emitted in the resonance fluorescence process:

$$R(\mathbf{f},\mathbf{g}) = c \sum_{\mu\mu'mm'} \frac{f_{\mu m} f_{m\mu'} g_{\mu'm'} g_{m'\mu}}{1 - 2\pi i \tau \nu(\mu,\mu')}, \qquad (2)$$

where $f_{\mu m} = (\mu|\mathbf{f}\cdot\mathbf{r}|m)$, etc.; τ is the mean lifetime of each excited state; $\nu(\mu,\mu') = (E_\mu - E_{\mu'})/h$; c is a parameter proportional to the intensity of the lamp, geometrical factors, etc.

For the case where the excited states are completely resolved, $2\pi\tau\nu(\mu,\mu')\gg1$ for all values of $\mu\neq\mu'$ and Eq. (2) reduces to

$$R(\mathbf{f},\mathbf{g}) = R_0 = c \sum_{\mu mm'} |f_{\mu m}|^2 |g_{\mu m'}|^2.$$

This is just the resonance fluorescence rate without any interference terms. Interference effects occur when two or more of the excited states are close enough together so that $2\pi\tau\nu(\mu,\mu')\lesssim1$.

In order to exhibit the features of this interference let us specialize to a system containing only one ground state, a, and two excited states b and c (Fig. 1). When the two excited states b and c are well resolved, then Eq. (2) becomes

$$R(\mathbf{f},\mathbf{g}) = R_0 = |f_{ab}|^2 |f_{ba}|^2 + |g_{ac}|^2 |g_{ca}|^2.$$

When the states b and c are "close," then Eq. (2) becomes

$$R(f,g) = R_0 + \frac{A}{1 - 2\pi i \tau \nu(b,c)} + \frac{A^*}{1 + 2\pi i \tau \nu(b,c)} \equiv R_0 + S, \quad (3)$$

where $A = f_{ba} f_{ac} g_{ca} g_{ab}$. For convenience the signal term

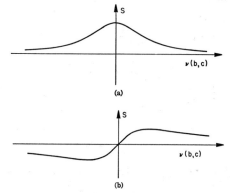

(a)

(b)

FIG. 3. The strength of the interference signal S [Eq. (4)] as a function of the excited state splitting $\nu(b,c)$. Figure 3(a) is the Lorentz lineshape which occurs when the matrix product A is real. Figure 3(b) is the lineshape which is found when A is pure imaginary.

[9] See, for example, R. H. Dicke and J. P. Wittke, *Introduction to Quantum Mechanics* (Addison Wesley Publishing Company, Reading, Massachusetts, 1960), pp. 336–337. I am indebted to R. H. Dicke, E. W. Johnston, and E. M. Purcell for several valuable discussions about this and related points.

[10] In a strong beam of resonance radiation the number of photons per mode in the appropriate frequency range is $\sim10^{-4}$. It is for this reason that the rate of absorption of resonance radiation per atom in such beams is some four orders of magnitude less than the rate of spontaneous emission.

S can be written

$$S=\frac{A+A^*}{1+4\pi^2\tau^2\nu^2(b,c)}+\frac{(A-A^*)2\pi i\tau\nu(b,c)}{1+4\pi^2\tau^2\nu^2(b,c)}. \quad (4)$$

For the case where the matrix product A is real, then S is just the well-known Lorentz lineshape [see Fig. 3(a)] with full half-width $\Delta\nu(b,c)=1/\pi\tau$. This width is just twice the natural width of each excited state.

For the case where the matrix product A is pure imaginary, S becomes

$$S=\frac{4\pi i A\tau\nu(b,c)}{1+4\pi^2\tau^2\nu^2(b,c)}. \quad (5)$$

This line shape is shown in Fig. 3(b). If the matrix product A is complex, then it is possible to have a mixture of the two pure forms shown in Fig. 3. The conditions for which A is real, imaginary, or complex depends on the direction and polarization of the incoming and outgoing beams of light. In general, all three cases can be realized experimentally.

ACKNOWLEDGMENTS

It is a pleasure to thank J. N. Dodd, R. R. Lewis, M. E. Rose, G. W. Series, and R. H. Sands for their very helpful contributions. I want particularly to acknowledge the enormous benefit of many discussions I enjoyed with Willis Lamb during the fall of 1959, and the many courtesies extended to me by the Clarendon Laboratory, Oxford.

APPENDIX 1. A SIMPLE DERIVATION OF THE BREIT FORMULA UNDER CONDITIONS OF PULSE EXCITATION

The sample atom is considered to have a set of ground states m, m', etc. and a set of excited states μ, μ', etc., which may exhibit partial or complete degeneracy. The sample atom will be exposed to a series of pulses of polarization f occuring at random times and far enough apart so that any process arising from the action of one pulse is finished before the arrival of the next. It is furthermore assumed that each pulse contains the Fourier components necessary for any of the possible absorptions from any ground state m to any excited state μ and that the duration of the pulse is short compared to the reciprocal of any of the frequency differences in the excited states. (These two conditions are clearly related.)

At the time $t=0$ the atom is assumed to be in some particular ground state m,[11] the energy of which, for convenience, is taken to be zero. Thus the wave function for the atom before the pulse is $\Psi_0=u_m$. At $t=0$ the atom is subjected to the pulse and the wave function

---

[11] This simplification is valid only for those experiments in which there is no preferred occurrence of specific configurations of the ground states m.

from that time on is given by

$$\Psi(t>0)=u_m+\sum_\mu f_{m\mu}u_\mu e^{-(i\omega_\mu+\frac{1}{2}\Gamma)t}. \quad (I,1)$$

The amplitude of the ground state m is still taken as unity because this is a first order calculation. The fact that the initial excited state amplitudes are given simply by the matrix elements $f_{m\mu}$ follows as a consequence of the brevity of the pulse. The subsequent radiation damping of the excited states is accounted for by the inclusion of the factor $\exp(-\frac{1}{2}\Gamma t)$. (The uninteresting constants of proportionality have been set equal to unity in this and in the following expressions.)

The instantaneous rate at which a photon of polarization g is emitted by the excited atom is given by

$$R(f,g,t)=\sum_m\sum_{m'}|(\Psi^*|g\cdot r|u_{m'})|^2$$

$$=\sum_{\mu\mu'mm'}f_{\mu m}f_{m\mu'}g_{\mu'm'}g_{m'\mu}e^{[2\pi i\nu(\mu,\mu')-\Gamma]t}, \quad (I,2)$$

where $2\pi\nu(\mu,\mu')=\omega_\mu-\omega_{\mu'}$ and the additional summation over m has been introduced because the initial ground state could have been any one of the set m.

If, now, the atom is subjected to N pulses (photons) per second, well separated in time, then the rate $R(f,g)$ at which photons of polarization f are absorbed and g are re-emitted is given by

$$R(f,g)=N\int_0^\infty R(f,g,t)dt$$

$$=N\sum_{\mu\mu'mm'}\frac{f_{\mu m}f_{m\mu'}g_{\mu'm'}g_{m'\mu}}{\Gamma-2\pi i\nu(\mu,\mu')}. \quad (I,3)$$

This expression is identical with the Breit formula, Eq. (2), since $\Gamma=1/\tau$.

APPENDIX II. THE DERIVATION OF THE BREIT FORMULA WITHOUT THE CONDITION OF PULSE EXCITATION

We shall follow the form of the derivation given in the preceding Appendix as much as possible. The decay constant of the source atoms γ and the decay constant of the sample atoms Γ will have arbitrary values. The source atoms are assumed to be excited and emit resonance radiation at random times (incoherently) and with random central frequencies (Doppler-broadened "white" light). Both of these assumptions are excellent for the lamp intensities usually employed in these experiments.

At $t=0$ we consider an excited source atom and a sample atom that is in a particular ground state $u_m(r)$,[11] the energy of which is taken to be zero. The state of the sample atom will be described at all times by

$$\Psi=u_m, \quad t<0$$

$$\Psi=\sum_\mu a_\mu(t)u_\mu+b_m(t)u_m, \quad t\geqslant0. \quad (II,1)$$

The sample atom experiences an electric field $\mathbf{E}$, for $t \geqslant 0$, due to the decay of the source atom:

$$\mathbf{E} = \mathbf{f}E_0 \cos\omega t e^{-\frac{1}{2}\gamma t}$$

$$= \mathbf{f}(E_0/2)e^{-i\omega t - \frac{1}{2}\gamma t},$$

where $\mathbf{f}$ is the polarization, ω is the central angular frequency of emission, and the rotating wave approximation has been employed.

The Hamiltonian is $\mathfrak{IC} = \mathfrak{IC}_0 + \mathfrak{IC}'$, where $\mathfrak{IC}_0$ is the complete Hamiltonian for the atom including the effects of all static electromagnetic fields and $\mathfrak{IC}' = e\mathbf{E} \cdot \mathbf{r}$.

The Schrödinger equation is

$$\dot{a}_\mu = -i\omega_\mu a_\mu + \frac{1}{i h}\sum_{\mu'}\mathfrak{IC}_{\mu\mu'}{}' a_{\mu'}(t) + \frac{1}{i h}\mathfrak{IC}_{\mu m}{}' b_m(t) - \tfrac{1}{2}\Gamma a_\mu,$$

where the term $-\frac{1}{2}\Gamma a_\mu$ has been added to account for the radiation damping of the excited states. The $\sum_{\mu'}$ term vanishes identically for all cases where the excited states have the same L value, and yields a negligible contribution otherwise. Since this is a first order calculation, we set $b_m(t) = 1$ for all times. Thus:

$$\dot{a}_\mu = B_\mu e^{-i\omega t - \frac{1}{2}\gamma t} - (\tfrac{1}{2}\Gamma + i\omega_\mu)a_\mu, \qquad \text{(II,2)}$$

where $B_\mu = (eE_0/2ih)(\mu|\mathbf{f}\cdot\mathbf{r}|m)$. Taking the boundary condition $a_\mu = 0$ at $t = 0$, the integration of (II,2) yields:

$$a_\mu(t) = B_\mu e^{-(\frac{1}{2}\Gamma + i\omega_\mu)t}\left[\frac{e^{i(\omega_\mu - \omega)t - \lambda t} - 1}{i(\omega_\mu - \omega) - \lambda}\right], \qquad \text{(II,3)}$$

where $\lambda = \frac{1}{2}\gamma - \frac{1}{2}\Gamma$.

The instantaneous rate at which a photon of polarization $\mathbf{g}$ is emitted by the excited atom is given by

$$R(\mathbf{f},\mathbf{g},t) = \sum_{m'}\left|\left(\sum_{\mu'} a_{\mu'}(t)u_{\mu'}|\mathbf{g}\cdot\mathbf{r}|u_{m'}\right)\right|^2. \qquad \text{(II,4)}$$

In order to find the rate $R(\mathbf{f},\mathbf{g})$ at which photons of polarization $\mathbf{f}$ are absorbed and $\mathbf{g}$ re-emitted for a "white" beam of incoming photons, we must first integrate (II,4) over t from 0 to ∞, then integrate ω from $-\infty$ to $+\infty$, and finally sum over all ground states m. It should be noted that the integration over time in this simple way is valid only for cases where the incoming light beam is weak enough so that each sample atom undergoes the entire resonance fluorescence process in a time short compared with the mean time between fluorescence events for this atom.[10] Combining (II,3) and (II,4) under the required integration yields:

$$R = \frac{e^2 E_0^2}{4\hbar^2}\sum_{\mu\mu'mm'} f_{m\mu'}f_{\mu m}g_{m'\mu}g_{\mu'm'}$$

$$\times \int_0^\infty dt \int_{-\infty}^\infty d\omega \frac{e^{-i\omega_{\mu\mu'}t - \Gamma t}}{[(\omega_\mu - \omega) + i\lambda][(\omega_{\mu'} - \omega) - i\lambda]}$$

$$\times [e^{+i\omega_{\mu\mu'} - 2\lambda t} - e^{i(\omega_\mu - \omega)t - \lambda t} - e^{-i(\omega_{\mu'} - \omega)t - \lambda t} + 1]. \qquad \text{(II,5)}$$

The integral over ω yields readily to contour integration owing to the simple singularities at $\omega_\mu + i\lambda$ and $\omega_{\mu'} - i\lambda$, and the integration over time is straightforward. The result is:

$$R(f,g,t) = \left(\frac{e^2 E_0^2}{4\hbar^2}\right)\left(\frac{2\pi}{\gamma}\right)\sum_{\mu\mu'mm'}\frac{f_{m\mu'}f_{\mu m}g_{m'\mu}g_{\mu'm'}}{\Gamma - i\omega(\mu,\mu')}. \qquad \text{(II,6)}$$

This expression is identical with the Breit formula, Eq. (2), since $\Gamma = 1/\tau$ and $\omega(\mu,\mu') = 2\pi\nu(\mu,\mu')$. The factor $2\pi/\gamma$ actually plays no role since the normalization over the light pulse (one photon condition) requires E_0^2/γ to be independent of γ.

Optical Detection of Level Crossing in the $(5s5p)$ $^3P_1$ State of Cd^{111} and Cd^{113}[†]

P. Thaddeus and R. Novick[*]

Columbia Radiation Laboratory, Columbia University, New York, New York

(Received November 28, 1961; revised manuscript received February 27, 1962)

The magnetic field at which crossing occurs for the $|F,m_F\rangle = |\frac{3}{2},\frac{3}{2}\rangle$ and $|\frac{1}{2},-\frac{1}{2}\rangle$ hyperfine levels of the $(5s5p)$ $^3P_1$ state of Cd^{111} and Cd^{113} has been measured to high precision by observing the change in intensity at an angle of 90° of the resonance fluorescence of the 3261 Å intercombination line. The measured crossing fields, in units of the nuclear magnetic resonance frequency of protons in mineral oil, are $H_c{}^{111} = 8363.408(30)$ kc/sec, $H_c{}^{113} = 8748.734(20)$ kc/sec. Using these results and the known values of the $(5s5p)$ $^3P_1$ hyperfine interval for the two isotopes, we find that the Lánde g_J factor for this state is $g_J{}^{111} = \frac{3}{2} - 160(9) \times 10^{-6}$, $g_J{}^{113} = \frac{3}{2} - 146(9) \times 10^{-6}$. These results include corrections for second-order interaction with the adjacent fine-structure levels of the $5s5p$ configuration.

INTRODUCTION

THE crossing of levels in a magnetic field may be detected by a change in the angular distribution of resonance fluorescence, as shown by Colegrove, Franken, Lewis, and Sands.[1] Using the 1-μ transition between the 2 $^3S_1$ and the 2 $^3P_{0,1,2}$ states of helium, they have succeeded in observing the crossing of several of the Zeeman components of the 2 ^3P states, and have determined the fine structure to high precision.

The level-crossing technique has been extended by Hirsch,[2] and by Dodd[3,4] to the hyperfine levels of the $(6s6p)$ $^3P_1$ state of Hg^{199} and Hg^{201}, while theoretical studies of the effect have been published by Franken,[5] and Rose and Carovillano,[6] following the early work of Breit[7] on resonance fluorescence with partial or complete degeneracy in the excited state. Kibble and Series[8] have studied the line shape of the change in resonance fluorescence at zero magnetic field for the even isotopes of mercury.

As a spectroscopic technique the level-crossing method offers the advantages of experimental simplicity and high resolution. A change in resonance fluorescence is experienced only when the two excited-state levels are separated by an energy of the order of their natural width, typically a small fraction of the Doppler width of the optical transition. This is a resolution usually associated with an optical double-resonance experiment, and in this respect the level-crossing effect may be regarded as a special case of double resonance for which the radio frequency is zero.

Particularly well suited to experiments of this kind are hyperfine levels of the lowest lying $^3P_1$ states of atoms with a $^1S_0$ ground state configuration, such as the alkaline earths, the rare gases, and the group II B metals zinc, cadmium, and mercury. For these elements the intercombination line lies in the ultraviolet, and the natural lifetime of the $^3P_1$ state is usually much longer than that of the $^1P_1$ state of the same configuration due to the close approximation to Russell-Saunders coupling. The hyperfine intervals are typically of the order of a few thousand Mc/sec, and crossings of various Zeeman components will occur in fields of a few kilogauss or less. Mercury, cadmium, and zinc all possess at least one odd isotope, and are especially convenient since they (a) have intercombination lines which do not lie too deeply in the ultraviolet, (b) have the required vapor pressures for maximum fluorescent scattering at much lower temperatures than the alkaline earths, and (c) are much less chemically active than these elements, allowing easy construction of resonance lamps and scattering cells.

For cadmium the lifetime of the $(5s5p)$ $^3P_1$ state is 2.43×10^{-6} sec, and the intercombination line falls at a wavelength of 3261 Å. The naturally occurring odd isotopes Cd^{111} and Cd^{113} each have an abundance of about 12%, and a nuclear spin of $\frac{1}{2}$. The hyperfine interval has been measured for either isotope in a double-resonance experiment.[9] Relevant atomic con-

TABLE I. Atomic constants for Cd^{111} and Cd^{113}.

Isotope	Cd^{111}	Cd^{113}
Fractional abundance	12.75%	12.26%
I	$\frac{1}{2}$	$\frac{1}{2}$
g_I [a]	$+64.80(1) \times 10^{-5}$	$+67.78(1) \times 10^{-5}$
$\tau(^1P_1)$ [b]	$1.59(8) \times 10^{-9}$ sec	$1.59(8) \times 10^{-9}$ sec
$\tau(^3P_1)$ [b,c]	$2.43(10) \times 10^{-6}$ sec	$2.43(10) \times 10^{-6}$ sec
$\Delta\nu(^3P_1)$ [d]	6185.72(2) Mc/sec	6470.79(2) Mc/sec
$\Delta\nu(^3P_2)$ [e]	8232.341(2) Mc/sec	8611.586(4) Mc/sec

[a] W. G. Proctor and F. C. Yu, Phys. Rev. **76**, 1728 (1949). Throughout we have followed the convention that the electron g factor is positive.
[b] A. Lurio and R. Novick (to be published).
[c] The value quoted was furnished by F. Byron and M. N. McDermott (private communication).
[d] See reference 9.
[e] W. Faust, M. N. McDermott, and W. Lichten, Phys. Rev. **120**, 469 (1960).

[9] R. F. Lacey (private communication). Preliminary results have appeared in R. F. Lacey, Ph.D. thesis, Massachusetts Institute of Technology, 1959 (unpublished).

† Work supported in part by a contract with the U. S. Air Force monitored by the Air Force Office of Scientific Research, and in part by a Joint Services Contract with the U. S. Army Signal Corps, the Office of Naval Research, and the Air Force Office of Scientific Research.
* Alfred P. Sloan Foundation Fellow.

[1] F. D. Colegrove, P. A. Franken, R. R. Lewis, and R. H. Sands, Phys. Rev. Letters **3**, 420 (1959).
[2] H. R. Hirsch, Bull. Am. Phys. Soc. **5**, 274 (1960).
[3] J. N. Dodd, Proc. Phys. Soc. (London) **77**, 669 (1961).
[4] J. N. Dodd, Proc. Phys. Soc. (London) **78**, 65 (1961).
[5] P. A. Franken, Phys. Rev. **121**, 508 (1961).
[6] M. E. Rose and R. L. Carovillano, Phys. Rev. **122**, 1185 (1961).
[7] G. Breit, Revs. Modern Phys. **5**, 91 (1933).
[8] B. P. Kibble and G. W. Series, Proc. Phys. Soc. (London) **78**, 70 (1961).

TABLE II. The dipole moment matrix connecting the $^3P_1$ state with the $^1S_0$ ground state, evaluated at the crossing point field $H_c \approx -A\,(^3P_1)/\mu_0 g_J$, where g_J is taken as $\frac{2}{3}$. Arbitrary units are used, and states are specified by their low-field quantum numbers.

		$^3P_1$					
F, m_F		$\frac{3}{2},\frac{3}{2}$	$\frac{3}{2},\frac{1}{2}$	$\frac{3}{2},-\frac{1}{2}$	$\frac{3}{2},-\frac{3}{2}$	$\frac{1}{2},\frac{1}{2}$	$\frac{1}{2},-\frac{1}{2}$
$^1S_0$	$\frac{1}{2},\frac{1}{2}$	$-(1/2)^{\frac{1}{2}}(\mathbf{i}+i\mathbf{j})$	$0.9291\mathbf{k}$	$(1/3)^{\frac{1}{2}}(\mathbf{i}-i\mathbf{j})$	0	$0.3691\mathbf{k}$	$(1/6)^{\frac{1}{2}}(\mathbf{i}-i\mathbf{j})$
	$\frac{1}{2},-\frac{1}{2}$	0	$-0.2610(\mathbf{i}+i\mathbf{j})$	$(1/3)^{\frac{1}{2}}\mathbf{k}$	$(1/2)^{\frac{1}{2}}(\mathbf{i}-i\mathbf{j})$	$0.6572(\mathbf{i}+i\mathbf{j})$	$-(2/3)^{\frac{1}{2}}\mathbf{k}$

stants are listed in Table I, while the Zeeman effect of the $^3P_1$ state is shown in Fig. 1. The crossing of the $|F,m_F\rangle = |\frac{3}{2},\frac{3}{2}\rangle$ and $|\frac{1}{2},-\frac{1}{2}\rangle$ levels satisfies, as will be shown in the next section, the requirements of a level-crossing experiment.

THEORY

For transitions from a single ground state $|a\rangle$ to two excited states $|b\rangle$ and $|c\rangle$, which are well separated in energy, Franken[5] obtains for the rate $R(\mathbf{f},\mathbf{g})$, in arbitrary units, at which photons of incoming polarization $\mathbf{f}$ and outgoing polarization $\mathbf{g}$ are scattered:

$$R(\mathbf{f},\mathbf{g}) = R_0 = |f_{ab}|^2|g_{ba}|^2 + |f_{ac}|^2|g_{ca}|^2, \quad (1)$$

where $f_{ab} = \langle a|\mathbf{f}\cdot\mathbf{r}|b\rangle$, etc.

In the vicinity of crossing

$$R(\mathbf{f},\mathbf{g}) = R_0 + \frac{A+A^*}{1+4\pi^2\tau^2\nu^2(b,c)} + \frac{(A-A^*)2\pi i\tau\nu(b,c)}{1+4\pi^2\tau^2\nu^2(b,c)}, \quad (2)$$

where $A = f_{ba}f_{ac}g_{ca}g_{ab}$, τ is the mean lifetime of each excited state, and $\nu(b,c) = (E_b - E_c)/h$.

When A is real, the change in resonance fluorescence S produced by the crossing has a Lorentzian line shape with a full half-width $\Delta\nu(b,c) = 1/\pi\tau$, while when A is pure imaginary the effect has a dispersion-type line shape, and in the general case of A complex, a mixture of these two profiles.

It is evident that crossing of Zeeman levels of different hyperfine states occurs when the Zeeman energy is comparable to the hyperfine energy, so that the mixing of states of different F, but the same m_F may be considerable. Using the hyperfine Hamiltonian,

$$\mathcal{H} = A\,(^3P_1)\mathbf{I}\cdot\mathbf{J} + g_J\mu_0 J_z H + g_I\mu_0 I_z H, \quad (3)$$

for the $^3P_1$ state of Cd^{111} and Cd^{113}, the crossing of the levels $|b\rangle$ and $|c\rangle$ (Fig. 1) may be shown to take place in a field H_c such that

$$g_J = -A\,(^3P_1)/\mu_0 H_c - \tfrac{1}{2}g_I. \quad (4)$$

In terms of the low-field states $|F,m_F\rangle$, $|c\rangle = |\frac{3}{2},\frac{3}{2}\rangle$ for all field values, while the composition of $|b\rangle$ at the crossing field H_c is, if we neglect the small contribution of g_I in Eq. (4),

$$|b\rangle = (2\sqrt{2}/3)|\tfrac{1}{2},-\tfrac{1}{2}\rangle - \tfrac{1}{3}|\tfrac{3}{2},-\tfrac{1}{2}\rangle. \quad (5)$$

The dipole-moment matrix in this intermediate representation connecting the various hyperfine levels of the

$^3P_1$ state with the $^1S_0$ ground state of the atom is given in Table II. From this matrix we can derive (a) the most convenient geometrical arrangement for the experiment, (b) the line shape as a function of the angle between the incoming and scattered light, and (c) the magnitude of the effect.

(a) Since neither states $|b\rangle$ nor $|c\rangle$ are connected to the ground state $|a\rangle = |^1S_0,\frac{1}{2},\frac{1}{2}\rangle$ by a photon polarized along the direction of the magnetic field (z axis), we are free, without loss of generality, to design the experiment with the incoming and scattered photons polarized and propagating in the transverse (xy) plane. The outgoing photon is then specified uniquely by the angle θ between its direction of polarization and the direction of polarization of the incident photon (which we will take as the x axis).

(b) The matrix elements of $\mathbf{f}$ and $\mathbf{g}$ then become, in the units of Table II,

$$f_{ab} = (1/6)^{\frac{1}{2}}, \quad g_{ab} = (1/6)^{\frac{1}{2}}(\cos\theta - i\sin\theta),$$
$$f_{ac} = -(1/2)^{\frac{1}{2}}, \quad g_{ac} = -(1/2)^{\frac{1}{2}}(\cos\theta + i\sin\theta), \quad (6)$$

and

$$A = (1/12)[\cos(2\theta) - i\sin(2\theta)]. \quad (6a)$$

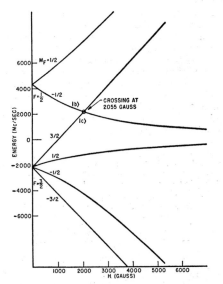

FIG. 1. Zeeman effect of the hyperfine structure of the $(5s5p)\,^3P_1$ state of Cd^{113}. The crossing point for Cd^{111} occurs near 1964 gauss.

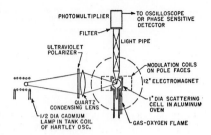

FIG. 2. Schematic illustration of the experimental apparatus.

Thus at $\theta = 0$, $90°$ we expect a pure Lorentzian, while at $\theta = 45°$ a pure dispersion-type line shape. For the line-width at $90°$,

$$\Delta H = (dH/d\nu(b,c))_{H_e}(1/\pi\tau)$$
$$= 45 \text{ mgauss, in the present case.}$$

An idea of the sharpness of the effect may be obtained using Eq. (4):

$$\Delta H/H = 45 \text{ mgauss} \times \mu_0 g_J/A(^3P_1) \approx 1/20\,000.$$

(c) Assuming that the scattering angle is $90°$, and that the light from the resonance lamp used has a line-width much larger than the hyperfine structure, the fractional change in the fluorescence at the crossing point is, for a single isotope, and considering all possible hyperfine transitions from the ground to the excited state for an incident x and scattered y or z photon,

$$S/R_0' = (A+A^*)/R_0' = 2A/R_0', \tag{7}$$

where, from Table II,

$$R_0' = \sum_{m,m',m''} |f_{mm'}|^2 |g_{m'm''}|^2 = 7/6,$$

giving

$$S/R_0' = 1/7. \tag{7a}$$

Besides being quite sharp, the crossing-point effect is seen to be relatively large.

DESCRIPTION OF THE EXPERIMENT

A schematic illustration of the experiment is shown in Fig. 2. Light from an electrodeless rf cadmium resonance lamp was passed through an ultraviolet polarizer, and focussed by a quartz lens onto a scattering cell which lay between the poles of a 12-in. electromagnet. 3261 Å light scattered at right angles was observed using a DuMont K 1306 ultraviolet photomultiplier tube. A Schott UG-11 filter effectively excluded other lines produced by the lamp, in particular, the 2288 Å, $^1P_1-{}^1S_0$ resonance transition, which is strongly scattered by the atomic vapor. To remove the photomultiplier from the magnetic field without sacrificing solid angle, a light pipe was used consisting of three feet of glass tubing aluminized on the inside.

The lamps used during this experiment gave about a watt of power (over 4π solid angle) at 3261 Å without self reversal. They consisted of a small sphere of quartz about $\frac{1}{2}$ in. in diameter, which had been baked at 1000°C for about half a day, and purged using an intense argon discharge for several hours, before being loaded with a small quantity of distilled cadmium, and about 1 mm Hg of spectroscopically pure argon. A lamp prepared in this way was found to run for many hours before the walls were discolored, or the discharge quenched by impurities driven from the walls. The lamp was excited by placing it within the tank coil of a strongly driven Hartley oscillator which operated in the region of 30 Mc/sec. Optimum lamp output was found to depend rather critically on the oscillator level.

The two scattering cells used were about an inch in diameter, and were prepared like the lamps, but were sealed off, without the addition of argon, at a pressure of typically 10^{-7} mm Hg. They had a thin tubular extension about 2 in. long at the bottom which was maintained at a slightly lower temperature than the rest of the cell, and determined the cadmium vapor pressure. The cell could be heated to at least 400°C by a single gas-oxygen flame which played on the outside of the oven. Temperature measurements were made with a thermocouple near the top of the cell, and do not therefore accurately reflect the true temperature of the cadmium reservoir.

To reduce instrumental scattering, the cell and oven were thoroughly blackened with a smoky acetylene flame, and small entrance and exit windows wiped on the quartz surfaces.

The photomultiplier current as a function of temperature for a magnetic field near 2000 gauss is shown in Fig. 3. It can be seen that instrumental scattering was small compared to fluorescent scattering above 200°C, while above 300°C the vapor pressure was so great that multiple scattering reduced the light reaching the photomultiplier.

This preliminary measurement of fluorescence allowed an estimate, on the basis of shot noise in the photomultiplier, to be made of the expected signal-to-noise

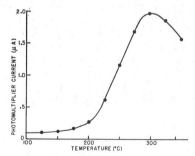

FIG. 3. Scattered power at an angle of $90°$ as a function of the cell temperature for a magnetic field near 2000 gauss.

ratio of the crossing effect. Using Eq. (7a),

$$\text{signal/noise} = (f/7)(i/2eGB)^{\frac{1}{2}} \approx 4, \qquad (8)$$

where e is the electronic charge, $f \approx 0.12$ is the fractional isotopic abundance, $G \approx 7 \times 10^4$ is the photomultiplier gain, $B \approx 1000$ cps is the approximate detector bandwidth for the oscilloscope display used, and $i \approx 1.7 \times 10^{-6}$ amp from Fig. 3.

EXPERIMENTAL RESULTS

The signal strength of the observed crossings, as shown in Fig. 4, agreed closely with the estimate given by Eq. (8). The line width is about twice that expected on the basis of the lifetime of the $^3P_1$ state, due presumably to field inhomogeneities over the sample. Field modulation at 30 cps was provided by rectangular coils attached to the magnet pole faces. In Fig. 5 are shown the signals obtained with narrow-band, phase-sensitive detection at the same modulation frequency, with an effective detector bandwidth of less than 1 cps, and at various scattering angles.

Measurements of the crossing field to an accuracy of better than one part in 10^5 were made with a small mineral-oil nuclear-magnetic-resonance probe, placed as close to the oven as possible, the proton resonance pip being superimposed on the crossing signal using a dual-beam oscilloscope, and the nuclear resonance oscillator frequency being read on a Hewlett-Packard Model 524C direct-reading frequency counter. To measure the slight differential field, of the order of one part in 10^4,

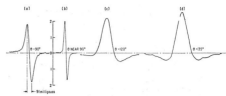

FIG. 5. Recorder traces of the crossing point effect for Cd[113], using phase-sensitive detection at 30 cps, with time constants of about 1 sec. The signal shown is the derivative of the true line shape, providing the field modulation is sufficiently small. In (a) the incoming and scattered light cones have been adjusted to give an effective scattering angle of 90°, and the upper and lower peaks are of equal size, while in (b) the lower half of the incoming light cone has been blocked out to give an effective scattering angle greater than 90°, with a consequent slight admixture of the dispersion-type line shape, and an asymmetry of the observed derivative. In (c) the scattering angle is 120° and in (d) 135°, where the signal is the derivative of a pure dispersion-type curve. The various apparent linewidths shown are due to different field-sweep rates.

between the probe and the scattering cell, a second, larger mineral-oil probe was constructed that approximated the cell in size, and could be placed accurately in the cell position. This was driven by a second oscillator, the two nuclear-resonance pips then being superimposed on the dual-beam oscilloscope, and the beat frequency measured by the counter. This scheme was quite flexible and had the virtue that no inaccuracies due to drifts in the magnet current, typically of the order of a part in 10^5 over a few seconds, were introduced.

The crossing was measured using the relatively weak signals obtained with oscilloscope display, rather than the strong narrow-band detector signals, primarily to avoid errors due to these long-term field fluctuations. Prior to a run, however, to ensure that the effective angle was exactly 90° and no admixture of the dispersion-type profile shifted the signal peak, the angles were adjusted so that the derivative curve in Fig. 5(a)

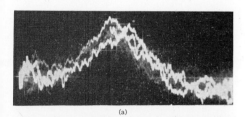

(a)

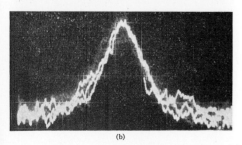

(b)

FIG. 4. Oscilloscope traces of the crossing point effect for (a) Cd[111] and (b) Cd[113], using 30-cps field modulation. The linewidth in either case is about 125 mgauss. The Cd[113] crossing point was consistently observed to be about twice as strong as that for Cd[111], due presumably to the isotope shift of the $^3P_1-^1S_0$ transition, and greater lamp output at the exact Cd[113] wavelength.

TABLE III. The measured values of the crossing-point fields in units of the nuclear magnetic resonance frequency of protons in mineral oil. To reduce systematic errors, following run II the large proton probe was dismantled and again assembled to approximate the cell position. The uncertainties given for each run are standard deviations, while the uncertainty in the final averages includes an estimated contribution of 15 cps for possible systematic errors.[a]

	Cd[111]		Cd[113]	
	Crossing field (kc/sec)	Number of readings	Crossing field (kc/sec)	Number of readings
Run I	8363.440(9)	10	8748.725(15)	18
	8363.384(11)	10	8748.722(11)	10
			8748.725(8)	10
Run II	8363.379(12)	10	8748.748(14)	10
			8748.741(10)	10
Run III	8363.427(7)	16	8748.730(9)	8
	8363.409(8)	8	8748.746(5)	16
Average	8363.408(30)		8748.734(20)	

[a] Preliminary results have appeared in Bull. Am. Phys. Soc. 6, 74 (1961) 5, 411 (1960).

TABLE IV. The matrix elements of the hyperfine Hamiltonian including second-order corrections relevant to the crossing of the levels $|b\rangle$ and $|c\rangle$, in the representation $|F,m_F\rangle$.

$$\langle \tfrac{3}{2},\tfrac{3}{2}|\mathcal{3C}|\tfrac{3}{2},\tfrac{3}{2}\rangle = \tfrac{1}{2}A(^3P_1)+(g_J+\tfrac{1}{2}g_I)\mu_0 H -\frac{\alpha^2}{4}\frac{\mu_0^2 H^2}{\delta_2}-\frac{\sqrt{3}\alpha}{8}\left[c_1 a_s-\left(c_1+c_2-\frac{5\sqrt{2}\xi}{8}\right)a_{\frac{1}{2}}\right]\frac{\mu_0 H}{\delta_2}$$

$$-\frac{\alpha^2\beta^2}{4}\frac{\mu_0^2 H^2}{\delta_1}+\frac{\alpha\beta}{8}\left[-3c_1 c_2 a_s+5\left(c_1 c_2+\frac{c_1^2-c_2^2}{4\sqrt{2}}\xi\right)a_{\frac{1}{2}}-2c_1 c_2 a_{\frac{1}{2}}\right]\frac{\mu_0 H}{\delta_1}$$

$$\langle \tfrac{3}{2},-\tfrac{1}{2}|\mathcal{3C}|\tfrac{3}{2},-\tfrac{1}{2}\rangle = \tfrac{1}{2}A(^3P_1)-(\tfrac{1}{3}g_J+\tfrac{1}{6}g_I)\mu_0 H +\frac{4\alpha^2}{9}\frac{\mu_0^2 H^2}{\delta_0}-\frac{11\alpha^2}{36}\frac{\mu_0^2 H^2}{\delta_2}+\frac{\sqrt{3}\alpha}{24}\left[c_1 a_s-\left(c_1+c_2-\frac{5\sqrt{2}\xi}{8}\right)a_{\frac{1}{2}}\right]\frac{\mu_0 H}{\delta_2}$$

$$-\frac{\alpha^2\beta^2}{12}\frac{\mu_0^2 H^2}{\delta_1}-\frac{\alpha\beta}{24}\left[-3c_1 c_2 a_s+5\left(c_1 c_2+\frac{c_1^2-c_2^2}{4\sqrt{2}}\xi\right)a_{\frac{1}{2}}-2c_1 c_2 a_{\frac{1}{2}}\right]\frac{\mu_0 H}{\delta_1}$$

$$\langle \tfrac{1}{2},-\tfrac{1}{2}|\mathcal{3C}|\tfrac{1}{2},-\tfrac{1}{2}\rangle = -A(^3P_1)-(\tfrac{2}{3}g_J-\tfrac{1}{6}g_I)\mu_0 H +\frac{2\alpha^2}{9}\frac{\mu_0^2 H^2}{\delta_0}-\frac{\alpha}{(6)^{\frac{1}{4}}}\left[c_2(a_s-a_{\frac{1}{2}})-c_1\frac{5\sqrt{2}\xi}{8}a_{\frac{1}{2}}\right]\frac{\mu_0 H}{\delta_0}-\frac{5\alpha^2}{18}\frac{\mu_0^2 H^2}{\delta_2}$$

$$-\frac{\alpha^2\beta^2}{6}\frac{\mu_0^2 H^2}{\delta_1}+\frac{\alpha\beta}{6}\left[-3c_1 c_2 a_s+5\left(c_1 c_2+\frac{c_1^2-c_2^2}{4\sqrt{2}}\xi\right)a_{\frac{1}{2}}-2c_1 c_2 a_{\frac{1}{2}}\right]\frac{\mu_0 H}{\delta_1}$$

$$\langle \tfrac{3}{2},-\tfrac{1}{2}|\mathcal{3C}|\tfrac{1}{2},-\tfrac{1}{2}\rangle = -\frac{\sqrt{2}}{3}(g_J-g_I)\mu_0 H -\frac{2\sqrt{2}\alpha^2}{9}\frac{\mu_0^2 H^2}{\delta_0}+\frac{\sqrt{3}\alpha}{6}\left[c_2(a_s-a_{\frac{1}{2}})-c_1\frac{5\sqrt{2}\xi}{8}a_{\frac{1}{2}}\right]\frac{\mu_0 H}{\delta_0}+\frac{\sqrt{2}\alpha^2}{36}\frac{\mu_0^2 H^2}{\delta_2}$$

$$-\frac{5\alpha}{8(6)^{\frac{1}{4}}}\left[c_1 a_s-\left(c_1+c_2-\frac{5\sqrt{2}\xi}{8}\right)a_{\frac{1}{2}}\right]\frac{\mu_0 H}{\delta_2}-\frac{\sqrt{2}\alpha^2\beta^2}{12}\frac{\mu_0^2 H^2}{\delta_1}$$

$$+\frac{\sqrt{2}\alpha\beta}{48}\left[-3c_1 c_2 a_s+5\left(c_1 c_2+\frac{c_1^2-c_2^2}{4\sqrt{2}}\xi\right)a_{\frac{1}{2}}-2c_1 c_2 a_{\frac{1}{2}}\right]\frac{\mu_0 H}{\delta_1}$$

was exactly symmetrical, and the signal a pure Lorentzian. The results of the crossing field measurements are summarized in Table III.

SECOND-ORDER CORRECTIONS TO g_J

Due to the high precision with which the $^3P_1$ hyperfine interval is known for both Cd[111] and Cd[113] (Table I), the primary value of the present experiment lies in a determination for this state of g_J to comparable accuracy. Equation (4) for g_J, however, does not take into account terms in the hyperfine and Zeeman energies off-diagonal in J, which are expected to contribute to g_J corrections of the order of the ratio of the hyperfine to fine structure energies, or about one part in 10^4, more than ten times that produced by the uncertainty in H_c. For mercury, Dodd[3] has derived an expression for the corrections due to the Zeeman terms off-diagonal in J, but has neglected similar terms in the hyperfine interaction which are of the same magnitude.

Our procedure for calculating these terms may be summed up as follows[10]: We have evaluated the hyperfine and Zeeman interactions for the p and s valance electrons in a representation $|j_1 j_2 J m_J\rangle$ following the relativistic treatment of Schwartz.[11,12] This Hamiltonian

involves four hyperfine constants, a_s, $a_{\frac{3}{2}}$, $a_{\frac{1}{2}}$, and ξ, in his notation. The ratio $a_{\frac{3}{2}}/a_{\frac{1}{2}}$, however, reduces to the ratio of radial integrals of the solution of the single particle Dirac equation, and is calculated by Schwartz[11] for an $l=1$ electron. For cadmium we obtain $a_{\frac{3}{2}}=6.42a_{\frac{1}{2}}$. ξ is a

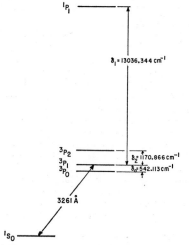

FIG. 6. Fine structure of the $(5s5p)$ cadmium configuration.

[10] A. Lurio, R. Novick, and M. Mandel, this issue [Phys. Rev. 126, 1758 (1961)].
[11] C. Schwartz, Phys. Rev. 97, 380 (1955).
[12] C. Schwartz, Phys. Rev. 105, 173 (1957).

TABLE V. The hyperfine coupling constants and second-order correction terms, calculated from Eq. (12) and the lifetime and hyperfine intervals given in Table I.

Isotope	Cd^{111}	Cd^{113}
a_s (kMc/sec)	$-12.354(33)$	$-12.923(35)$
$a_{\frac{1}{2}}$ (kMc/sec)	$-1.752(71)$	$-1.833(75)$
$a_{\frac{3}{2}}$ (kMc/sec)	$-0.273(11)$	$-0.285(12)$
$+[(3)^{\frac{1}{2}}\alpha/6]\{c_1 a_s-[c_1+c_2(5\sqrt{2}\xi/8)]a_{\frac{1}{2}}\}(1/\delta_2)$	$-52.0(3)\times10^{-6}$	$-54.4(3)\times10^{-6}$
$+(\alpha^2\mu_0 H_c/24)[(8/\delta_0)-(1/\delta_2)]$	$+53.0(1)\times10^{-6}$	$+55.5(1)\times10^{-6}$
$-[(6)^{\frac{1}{2}}\alpha/6][c_2(a_s-a_{\frac{1}{2}})-c_1(5\sqrt{2}\xi/8)a_{\frac{1}{2}}](1/\delta_0)$	$+220.4(20)\times10^{-6}$	$+230.5(20)\times10^{-6}$
Total correction	$+221.4(24)\times10^{-6}$	$+231.6(24)\times10^{-6}$

second-order correction of the order of unity, estimated to be

$$\xi=+[1+3\alpha^2 Z^2/2l(l+1)n^*]^{\frac{1}{2}}G/F_{\frac{3}{2}}, \quad (9)$$

where n^* is the effective quantum number of the $^3P_1$ state, and the relativistic correction factors G and $F_{\frac{3}{2}}$ for an $l=1$ electron are also given in Fig. 1 of reference 11, and in Kopfermann.[13] Only two independent hyperfine constants remain, which ultimately are determined from the known $^3P_2$ and $^3P_1$ hyperfine intervals.

The diagonalization of this Hamiltonian is most conveniently accomplished in two operations. Initially, a transformation is made from the jj coupling scheme into the nearly LS representation which applies to the fine structure of the $5s5p$ configuration, shown in Fig. 6. As is well known, the fine-structure intervals are not a reliable indication of the exact degree of intermediate coupling due to spin-spin, spin-other-orbit, etc. fine-structure interactions in addition to the spin-orbit interaction mainly responsible for the breakdown of LS coupling.[14] The lifetimes of the $^1P_1$ and $^3P_1$ states are reasonably well known for cadmium, however (Table I), and give a direct measure of the mixture of the two states. If we write for the nominally $^3P_1$ state

$$\psi=\alpha|^3P_1\rangle+\beta|^1P_1\rangle, \quad (10)$$

then

$$\frac{\beta^2}{\alpha^2}=\frac{\tau(^1P_1)}{\tau(^3P_1)}\frac{\lambda^3(^3P_1-^1S_0)}{\lambda^3(^1P_1-^1S_0)}=(1.89\pm0.10)\times10^{-3}, \quad (11)$$

and $\alpha=0.99906(5)$, $\beta=-0.0434(23)$ while the c coefficients which transform from the jj representation are[10]: $c_1=(1/3)^{\frac{1}{2}}\alpha+(2/3)^{\frac{1}{2}}\beta=0.5414(20)$, $c_2=(2/3)^{\frac{1}{2}}\alpha-(1/3)^{\frac{1}{2}}\beta=0.8408(13)$. The uncertainties in these coefficients arise from the experimental uncertainties in the determination of the lifetimes (see Table I). It is reassuring to note that we obtain $\beta^2/\alpha^2=2.22\times10^{-3}$ from the observed fine structure when we include the correction for the spin-other-orbit interaction (Wolfe correction). However, since we believe the lifetime method to be more reliable we will use the result given by Eq. (11) when estimating the second-order corrections.

With the Hamiltonian in this representation, terms off-diagonal in J may be treated as a perturbation on

the diagonal terms, most conveniently using the transformation method of Van Vleck.[15] The final matrix elements relevant to the levels $|b\rangle$ and $|c\rangle$ are given in Table IV. When the quadratic secular equation is solved, and the energies of states $|b\rangle$ and $|c\rangle$ equated, we find that

$$g_J=\frac{g_p A(^3P_1)}{h\nu_p}-\frac{g_I}{2}+\frac{\alpha^2\mu_0 H_c}{24}\left(\frac{8}{\delta_0}+\frac{3\beta^2}{\delta_1}-\frac{1}{\delta_2}\right)$$
$$-\frac{(6)^{\frac{1}{2}}\alpha}{6}\left[c_2(a_s-a_{\frac{1}{2}})-c_1\frac{5\sqrt{2}\xi}{8}a_{\frac{1}{2}}\right]\frac{1}{\delta_0}$$
$$+\frac{(3)^{\frac{1}{2}}\alpha}{6}\left[c_1 a_s-\left(c_1+c_2\frac{5\sqrt{2}\xi}{8}\right)a_{\frac{1}{2}}\right]\frac{1}{\delta_2}, \quad (12)$$

where g_p is the proton g factor, ν_p the nuclear magnetic resonance frequency of protons at the crossing field, α and β the mixing coefficient given above, and δ_0, δ_1 and δ_2 are the magnitude of the fine structure separations shown in Fig. 6. The term arising from the interaction with the $^1P_1$ state contributes less than one part in 10^7 to the final value of g_J. In Eq. (12) and Table IV, all field-independent terms involving the square of the hyperfine constants following the Van Vleck transformation have been absorbed into A ($^3P_1$). At low magnetic fields, such as in a double-resonance experiment, this is therefore the directly measured $\mathbf{I}\cdot\mathbf{J}$ constant. The terms in $8/\delta_0$ and $1/\delta_2$ proportional to H_c of Eq. (12) are identical with Dodd's Zeeman corrections.[3]

The numerical values of the hyperfine coupling constants as determined from the intervals in the $^3P_1$ and $^3P_2$ states, and the second-order correction terms, are listed in Table V. Using the recent value $1/657.462(3)$ reported by Liebes and Franken[16] for $g_p/2$ in mineral oil, g_J is calculated as

$$g_J^{111}=\tfrac{3}{2}-160(9)\times10^{-6},$$
$$g_J^{113}=\tfrac{3}{2}-146(9)\times10^{-6}.$$

The difference between these results is not believed to be significant.

---

[13] H. Kopfermann, *Nuclear Moments* (Academic Press Inc., New York, 1958), Table VIII.
[14] G. Araki, Progr. Theoret. Phys. (Kyoto) 3, 262 (1948).

[15] E. C. Kemble, *Fundamental Principles of Quantum Mechanics* (McGraw-Hill Book Company, Inc., New York, 1937), p. 394.
[16] S. Liebes and P. Franken, Phys. Rev. 116, 633 (1959).

A theoretical estimate of g_J exclusive of relativistic and diamagnetic effects is given by

$$g_J = \tfrac{1}{2}\alpha^2(g_L + g_S) + \beta^2 g_L, \qquad (13)$$

where α and β are again the mixing coefficients of Eq. (10).

Using $g_L = 1 - m/M$ and $g_S = 2(1.0011596)$, we find

$$g_J = \tfrac{3}{2} - \tfrac{1}{2}\beta^2 + \alpha^2(0.0011596) - \tfrac{1}{2}(m/M).$$

Applying this formula to cadmium, we obtain

$$g_J = \tfrac{3}{2} - 18(80) \times 10^{-6}.$$

The uncertainty in this result arises almost entirely from the uncertainty in β.

By comparing this result with the mean of the experimental values, we find that the relativistic and diamagnetic corrections are

$$\Delta g_{\text{rel}} + \Delta g_{\text{diam}} = -135(81) \times 10^{-6},$$

a figure not unreasonable in the light of previous estimates[17,18] for other atoms. Theoretical calculations of these corrections for cadmium and other group II elements are in progress and will be reported in a later publication.

ACKNOWLEDGMENTS

We are indebted to the staff of the Columbia Radiation Laboratory, and in particular to C. Dechert and A. Deery for their assistance during the course of this work. Discussions with Professor P. Franken and Professor H. Foley are gratefully acknowledged, as are the services of A. Landman, who checked many of the calculations.

---

[17] A. Abragam and J. H. Van Vleck, Phys. Rev. **92**, 1448 (1953).
[18] A. Lurio, G. Weinreich, C. W. Drake, V. W. Hughes, and J. A. White, Phys. Rev. **120**, 153 (1960).

From: *Astrophys. J.* **124**, 542–549 (1956)

INFLUENCE OF COLLISIONS UPON POPULATION OF HYPERFINE STATES IN HYDROGEN

Edward M. Purcell and George B. Field*
Harvard University and Harvard College Observatory
Received June 14, 1956

ABSTRACT

In a collision between two hydrogen atoms in their ground states, the electron spins may exchange. Such exchanges affect the relative populations of the hyperfine levels and are therefore important in determining the rate of 21-cm transitions in an assembly of atoms undergoing collision. A cross-section is computed for electron exchange over a range of gas kinetic temperatures, and the competition between collisions and radiation in establishing the hyperfine populations is analyzed. The results are applied to typical situations encountered in 21-cm radio astronomy.

INTRODUCTION

The intensity of emission or absorption by atomic hydrogen at the 21-cm resonance depends on the populations of the two levels into which the ground state of the atom is split by the hyperfine interaction. It is convenient to describe the relative occupation of these levels by a "spin temperature," T_S, defined by the relation

$$\frac{n_1}{n_0} = 3 \exp - \frac{\hbar\omega}{kT_S},$$

in which n_1 and n_0 are, respectively, the populations of the upper ($F = 1$) and lower ($F = 0$) levels and $\hbar\omega$ is the energy difference. If we observe with a radio telescope an extended, homogeneous, optically thick hydrogen source, the power received per unit band width will be simply kT_S. The spin temperature of the source in other situations is not so directly accessible. In the limiting case of low opacity and negligible background radiation, the observed emission intensity will be practically independent of T_S, so long as T_S is much greater than $\hbar\omega/k$. In that case the power received is determined simply by the probability of spontaneous emission and the number of hydrogen atoms (nearly three-fourths of which are in the upper level) in a column of unit cross-section extending through the source. But in any case the degree of opacity of a given source depends on T_S, among other factors. All this is well known (Wild 1952) and is repeated here only to recall the role of the level occupations, or the spin temperature, in the interpretation of 21-cm observations. This note is concerned with processes which, in typical astrophysical situations, may establish the level occupations and hence the spin temperature.

In an earlier publication (Ewen and Purcell 1951) the effect of atomic collisions was estimated and was asserted to be the dominant effect in determining T_S in the galactic H I regions then observed. The conclusion was, as it turns out, correct, but the reason was wrong; for the most important process at work during collisions had been overlooked, one which may be called "spin exchange." Its importance was pointed out in a private communication by V. F. Weisskopf and N. F. Ramsey. Subsequent calculations by the senior author yielded an approximate cross-section for the process.

A closely related question had arisen in the laboratory experiments of Wittke and Dicke (1956), who developed the theory of the effect for their purposes, along slightly different lines. They have provided us with much help and illumination; indeed, the conclusions presented here are to a considerable extent the result of a common effort.

---

* Junior Fellow, Society of Fellows.

EXCHANGE COLLISIONS

We are interested in this question: A hydrogen atom in a given hyperfine state, say $F = 1$, collides with a random hydrogen atom; what is the probability that the first atom will be left after the collision in the state $F = 0$? One interaction which occurs during a collision is the direct magnetic interaction of the electron spins. The energy of such an interaction is, in order of magnitude, β^2/d^3, β being the Bohr magneton and d the distance between the two electrons. If we take $d = 10^{-8}$ cm as representative of the situation during a collision, the duration of which is some 10^{-13} sec, we may estimate the probability that a hyperfine transition is induced. It is (interaction energy $\times$ duration$/\hbar)^2$, or roughly 10^{-4}. This crude estimate could be refined, but there is no point in doing so, for the spin-exchange process, which we shall now discuss, is so much more effective in all circumstances.

The collision of two hydrogen atoms presents us, temporarily, with a hydrogen molecule, in the structure of which electron exchange plays a prominent part. Speaking very loosely, we may say that the atoms exchange electron spins at a rate given by $(V_t - V_s)/\hbar$, where $V_t - V_s$ is the difference in energy between the triplet electronic state of the molecule and the singlet electronic state. If the collision is close enough and lasts long enough for the exchange to occur several times, the chance that a given proton will leave the collision with its electron in a new orientation is simply $\frac{1}{2}$. In some fraction of these cases the orientation of the new direction of the electron spin, relative to that of the proton spin, will be such that the atom is in a hyperfine state different from its state prior to the collision.

The argument can be developed rigorously along these lines, following Wittke and Dicke. Consider a system of two atoms whose state before the collision is specified, so far as all spin co-ordinates are concerned, by the four quantum numbers F_1, m_1, F_2, m_2, appropriate to isolated atoms individually in well-defined hyperfine states. To treat the collision, write the spin function of the initial state (F_1, m_1, F_2, m_2) as a linear combination of molecular spin functions which have been properly symmetrized with respect to electron co-ordinates. (The nuclear spin co-ordinates need not be so treated.) Our initial spin state for the separated atoms is then expressed as a superposition of singlet and triplet electronic spin states of the molecule, multiplied by the nuclear spin functions. The effect of a collision can now be described precisely: it brings about a relative phase shift, ϕ_{ts}, between the amplitude of the singlet component and the amplitudes of the triplet components of the electron spin function; so that when we revert to a representation in terms of our original spin functions, we find, in general, a mixture of several (F_1, m_1, F_2, m_2) states, not merely the pure state we began with. The decisive quantity is therefore

$$\phi_{ts} = \int dt \, \frac{V_t - V_s}{\hbar}, \tag{2}$$

where V_t is the energy of the triplet ("repulsive") electronic state, V_s is the energy of the singlet ("attractive") state, and the integration extends over the whole duration of the collision.

The matrices which transform the representation in the manner described have been given by Wittke and Dicke. Our problem is simpler than theirs in several respects: we need not worry about a correlation in phase among spin functions for different atoms which can arise in their experiments through the coupling to the radio-frequency field in their cavity; we are interested only in the probability of transitions from $F = 0$ to $F = 1$ and vice versa, and we need not sort out the m-substates of $F = 1$, which remain degenerate under all conditions of interest to us. Because of this, the only result we shall need can be deduced from one simple case.

Let the spin functions for an atom consisting of electron (1) and proton (1) be $a(1)a(1)$, $[a(1)\beta(1) + b(1)a(1)]/\sqrt{2}$, $b(1)\beta(1)$, and $[a(1)\beta(1) - b(1)a(1)]/\sqrt{2}$, where a and b are normalized spin functions for a proton and α and β are normalized spin functions for an electron. Suppose that atom (1) is initially in one of the $F = 1$ states, say $a(1)a(1)$. It meets in collision an arbitrary second atom. The nuclear spin of this atom is not correlated with that of atom (1); hence the spin of electron (2) is directed at random; this would be true even if the quantum number F_2 were specified (though not, of course, if we further specified m_2). We may, therefore, write for the spin functions of the unpolarized electron (2), $[a(2)e^{i\gamma} + \beta(2)]/\sqrt{2}$; and the nature of its nuclear spin function $S(2)$ is irrelevant. The factor $e^{i\gamma}$, a particular value of which would imply more about the spin of electron (2) than we may specify, is introduced explicitly to show that it does not affect the final result. The entire spin function, prior to collision, may now be written

$$\psi_{\text{before}} = 2^{-1/2}a\,(1)\,a\,(1)\,[\,a\,(2)\,e^{i\gamma} + \beta\,(2)\,]\,S\,(2)\,. \tag{3}$$

This is readily expanded in symmetrical and antisymmetrical electronic spin functions:

$$\psi_{\text{before}} = 2^{-3/2}a\,(1)\,S\,(2)\,\{2\,a\,(1)\,a\,(2)\,e^{i\gamma} + [\,a\,(1)\,\beta\,(2) + \beta\,(1)\,a\,(2)\,]$$
$$+ [\,a\,(1)\,\beta\,(2) - \beta\,(1)\,a\,(2)\,]\,\}. \tag{4}$$

With the symmetrical parts is associated the phase factor $\exp(-iV_t t/\hbar)$ and with the antisymmetrical component, $\exp(-iV_s t/\hbar)$. Hence, apart from an irrelevant common phase factor, the spin function after collision is

$$\psi_{\text{after}} = 2^{-3/2}a\,(1)\,S\,(2)\,\{2\,a(1)\,a(2)\,e^{i\gamma} + [\,a(1)\,\beta\,(2) + \beta(1)\,a(2)\,]$$
$$+ e^{i\phi_{ts}}[\,a\,(1)\,\beta\,(2) - \beta\,(1)\,a\,(2)\,]\,\}, \tag{5}$$

with ϕ_{ts} given by equation (2). From this we easily compute the probability that atom (1) is in the state $F = 0$, with spin function $[a(1)\beta(1) - b(1)a(1)]/\sqrt{2}$ after the collision; it is $|1 - e^{i\phi_{ts}}|^2/16$, or $\frac{1}{4}\sin^2(\phi_{ts}/2)$.

We define a *strong* collision as one for which $\phi_{ts} \gg 1$. For such collisions as a class the average value of $\sin^2(\phi_{ts}/2)$ will be $\frac{1}{2}$. We therefore conclude that an atom in the state $F = 1$, which experiences a strong collision with an arbitrary atom of the gas, has a chance of $\frac{1}{8}$ of departing the collision in the state $F = 0$. This probability we call W_{10}. It is clearly necessary that the converse probability, W_{01}, that is, the probability that an atom initially in $F = 0$ will leave a strong collision in $F = 1$, be $\frac{3}{8}$.

It is worth noting that the conclusion reached here is independent of the prior state of the collision partner; in other words, the probability that a selected atom in its next strong collision will be thrown into the other hyperfine state is independent of the relative occupation of the two states in the gas as a whole. However, W_{10} may depend on the gas kinetic temperature, T_K. Indeed, it must, because the ratio of the upward to the downward probability has, by detailed balancing, the value appropriate to thermal equilibrium with only collisions acting, namely, $3 \exp(-\hbar\omega/kT_K)$. Detailed examination of the collisions with the kinetic and spin co-ordinates given full and equal treatment would necessarily yield probabilities biased in favor of downward transitions. In our case the bias is relatively small because $\hbar\omega/kT_K$ is a small quantity for all temperatures of interest ($\hbar\omega/k = 0.068°$ K). We may therefore use

$$W_{10} = W\,,$$

$$W_{01} = 3W \exp\left(-\frac{\hbar\omega}{kT_K}\right), \tag{6}$$

and take W to be $\frac{1}{8}$. The error in so doing (of order $\hbar\omega/kT_K$) resides entirely in W and can cause, at worst, a wholly negligible error in the net transition rate. The *ratio* of upward to downward probability is given correctly by equations (6), although, of course, to the accuracy we require, the Boltzmann factor can be replaced by $(1 - \hbar\omega/kT_K)$.

Finally, to quiet any misgivings about the preservation of an atom's identity through a collision, we remark that all interactions involving the nuclear spin, including the hyperfine interaction itself, are, in fact, weak compared to ($\hbar$/collision duration), so that the orientation of the proton spin is an admissible label. The same argument justifies our brusque treatment of the nuclear spin co-ordinates in the calculation.

CROSS-SECTIONS

In the picture of the collision outlined previously, we may view the colliding pair as being in a mixture of space-symmetric and space-antisymmetric electronic states. Each state evolves independently of the other, and a phase shift ϕ_{ts} develops between the two. It is clear that in the development of the symmetric state, which is attractive, closer distances of approach will be involved for given initial conditions than in the development of the antisymmetric. The phase shift will thus arise chiefly from the behavior of the symmetric state. We need consider, therefore, only what happens in a "symmetric collision."

We shall treat the kinematics of the collision classically, justifying this approximation later by showing that, over most of the range of interest, the angular momentums involved are fairly large. The internuclear force for a given instantaneous nuclear separation will be assumed to be that appropriate to the same configuration at rest. That is, we shall work in the usual adiabatic approximation.

We shall concentrate our attention on strong collisions at the outset. If no angular momentum were involved, all collisions would be strong in the sense that the attractive force would bring the atoms together until the repulsive core of the molecular potential began to act, thus conducting them through a region of large exchange energy. Such a collision would result in a phase shift of hundreds of radians. The centrifugal barrier prevents this from happening in many cases, however. Consider the motion of a pair of atoms in center-of-mass co-ordinates. Let E be the energy of one of the atoms at infinity, where it moves in a trajectory specified by the impact parameter r_0 (measured to the center of the mass). The atom will be repelled by a centrifugal barrier Er_0^2/r^2. Only when r_0 is small enough will the atom surmount the barrier and proceed on to the repulsive core. If r_0 is too big, the atom is repelled by the centrifugal barrier and never reaches the region of large exchange energy. Evidently, there is a critical value of r_0 (a function of E), dividing strong from not-strong collisions. With the critical r_0, the atom arrives at the top of the potential barrier with zero velocity. The strong collision cross-section σ for the energy E is then $4\pi r_0^2$. In actual computations, $r_0(E)$ is computed parametrically through its dependence on r_1, the turning-point radius. If $S(r) = d(\log V)/2d(\log r)$, with V the potential per atom, then $E = V(r_1)[1 + S(r_1)]$ and $r_0^2 = r_1^2 S(r_1)/[1 + S(r_1)]$.

Values of $V(r)$ for r between $2a_0$ and $6a_0$ (nuclear separations between $4a_0$ and $12a_0$) were taken from Hirschfelder, Curtiss, and Bird (1954). Two additional points at $r = 6.5a_0$ and $7a_0$ were computed with the formulae of Pauling and Beach (1935) recommended by Hirschfelder *et al.* (The latter authors review various experimental curves, exchange and variational calculations, and van der Waals' calculations and select a "most likely potential" for both symmetric and antisymmetric cases.)

The calculated r_0 varies only slowly with E, a behavior which reflects the steepness of $V(r)$. It is not hard to take this variation into account for a gas having a Maxwellian velocity distribution. We use an equation adapted from Jeans (1925):

$$\bar{\sigma} = \int^{\infty} \sigma(u)\, u\, e^{-u} du\,; \qquad u = \frac{2E}{kT_K}. \tag{7}$$

If $\sigma(E)$ were given by a power law $\sigma \sim E^{-\mu}$, the effective cross-section appropriate to the kinetic temperature T_K, $\bar{\sigma}(T_K)$, would be found as follows:

$$\bar{\sigma}(T_K) = \sigma(E^*) = 4\pi r_0^2(E^*) , \tag{8}$$

with

$$E^* = \tfrac{1}{2}kT_K[\Gamma(2-\mu)]^{-1/\mu} .$$

Our results are fairly well represented by $\mu = 0.27$. Inserting this value into equation (8) gives $E^* = 0.70\,kT_K$. That is, we get the correct strong-collision rate in a Maxwellian gas at T_K by finding the r_0 that corresponds to $E = 0.70\,kT_K$ and using $4\pi r_0^2$ as a "hard sphere" cross-section in the Maxwellian formula,

$$\nu = \sqrt{2}\,n\bar{\sigma}\left(\frac{8\,kT_K}{\pi M}\right)^{1/2} . \tag{9}$$

The errors in this procedure due to imprecision in the power law and the assumption of the same power law for the tails of the velocity distribution were investigated and found to be no more than a few per cent.

TABLE 1

STRONG-COLLISION CROSS-SECTION AS FUNCTION
OF KINETIC TEMPERATURE

T_K (° K)	$\bar{\sigma}(10^{-15}$ cm$^2)$	Angular Momentum ($\hbar$)	y/n	T_K (° K)	$\bar{\sigma}(10^{-15}$ cm$^2)$	Angular Momentum ($\hbar$)	y/n
1.........	19.6	1.4	1200	300.......	4.42	11	16
3.........	13.7	2.0	490	1000.......	3.45	17	6.7
10.........	9.50	3.0	190	3000.......	2.62	26	3.3
30.........	7.42	4.5	85	10000.......	1.90	40	1.3
100.........	5.65	7.4	35				

The effective cross-section for strong collisions thus computed is given in Table 1 for various kinetic temperatures. At 1° K the cross-section $\bar{\sigma}$ is more than two hundred times πa_0^2. It decreases slowly with rising gas temperature, varying approximately as $T_K^{-0.27}$, as already noted. It is perhaps worth remarking that the cross-section for ordinary gas collisions between hydrogen atoms (that is, the cross-section for momentum transfer) is likewise large, being, in fact, not much different from the cross-section given in Table 1. This should be borne in mind when one is considering transport properties of interstellar or intergalactic H I gas.

The third column of the table gives the angular momentum, in units of $\hbar$, of a typical collision. This provides some justification for our classical treatment of the impact. Note that at the lowest temperatures the angular momenta are *not* very large; the accuracy of our results there is uncertain.

It remains to examine the contribution of collisions which are not strong. Consider the value of ϕ_{ts}: evidently, as we increase r_0 from its critical value at the energy E, we reach a point where $\phi_{ts} = \pi$. An exchange is likely in the *intermediate region* between $\phi_{ts} = \infty$ and $\phi_{ts} = \pi$, and so its area should be added to the strong-collision cross-section. Beyond the point where $\phi_{ts} = \pi$, ϕ_{ts} will decrease uniformly outward, implying a rather small probability, $\tfrac{1}{8}\sin^2(\phi_{ts}/2)$, of exchange. This *region of weak collisions* will contribute something to the total cross-section if the annular areas weighted by the exchange probability are summed. Closer examination shows that both these effects become considerable above $T_K = 1000°$, so that the strong-collision approximation is not accurate above that temperature.

The deviation from the critical r_0 for which $\phi_{ts} = \pi$ depends very sensitively on the critical impact parameter itself, and thus the contribution of the intermediate region will drop very sharply as r_0 is increased. However, it amounts to 10 per cent of the strong-collision cross-section at $r_0 = 1.66 \times 10^{-8}$ cm, which corresponds to 1000°. At that radius the contribution of weak collisions of the same energy is 25 per cent, falling exponentially as r_0 is increased. We conclude that the strong-collision approximation breaks down for $T_K = 1000°$. The cross-sections for 3000° and 10000° are therefore in error by an uncertain amount. On the other hand, we may be sure that they are *less* than the 1000° value of 3.45×10^{-15} cm^2, since in a higher-energy collision the phase shifts will be less for every impact parameter.

APPLICATIONS

In view of the effectiveness of the hydrogen-hydrogen collisions and the rarity of collisions of any other sort in the interstellar medium, the only collision process we shall need to consider is the spin exchange examined earlier. To be sure, a similar spin exchange could occur between a hydrogen atom and a free electron, but this would assume relative importance only in an H I region containing electrons with more than a few per cent of the hydrogen abundance—an unlikely state of affairs.

Radiative processes may be of two types—radio-frequency and optical. The latter, notably absorption of Lyman radiation, can excite atoms in the singlet ground state, whereupon they re-emit and land on the triplet. For 21-cm processes the radiation intensity is important; for Lyman transitions the spectral gradient over the 1420-megacycle interval is important also. Wouthuysen (1952) has considered this effect for trapped Lyman-a radiation and has shown that the color temperature of such radiation will approach the kinetic temperature of the gas. It now seems likely, however, that Lyman radiation processes will be unimportant in interstellar space, owing to the large effective opacity of the dust for the highly scattered Lyman-a (van de Hulst, Muller, and Oort 1954). We shall confine our attention here to radio-frequency transitions. We want to examine the competition between exchange collisions and radiation in establishing the spin temperature.

Let P_{10} be the probability per second that an atom in the triplet state will go to the singlet as a result of a collision; it is equal to $\nu/8$, with ν the collision rate previously given in equation (9). The probability of the inverse process is, then, $3P_{10} \exp(-\hbar\omega/kT_K)$. The equation of equilibrium is

$$n_1 \left(P_{10} + A_{10} + A_{10} \frac{\lambda^2}{2\hbar\omega} I \right) = 3n_0 \left[P_{10} \exp\left(-\frac{\hbar\omega}{kT_K} \right) + A_{10} \frac{\lambda^2}{2\hbar\omega_K} I \right]. \tag{10}$$

Here λ and ω refer to 21 cm, and I is the specific intensity of 21-cm background radiation. By "background radiation" we mean the 21-cm radiation of any origin whatever, incident on the region in question. Usually this background radiation will not be isotropic, so we must understand I to mean an average taken over all directions of incidence. We define in terms of I a radiation temperature, T_R, by the relation

$$I = \frac{2\hbar\omega}{\lambda^2} \left[\exp\left(\frac{\hbar\omega}{kT_R} \right) - 1 \right]^{-1}. \tag{11}$$

No matter what the source of the radiation is, T_R is the temperature to which the spin populations of atoms exposed to this radiation would adjust in the absence of competing mechanisms. If it happens that the T_R so defined is large compared to $\hbar\omega/k$, it coincides with the brightness temperature, T_B, usually defined in radio astronomy by

$$I = \frac{2kT_B}{\lambda^2}. \tag{12}$$

It follows from equations (1), (10), and (11) that

$$e^{-\hbar\omega/kT_S} = \frac{P_{10}\,e^{-\hbar\omega/kT_K}\,(e^{\hbar\omega/kT_R} - 1) + A_{10}}{(P_{10} + A_{10})\,(e^{\hbar\omega/kT_R} - 1) + A_{10}}. \tag{13}$$

Usually, both kT_K and kT_R will be large compared to $\hbar\omega$. We may be sure that kT_S will then be large compared to $\hbar\omega$ also, since T_S will necessarily lie between T_K and T_R. Making the appropriate approximations in equation (13), we obtain the simpler relation,

$$T_S = \frac{y}{1+y}\,T_K + \frac{1}{1+y}\,T_R, \tag{14}$$

where we have introduced the abbreviation

$$y = \frac{\hbar\omega P_{10}}{kT_K A_{10}}. \tag{15}$$

The dependence of the parameter y on the density of atoms n, the kinetic temperature T_K, and the strong-collision cross-section $\bar{\sigma}$ is shown explicitly in equation (16):

$$y = \frac{\hbar\omega}{2k A_{10}} \left(\frac{k}{\pi M}\right)^{1/2} n\bar{\sigma} T_K^{-1/2}. \tag{16}$$

Since $\bar{\sigma} \sim T_K^{0.27}$ approximately, y varies as $T_K^{-0.77}$. It expresses the effectiveness of collisions relative to that of radiation processes in establishing the spin temperature. In the last column of Table 1 the values of y/n for various T_K are given. Here $A_{10} = 2.85 \times 10^{-15}$ sec^{-1} was used (Wild 1952). To employ equation (14), then, we multiply n by the y/n from Table 1 and insert the result in equation (14).

The statement that collisions are most important in the standard galactic interstellar H I situation (Shklovsky 1949; Ewen and Purcell 1951; Wild 1952) follows if we recognize that T_R, even at the galactic center, is only about 10°. For then, at densities comparable with unity and practically all kinetic temperatures, y is large, and collisions dominate. For example, if we take $T_K = 100°$ K, $n = 1$ cm^{-3}, and $T_R = 10°$ K, y is 35, and T_S differs from T_K by only 2.5° K. If n were as small as 0.01 cm^{-3}, on the other hand, T_S would fall to 33° K, illustrating the importance of spontaneous emission at low densities. Care should therefore be exercised in interpreting weak absorption lines in terms of total numbers of atoms. If the derived densities are low, on the basis of assumed kinetic temperatures, the spin temperature may differ considerably from T_K, and the derived densities should be re-examined.

There are particular conditions under which we might expect collisions to be unimportant relative to radiation. In the intergalactic medium, for example, y will be small for even the lowest kinetic temperatures, if the density is as low as has been suggested (10^{-4} cm^{-3}). Also, even in dense regions, the radiation temperature may reach such values as to make T_R dominant. For example, absorbing clouds in the near vicinity of a bright radio source should exhibit spin temperatures far from the kinetic temperature. It is easy to show that the apparent absorption $(T_{\text{cont}} - T_{\text{line}})/T_{\text{cont}} = (1 - e^{-\tau})$ $(1 - T_S/T_R)$, where τ is the opacity of the absorbing layer. In the particular case of Lilley and McClain's (1956) observations of H I absorption in Cyg A, we may draw some interesting conclusions from a consideration of the effects of the continuum radiation on the spin temperature of the H I in front of the source. From the angular dimensions given by Baade and Minkowski (1954) and the continuum flux near 21 cm given by

Hagen, McClain, and Hepburn (1955), we estimate an average radiation density in the neighborhood of the source which corresponds to a radiation temperature T_R approximately equal to 1.0×10^5 ° K. On the other hand, if we take $r = 1$ cm^{-3} and $T_K = 100°$ for the H i, following Lilley and McClain, we find that $y = 35$. Thus the 2880° K contribution by the radiation term far outweighs that of 97° K by the collision term. The *direct* effect of increasing T_S is to increase the H i emission, thus reducing the apparent absorption, and is accounted for by the second term in the expression for the apparent absorption. Evidently, we may neglect the direct effect in the present case, since T_S/T_R is only $\frac{1}{36}$.

On the other hand, increasing T_S decreases the effective opacity in the ratio $\hbar\omega/kT_S$ (Wild 1952). Thus the τ deduced by using our expression for the apparent absorption can be related to the number of absorbing atoms only if T_S is known. In fact, the number of absorbing atoms estimated from the apparent absorption will be proportional to T_S. Lilley and McClain adopted 100° K for the latter and derived $7 \times 10^7 \times A$ suns for the mass of absorbing H i, with A the absorbing area in square kiloparsecs. We have shown that T_S is, in fact, thirty times as great as they assumed, from which it follows that the mass estimate should be revised upward to $2.0 \times 10^9 \times A$ suns. The latter figure approaches the mass of H i in a typical spiral galaxy if the dimensions of the absorbing region are of the order of 10 kpc. That this should be so does not disagree with the radio dimensions of 10×40 kpc; or with Baade and Minkowski's characterization of the system as a giant one. It should be noted that the estimate of number of atoms absorbing the radiation from Cyg A is still sensitive to the density and temperature assumed for the H i. We conclude that in the case of Cyg A and in similar cases one needs to know something about the radiation density as well as something about the gas density and temperature in the cloud, in order to interpret absorption measurements properly in terms of numbers of atoms.

REFERENCES

Baade, W., and Minkowski, R. 1954, *Ap. J.*, 119, 206.
Ewen, H. I., and Purcell, E. M. 1951, *Nature*, 168, 356.
Hagen, J. P., McClain, E. F., and Hepburn, N. 1954, *Proc. I.R.E.*, 42, 1811.
Hirschfelder, J. O., Curtiss, C. F., and Bird, R. B. 1954, *Molecular Theory of Gases and Liquids* (New York: John Wiley & Sons).
Hulst, H. C. van de, Muller, C. A., and Oort, J. H. 1954, *B.A.N.*, 12, No. 452, 117.
Jeans, Sir J. 1925, *Dynamical Theory of Gases* (Cambridge: At the University Press), p. 36.
Lilley, A. E., and McClain, E. F. 1956, *Ap. J.*, 123, 172.
Pauling, L., and Beach, J. Y. 1935, *Phys. Rev.*, 47, 686.
Shklovsky, I. S. 1949, *Astr. J. U.S.S.R.*, 26, 10.
Wild, J. P. 1952, *Ap. J.*, 115, 206.
Wittke, J. P., and Dicke, R. H. 1956, *Phys. Rev.*, 103, 620.
Wouthuysen, S. 1952, *Physica*, 18, 75.

From: *Phys. Rev.* **109**, 381–385 (1958)

Spin Resonance of Free Electrons Polarized by Exchange Collisions*†

H. G. Dehmelt
Department of Physics, University of Washington, Seattle, Washington
(Received September 16, 1957)

An experiment is described in which thermal electrons, $t_e \approx 400°K$, become polarized in detectable numbers by undergoing exchange collisions with oriented sodium atoms during which the atom orientation is transferred to the electrons. The collisions establish interrelated equilibrium values for the atom and electron polarizations which depend upon the balance between the polarizing agency acting upon the atoms (optical pumping) and the disorienting relaxation effects acting both on atoms and electrons. When now the electrons are furthermore artificially disoriented by gyromagnetic spin resonance, an additional reduction of the atom polarization ensues which is detected by an optical monitoring technique, thereby allowing a determination of the free-electron spin g factor, g_s. Since it was experimentally convenient, at this stage only the ratio $g_J(Na)/g_s = 1.000026$

± 0.00003 was determined, showing no significant difference between g_s and $g_J(Na)$, the g factor of the $^2S_{\frac{1}{2}}$ sodium ground state. From the experimental strength and width of the electron disorientation signal a lower limit was obtained for the sodium exchange cross section with thermal electrons: $Q > 2.3 \times 10^{-14}$ cm². This may be compared with a theoretical exchange cross section, $Q = 2.3 \times 10^{-14}$ cm², which is derived under the assumption that the $3s^2 \, S_0$ state of the Na⁻ ion has essentially zero binding energy, thereby causing strong singlet scattering while the triplet scattering is negligible in comparison. Spin-orbit coupling during collisions of the electrons with the atoms of the inert argon buffer employed to slow down wall diffusion is discussed as the chief cause for the shortness of the observed free-electron spin relaxation time, $T_e \approx 6 \times 10^{-5}$ sec.

INTRODUCTION

CONSIDERABLE interest exists in experimental determinations of the free-electron spin magnetic moment μ_s in terms of the Bohr magneton μ_0 with accuracies high enough to provide further tests for the theoretical values,

$$\mu_s/\mu_0 = 1 + (\alpha/2\pi) + \text{higher terms},$$

obtained from quantum electrodynamics.[1-3] There are experimental values available[4,5] with an accuracy of about 10^{-6} for $g_J(H)/g_p$, the ratio of the g factors of the hydrogen ground state to that of the proton, which after a small relativistic bound state correction yield accurate g_s/g_p values that can be combined with other experimental data for[6] μ_p/μ_0 to obtain the desired ratio μ_s/μ_0. However, a *direct* experimental determination of the free-electron spin g factor in terms of g_p or $g_J(H)$ with an accuracy of 10^{-6} or better would be highly desirable. Various experimental schemes[7] have been proposed to accomplish this; however, no accuracies higher than 5×10^{-3} appear to have been reported so far. The present experiment was carried out on thermal electrons and an accuracy of 3×10^{-5} was achieved in preliminary measurements which also indicated that an increase in accuracy by one or two orders of magnitude should be possible.

PRINCIPLE OF EXPERIMENT AND APPARATUS

The electrons were polarized by allowing them to undergo exchange collisions with oriented sodium atoms in which the total spin component with respect to the axis of orientation, a magnetic field H_0, is conserved and the orientation of the atoms is transferred to the initially unpolarized electrons by exchange of the spin directions. Electrons and atoms, the latter polarized by optical pumping, were allowed to diffuse in an inert buffer, argon or helium at pressures of a few centimeters Hg. Since the electron-sodium collisions tend to equalize the polarization ratios of sodium atoms and electrons, the mere presence of free electrons reduced the sodium equilibrium polarization because the disorienting relaxation effects acting upon the electrons are passed on to the sodium atoms. In the same fashion, resonance disorientation of the electrons by a magnetic rf field of the proper frequency fulfilling the gyromagnetic resonance condition,

$$\nu_s = g_s \mu_0 H_0/h,$$

caused a further decrease in the sodium orientation. This orientation decrease was detected by an optical-absorption monitoring technique, thereby allowing a determination of the free-electron spin g factor g_s. A typical experiment (see Fig. 1) employed a spherical

* Supported by the U. S. Office of Ordnance Research.
† Early results of this work were reported at the 123rd meeting of the American Association for the Advancement of Science, December 26, 1956.
[1] J. Schwinger, Phys. Rev. **73**, 416 (1948).
[2] R. Karplus and N. Kroll, Phys. Rev. **77**, 536 (1950).
[3] C. M. Sommerfield, Phys. Rev. **107**, 328 (1957).
[4] Koenig, Prodell, and Kusch, Phys. Rev. **88**, 191 (1952).
[5] R. Beringer and M. A. Heald, Phys. Rev. **95**, 1474 (1954).
[6] J. H. Gardner and E. M. Purcell, Phys. Rev. **76**, 1262 (1949).
[7] Reviewed by H. A. Tolhoek, Revs. Modern Phys. **28**, 277 (1956).

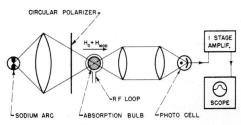

Fig. 1. Free-electron spin resonance apparatus.

200-cm³ absorption bulb heated to around 140°C which contained 70 mm of 2.5×10¹⁸ atoms per cm³ argon and sodium vapor of a density of about 8×10⁹ per cm³, corresponding roughly to a pressure of 10⁻⁷ mm. The sodium density N was estimated from the ratio of the transmitted to the indident light fluxes I_1/I_0 with the help of the formula[7a] for "line absorption"

$$1-(I_1/I_0) \approx 1.4(\pi \ln 2)^{\frac{1}{2}} r_0 c N d/\Delta\nu_A,$$

which holds for small absorption and the source width equal to the absorber width $\Delta\nu_A$, r_0 being the classical electron radius and d the thickness of the absorbing layer. The value 3×10^9 sec⁻¹ was taken for the pressure-broadened absorption line width $\Delta\nu_A$. For the purpose of ionization and generation of free electrons, the absorption bulb was placed between two capacitor plates (not shown in Fig. 1) to which 25-Mc/sec rf pulses of around 10^{-3} sec duration at a repetition rate of about 10 per second were applied synchronously with the sweep of the oscilloscope used for the observation of the disorientation signals and the sawtooth modulating field H_{mod}. Under these conditions, after each discharge pulse the electron temperature drops within 50 microseconds to the gas temperature. The electron density,[8,9] n, decays due to volume recombination approximately according to $1/n = (1/n_0) + \alpha t$, since wall diffusion of the electrons and ions can be neglected as long as the observation interval is short compared with the average ambipolar wall diffusion time $T_D = (1/D_a)(R/\pi)^2$ which, with $D_a(\text{argon}) = 91$ cm²/sec at 1 mm pressure, is about 1 sec. Rough measurements of the rf conductivity σ of the decaying plasma at 25 Mc/sec indicated a decay of n from 3.2 ×10⁸ cm⁻³ to 1.6×10⁸ cm⁻³ during the 0.1 sec long usable portion of the observation interval, the connection[10] between n and σ being given by $n = (m/e^2)\omega_c \sigma$. The value 2×10^{10} sec⁻¹ was assumed for the electron collision frequency ω_c in the argon buffer.

The optical system[11] now functioned in the following way: Light from the sodium arc was made circular polarized by a commercial polarizing plate and served to orient the sodium atoms in the bulb by optical pumping.[12] The transmitted light then was focussed upon a vacuum photocell connected to an oscilloscope through an amplifier. The amplified photocurrent was a measure of the sodium orientation P since the oriented atoms absorb less than unoriented ones. The axial magnetic field $H_0 \approx 21.4$ gauss was provided by a Helmholtz coil 30 inches in diameter. The modulation field was furnished by a separate ring coil. The rf loop was

energized from a 62.08-Mc oscillator for the electron spin disorientation field and simultaneously from a second tunable oscillator in order to induce consecutively the four $\Delta m_F = \pm 1$ transitions between the magnetic sublevels of the $F = 2$ sodium hfs level at about 15.10, 15.36, 15.63, and 15.92 Mc which served to calibrate the magnetic field H_0.

INTERDEPENDENCE OF POLARIZATIONS

We now consider the factors relating the electron and sodium polarizations p and P. Of the N atoms, disregarding their nuclear spins, and the n electrons contained in one cubic centimeter, N_+ and n_+ have their spins up, N_- and n_- have them down. We define $P = (N_+ - N_-)/N$; $p = (n_+ - n_-)/n$. The cross section for exchange of the spin direction when oppositely oriented electrons and atoms meet will be denoted by Q For simplicity the atoms are considered at rest, wh.ile at absolute temperature t_e the electrons are assumed to move with fixed speed $v = (3kt_e/m)^{\frac{1}{2}}$, their velocity distribution being neglected. Then the time variation of n_+ due to electron-sodium collisions alone is given by $\dot{n}_+ = vQ[N_+ n_- - N_- n_+]$ which leads to $\dot{p} = f(P - p)$ for the electron polarization and $\dot{P} = F(p - P)$ for the atom polarization. Here the frequency of collision of an electron with sodium atoms, $f = vQN$, and that for a sodium atom to be hit by electrons, $F = vQn$, have been introduced. On the other hand, the atoms are continuously polarized by optical pumping and depolarized by relaxation effects of characteristic time T_a. In the absence of free electrons the time variation of P due to these processes is described[11] by

$$\dot{P} = cI_0(\bar{P} - P) - (1/T_a)P,$$

which can be rewritten

$$\dot{P} = (1/\tau)(P_I - P), \quad \tau = T_a/(cI_0 T_a + 1),$$

where $P_I = cI_0 T_a \bar{P}/(cI_0 T_a + 1)$ is the equilibrium polarization corresponding to a finite light intensity I_0 and $\bar{P}$ is the saturation polarization obtainable with the optical pumping. The relaxation effects of characteristic time T_e acting on the electrons in the absence of sodium atoms would cause their polarization to decay according to $\dot{p} = -(1/T_e)p$. By combining all these contributions to $\dot{P}$ and $\dot{p}$ when the corresponding processes are simultaneously present, we get

$$\dot{p} = f(P - p) - (1/T_e)p,$$
$$\dot{P} = F(p - P) + (1/\tau)(P_I - P).$$

By setting $\dot{p}$ and $\dot{P}$ equal to zero, we now obtain the equilibrium polarizations **p** and **P**,

$$\mathbf{p} = fT_e(fT_e + F\tau + 1)^{-1}P_I,$$
$$\mathbf{P} = (fT_e + 1)(fT_e + F\tau + 1)^{-1}P_I.$$

The effect of resonance disorientation of the electrons

[7a] A. C. G. Mitchell and M. W. Zemansky, *Resonance Radiation and Excited Atoms* (Cambridge University Press, 1934), Chap. III.
[8] M. A. Biondi and S. C. Brown, Phys. Rev. **75**, 1700 (1949).
[9] A. von Engel, *Ionized Gases* (Clarendon Press, Oxford, 1955).
[10] Cf. e.g., H. Belcher and T. M. Sugden, Proc. Roy. Soc. (London) **A201**, 480 (1950).
[11] Cf. H. G. Dehmelt, Phys. Rev. **105**, 1487 (1957); **105**, 1924 (1957).
[12] Cf., e.g., A. Kastler, J. Opt. Soc. Am. **47**, 460 (1957).

by a magnetic rf field[13] is equivalent to shortening the electron relaxation time. It can be described by substituting for $1/T_e$ the modified quantity $1/T_e' = (1/T_e) + (1/T_{rf})$, where T_{rf} is the rf disorientation time which we define for exact resonance and which is connected with the rf field amplitude H_1 and the characteristic time T_2^* by $\omega_1^2 T_2^* T_{rf} = 1$. Here $\omega_1 = \pi g_s \mu_0 H_1/h$ would be the precession circular frequency in the field $H_1/2$. The time $T_2^* = 1/\pi \Delta \nu$ is a measure of the total experimental electron line width $\Delta \nu$ and, assuming small atom polarization, is given by

$$1/T_2^* \approx (1/T_e) + f + (1/T_2'),$$

while T_2' represents the contribution by the magnetic field inhomogeneity. As a consequence of the foregoing, the atom polarization is a function of the rf field H_1 acting upon the electrons, $\mathbf{P} = \mathbf{P}(H_1)$. For a given light intensity I_0 and therefore given τ, a measure of the optical signal resulting when the magnetic field $H_0 + H_{mod}$ is swept through the resonance value is provided by

$$S(H_1) = [\mathbf{P}(0) - \mathbf{P}(H_1)]/P_I,$$

the maximum possible signal being

$$S(\infty) = f T_e F \tau (F \tau + 1)^{-1} (f T_e + F \tau + 1)^{-1}.$$

Radio-frequency saturation will become appreciable for $H_1 > H_1^*$, the latter quantity being defined by $S(H_1^*) = \frac{1}{2} S(\infty)$. For the corresponding critical disorientation time T_{rf}^*, one obtains

$$1/T_{rf}^* = f(F \tau + 1)^{-1} + (1/T_e).$$

In order to use the experimentally observed signal $S_{exp} \approx 0.1$ to put a lower limit on Q, we note that

$$0.1 = S_{exp} < S(\infty) < f T_e F \tau = n N T_e \tau v^2 Q^2.$$

With the experimental values $v = 1.1 \times 10^7$ cm sec^{-1}, $N = 8 \times 10^9$ cm^{-3}, $n = 1.6 \times 10^8$ cm^{-3}, $\tau = 2 \times 10^{-2}$ sec, and $T_e = 6 \times 10^{-5}$ sec, we have

$$Q > 2.3 \times 10^{-14} \text{ cm}^2.$$

Here T_e was obtained from the experimental line width data by assuming

$$\Delta \nu(\text{electron}) - 4 \Delta \nu(\text{Na}) \approx 1/\pi T_e \approx 5.6 \times 10^3 \text{ sec}^{-1}.$$

EXCHANGE CROSS SECTION

The large observed exchange cross section Q can be understood as follows: There is evidence that the $3s^2\,{}^1S_0$ state of the Na$^-$ ion exists,[14,15] its binding energy W being close to zero. In this case the cross section for singlet s scattering, Q_- (only s-wave scattering need be considered at the low energies of interest

here) can be expressed approximately for small energies E of the impinging electron by[16,17]

$$Q_- = 4\pi(\hbar^2/2m)(E + |W|)^{-1}.$$

This approaches the maximum possible cross section $4\pi\lambda^2$ for $|W| \ll E$. The cross section for triplet scattering, Q_+, should be much smaller than Q_- since no bound triplet level exists and the above resonance effect does not occur. Therefore, as an approximation we neglect Q_+. Under this assumption one finds for the exchange cross section, $Q = \frac{1}{4} Q_-$. For thermal electrons (400°K) and $|W| \ll E$, the exchange cross section‡ then assumes nearly its upper limit $\bar{Q}$,

$$\bar{Q} = (\pi\hbar^2/3mkt_e) = 2.3 \times 10^{-14} \text{ cm}^2,$$

which in accordance with the earlier simplifying assumption of a fixed electron velocity has not been averaged over the electron energy distribution. In order to see that the exchange cross section Q is one-fourth as large as the singlet scattering cross section Q_-, we consider the asymptotic behavior of a mixed state Ψ which consists of equal parts of properly symmetrized singlet and triplet states,

$$\Psi = \frac{1}{2}[f(1)g(2) + f(2)g(1)][v_+(1)v_-(2) - v_+(2)v_-(1)] + \frac{1}{2}[f(1)g(2) - f(2)g(1)][v_+(1)v_-(2) + v_+(2)v_-(1)].$$

For the case of interest here, that the electron 1 in the free state f is initially at a large distance from the scattering atom in whose ground state g the electron 2 moves, $f(2)g(1)$ is nearly zero and can be neglected. The state then reduces to $\Psi = f(1)g(2)\,v_+(1)v_-(2)$, which corresponds to a definite situation where the electron 1 is free and has its spin up while the bound one 2 has its spin down; v_+ and v_- denote the spin functions with $m_s = +1$ and $m_s = -1$, respectively. If we now, as usual, represent $f(1)$ as a plane wave, Ψ will be associated with an electron stream of current density j of which $j/2$ will correspond to the singlet and $j/2$ to the triplet wave. Since only the singlet part is assumed to be scattered by the atom, the total scattered (singlet) current is given by $i_- = \frac{1}{2} j Q_-$. This current now consists of electrons 50% of which have exchanged their spins with the scattering atom. For the total current of spin-exchanged electrons, $i = \frac{1}{2} i_-$, we obtain therefore

$$i = \frac{1}{4} j Q_-, \quad \text{or} \quad Q = \frac{1}{4} Q_-.$$

ELECTRON SPIN RELAXATION

The main electron spin relaxation mechanism appears to be spin-orbit coupling during electron-argon collisions, which can be fairly accurately analyzed. First

---

[13] Cf., e.g., Bloembergen, Purcell, and Pound, Phys. Rev. **73**, 679 (1948).

[14] G. Glocker, Phys. Rev. **46**, 111 (1934).

[15] D. R. Hartree and W. Hartree, Proc. Cambridge Phil. Soc. **34**, 550 (1938).

[16] E. Wigner, Z. Physik **83**, 253 (1933).

[17] N. F. Mott and H. S. W. Massey, *Theory of Atomic Collisions* (Clarendon Press, Oxford, 1947), Chap. 2.

‡ For the exchange cross section Q to approach its maximum value, $\bar{Q} = \pi\lambda^2$, it would be sufficient that a level of one multiplicity, singlet or triplet, bound or virtual, lie much closer to zero than the free electron energy E, while the closest level of the other multiplicity is much further away than E.

we try to find the angle α through which a spin precesses during such a collision. Noting that simultaneously appreciable precession angles and scattering cross sections will occur only in p scattering and that the penetrating parts of the orbitals of a free, low-energy p electron around an argon atom and of a loosely bound p electron in a potassium atom should be very similar, we can calculate α from the doublet splitting $\delta\nu$ [cm^{-1}] and the classical period of revolution, $T = h^3(4\pi^2 me^4)^{-1}n^3$, for potassium p orbitals of high principal quantum number n. We obtain

$$\alpha = 2\pi c \sin\vartheta\, T\delta\nu = 2.8\times10^{-5} \sin\vartheta\, n^3\delta\nu,$$

where ϑ is the angle which the spin direction makes with the resultant of spin and orbital angular momentum. Numerically, with $n^3\delta\nu = 10^3$ cm^{-1} which for $n > 12$ is practically constant, we find

$$\alpha = 0.028 \sin\vartheta.$$

The relaxation time T_e which is associated with the random walk steps α which the tip of the unit spin vector executes on the unit sphere and with the frequency of collisions with argon atoms, f_p, is given by[17a]

$$1/T_e = \tfrac{1}{2}f_p\langle\alpha^2\rangle_{\mathrm{Av}} = \tfrac{1}{2}vq_pN_A\langle\alpha^2\rangle_{\mathrm{Av}}.$$

With $\langle\sin^2\vartheta\rangle_{\mathrm{Av}} \approx \tfrac{2}{3}$ and the experimental value $T_e = 6\times10^{-5}$ sec and taking $N_A = 2.5\times10^{18}$ cm^{-3}, $v = 1.1\times10^7$ cm/sec, we find from this for q_p, the partial cross section for p scattering,

$$q_p = 2.5\times10^{-18} \text{ cm}^2.$$

This value can be compared with a theoretical value extrapolated from Holtsmark's calculations.[18] Since in the limit of large de Broglie wavelength or small electron energy E the exact shape of the short-range scattering potential is immaterial, a square well may be substituted, for which it can be shown[17] that $q_p \propto E^2$ for $E\to0$. In this way one finds $q_p = 1.03\times10^{-24}t_e^2$ cm^2, where t_e is the absolute electron temperature. Again for simplicity we have not taken an average over the energy distribution of the electrons, assuming instead a fixed energy $E = \tfrac{3}{2}kt_e$. With $t_e = 400°$K we get numerically

$$q_p = 1.65\times10^{-19} \text{ cm}^2.$$

The strong temperature dependence of q_p and therefore T_e is in agreement with the experimentally observed quenching of the electron signal by weak electric rf fields which heat up the electrons. It is likely that even the electric rf field associated with the H_1 field caused appreciable heating of the electrons since the electron signal got weaker and weaker with increasing frequency and at 120 Mc/sec no signal could be observed in the present apparatus. The assumption of some increase in t_e by this H_1 heating and proper averaging would make the theoretical and experimental q_p values more nearly equal also.

[17a] D. Pines and C. P. Slichter, Phys. Rev. **100**, 1014 (1955).
[18] T. Holtsmark, Z. Physik **55**, 437 (1929).

ELECTRON-SODIUM g-FACTOR RATIO

As the chief goal of the present experiment a preliminary determination of the free electron spin g factor in terms of the g factor of the $S_{\frac{1}{2}}$ Na ground state was carried out by comparing the free-electron precession frequency ν_s with the sum of the four $\Delta m_F = \pm1$ transition frequencies associated with the $F = 2$ hfs level of the sodium atoms in the same sample and the same magnetic field. The sodium transitions were observed also by the optical method discussed earlier. During a run the free electron resonance was continuously displayed on the oscilloscope screen while the four Na resonances ν_1 to ν_4 were consecutively superimposed on the free-electron resonance. Typical resonances are shown in Fig. 2. The sodium frequency sum has the value

$$\sum\nu = (g_J\mu_0 + 2\mu_I)H_0/h,$$

where g_J denotes the electronic g factor of the sodium ground state and μ_I is the magnetic moment of the sodium nucleus. By using the field-independent ratio, $(\nu_s - \sum\nu)/\nu_s$, we can now form with $I = \tfrac{3}{2}$

$$g_J/g_s = 1 - 3(g_I/g_s) - (\nu_s - \sum\nu)/\nu_s.$$

Employing the atomic-beam value[19] $g_J/g_I = -2487.8$,

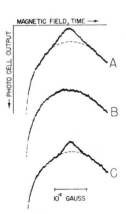

FIG. 2. Oscilloscope traces of electron and sodium resonances. The blank trace B was obtained by operating the equipment with the frequencies of the rf fields for electron and sodium resonances adjusted to off-resonance values. This trace served only to establish the dashed baselines which are shown in trace A, depicting the electron signal at about 62.1 Mc/sec and in trace C which displays one of the four sodium signals, namely that at about 15.9 Mc/sec. The signal peak intensities have been adjusted to about the same value and one easily notices the larger width of the electron resonance on a magnetic field scale. On a frequency scale the electron and sodium signal line widths turn out to be about 14.4 kc/sec and 2.2 kc/sec, respectively. The high light-intensity spikes at the beginning of the traces are the result of the ionizing discharge pulse at the beginning of each sweep cycle. The slow curvature of the remaining part of the baseline was either connected with afterglow effects in the decaying plasma or imperfections in the electronic equipment which were not further analyzed.

[19] P. Kusch and H. Taub, Phys. Rev. **75**, 1477 (1948).

in place of g_s/g_I, we finally have

$$g_J/g_s = 1 + 1.2059 \times 10^{-3} - (\nu_s - \sum \nu)/\nu_s.$$

With our preliminary experimental value for

$$(\nu_s - \sum \nu)/\nu_s = (118 \pm 3) \times 10^{-5},$$

we now obtain,

$$g_J/g_s = 1.000026 \pm 0.00003,$$

showing no difference in our limit of accuracy between the g factors of the free electron and the sodium ground state. Further experiments with the aim of improving the experimental accuracy and extending the method to much lower buffer gas pressures and eventually to near vacuum are in progress.

ACKNOWLEDGMENTS

The author wishes to express his appreciation for discussions with Dr. G. C. Wick of the Carnegie Institue of Technology and with his colleagues, especially Dr. R. Geballe and Dr. E. M. Henley. J. Jonson built the various absorption bulbs while F. Thoene designed the Helmholz coils and N. Pakinas helped with the electronic equipment.

Hyperfine Structure of Hydrogen, Deuterium, and Tritium*

L. Wilmer Anderson† and Francis M. Pipkin‡
Lyman Laboratory, Harvard University, Cambridge, Massachusetts

AND

James C. Baird, Jr.§
Mallinckrodt Laboratory, Harvard University, Cambridge, Massachusetts
(Received June 3, 1960)

The optical transmission of an optically oriented rubidium vapor in spin-exchange equilibrium with atomic hydrogen, deuterium, and tritium has been used to measure with high precision the hyperfine splittings of these paramagnetic atoms. The results are

$$\Delta\nu(\text{H}) = 1420.405726 \pm 0.000030 \text{ Mc/sec},$$
$$\Delta\nu(\text{D}) = 327.384349 \pm 0.000005 \text{ Mc/sec},$$

and

$$\Delta\nu(\text{T}) = 1516.701396 \pm 0.000030 \text{ Mc/sec}.$$

These results are based on a value of the hyperfine splitting of Cs^{133} which is taken to be

$$\Delta\nu(\text{Cs}^{133}) = 9192.631840 \text{ Mc/sec}.$$

These measurements were made in various buffer gases which caused a shift in the observed hyperfine splitting, and the results given represent extrapolations to zero pressure. The pressure shifts were measured for H in argon, neon, helium, and molecular hydrogen and were measured for D and T in argon and neon. The assigned limits of error represent the range of disagreement of the zero-pressure extrapolations in the different buffer gases.

INTRODUCTION

THE three simplest atoms which exist in nature are those of the hydrogen isotopes—hydrogen, deuterium, and tritium. The ground state of these atoms has a characteristic hyperfine splitting which results from the interaction of the nuclear magnetic moment with the electronic magnetic moment. The hyperfine splittings of the hydrogen isotopes have been extensively investigated both theoretically and experimentally with the hope of completely understanding these simple systems. Only the experimental work will be reviewed here; other references should be consulted for theoretical treatments.[1]

Nafe and Nelson used the atomic beam resonance technique to make the first precision measurement of the hyperfine splittings of atomic hydrogen,[2] deuterium, and tritium.[3] Later, Prodell and Kusch[4,5] used an improved atomic beam apparatus to redetermine these hyperfine splittings with greater precision. The precision of these measurements was limited by the 20-

kc/sec linewidth due to the short transit time in their beam apparatus *C* field.

Wittke and Dicke employed a paramagnetic resonance method to measure the hyperfine splitting of atomic hydrogen.[6] They used a buffer gas to reduce the Doppler broadening of the hyperfine resonance line[7] and obtained lines as narrow as 4 kc/sec. This residual linewidth was due to spin-exchange collisions between hydrogen atoms. Their result, even without an unjustified extrapolation to zero buffer gas pressure, was in disagreement with the measurement of Prodell and Kusch.[5] Subsequently, Kusch[8] remeasured the hyperfine splitting of hydrogen and deuterium. His new result for hydrogen agreed with the measurement of Wittke and Dicke with no pressure shift extrapolation.

The discovery[9-12] that the hyperfine transitions in an atom with an *S* atomic state can be detected by spin-exchange collisions with optically oriented rubidium atoms has furnished a new method for measuring the hyperfine splittings of the hydrogen isotopes. This paper reports a precision measurement of these three hyperfine splittings by this technique.

THE DETECTION MECHANISM

The paramagnetic resonance of atomic hydrogen can be detected in an extremely sensitive manner through spin-exchange collisions. A spherical flask containing a

* This research was supported in part by Harvard University funds and in part by a grant from the Research Corporation.

† National Science Foundation predoctoral fellow, 1958–59 and 1959–60. Now in the Physics Department, University of Wisconsin, Madison, Wisconsin.

‡ Alfred P. Sloan Research Fellow, 1959–61.

§ Research Fellow in Chemistry, supported by the Office of Naval Research. Now at the California Research Corporation, Richmond, California.

[1] Most of the older references are given by H. A. Bethe and E. E. Salpeter, in *Quantum Mechanics of One- and Two-Electron Systems* (Academic Press, Inc., New York, 1957), pp. 107–114. Some more recent references are C. K. Iddings and P. M. Platzman, Phys. Rev. **113**, 192 (1959); A. C. Zemach, Phys. Rev. **104**, 1771 (1956).

[2] J. E. Nafe and E. B. Nelson, Phys. Rev. **73**, 718 (1948).

[3] E. B. Nelson and J. E. Nafe, Phys. Rev. **75**, 1194 (1948).

[4] A. G. Prodell and P. Kusch, Phys. Rev. **88**, 184 (1957).

[5] A. G. Prodell and P. Kusch, Phys. Rev. **106**, 87 (1957).

[6] J. P. Wittke and R. H. Dicke, Phys. Rev. **103**, 620 (1956).

[7] R. H. Dicke, Phys. Rev. **89**, 472 (1953).

[8] P. Kusch, Phys. Rev. **100**, 1188 (1955).

[9] H. G. Dehmelt, Phys. Rev. **109**, 381 (1958).

[10] P. Franken, R. Sands, and J. Hobart, Phys. Rev. Letters **1**, 52 (1958); **1**, 188(E) (1958).

[11] R. Novick and H. E. Peters, Phys. Rev. Letters **1**, 54 (1958).

[12] L. W. Anderson, F. M. Pipkin, and J. C. Baird, Jr., Phys. Rev. Letters **1**, 229 (1958).

small amount of vacuum-distilled rubidium, some molecular hydrogen, and a buffer gas such as neon or argon is prepared. The resonance radiation from a rubidium light source, after being circularly polarized and filtered to remove the D_2 line ($^2S_{1/2} \leftrightarrow {}^2P_{3/2}$), is used to illuminate the flask. The direction of propagation of the light is chosen to coincide with the direction of the static magnetic field, and the transmission of the light by the flask is monitored with a vacuum photocell. The absorption of a circularly polarized light quantum followed by the emission of a quantum in a different state of polarization causes the rubidium atoms in the flask to become oriented along the direction of propagation of the light. As the polarization of the rubidium in the flask increases, the cell becomes less absorbent and the light transmitted to the photocell increases. A steady state is reached when the rate of transfer of angular momentum to the rubidium by the light is equal to the angular momentum lost from the rubidium by collisions with the buffer gas and the walls of the cell. Atomic hydrogen is then produced from the molecular hydrogen in the flask by a short pulsed radio-frequency discharge. The hydrogen atoms become polarized through spin-exchange collisions with the polarized rubidium. A radio-frequency magnetic field applied to the sample at a frequency corresponding to a transition in the hydrogen atom will alter the hydrogen polarization. Through spin-exchange collisions the polarization of the rubidium is reduced, and hence the light transmitted to the photocell decreases. In this fashion the light transmission can be used to detect the paramagnetic resonance of atomic hydrogen.

ENERGY LEVELS OF THE ISOTOPES OF ATOMIC HYDROGEN

The energy levels of the hydrogen isotopes can be computed from the Hamiltonian

$$\mathcal{3C} = A\mathbf{I}\cdot\mathbf{J} - g_J\mu_0\mathbf{J}\cdot\mathbf{H} - g_I\mu_0\mathbf{I}\cdot\mathbf{H},$$

where A is the magnetic hyperfine structure constant, μ_0 is the Bohr magneton, H is the magnetic field, $\mathbf{J}$ is the electronic angular momentum of the atom, $\mathbf{I}$ is the nuclear spin, and g_J and g_I are the electronic and nuclear g factors, respectively. The gyromagnetic ratio of the electron is taken to be negative and A is positive for a positive nuclear magnetic moment. The ground state of hydrogen and tritium, for which $I=\frac{1}{2}$, contains two hyperfine levels characterized in a low magnetic field by the total angular momentum $F=|\mathbf{I}+\mathbf{J}|=1, 0$. The energy levels for H and T are shown in Fig. 1. The ground state of atomic deuterium, for which $I=1$, contains two hyperfine levels characterized in a low magnetic field by $F=\frac{3}{2}, \frac{1}{2}$. The energy levels of D are shown in Fig. 2. Since magnetic fields of less than 0.2 gauss were always used, the energies of the levels shown in Fig. 1 and Fig. 2 are given only to second order in the magnetic field.

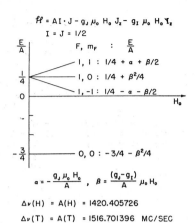

FIG. 1. The energy levels of the ground state of atomic H or T ($1\,^2S_{1/2}$) in a small magnetic field.

SPIN-EXCHANGE COLLISIONS

The spin-exchange collisions of rubidium and hydrogen make the detection of the paramagnetic resonance of the atomic hydrogen possible. This process also partially determines the various state populations and the linewidths which are obtained. In order to understand these effects, it is instructive to study the details of the spin-exchange process for two colliding hydrogen atoms. This problem has been considered by Purcell and Field,[13] by Wittke and Dicke,[6] and by the

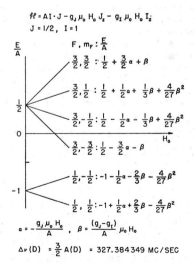

FIG. 2. The energy levels of the ground state of atomic D ($1\,^2S_{\frac{1}{2}}$) in a small magnetic field.

[13] E. M. Purcell and G. B. Field, Astrophys. J. **124**, 542 (1956).

present authors in another paper.[14] The detailed arguments will not be reproduced here; only the essential results which have a bearing on the interpretation of this experiment will be repeated.

During the collision of two hydrogen atoms the wave function for the electronic state can be written as the superposition of triplet and singlet spin components. The phase of these two components will develop at a different rate due to the difference in the interaction energy in the two states. Thus, in general, when the wave function after the collision is written in terms of the wave functions of two isolated hydrogen atoms, there will be new components in the wave function. In this type of collision the z component of the total spin angular momentum is a constant of the motion. The magnitude of the cross section can be estimated by defining some region of strong collisions where both the singlet and triplet electronic states will be involved. Purcell and Field take the maximum impact parameter for which such collisions occur to be that for which the classical turning point of the motion occurs at the top of the centrifugal barrier for the attractive $^1\Sigma$ potential. They estimate the reaction cross section for hydrogen-hydrogen spin-exchange collisions at $T=325°K$ to be

$$\sigma = 4.39 \times 10^{-15} \text{ cm}^2.$$

Another viewpoint is advantageous to obtain the populations of the various magnetic sublevels. The optical pumping process can be viewed as one in which the absorption of light introduces a certain net angular momentum; this is redistributed among the magnetic substates by the spin-exchange col'isions; and finally it is passed to the walls and the buffer gas by relaxation collisions. If it is assumed that the time for spin-exchange equilibrium is much less than the time required to produce orientation in the rubidium by optical pumping and the relaxation time for the orientation, then the relative populations will be dominated by the spin-exchange collisions. In equilibrium the populations of the magnetic substates will be the most probable distribution which carries the given total component of spin angular momentum along the axis of quantization. This is just a Boltzmann-like distribution in angular momentum. Each state will have a relative population given by

$$n_{mF} = Ce^{-\beta m F_1},$$

where β is determined so that the angular momentum has the prescribed value and C is a normalization constant. This distribution can be derived by the methods of elementary statistical mechanics. It can also be shown that this distribution is the steady-state solution to the equations describing the time dependence of the state populations under binary spin-exchange collisions.[14] Figure 3 shows the relative populations of

[14] L. W. Anderson, F. M. Pipkin, and J. C. Baird, Jr., Phys. Rev. 116, 87 (1959).

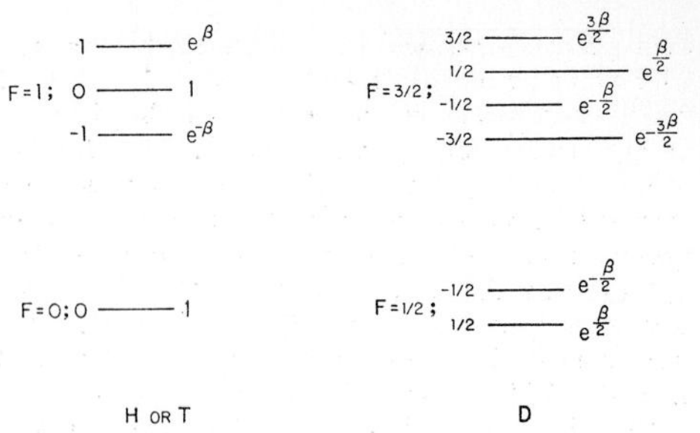

FIG. 3. The relative populations of the various sublevels of H, D, and T in spin-exchange equilibrium with a sea of similar atoms.

H, D, and T in spin-exchange equilibrium. This theory is applied in the section on experimental results.

APPARATUS AND EXPERIMENTAL PROCEDURE

A. Apparatus

The apparatus consisted of three parts, the first to generate and measure the microwave frequencies which produce the transitions, the second to produce oriented hydrogen, and the third to detect these transitions when they occur. A block diagram of the apparatus is shown in Fig. 4.

It was desired to produce and measure the three hyperfine frequencies with the same apparatus by changing only the frequency of the microwave oscillator. The oscillator used to drive the transitions was phase-locked to the sum of a stable high-frequency source and a variable frequency oscillator. The basic frequency standard used was an Atomichron made by the National Company, which was operated by Mr. J. A. Pierce of the Cruft Laboratory. A Gertsch AM-1 frequency meter generated a signal of 27 Mc/sec for H and D and of 25 Mc/sec for T. These frequencies were selected, as will be seen later in this paragraph, in order that the

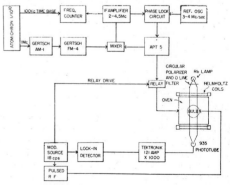

FIG. 4. A block diagram of the apparatus used in the experiment.

same i.f. amplifier could be used for all three isotopes without retuning. The AM-1 was altered so that its basic input reference frequency was the 1-Mc/sec output of the Atomichron rather than the 100-kc/sec, which it normally requires. Also, the 1-Mc/sec signal from the Atomichron was used to replace the variable low-frequency oscillator in the AM-1 and as an input to the Gertsch FM-4 500–1000 Mc/sec locked oscillator. The harmonics of the signal generated by the AM-1 were used as the high-frequency input for the FM-4. A T-116/APT-5 coaxial line grounded grid oscillator (a World War II radar-jamming oscillator) was used to supply the microwave frequency to drive the hyperfine transitions in all three isotopes. A probe was inserted into the cavity of this oscillator to provide an auxiliary output for the frequency stabilization circuits and this signal was mixed with the output of the FM-4. The FM-4 supplied signals at 712 Mc/sec for H, 760 Mc/sec for T, and 658 Mc/sec for D. The hyperfine frequencies are approximately 1420.406 Mc/sec for H, 1516.701 Mc/sec for T, and 327.384 Mc/sec for D. The 1420.406 Mc/sec upon being mixed with the second harmonic of 712 Mc/sec gives a beat at 3.594 Mc/sec; the 1516.701 Mc/sec upon being mixed with the second harmonic of 760 Mc/sec gives a beat of 3.299 Mc/sec; the second harmonic of 327.385 Mc/sec upon being mixed with the 658-Mc/sec signal gives a beat of 3.232 Mc/sec. The appropriate beat frequency was amplified in an i.f. amplifier whose bandwidth was 2 to 4.5 Mc/sec. One output of the i.f. amplifier was measured by a Northeastern Engineering 14–20 electronic counter, whose time base was provided by the 100-kc/sec output of the Atomichron. Another output of the i.f. amplifier was compared in a phase-detecting circuit with a General Radio 616D variable-frequency oscillator. The output of the phase detection circuit was sent to one of the grids of the differential amplifier in the voltage regulation circuit for the plate power supply of the APT-5. The changes in the plate voltage of the APT-5 generated this way were sufficient to phase lock the APT-5 over a reasonable range (about 150 kc/sec at 1420 Mc/sec). The tuning of the APT-5 was accomplished by varying the cavity dimensions until the oscillator was near the desired frequency. The fine tuning to bring the oscillator into the locking range was performed by varying the position of a micrometer head which was inserted into the lecher wire port near the grid of the oscillator.

The output of the APT-5 was fed into an isolator at 1420 Mc/sec and at 1516 Mc/sec or into a 20-db attenuator at 327 Mc/sec to buffer it from the remainder of the system. This output was amplitude modulated in a square wave by a relay driven at approximately 18 cycles/sec. The relay used to modulate the radio frequency was made by the James Vibra Power Company to work at L band (1400 Mc/sec). To excite transitions in the absorption flask, the modulated microwave power was fed into a crude cavity consisting

of two brass plates approximately 21 cm apart for the 1420- and 1516-Mc/sec and into a 10-turn solenoid for the 327-Mc/sec signal.

A General Radio 805B oscillator was used to drive the low-frequency Zeeman transitions. The output of this oscillator was amplitude modulated in a square wave with a Western Electric mercury relay and fed into the 10-turn solenoid. In order to measure the frequency of the Zeeman transitions, a signal was taken off before the amplitude modulation occurred, and the frequency was determined directly with the electronic counter.

The rubidium lamp consisted of a 25-cc spherical flask in which there was a small amount of rubidium and 1 mm Hg of argon. The rubidium spectrum was excited by placing the flask in the coil of the tank circuit of a power amplifier excited by a 7.5-Mc/sec crystal controlled oscillator. This provided a very stable, intense source of rubidium resonance radiation. The resonance radiation was circularly polarized by passing it through a sheet of polaroid followed by a quarter-wave plate, both of which were made by the Polaroid Company. The resonance radiation then passed through an interference filter which was manufactured by the Spectrolab Corporation and which transmitted only the D_1 ($^2S_{1/2} \leftrightarrow {}^2P_{1/2}$) line. Franzen and Emslie[15] have shown that the use of only D_1 resonance radiation increases substantially the efficiency of orientation over that obtained when both D lines are used. The filtered beam of light passed through the absorption cell which consisted of a 500-cm³ flask containing a small amount of vacuum-distilled rubidium, some spectroscopically pure hydrogen, and a spectroscopically pure rare gas such as argon or neon. The transmitted light was detected by a 935 photocell and the output of the photocell was clipped in order to reduce the overload effects of the discharge which created an intense flash of light. The signal was then amplified by a Tektronix 121 preamplifier whose gain was set at 1000, and the output sent to a lock-in detector. The lock-in detector employed a 6AR8 beam-switching beam, and it was gated in proper phase with the rf switching.

The flask containing the hydrogen was provided with two glass-covered tungsten leads which were used to excite the discharge for producing atomic hydrogen. The glass covering served to reduce the recombination rate for the hydrogen atoms. The 30-Mc/sec radiofrequency discharge was pulsed on for a time of one to three milliseconds at a rate of 36 or 18 times/sec. The discharge was usually run at a rate of 36 times/second and phased in such a way that pulses occurred both at the midpoint of the time when the modulation relay was open and when the relay was closed. In this mode the effects of the discharge pulse on the lock-in detector were easily averaged out. However, an 18-times/sec

---

[15] W. Franzen and A. G. Emslie, Phys. Rev. **108**, 1453 (1957).

rate for the discharge and any phasing could be used. Tests were made showing that neither of these adjustments could change the observed hyperfine frequencies. The bulb was mounted in an oven whose temperature was maintained at 50°C. The static magnetic field was the horizontal component of the earth's field. The vertical component was canceled out by a pair of Helmholtz coils.

The construction of the bulbs was quite simple. They were evacuated to a pressure of 5×10^{-6} mm Hg or better and then thoroughly outgassed by heating with a torch until the yellow sodium flame appeared indicating a softening of the glass. This was repeated until no appreciable rise in the pressure occurred upon heating. The rubidium was then distilled into the flask and boiled around for some time to eliminate any gas trapped in the rubidium. The flasks were then filled with a known amount of hydrogen and rare gas as required, and the gas pressure was measured with an oil manometer. The flask was subsequently sealed off. The pressure in the system was again noted and the pressure in the flask was corrected by using the perfect gas law and the volumes of the system and the bulb. The deuterium was purified by passing it through a palladium leak. For the tritium the purification consisted only in allowing the tritium to stand in contact with a liquid air trap for fifteen minutes. This could leave an impurity such as nitrogen or helium. These are estimated by the Atomic Energy Commission as being less than 0.5% of the total gas.

The splitting observed depends upon the nature and pressure of the buffer gas which is used. For this reason the frequency of the hyperfine splitting was measured in several buffer gases and at several pressures of each buffer gas. These data were then used to make an extrapolation of the observed frequency to that which would be observed at zero buffer gas pressure. Since the buffer gas shifts the observed frequency somewhat, it might appear unwise to use such a gas. The buffer gas is, however, advantageous for two reasons. First, it reduces the Doppler broadening of the line. The normal Doppler width is approximately 17 kc/sec; the Doppler width with 1 mm Hg of buffer gas is only 2 cycles/sec. Secondly, the buffer gas prevents the hydrogen and rubidium from diffusing to the wall of the container and thus losing their orientation.

B. Influence of Ions

Because of the manner in which the hydrogen atoms were produced, the measurements were always made while there were ions and electrons present in the bulb. In this section it will be shown that the effect of the plasma upon the hyperfine splitting should be negligible. Schwartz[16] has computed a theoretical expression for the Stark shift of the hydrogen hyperfine splitting. He finds that the change $\Delta(\mathcal{E})$ in the hyperfine splitting is

given by the expression

$$\Delta(\mathcal{E}) = -\frac{1193}{80} \frac{(a_0)^4}{e^2} \mathcal{E}^2 \Delta\nu(H),$$

where a_0 is the Bohr radius, e is the charge of the electron, $\mathcal{E}$ is the electric field, and $\Delta\nu(H)$ is the hyperfine splitting in the absence of the electric field. To estimate the shift in the hyperfine splitting due to the ionized atmosphere, the average of the square of the electric field at a typical hydrogen atom must be computed. This will be done in two ways; first by assuming a collision model with classical straight-line paths, and second by using an expression derived in the theory of the Stark broadening of spectral lines.

The time average of the square of the electric field due to an ion which passes at a distance b from the hydrogen atom is

$$\langle \mathcal{E}^2 \rangle_t = \frac{v}{2L} \int_{-L/v}^{L/v} \frac{e^2 dt}{[b^2 + (vt)^2]^2},$$

where $2L$ is the total length of the path, v is the ion velocity and the duration of the collision is $2L/v$. Evaluation of the integral gives

$$\langle \mathcal{E}^2 \rangle_t = \frac{e^2}{2Lb^3} \tan^{-1}\left(\frac{L}{b}\right) \sim \frac{\pi e^2}{4Lb^3}.$$

If it is assumed that all values of the impact parameter are equally probable, then for the average collision

$$\langle \mathcal{E}^2 \rangle_{t,b} = \frac{1}{\pi R_0^2} \int_{a_0/10}^{R_0} \frac{\pi e^2}{4Lb^3} 2\pi b\,db.$$

The lower limit of the integral has been conservatively chosen as $a_0/10$. The length R_0 represents some maximum impact parameter. Since the value of the integral is not sensitive to R_0, it will be taken as the radius of a circle of unit area. In this case

$$\langle \mathcal{E}^2 \rangle_{t,b} = 10\pi^2 e^2 / 2La_0.$$

The shift in the hyperfine splitting can now be computed from this average field, the average duration of a collision, and the number n of ions/cm³.

$$\Delta = -\frac{1193}{80} \frac{(a_0)^4}{e^2} \Delta\nu(H)(nv)\left(\frac{2L}{v}\right)\frac{10\pi^2 e^2}{2La_0}$$

$$= -\frac{1193}{8}(a_0)^3 \pi^2 n \Delta\nu(H)$$

$$= -3 \times 10^{-13} n \text{ cycles/sec.}$$

A conservative estimate of the number of ions and electrons in the bulbs is $10^{11}/\text{cm}^3$. This number is based on Dehmelt's[9] results on experiments with the free electron, where he found there were about $3\ 2 \times 10^8$

---

[16] R. D. Haun and J. R. Zacharias, Phys. Rev. 107, 107 (1957).

electrons/cm³, and on the radioactive decay of the tritium. In our experiment, each tritium bulb was a 500-cm³ flask and contained 2 curies of tritium. The beta ray emitted by the tritium has an energy of 17 kev and one ion pair is produced for each 30-ev energy loss in the gas. This would give 5×10^{10} ion pairs/cm³ produced per second by the decay of the tritium. The recombination time is much less than 1 second so this procedure overestimates the number at equilibrium.

In the Holtzmark theory of Stark shift line broadening, it is shown that the probability distribution of the electric field $\mathscr{E}$ at the site of a neutral atom is[17]

$$dp(\mathscr{E}) = \frac{3}{2\mathscr{E}} \left(\frac{\mathscr{E}_0}{\mathscr{E}}\right)^{\frac{3}{2}} \exp\left[-\left(\frac{\mathscr{E}_0}{\mathscr{E}}\right)^{\frac{3}{2}}\right] d\mathscr{E},$$

where

$$\mathscr{E}_0 = \left(\frac{4\pi}{3}n\right)^{\frac{2}{3}} e,$$

and n is the number of ions/cm³. Thus the average of the square of the electric field is

$$\langle \mathscr{E}^2 \rangle_{\text{prob}} = \int_0^\infty \mathscr{E}^2 dp(\mathscr{E}) = 2.5(\mathscr{E}_0)^2.$$

Hence

$$\langle \mathscr{E}^2 \rangle_{\text{prob}} = \left(\frac{4\pi}{3}n\right)^{\frac{4}{3}} e^2.$$

The hyperfine Stark shift for this field is

$$\Delta = -\frac{1193}{80}(a_0)^4 \left(\frac{4\pi n}{3}\right)^{\frac{4}{3}} \Delta\nu(\text{H})$$

$$= -0.96 \times 10^{-22} n^{\frac{4}{3}}.$$

This estimate is even smaller than the previous one.

C. Measurement Procedure

In making a set of measurements the following procedure was used. The bulb was inserted into the oven and checks were made to see that the lines had a Lorentz-like shape and that there was no appreciable power broadening. This was done by sweeping the frequency through the line slowly and observing the shape and half-width. In all cases two lines were measured which had the opposite dependence upon magnetic field. The measurements were made by observing the output of the lock-in detector on a Brown recorder. One observer would set the frequency of the oscillator so that the line intensity was at its maximum value, then a second observer would read the frequency, and the third observer would record the number. The output time constant of the lock-in detector was usually set at 0.1 sec. The procedure was to measure the frequency first of one of the field-dependent lines, then of the other; the cycle was then repeated in reverse order.

[17] H. Margenau and M. Lewis, Revs. Modern Phys. **31**, 569 (1959).

Only ten such measurements on a particular bulb were made at one time. In order to eliminate any observer bias, the roles of the various observers were changed after each ten measurements when a new bulb was inserted. All of the measurements on H and T were made during the hours of 1 a.m. to 5 a.m. when the magnetic activity (i.e., that due to trolleys) in the neighborhood was a minimum.

During the period when the measurements were made, the Atomichron being used (111) was compared by Mr. J. A. Pierce with another Atomichron (112). The total drift over this entire period was less than three parts in 10^{10}. Thus the error introduced by the frequency standard should be small. There is a correction, however, to change the results from Atomichron time to some other time standard. All results given are in Atomichron time; the correction to the A-1 time scale will be given at the end of this paper.

RESULTS

The most important result of the discussion of the spin-exchange induced state populations is the predicted equality of the populations of the states ($F=1$, $m=0$) and ($F=0$, $m=0$) in atomic hydrogen and tritium. This indicates that transitions between these two states would be unobservable. An intensive search was made for the $0 \leftrightarrow 0$ transition in atomic hydrogen. No evidence could be found for this transition; at the maximum it was less than 1/500 of the other hyperfine transitions.

In order to further verify that the populations in H were the predicted ones, the sample was placed in a low magnetic field so that the two Zeeman transitions were not resolved, and a radio-frequency field of sufficient strength to saturate these transitions was applied to the sample. This equalized the populations of the three $F=1$ substates. At the same time a search was made for the $0 \leftrightarrow 0$ hyperfine transition. A negative result was obtained. This implies that the state popu-

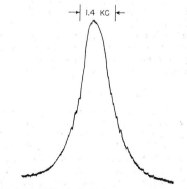

FIG. 5. A typical line profile of the ($F=1$, $m=1 \leftrightarrow F=0$, $m=0$) transition in atomic H in a buffer gas of molecular hydrogen. The lock-in detector time constant was 0.1 sec.

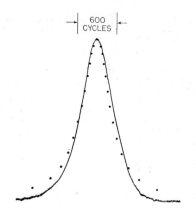

FIG. 6. A typical line profile of the Rb Zeeman transitions in a 0.15-gauss magnetic field. The lock-in detector time constant was 0.1 sec. The heavy dots represent a Lorentzian line which was fitted to one side of the curve, and they serve to emphasize the asymmetry.

lations before the equalization by the Zeeman frequency were

$$n_{1,1}:n_{1,0}:n_{1,-1}:n_{0,0}=(1+\delta):1:(1-\delta):1,$$

and after the application of the saturating field they were

$$n_{1,1}:n_{1,0}:n_{1,-1}:n_{0,0}=1:1:1:1.$$

In another experiment the static magnetic field was increased until the transitions ($F=1$, $m=1 \leftrightarrow F=1$, $m=0$) and ($F=1$, $m=0 \leftrightarrow F=1$, $m=-1$) were resolved. The transition ($F=1$, $m=1 \leftrightarrow F=1$, $m=0$) was then saturated. Under these conditions the state populations are predicted to be

$$n_{1,1}:n_{1,0}:n_{1,-1}:n_{0,0}=(1+\tfrac{1}{2}\delta):(1+\tfrac{1}{2}\delta):(1-\delta):1,$$

and hence the ($F=1$, $m=0 \leftrightarrow F=0$, $m=0$) transition is detectable. This was found to be the case. It was also observed that upon saturating both the Zeeman transitions the transition ($F=1$, $m=0 \leftrightarrow F=0$, $m=0$) could no longer be detected.

When the field-dependent transition was detected in this fashion, it was found to be as broad as the field-dependent transitions and its frequency depended somewhat upon the frequency of the oscillator producing the Zeeman transitions. It was decided to determine the hyperfine splitting in hydrogen and tritium by measuring the ($F=1$, $m=\pm1 \leftrightarrow F=0$, $m=0$) field-dependent transitions since they could be measured without an auxiliary oscillator.

A typical line profile for the ($F=1$, $m=1 \leftrightarrow F=0$, $m=0$) transition in atomic hydrogen is shown in Fig. 5. In recording this line and all the others which are reproduced here, the output time constant of the lock-in detector was 0.1 sec. The line is typically 1.4 kc/sec full width at half maximum, and it is somewhat asymmetrical. The rapid falloff occurred on the low-frequency

side of one of the hyperfine lines and on the high-frequency side of the other. The magnitude of the asymmetry varied with the nature and pressure of the buffer gas. Figure 6 shows a typical line profile for the rubidium Zeeman transitions in a low magnetic field with no discharge. This line has about 600 cycles/sec full width at half maximum and is slightly asymmetrical. The width and asymmetry in this line are most probably due to inhomogeneities in the magnetic field and magnetic noise. The transitions in atomic hydrogen were more than twice as broad as the rubidium transitions and more asymmetrical. The Zeeman transitions in hydrogen fell sharply on the low-frequency side of the line while the Zeeman transitions in rubidium fell sharply on the high-frequency side of the line. In order to ascertain the hyperfine splitting of atomic H and T, the transitions ($F=1$, $m=\pm1 \leftrightarrow F=0$, $m=0$) were both measured, and the results were averaged to obtain a nearly field-independent quantity. It was assumed that when the frequencies of the two lines were averaged, the effect of the asymmetry could be ignored. The difference of the frequencies of these two lines was used to compute the second-order correction to obtain the hyperfine splitting.

Table I shows the values of the observed hyperfine splitting of hydrogen for the different buffer gases at

TABLE I. The data taken on the observed hyperfine splitting of H at various pressures of argon, neon, helium, and molecular hydrogen. There are no errors quoted as the statistical ones are much smaller than the disagreement between the various values of $\Delta\nu$ obtained for each buffer gas to zero pressure. The least-squares fit for the data obtained with each buffer gas is

$$\Delta\nu_{\mathrm{obs}}-1\,420\,405\,000 \text{ (cps)}=-0.35\,p(\mathrm{H_2})+721,$$
$$\Delta\nu_{\mathrm{obs}}-1\,420\,405\,000 \text{ (cps)}=-5.38\,p(\mathrm{A})+712,$$
$$\Delta\nu_{\mathrm{obs}}-1\,420\,405\,000 \text{ (cps)}=4.24\,p(\mathrm{He})+698,$$

and

$$\Delta\nu_{\mathrm{obs}}-1\,420\,405\,000 \text{ (cps)}=2.44\,p(\mathrm{Ne})+753.$$

The data with He as a buffer gas was taken primarily for the pressure shift and hence only a few measurements were made. The density of the oil is about 1 g/cc. The partial pressure of H_2 in all Ne, A, and He bulbs was 0.7 mm Hg.

Buffer gas	p (cm of oil)	No. of measurements	$\Delta\nu_{\mathrm{obs}}-1\,420\,405\,000$ (cps)
H₂	25.86	40	722
H₂	44.65	40	684
H₂	58.98	40	709
H₂	71.19	40	698
A	27.88	40	570
A	37.50	40	531
A	53.28	40	372
A	74.77	40	335
He	29.16	10	817
He	35.01	10	857
He	53.33	10	917
He	84.83	10	1058
Ne	69.06	20	886
Ne	27.07	20	776
Ne	35.67	20	841
Ne	42.86	20	872
Ne	27.04	20	828
Ne	42.92	20	891
Ne	56.28	20	915
Ne	81.02	20	953

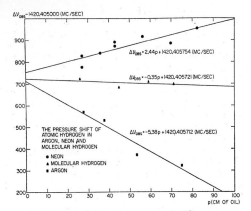

FIG. 7. A plot of $\Delta\nu_{obs}$ versus pressure for H in argon, neon, and molecular hydrogen buffer gases.

TABLE II. The data on the observed hyperfine structure of T at various pressures of neon and argon. The least-squares fit to the data for each gas is

$$\Delta\nu_{obs}-1\ 516\ 701\ 000\ (cps)=-2.97\ p(A)+382,$$

and

$$\Delta\nu_{obs}-1\ 516\ 701\ 000\ (cps)=4.49\ p(Ne)+410.$$

The oil has a density of about 1 g/cc. The partial pressure of T_2 in each bulb was 1.2 mm Hg.

Buffer gas	p (cm of oil)	No. of measurements	$\Delta\nu_{obs}-1\ 516\ 701\ 000$ (cps)
A	27.27	40	304
A	42.69	40	249
A	60.15	40	206
Ne	27.01	40	525
Ne	42.69	40	614
Ne	62.18	40	684

the various pressures. The results of these measurements are shown graphically in Fig. 7 and Fig. 8. The same quantities for tritium are given in Table II and Fig. 9. The values of the hyperfine splittings of H and T seemed to fluctuate in a nonstatistical manner from night to night. As an example of this behavior, Table III gives all the data on one of the H bulbs. The amount by which the lines determined for the various buffer gases fail to meet in a point at zero pressure has been taken as a measure of the error in the hyperfine splitting of the two isotopes. (See footnote 19.) The results are

$$\Delta\nu(H)=1420.405726\pm0.000030,$$

$$\Delta\nu(T)=1516.701396\pm0.000030.$$

The result for hydrogen agrees very well with the most recent atomic beam result of Kusch[8] and the paramagnetic resonance result of Wittke and Dicke[6] with

no pressure shift correction. The value for tritium disagrees with the atomic beam measurement of Prodell and Kusch.[5]

In deuterium the two lines ($F=\frac{3}{2}$, $m=\pm\frac{1}{2} \leftrightarrow F=\frac{1}{2}$, $m=\mp\frac{1}{2}$) are nearly field independent; they differ by only $2g_I\mu_0H/h$. Both of these lines were detected, and they were equal in intensity as is predicted by the spin-exchange theory. These two lines were measured in order to determine the hyperfine splitting in D. A typical line profile is shown in Fig. 10. The linewidth was approximately 175 cycles/sec. This width increased rapidly when the discharge intensity and hence the atom concentration was increased. If it is assumed that this linewidth is entirely due to the spin-exchange collisions of the deuterium atoms, then this linewidth can be used to estimate the concentration of atoms. The result is

$$N(D)=\frac{2\pi\delta\nu}{\sqrt{2}v\bar{\sigma}}=\frac{6.28\times175}{1.41\times4.4\times10^{-15}\times2.0\times10^5}$$

$$=10^{12}\ atoms/cm^3,$$

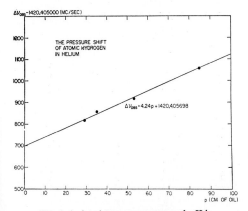

FIG. 8. A plot of $\Delta\nu_{obs}$ versus pressure for H in a helium buffer gas.

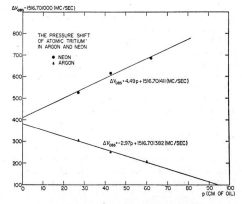

FIG. 9. A plot of $\Delta\nu_{obs}$ versus pressure for T in neon and argon buffer gases.

TABLE III. The data for the bulb at 44.65 cm of oil pressure of pure H_2. The errors quoted are $2\sigma/\sqrt{n}$ where

$$\sigma = [\Sigma(\epsilon_i)^2/(n-1)]^{\frac{1}{2}};$$

$n=$ the total number of measurements, and $\epsilon_i=$ the deviation from the average for each individual measurement. The total average for the four nights is $\Delta\nu_{obs}=1420.405684\pm0.000012$, where the error here, is also, $2\sigma/\sqrt{n}$. It is clear that the measurements from one night do not always overlap the measurements from the other nights. It is also clear from Fig. 7 that the measurements on this bulb do not overlap the least-squares fit to the line through all the points taken on pure H_2 bulbs. This type of data on H and T led us to believe that the errors were not altogether statistical and led us to assign the amount by which the lines determined for the various buffer gases fail to meet in a point at zero pressure as an estimate of our error. In the case of D the errors appeared to be statistical.

	Hyperfine splitting (Mc/sec)		
First night	Second night	Third night	Fourth night
1420.405666	1420.405689	1420.405738	1420.405693
680	688	765	710
625	670	666	726
698	663	683	698
586	716	710	686
663	739	718	702
558	656	707	694
586	694	765	679
621	681	675	697
673	693	700	694
1420.405635±0.000033	1420.405690±0.000015	1420.405698±0.000007	1420.405698±0.000007

where $\bar{\sigma}$ is the spin-exchange cross section (4.4×10^{-15} cm²) and v is the velocity of the deuterium atom (2.0×10^5 cm/sec). The concentration of rubidium atoms can be determined from the known vapor pressure of rubidium. It is

$$N(\text{Rb}) = 9\times10^{10} \text{ atoms/cm}^3.$$

The Zeeman transitions in D were used to compute the second-order correction. Table IV gives the data obtained for D; Fig. 11 shows a plot of these data. In the case of deuterium, where the observed transitions are field independent, the errors appear to be purely sta-

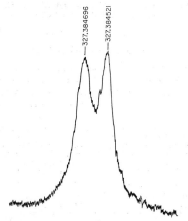

FIG. 10. A typical line profile for the $(F=\frac{3}{2}, m=-\frac{1}{2} \leftrightarrow F=\frac{3}{2}, m=\frac{1}{2})$ and $(F=\frac{3}{2}, m=\frac{1}{2} \leftrightarrow F=\frac{3}{2}, m=-\frac{1}{2})$ hyperfine transitions of atomic deuterium in a neon buffer gas. The separation of the two peaks is equal to twice the nuclear resonance frequency for the deuteron in a field of 0.15 gauss. The markers were made with only one direction of frequency sweep and serve only to mark the separation of the two peaks and the linewidth. The lock-in detector time constant was 0.1 sec.

tistical. The value obtained for the zero-field hyperfine splitting is

$$\Delta\nu(\text{D}) = 327.384349\pm0.000005 \text{ Mc/sec}.$$

This value is only slightly outside the quoted error of the atomic beam result of Kusch.[8] The final results of the measurements on the hyperfine structures of H, D, and T obtained by extrapolating to zero pressure are shown in Table V.

The results of the work on the pressure shifts of the hyperfine splittings of H, D, and T are given for $T=50°C$ in Table VI. In Fig. 12 these fractional pressure shifts (the pressure shift divided by the hyperfine separation) have been plotted versus the optical polarizability of the buffer gas as has been suggested by Rank, Birtley, Eastman, and Wiggins.[18]

TABLE IV. The data taken on the observed hyperfine structure of D at various pressures of neon and argon. Each error quoted is

$$\sigma = [\Sigma(\epsilon_i)^2/(n-1)]^{\frac{1}{2}},$$

where ϵ_i is the deviation of an individual measurement from the mean and n is the total number of measurements. The least squares fit to the points (for each gas) is

$$\Delta\nu_{obs} - 327\ 384\ 000 \text{ (cps)} = 0.95\ p(\text{A}) + 350\pm5,$$

and

$$\Delta\nu_{obs} - 327\ 384\ 000 \text{ (cps)} = 0.65\ p(\text{Ne}) + 347\pm5,$$

where the errors quoted in the zero-pressure extrapolation are one standard deviation. The oil has a density of about 1 g/cc. The partial press of D_2 was 0.7 mm Hg in all bulbs.

Buffer gas	p (cm of oil)	No. of measurements	$\Delta\nu_{obs} - 327\ 384\ 000$ (cps)
A	28.80	20	324±3
A	43.82	20	310±5
A	64.99	20	291±5
Ne	26.07	15	365±6
Ne	40.55	15	374±6
Ne	55.10	15	380±6
Ne	72.62	15	396±6

[18] D. H. Rank, W. B. Birtley, D. P. Eastman, and T. A. Wiggins, J. Chem. Phys. 32, 298 (1960).

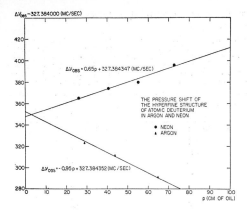

FIG. 11. A plot of $\Delta\nu_{obs}$ versus pressure for D in neon and argon buffer gases. The second value of the term $\Delta\nu_{obs}$ should read 350.

There is an apparent dependence of the pressure shift upon the hydrogen isotope being studied. In view of the behavior of the data taken on the hydrogen and tritium bulbs, it is not clear whether or not the apparent shift is statistically significant.[19]

Since the ratio of the nuclear magnetic moments of H and T has recently been remeasured with high precision,[20] a new value for the hyperfine anomaly can

TABLE V. The measured hyperfine splittings obtained by extrapolating to zero pressure.

Hydrogen isotope	Buffer gas	Number of bulbs at different pressures	Number of observations per blub	Hyperfine splitting in Mc/sec
H	A	4	40	1420.405712
H	Ne	8	20	753
H	H_2	4	40	721
H	He	4	10	698
Average				1420.405726
D	A	3	20	327.384350
D	Ne	4	15	347
Average				327.384349
T	A	3	40	1516.701382
T	Ne	3	40	410
Average				1516.701396

[19] *Note added in proof.* Since this article was submitted for publication, the apparatus has been improved, and it has been found possible to reduce the linewidth of the magnetic field dependent transitions in hydrogen and tritium from 1400 cps to 300 cps. Measurements made with the narrower line indicate that even with the procedure used in this paper the shape of the magnetic field dependent line is not stable enough to make meaningful the repeatability with which the center of the line can be measured. These further measurements indicate that the variation of the fractional pressure shifts from tritium to deuterium is less than 10%. These measurements also indicate that the value of the tritium hyperfine splitting quoted in this paper is too small by approximately 80 cps.
[20] W. Duffy, Jr., Phys. Rev. **115**, 1012 (1959).

be determined. The result is

$$\delta_{H-T} = \frac{[A(H)/A(T)][m(T)/m(H)]}{g(H)/g(T)} - 1$$
$$= 0.0000058 \pm 0.0000001,$$

where A is the magnetic hyperfine structure interaction constant, g is the nuclear g factor, and m is the reduced mass. The H-D hyperfine anomaly is essentially unchanged from its previous value. This value is

$$\delta_{H-D} = \frac{[A(H)/A(D)][m(D)/m(H)]}{g(H)/g(D)} - 1$$
$$= 0.0001703 \pm 0.0000005.$$

CORRECTION FROM THE ATOMICHRON TIME SCALE TO THE A-1 TIME SCALE

In the A-1 time scale the Cs frequency is

$$\Delta\nu = 9192.631770 \pm 0.000020 \text{ Mc/sec}.$$

The Atomichron was designed on the assumption that $\Delta\nu = 9192.631840$ Mc/sec. Thus a small correction is necessary to change the frequencies previously quoted to the A-1 time scale. The frequencies based on the

TABLE VI. The pressure shift data. The pressure in each bulb was measured at room temperature with an oil manometer when the bulb was prepared; the measurements of the hyperfine splittings were made with the bulb at 50°C. In computing the pressure shifts at 50°C the perfect gas law was used to correct the pressure. The error in the pressure shifts is estimated to be 20%.

Hydrogen isotope	Buffer gas	Pressure shift cycles/sec mm Hg	Pressure shift/$\Delta\nu$ (mm Hg)$^{-1} \times 10^{-9}$
H	A	−3.59	−2.53
H	He	+2.83	+2.00
H	Ne	+1.62	+1.14
H	H_2	−0.24	−0.17
D	A	−0.63	−1.94
D	Ne	+0.44	+1.34
T	A	−1.98	−1.31
T	Ne	+2.99	+1.98

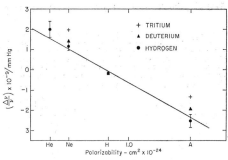

FIG. 12. A plot of the pressure shifts of the hydrogen isotopes versus the optical polarizability of the buffer gas.

A-1 time scale are

$$\Delta\nu(\mathrm{H}) = 1420.405716 \pm 0.000030,$$

$$\Delta\nu(\mathrm{D}) = 327.384347 \pm 0.000005,$$

and

$$\Delta\nu(\mathrm{T}) = 1516.701386 \pm 0.000030$$

ACKNOWLEDGMENTS

We are particularly indebted to Mr. Larry Donaldson for his aid as a glassblower in the preparation of the many bulbs. We also wish to thank Mr. J. A. Pierce for his cooperation in permitting us to take frequency standards from the output of the Atomichron.

Reprinted from The Physical Review, Vol. 121, No. 6, 1864, March 15, 1961
Printed in U. S. A.

Hyperfine Structure of Hydrogen, Deuterium, and Tritium,

L. Wilmer Anderson, Francis M. Pipkin, and James C. Baird, Jr. [Phys. Rev. **120**, 1279 (1960)]. On page 1288, the expression

$$\delta_{\mathrm{H-T}} = \frac{[A(\mathrm{H})/A(\mathrm{T})][m(\mathrm{T})/m(\mathrm{H})]}{g(\mathrm{H})/g(\mathrm{T})} - 1$$

$$= 0.0000058 \pm 0.0000001$$

should read

$$\delta_{\mathrm{H-T}} = \frac{[A(\mathrm{H})/A(\mathrm{T})][m(\mathrm{T})/m(\mathrm{H})]^3}{g(\mathrm{H})/g(\mathrm{T})} - 1$$

$$= 0.0000058 \pm 0.0000001.$$

A similar omission was made for $\delta_{\mathrm{H-D}}$.

Reprinted from The Physical Review, Vol. 122, No. 6, 1962, June 15, 1961
Printed in U. S. A.

Hyperfine Structure of Hydrogen, Deuterium, and Tritium,

L. Wilmer Anderson, Francis M. Pipkin, and James C. Baird, Jr. [Phys. Rev. **120**, 1279 (1960)]. In constructing Table VI, the pressure shifts in cycles/sec mm Hg were calculated incorrectly from the measured pressure shifts in cycles/sec cm oil. The correct entries for Table VI are:

Hydrogen isotope	Buffer gas	Pressure shift cycles/sec mm Hg	(Pressure shift/$\Delta\nu$) $\times 10^9$ (mm Hg)$^{-1}$
H	A	−6.6	−4.7
H	He	+5.2	+3.7
H	Ne	+3.0	+2.1
H	H_2	−0.44	−0.31
D	A	−1.2	−3.6
D	Ne	+0.81	+2.5
T	A	−3.7	−2.4
T	Ne	+5.5	+3.7

Because of this correction the ordinate scale in Fig. 12 should read

$$(1/1.86)(\Delta\nu/\nu) \times 10^{+9}/\mathrm{mm\ Hg}.$$

The most recent values for the pressure shift of the hyperfine interaction in H and T are given in the following abstract:

Reprinted from The Physical Review, Vol. 127, No. 3, 787–792, August 1, 1962
Printed in U. S. A.

Hyperfine Splittings of Hydrogen and Tritium. II*†

F. M. Pipkin‡ and R. H. Lambert§
Lyman Laboratory, Harvard University, Cambridge, Massachusetts
(Received March 22, 1962; revised manuscript received April 20, 1962)

The spin-exchange optical polarization method was used to remeasure the zero-field hyperfine splittings of atomic hydrogen and atomic tritium. The transmission of circularly polarized rubidium resonance radiation through a flask containing rubidium, atomic hydrogen, or atomic tritium, and a buffer gas was monitored as a function of the frequency of an applied radio-frequency field. Measurements were made for hydrogen in helium, neon, molecular hydrogen, and argon buffer gases and for tritium in neon and argon buffer gases. The values of the hyperfine splittings obtained are $\Delta\nu(\mathrm{H}) = 1\ 420\ 405\ 749.1 \pm 6.0$ cps; $\Delta\nu(\mathrm{T}) = 1\ 516\ 701\ 476.8 \pm 6.0$ cps. The assigned limits of error represent the range of disagreement of the zero-pressure extrapolations in the different buffer gases. The fractional pressure shifts [pressure shift in cps/mm Hg divided by hyperfine splitting in kMc/sec] for hydrogen in helium, neon, molecular hydrogen, and argon are 4.80 ± 0.09, 2.88 ± 0.05, -0.56 ± 0.10, and -4.77 ± 0.12, respectively. Those for tritium in neon and argon are 3.24 ± 0.09 and -5.05 ± 0.15, respectively.

From: *Phys. Rev.* **132**, 2154–2158 (1963)

Effect of Hydrogen-Hydrogen Exchange Collisions

P. L. BENDER

Joint Institute for Laboratory Astrophysics, Boulder, Colorado

(Received 23 July 1963)

Exchange collisions between ground-state hydrogen atoms are considered. The density matrix after collision is calculated for pairs of atoms which initially had the same density matrix. The result is applied to the hydrogen maser with the assumption that only exchange collisions and the escape of atoms from the storage bulb influence the linewidth for the field-independent hyperfine transition. Under normal operating conditions a frequency shift of roughly 5% of the exchange collision contribution to the linewidth is predicted.

1. INTRODUCTION

THE effect of exchange collisions between ground-state hydrogen atoms has been treated by a number of authors.[1-6] In particular, Wittke and Dicke considered a case where departures from thermal equilibrium were small and the only nonzero off-diagonal elements of the density matrix for the ground-state sublevels were those corresponding to the magnetic field-independent $(F=1, M_F=0) \rightarrow (F=0, M_F=0)$ component of the hyperfine transition. The nuclear spins and all magnetic interaction energies can be neglected during collisions and the electron wave functions for the two colliding atoms can be combined to form triplet and singlet states. The effect of a collision is to multiply the triplet and singlet parts of the wave function by $e^{-i\Delta_T}$ and $e^{-i\Delta_S}$ respectively. Δ_T is the integral of $(E_T/\hbar)$ over the time of the collision, where E_T is the triplet state hydrogen-hydrogen interaction energy, and Δ_S is defined similarly. Wittke and Dicke made the approximation that only "strong" collisions were important, where "strong" collisions are those in which the relative phase shift $\Delta = \Delta_T - \Delta_S$ is large enough so that the relative phase after the collision can be considered random.

In the present paper the approximations of strong collisions and of small departures from equilibrium are removed. The effect on the density matrix of a single hydrogen-hydrogen collision for each atom in the

sample is given in Sec. 2. The resulting effect on operation of the hydrogen maser[7] is discussed in Sec. 3. The expected frequency shift is estimated in Sec. 4 using straight-line paths with the triplet and singlet interaction potentials of Dalgarno and Lynn.[4,8] A shift in the field-independent hyperfine transition of up to 5% of the exchange collision contribution to the linewidth is predicted.

2. EFFECT OF A SINGLE COLLISION WITH ARBITRARY PHASE SHIFT

The initial 4×4 density matrix[9] ρ^i for the magnetic sublevels of ground-state hydrogen atoms is written in the F, M_F representation:

$$\rho^i = \begin{array}{c|cccc} {}_{F, M_F}\diagdown^{F, M_F} & 1,1 & 1,0 & 1,-1 & 0,0 \\ \hline 1,1 & a & e^* & f^* & h^* \\ 1,0 & e & b & g^* & j^* \\ 1,-1 & f & g & c & k^* \\ 0,0 & h & j & k & d \end{array} \quad (1)$$

The 16×16 density matrix σ^i for a pair of colliding atoms just before collision in the $F_1 M_{F_1} F_2 M_{F_2}$ representation is the direct product of ρ^i with itself. σ^i is transformed by a unitary transformation Γ to a representation $SM_S I M_I$ where the two electron spins and

[1] J. P. Wittke and R. H. Dicke, Phys. Rev. **103**, 620 (1956).
[2] J. P. Wittke, Thesis, Princeton University, 1955 (unpublished).
[3] E. M. Purcell and G. B. Field, Ap. J. **124**, 542 (1956).
[4] A. Dalgarno, Proc. Roy. Soc. (London) **A262**, 132 (1961).
[5] A. F. Hildebrandt, F. B. Booth, and C. A. Barth, J. Chem. Phys. **31**, 273 (1959).
[6] R. M. Mazo, J. Chem. Phys. **34**, 169 (1961).

[7] D. Kleppner, H. M. Goldenberg, and N. F. Ramsey, Phys. Rev. **126**, 603 (1962).
[8] A. Dalgarno and N. Lynn, Proc. Phys. Soc. (London) **A69**, 821 (1956).
[9] U. Fano, Rev. Mod. Phys. **29**, 74 (1957); see also C. P. Slichter, *Principles of Magnetic Resonance* (Harper and Row, New York, 1963), Chap. 5.

TABLE I. Representation transformation matrix $\Gamma = \langle SM_SIM_I | F_1M_{F_1}F_2M_{F_2} \rangle$.

SM_SIM_I \ $F_1M_{F_1}$, $F_2M_{F_2}$	11, 11	11, 10	11, 1 −1	11, 00	10, 11	10, 10	10, 1 −1	10, 00	1 −1, 11	1 −1, 10	1 −1, 1 −1	1 −1, 00	00, 11	00, 10	00, 1 −1	00, 00
11, 11	1	0	0	0	0	0	0	0	0	0	0	0	0	0	0	0
11, 10	0	½	0	½	½	0	0	0	0	0	0	0	½	0	0	0
11, 1 −1	0	0	0	0	0	½	0	½	0	0	0	0	0	½	0	½
11, 00	0	½	0	½	−½	0	0	0	0	0	0	0	−½	0	0	0
10, 11	0	½	0	−½	½	0	0	0	0	0	0	0	−½	0	0	0
10, 10	0	0	½	0	0	½	0	0	½	0	0	0	0	0	0	−½
10, 1 −1	0	0	0	0	0	0	½	0	0	½	0	½	0	0	0	0
10, 00	0	0	½	0	0	0	0	½	−½	0	0	0	0	−½	½	0
1 −1, 11	0	0	0	0	0	½	0	−½	0	0	0	0	0	−½	0	½
1 −1, 10	0	0	0	0	0	0	½	0	0	½	0	−½	0	0	−½	0
1 −1, 1 −1	0	0	0	0	0	0	0	0	0	0	1	0	0	0	0	0
1 −1, 00	0	0	0	0	0	0	½	0	0	−½	0	½	0	0	−½	0
00, 11	0	½	0	−½	−½	0	0	0	0	0	0	0	½	0	0	0
00, 10	0	0	½	0	0	0	0	−½	−½	0	0	0	0	½	0	0
00, 1 −1	0	0	0	0	0	0	½	0	0	−½	0	−½	0	0	½	0
00, 00	0	0	½	0	0	−½	0	0	½	0	0	0	0	0	0	½

the two nuclear spins are coupled:

$$\sigma^{ci} = \Gamma \sigma^i \Gamma^*. \tag{2}$$

The matrix Γ (see Wittke,[2] Appendix 2) is reproduced in Table I.

The effect of a collision yielding a phase shift Δ between the parts of the density matrix corresponding to triplet and singlet electron states can be given by a unitary transformation A:

$$\sigma^{cf} = A\sigma^{ci}A^*. \tag{3}$$

A is diagonal and has unit diagonal elements except for the elements connecting $S=0$, $M_S=0$ states, which are $e^{i\Delta}$. We can also write A as follows:

$$A = I - (x/4)B, \tag{4}$$

where $x = (1-e^{i\Delta})$, B has all elements zero except the last four diagonal elements which are 4, and I is the identity matrix. Transforming back to the $F_1M_{F_1}F_2M_{F_2}$ representation,

$$\sigma^f = \Gamma^* A \Gamma \sigma^i \Gamma^* A^* \Gamma = \left[I - \left(\frac{x}{4}\right)C\right]\sigma^i\left[I - \left(\frac{x^*}{4}\right)C^*\right],$$
$$\sigma^f = \sigma^i + \tfrac{1}{16}|x|^2 C\sigma^i C^* - \tfrac{1}{4}[xC\sigma^i + x^*\sigma^i C^*], \tag{5}$$

where $C = \Gamma^* B \Gamma$ is given in Table II. Since $C^* = C$ and

TABLE II. Matrix $C = \Gamma^* B \Gamma$.

$F_1M_{F_1}$, $F_2M_{F_2}$ \ $F_1M_{F_1}$, $F_2M_{F_2}$	11, 11	11, 10	11, 1 −1	11, 00	10, 11	10, 10	10, 1 −1	10, 00	1 −1, 11	1 −1, 10	1 −1, 1 −1	1 −1, 00	00, 11	00, 10	00, 1 −1	00, 00
11, 11	0	0	0	0	0	0	0	0	0	0	0	0	0	0	0	0
11, 10	0	+1	0	−1	−1	0	0	0	0	0	0	0	+1	0	0	0
11, 1 −1	0	0	+2	0	0	−1	0	−1	0	0	0	0	0	+1	0	+1
11, 00	0	−1	0	+1	+1	0	0	0	0	0	0	0	−1	0	0	0
10, 11	0	−1	0	+1	+1	0	0	0	0	0	0	0	−1	0	0	0
10, 10	0	0	−1	0	0	+1	0	0	−1	0	0	0	0	0	0	−1
10, 1 −1	0	0	0	0	0	0	+1	0	0	−1	0	−1	0	0	+1	0
10, 00	0	0	−1	0	0	0	0	+1	+1	0	0	0	0	−1	0	0
1 −1, 11	0	0	0	0	0	−1	0	+1	+2	0	0	0	0	−1	0	+1
1 −1, 10	0	0	0	0	0	0	−1	0	0	+1	0	+1	0	0	−1	0
1 −1, 1 −1	0	0	0	0	0	0	0	0	0	0	0	0	0	0	0	0
1 −1, 00	0	0	0	0	0	0	−1	0	0	+1	0	+1	0	0	−1	0
00, 11	0	+1	0	−1	−1	0	0	0	0	0	0	0	+1	0	0	0
00, 10	0	0	+1	0	0	0	0	−1	−1	0	0	0	0	+1	0	0
00, 1 −1	0	0	0	0	0	0	+1	0	0	−1	0	−1	0	0	+1	0
00, 00	0	0	+1	0	0	−1	0	0	+1	0	0	0	0	0	0	+1

TABLE III. Density matrix elements after collision with another hydrogen atom having the same initial density matrix.

$\rho_{11}{}^f = a - \frac{1}{4}(1 - \cos\Delta)\{2ac - \frac{1}{2}(b+d)^2 + |j|^2\} - \frac{1}{4}i(\sin\Delta)\{eg^* - ge^*\}$

$\rho_{22}{}^f = b - \frac{1}{4}(1 - \cos\Delta)\{2b - a(1-a) - c(1-c) - \frac{1}{2}(b+d)^2 - |j|^2 - (|e|^2 + |g|^2 - |h|^2 - |k|^2) - (eg^* + ge^*)\} - \frac{1}{4}i(\sin\Delta)\{-2(eg^* - ge^*)\}$

$\rho_{33}{}^f = c - \frac{1}{4}(1 - \cos\Delta)\{2ac - \frac{1}{2}(b+d)^2 + |j|^2\} - \frac{1}{4}i(\sin\Delta)\{eg^* - ge^*\}$

$\rho_{44}{}^f = d - \frac{1}{4}(1 - \cos\Delta)\{2d - a(1-a) - c(1-c) - \frac{1}{2}(b+d)^2 - |j|^2 + (|e|^2 + |g|^2 - |h|^2 - |k|^2) + (eg^* + ge^*)\}$

$\rho_{21}{}^f = e - \frac{1}{4}(1 - \cos\Delta)\{e(b+d+2c) - g(b+d+2a) + jk^* - hj^*\} - \frac{1}{4}i(\sin\Delta)\{e(c-b) + g(a-b) + f(e^* + g^*)\}$

$\rho_{31}{}^f = f - \frac{1}{4}(1 - \cos\Delta)\{2f - (e^* + g^*) - 2hk^*\} - \frac{1}{4}i(\sin\Delta)\{2f(c-a) + (e^2 - g^2)\}$

$\rho_{32}{}^f = g - \frac{1}{4}(1 - \cos\Delta)\{g(b+d+2a) - e(b+d+2c) + hj^* - jk^*\} - \frac{1}{4}i(\sin\Delta)\{e(b-c) + g(b-a) - f(e^* + g^*)\}$

$\rho_{41}{}^f = h - \frac{1}{4}(1 - \cos\Delta)\{h(b+d+2c) - j(e+g)\} - \frac{1}{4}i(\sin\Delta)\{h(c-d) + fk - gj\}$

$\rho_{42}{}^f = j - \frac{1}{4}(1 - \cos\Delta)\{j - k(e+g) - h(e^* + g^*)\} - \frac{1}{4}i(\sin\Delta)\{j(b-d) - ek - hg^*\}$

$\rho_{43}{}^f = k - \frac{1}{4}(1 - \cos\Delta)\{k(b+d+2a) - j(e^* + g^*)\} - \frac{1}{4}i(\sin\Delta)\{k(a-d) + hf^* - je^*\}$

$|x|^2 = 2(1 - \cos\Delta),$

$\sigma^f = \sigma^i - \frac{1}{4}(1 - \cos\Delta)(C\sigma^i + \sigma^i C - \frac{1}{2}C\sigma^i C)$
$\qquad - \frac{1}{4}i(\sin\Delta)(\sigma^i C - C\sigma^i). \quad (6)$

Ignoring the correlation between the atoms which have just collided, the elements of the final 4×4 density matrix ρ^{ft} for all atoms in the sample which underwent collisions at time t are given by a partial contraction of σ^f with respect to F and M_F for one of the two atoms:

$$\rho^{ft}(F_2 M_{F_2}, F_2' M_{F_2'}) = \sum_{F_1 M_{F_1} F_1' M_{F_1'}} \delta(F_1 F_1')\delta(M_{F_1} M_{F_1'})$$
$$\times \sigma^f(F_1 M_{F_1} F_2 M_{F_2}, F_1' M_{F_1'} F_2' M_{F_2'}). \quad (7)$$

We now average over the times at which collisions occur and call the resulting final density matrix ρ^f. Each density matrix element has associated with it a frequency corresponding to the energy difference of the two states connected by that element. If an element of ρ^{ft} contains an element of σ^i having a frequency different by an amount large compared with the reciprocal of the averaging time, then the contribution to ρ^f will be zero. Thus we can break up σ^i into terms having different frequency dependences,

$$\sigma^i = \sigma^i(0) + \sigma^i(\omega_1) + \sigma^i(\omega_2) + \cdots \quad (8)$$

and only the contribution of $\sigma^i(\omega_n)$ to the corresponding elements of $\sigma^f(\omega_n)$ and thereby $\rho^f(\omega_n)$ should be included.

With the above prescription and Eqs. (6) and (7), we can now calculate ρ^f in terms of ρ^i. We assume the low field case where the two Zeeman frequencies are equal but all other frequencies are quite different. The results for ρ^f are given in Table III. The phase shift in $\rho_{42}{}^f$ is particularly significant, since this corresponds to a small frequency shift in the magnetic-field-independent hyperfine component whose frequency ω_H can be measured precisely in the hydrogen maser.

3. APPLICATION TO THE HYDROGEN MASER

The rate of change of the density matrix for hydrogen atoms in a hydrogen maser[7] can be written as the sum of three terms:

$$\left(\frac{d\rho}{dt}\right) = \left(\frac{d\rho}{dt}\right)_{\text{flow}} + \left(\frac{d\rho}{dt}\right)_{\text{exchange}} + \left(\frac{d\rho}{dt}\right)_{\text{radiation}} \quad (9)$$

Here the flow term corresponds to atoms entering and leaving the storage bulb, the exchange term represents exchange collisions between hydrogen atoms, and the radiation term involves the effects of a microwave field capable of producing transitions between the (1,0) and (0,0) states. The effect of the energy separation between the levels is included in the radiation term. Possible line broadening and frequency shifts due to collisions with the walls or anything else except exchange collisions with hydrogen atoms are not included and we assume that the only off-diagonal elements of the density matrix are those corresponding to the desired hyperfine transition component.

We take the flow term with the same ordering of states as in Eq. (1) to be

$$\left(\frac{d\rho}{dt}\right)_{\text{flow}} = r \begin{vmatrix} \frac{1}{2} & & & \\ & \frac{1}{2} & & \\ & & 0 & \\ & & & 0 \end{vmatrix} - r\rho, \quad (10)$$

where r corresponds to the rate at which hydrogen atoms flow into and out of the storage bulb. We have assumed that only atoms in the (1,1) and (1,0) states are passed by the state selector. Here $(1/r)$ is the mean time that atoms spend in the bulb.

The exchange term is given approximately by:

$$\left(\frac{d\rho}{dt}\right)_{\text{exchange}} = -2\pi n\bar{v}_{\text{rel}}\left[\int_0^\infty \{\rho - \rho^f[\Delta(R)]\}R\,dR\right], \quad (11)$$

where n is the number of hydrogen atoms per cm³ and $\bar{v}_{\text{rel}}$ is the mean relative velocity. $\rho^f[\Delta(R)]$ is the density matrix for an atom after an exchange collision with impact parameter R and relative velocity $\bar{v}_{\text{rel}}$ with another atom also having the initial density matrix ρ. The elements of $(\rho - \rho^f[\Delta])$ in terms of the elements of ρ may be obtained from Table III.

The nonzero elements of the radiation term can most easily be obtained from the equations of time-dependent perturbation theory for an undisturbed atom:

$$\dot{a}_2 = -i(\omega_0/2)a_2 - i\beta e^{-i\omega t}a_4,$$
$$\dot{a}_4 = i(\omega_0/2)a_4 - i\beta e^{i\omega t}a_2. \tag{12}$$

a_2 and a_4 correspond to the $(1,0)$ and $(0,0)$ levels, respectively, and ω_0 is the unperturbed transition frequency between these two levels. The nonzero matrix elements of the term in the Hamiltonian giving the effect of an oscillating magnetic field near this transition frequency are taken to be

$$H_{42} = \hbar\beta e^{-i\omega t}, \quad H_{24} = H_{42}^*, \tag{13}$$

where β is real. The oppositely rotating terms in the matrix elements have been omitted since they are unimportant for weak oscillating fields. The results are

$$(d/dt)(a_4a_2^*) = \dot{a}_4a_2^* + a_4\dot{a}_2^* = i\omega_0 a_4 a_2^*$$
$$- i\beta(|a_2|^2 - |a_4|^2)e^{i\omega t}, \tag{14}$$

$$(d/dt)|a_2|^2 = -(d/dt)|a_4|^2 = 2\beta \operatorname{Im}(a_4 a_2^* e^{-i\omega t}).$$

This gives for the density matrix:

$$(d/dt)(\rho_{42})_{\mathrm{rad}} = i\omega_0\rho_{42} - i\beta(\rho_{22}-\rho_{44})e^{i\omega t}, \tag{15}$$

$$(d/dt)(\rho_{22})_{\mathrm{rad}} = -(d/dt)(\rho_{44})_{\mathrm{rad}}$$
$$= 2\beta \operatorname{Im}(\rho_{42}e^{-i\omega t}). \tag{16}$$

From Eq. (9) and Table III we have:

$$d(\rho_{42})/dt = -r\rho_{42} - \tfrac{1}{4}\{U + iV(\rho_{22}-\rho_{44})\}\rho_{42}$$
$$+ i\omega_0\rho_{42} - i\beta(\rho_{22}-\rho_{44})e^{i\omega t}, \tag{17}$$

$$d(\rho_{22}-\rho_{44})/dt = \tfrac{1}{2}r - (\rho_{22}-\rho_{44})r - \tfrac{1}{2}U(\rho_{22}-\rho_{44})$$
$$+ 4\beta \operatorname{Im}(\rho_{42}e^{-i\omega t}), \tag{18}$$

where

$$U = 2\pi n\bar{v}_{\mathrm{rel}}\int_0^\infty [1 - \cos\Delta(R)]R\,dR, \tag{19}$$

$$V = 2\pi n\bar{v}_{\mathrm{rel}}\int_0^\infty [\sin\Delta(R)]R\,dR.$$

These equations have a quasistationary solution obtained by setting

$$(d/dt)(\rho_{mm}) = 0, \quad \rho_{42} = \delta e^{i\omega t}. \tag{20}$$

This solution is:

$$\delta = -i\beta(\rho_{22}-\rho_{44})/[K + i(\omega-\omega')], \tag{21}$$

$$(\rho_{22}-\rho_{44}) = \{2 + (U/r)$$
$$+ (8\beta^2 K/r)/[K^2 + (\omega-\omega')^2]\}^{-1}, \tag{22}$$

where

$$K = r + \tfrac{1}{4}U, \tag{23}$$

$$\omega' = \omega_0 - \tfrac{1}{4}(\rho_{22}-\rho_{44})V. \tag{24}$$

The rate of emission per atom is given by

$$\frac{d}{dt}(\rho_{22})_{\mathrm{rad}}$$
$$= \frac{2\beta^2 K}{\{[K^2 + (\omega-\omega')^2][2 + (U/r)] + (8\beta^2 K/r)\}}. \tag{25}$$

From the above expression the stimulated emission is maximum for $\omega = \omega'$. The frequency shift due to exchange collisions is thus given by Eq. (24). At low power levels the full linewidth at half-power is

$$\Delta\omega = 2K. \tag{26}$$

The ratio of the frequency shift to the part of the linewidth due to exchange collisions is then

$$\tfrac{1}{4}(V/U)[1 + (U/2r)]^{-1}. \tag{27}$$

Alternately, the ratio of the frequency shift to the limiting linewidth for low hydrogen density is

$$\tfrac{1}{8}(V/U)[(U/2r)]/[1 + (U/2r)]. \tag{28}$$

4. ESTIMATE OF PARAMETERS FOR HYDROGEN-HYDROGEN COLLISIONS

Given initially that the electron spin for atom 1 is $+\tfrac{1}{2}$ and for atom 2 is $-\tfrac{1}{2}$, the exchange cross section σ_{ex} is associated with the probability that if we make a measurement at a later time we will find $-\tfrac{1}{2}$ for the electron spin of atom 1. In this paper we use the term "exchange collision" more generally to mean an encounter in which an appreciable phase shift between the triplet and singlet parts of the electron wave function occurs, even though the electron spin is not measured after the encounter and therefore we cannot say whether exchange actually occurred. In fact, measuring the electron spin shortly after the encounter would force the phase difference to be a multiple of π and would thereby remove the possibility of obtaining a frequency shift.

The most recent work on the triplet and singlet potentials between two hydrogen atoms in their ground states is that of Dalgarno and Lynn.[4,8] The difference between the triplet and singlet energies can be adequately represented from $4a_0$ to $12a_0$ by[4]

$$\delta(r) = 6.87r^2 e^{-kr}, \tag{29}$$

where r is the distance between the atoms in units of a_0, $k = 1.974$, and δ is in rydbergs. Integrating $[R_\infty c\hbar\delta(r)/\hbar]$ over a straight-line path with impact parameter R to obtain the triplet phase shift minus the singlet phase shift:

$$\Delta(R) = (6.87)(4\pi a_0 c R_\infty/v_{\mathrm{rel}})$$
$$\times \int_0^\infty (x^2 + R^2)e^{-k(x^2+R^2)^{1/2}}dx. \tag{30}$$

Expanding $(x^2+R^2)^{1/2}$ gives:

$$\int_0^\infty (x^2+R^2)e^{-k(x^2+R^2)^{1/2}}dx$$

$$= R^2 e^{-kR} \int_0^\infty e^{-(kx^2/2R)}\left[1+\frac{x^2}{R^2}+\left(\frac{kR}{8}\right)\frac{x^4}{R^4}\right.$$

$$\left. -\left(\frac{kR}{16}\right)\frac{x^6}{R^6}+\cdots\right]dx$$

$$= (\pi R/2k)^{1/2}R^2 e^{-kR}[1+(kR)^{-1}+\tfrac{3}{8}(kR)^{-1}$$

$$-\tfrac{15}{16}(kR)^{-2}+\cdots]. \qquad (31)$$

Since $kR\sim 13$ when $\Delta(R)\sim 1$, we keep only the first term. Setting $v_{\rm rel}=\sqrt{2}\bar{v}$, where $\bar{v}$ is the mean speed, we have:

$$\Delta(R)\simeq KR^{5/2}e^{-kR}, \qquad (32)$$

with

$$K = (13.74)\pi^{3/2}(a_0 c R_\infty/\bar{v})k^{-1/2}. \qquad (33)$$

At 300°K, $\bar{v}=2.51\times 10^5$ cm/sec and $K=3.78\times 10^3$. This gives $\Delta\simeq 1$ at $R=6.55$, and Δ ranges approximately from 0.003 at $R=10$ to 45 at $R=4$.

Using Eq. (32) for $\Delta(R)$, we find:

$$[V/n\bar{v}_{\rm rel}]=2\pi a_0^2 \int_0^\infty R(\sin\Delta)dR$$

$$\simeq 2\pi a_0^2 \int_0^\infty \frac{R}{[k-(2.5/R)]}\left(\frac{\sin\Delta}{\Delta}\right)d\Delta. \qquad (34)$$

By numerical integration up to $\Delta(4)$, using the fact that the first factor under the integral is slowly varying, and ignoring the remainder of the integral:

$$[V/n\bar{v}_{\rm rel}]\simeq 13\pi a_0^2. \qquad (35)$$

Similarly, ignoring $\cos\Delta$ for R up to 4 and making the transformation of Eq. (34) for the rest of the interval,

$$[U/n\bar{v}_{\rm rel}]\simeq 48\pi a_0^2 = 42\times 10^{-16}\ {\rm cm^2}. \qquad (36)$$

Thus the straight-line path approximation gives (V/U) ~ 0.27.

Since $(1/2)[U/n\bar{v}_{\rm rel}]$ is the exchange cross section, Eq. (36) is equivalent to $\sigma_{\rm ex}\simeq 21\times 10^{-16}$ cm², in agreement with Dalgarno's result.[4] Wittke and Dicke[1] found $\sigma_{\rm ex}=23\times 10^{-16}$ cm² using somewhat different potentials and assuming that the phase-shift difference is random if the singlet part of the wave function experiences a close collision by overcoming the centrifugal potential barrier and is zero otherwise. Purcell and Field[3] made essentially the same assumption as Wittke and Dicke and found a strong collision cross section at 300°K which can be converted to $\sigma_{\rm ex}\simeq 22\times 10^{-16}$ cm². Mazo[6] used the experimental linewidth data of Hildebrandt, Booth, and Barth[5] to obtain an experimental exchange cross section at 325°K of $\sigma_{\rm ex}=28.5\times 10^{-16}$ cm². Since the assumptions of Wittke and Dicke, of Purcell and Field, and of Dalgarno all may tend to underestimate the cross section, there is no significant indication that the potentials are inadequate. A complete treatment of the exchange line broadening and frequency shift can be obtained from the method of Baranger.[10,11] For the present purposes we will use the straight-line path value of V and a value of U deduced from the experimental exchange cross section to give an estimated value of 0.2 for (V/U).

5. CONCLUSION

From Secs. 3 and 4 the estimated maximum frequency shift as a function of hydrogen density for the $(1,0)\rightarrow (0,0)$ transition is about 1% of the linewidth and should thus be observable. Under normal hydrogen maser operating conditions, where the exchange broadening is considerably less than the transit time broadening, the shift will be roughly 5% of that part of the linewidth due exchange broadening. While the shift is small, it is of interest both because of the high potential long term stability of hydrogen masers and because of the information the shift can give us about the interaction potentials. The size of the shift is related to the logarithmic derivative of the potential difference curve near the strong collision radius. Similar shifts occur for magnetic-field-dependent transitions, but these would be much harder to observe. The ratio of shift to exchange broadening may be even larger for alkali atoms than for hydrogen.

[10] M. Baranger, Phys. Rev. 112, 855 (1958).
[11] P. L. Bender (to be published).

Spin Exchange in a Cesium–Electron System*

L. C. Balling and F. M. Pipkin

Lyman Laboratory of Physics, Harvard University, Cambridge, Massachusetts

(Received 1 May 1964)

A spin-exchange optical pumping experiment to study collisions between cesium atoms and quasifree electrons is reported. In this experiment, electrons in a weak magnetic field were polarized through spin-exchange collisions with optically pumped cesium atoms. The cesium-electron collisions were the principal source of the electron-resonance linewidth, and they also gave rise to a shift in the center frequency of the electron resonance. The magnitudes of the linewidth and frequency shift depend upon the two-body scattering amplitude for elastic collisions, the cesium polarization, and the cesium density. From measurements of the electron linewidth and the frequency shift, a value is derived for the electron-cesium spin-flip cross section. The spin-flip cross section at 20°C is found to be approximately 3.5×10^{-14} cm^2. The expressions for the linewidth and frequency shift due to spin-exchange collisions of electrons with alkali-metal atoms are generalized to cover the case where there is a spin-orbit interaction between the electron–alkali-metal-atom systems.

INTRODUCTION

R ECENTLY, interest in the scattering of low-energy electrons from alkali atoms has increased. This interest has resulted in the appearance in the literature of new measurements of the momentum transfer cross section for the scattering of low-energy electrons by cesium atoms[1,2] and theoretical calculations for the electron-cesium scattering phase shifts.[3,4] Values for the electron-cesium momentum transfer cross section in the temperature range of 450 to 550°K were obtained by Chen and Raether using microwave techniques to measure the electrical conductivity of a cesium-electron plasma. Flavin and Meyerand used the electron cyclotron resonance to measure the same cross section in the temperature range of 650 to 975°K. This paper reports a spin-exchange optical-pumping experiment performed to study the elastic collisions of electrons and cesium atoms at temperatures near 300°K.

In this experiment, cesium vapor in a magnetic field is polarized by the absorption of circularly polarized optical-resonance radiation incident along the direction of the magnetic field. The polarization is monitored by observing the transmission of the resonance radiation through the flask containing the cesium atoms. Free electrons produced in the flask by the ionizing radiation of tritium or by a radio-frequency discharge are polarized by spin-exchange collisions with the cesium atoms. If a radio-frequency field is adjusted so as to depolarize the electrons, the cesium atoms will also be partially depolarized through the spin-exchange collisions with the electrons, and the intensity of the light transmitted through the flask will decrease accordingly. Under suitable conditions, the electron-cesium collisions dominate other electron spin relaxation mechanisms, such as

collisions with the buffer gas, and are the principal source of the width of the electron resonance signal. They also give rise to a shift in the resonance frequency. Both the frequency shift and the linewidth are functions of the electron-cesium scattering phase shifts. If the scattering is entirely s wave, measurements of the frequency shift and of the linewidth in the limit of zero radio-frequency field yield a value for the spin-flip cross section even if the number of cesium atoms in the flask is unknown.

In a recent paper a complete theoretical treatment of spin-exchange optical-pumping experiments was given, and an experimental study of rubidium-electron collisions was reported.[5] The experiments reported in the present paper are similar to the experiments reported in that paper. The agreement of the cesium-electron measurements with the theory is not completely satisfactory, however. One possible source of this discrepancy could be a spin-orbit interaction in the electron-cesium system. The previous theory assumed there was no spin-orbit interaction. In this paper the theoretical expressions for the electron linewidth and frequency shift are generalized to cover the situation where there is spin-orbit coupling. The first part of this paper summarizes and extends the theory; the second part summarizes the measurements; the third part compares the results of these measurements on the electron-cesium system with the available theoretical calculations and other measurements.

THEORY

In this section we will be primarily concerned with summarizing the theoretical expressions for the electron linewidth and frequency shift and generalizing them to the case where there is spin-orbit coupling. We shall assume that the alkali metal or cesium atom has no nuclear spin. The basic problem in this calculation is to determine the rate of change of the cesium and electron spin-space density matrices due to spin-

* Research supported by a grant from the National Science Foundation (G–19736).

[1] C. L. Chen and M. Raether, Phys. Rev. **128**, 2679 (1962).

[2] R. K. Flavin and R. G. Meyerand, Jr., IEEE Thermionic Converter Specialist Conference, Gatlinburg, Tennessee, October 1963 (unpublished).

[3] L. B. Robinson, Phys. Rev. **127**, 2076 (1962).

[4] P. M. Stone and J. R. Reitz, Phys. Rev. **131**, 2101 (1963).

[5] L. C. Balling, R. J. Hanson, and F. M. Pipkin, Phys. Rev. **133**, A607 (1964).

exchange collisions. For a more complete treatment of the theory the reader should refer to the previous paper.[5]

To describe the electron-cesium scattering, it is convenient to employ the center-of-mass system and to use the coordinates of the electron relative to the cesium atom. The incoming wave for the electron-cesium scattering problem can be written in the form

$$\frac{1}{L^{3/2}} \exp(i\mathbf{k}_0 \cdot \mathbf{r})|s_0\rangle, \qquad (1)$$

where s_0 is the initial electron-cesium atom spin state and the normalization is such that we have one electron in the box. The scattered wave will be

$$\psi(r,\mathbf{k},s)$$
$$= \frac{1}{L^{3/2}}\left[\exp(i\mathbf{k}_0\cdot\mathbf{r})|s_0\rangle + \left(\frac{e^{ikr}}{r}\right)M_{ss_0}(\mathbf{k};\mathbf{k}_0)|s_0\rangle\right], \quad (2)$$

where $M_{ss_0}(\mathbf{k};\mathbf{k}_0)$ is a function of the angle between $\mathbf{k}$ and $\mathbf{k}_0$ and is in general a matrix in spin space which allows for the possibility of changes in spin states during a collision. In the earlier paper it was shown that in terms of the M matrix the time rate of change of the electron density matrix due to spin-exchange collisions with the alkali-metal atom A was

$$d\rho(e)/dt = v_{eA}N_A \,\mathrm{Tr}_A\Big[(2\pi i/k)[M(\theta=0, \phi=0)\rho(e,A)$$
$$- \rho(e,A)M^\dagger(\theta=0, \phi=0)]$$
$$+ \int d\Omega M(\theta,\phi)\rho(e,A)M^\dagger(\theta,\phi)\Big]. \quad (3)$$

Here v_{eA} is the relative velocity of the electrons and the alkali-metal atoms, N_A is the number of alkali atoms per cm³, Tr_A stands for the trace over the alkali-atom spin coordinates, $\rho(e,A)$ is the electron-alkali atom spin-space density matrix, $M(\theta,\phi)$ is an abbreviation for $M_{ss_0}(k;k_0)$, and θ, ϕ are the polar coordinates of the vector $\mathbf{k}$ with respect to $\mathbf{k}_0$. An analogous expression for the time-rate change of the alkali-metal atom can be derived by interchanging A and e. In the earlier paper it was assumed that there was no spin-orbit coupling and that M could be written in the form

$$M = f_3(\theta)P_3 + f_1(\theta)P_1, \qquad (4)$$

where P_3 and P_1 are the projection operators for the triplet and singlet electronic states, f_3 and f_1 are the triplet and singlet scattering amplitudes. In terms of the Pauli spin matrices the projection operators are

$$P_3 = \tfrac{1}{4}(3 + \sigma_e \cdot \sigma_A), \qquad (5)$$

and

$$P_1 = \tfrac{1}{4}(1 - \sigma_e \cdot \sigma_A). \qquad (6)$$

In terms of the triplet and singlet phase shifts, the scattering amplitudes are

$$f_3 = (1/2ik)\sum_{l=0}^{\infty}(2l+1)(e^{2i\delta_l^3}-1)P_l(\cos\theta), \qquad (7)$$

and

$$f_1 = (1/2ik)\sum_{l=0}^{\infty}(2l+1)(e^{2i\delta_l^1}-1)P_l(\cos\theta). \qquad (8)$$

It was further shown that if the alkali metal atom was replaced by an equivalent spin-$\tfrac{1}{2}$ system, the time dependence of the electron density matrix was given by the expression

$$\frac{d\rho(e)}{dt} = \begin{bmatrix} \dfrac{P(A)-P(e)}{2T_{ee}} & \dfrac{1-i\kappa P(A)}{T_{ee}}\rho_{12}(e) \\[2ex] -\dfrac{1+i\kappa P(A)}{T_{ee}}\rho_{21}(e) & \dfrac{P(e)-P(A)}{2T_{ee}} \end{bmatrix}, \qquad (9)$$

where $P(A)$ and $P(e)$ are the electron polarization and the alkali-atom electronic polarization given by the equations

$$P(e) = \rho_{11}(e) - \rho_{22}(e), \qquad (10)$$

and

$$P(A) = \rho_{11}(A) - \rho_{22}(A), \qquad (11)$$

and the spin-exchange relaxation time is given by the equation

$$1/T_{ee} = v_{eA}N_A\sigma_{\mathrm{SF}}. \qquad (12)$$

In terms of the phase shifts, the spin-flip cross section σ_{SF} and the frequency shift parameter κ are given by the equations

$$\sigma_{\mathrm{SF}} = (\pi/k^2)\sum_{l=0}^{\infty}(2l+1)\sin^2(\delta_l^3-\delta_l^1), \qquad (13)$$

and

$$\kappa = (1/\sigma_{\mathrm{SF}})(\pi/2k^2)\sum_{l=0}^{\infty}(2l+1)\sin2(\delta_l^3-\delta_l^1). \qquad (14)$$

The corresponding equations for the time rate of change of the alkali-atom density matrix are

$$\frac{d\rho(A)}{dt} = \begin{bmatrix} \dfrac{P(e)-P(A)}{2T_{eA}} & 0 \\[2ex] 0 & \dfrac{P(A)-P(e)}{2T_{eA}} \end{bmatrix}, \qquad (15)$$

where

$$1/T_{eA} = v_{eA}N_e\sigma_{\mathrm{SF}}. \qquad (16)$$

In this paper we wish to derive the generalization of these expressions when there is also spin-orbit coupling. We shall assume that the potential which describes the interaction between the electron and the alkali atom can be written in the form

$$V(r)+V_1(r)\mathbf{S}\cdot\mathbf{L},\tag{17}$$

where $\mathbf{L}$ is the orbital angular momentum of the electron with respect to the rubidium atom and

$$\mathbf{S}=\tfrac{1}{2}(\boldsymbol{\sigma}_e+\boldsymbol{\sigma}_A).\tag{18}$$

For an interaction of this form there will be a different phase shift for each of the total angular-momentum states derived by coupling $\mathbf{S}$ to $\mathbf{L}$. If we introduce the total angular momentum,

$$\mathbf{J}=\mathbf{S}+\mathbf{L},\tag{19}$$

then in terms of the notation

$$P_{l,j}{}^{2s+1},\tag{20}$$

the projection operators for the states of total angular momemtum j derived from a total spin state s and an angular-momentum state l by coupling $\mathbf{S}$ and $\mathbf{L}$ together in various fashions can be written in the form

$$P_{l,l}{}^{1}=1,\tag{21}$$

$$P_{l,l+1}{}^{3}=\frac{(\mathbf{S}\cdot\mathbf{L}+1)(\mathbf{S}\cdot\mathbf{L}+l+1)}{(l+1)(2l+1)},\tag{22}$$

$$P_{l,l}{}^{3}=\frac{(l-\mathbf{S}\cdot\mathbf{L})(\mathbf{S}\cdot\mathbf{L}+l+1)}{l(l+1)},\tag{23}$$

$$P_{l,l-1}{}^{3}=\frac{(\mathbf{S}\cdot\mathbf{L}-l)(\mathbf{S}\cdot\mathbf{L}+1)}{l(2l+1)}.\tag{24}$$

In terms of these projection operators the M matrix is

$$M(\theta,\phi)=(1/k)\{[\sum_{l=0}^{\infty}(2l+1)e^{i\delta_{ll}{}^{1}}\sin\delta_{ll}{}^{1}P_l(\cos\theta)]\tfrac{1}{4}(1-\boldsymbol{\sigma}_e\cdot\boldsymbol{\sigma}_A)+[e^{i\delta_{01}{}^{3}}\sin\delta_{01}{}^{3}+\sum_{l=1}^{\infty}(2l+1)(e^{i\delta_{l,l+1}{}^{3}}\sin\delta_{l,l+1}{}^{3}P_{l,l+1}{}^{3}$$
$$+e^{i\delta_{l,l}{}^{3}}\sin\delta_{l,l}{}^{3}P_{l,l}{}^{3}+e^{i\delta_{l,l-1}{}^{3}}\sin\delta_{l,l-1}{}^{3}P_{l,l-1}{}^{3})P_l(\cos\theta)]\tfrac{1}{4}(3+\boldsymbol{\sigma}_e\cdot\boldsymbol{\sigma}_A)\}.\tag{25}$$

If this expression is inserted into Eq. (3) and we retain only states of orbital angular momentum 0 and 1, the following expression is obtained for the time rate of change of the electron density matrix:

$$\frac{d\rho(e)}{dt}=\begin{bmatrix}\dfrac{P(A)-P(e)}{2T_{ee1}}-\dfrac{P(A)+P(e)}{2T_{ee3}} & \dfrac{1-i\kappa_1 P(A)}{T_{ee2}}\rho_{12}(e)\\[3mm]-\dfrac{1+i\kappa_1 P(A)}{T_{ee2}}\rho_{21}(e) & \dfrac{P(e)-P(A)}{2T_{ee1}}+\dfrac{P(A)+P(e)}{2T_{ee3}}\end{bmatrix},\tag{26}$$

where

$$1/T_{ee1}=v_{eA}N_A(\pi/k^2)[\sin^2(\delta_{01}{}^{3}-\delta_{00}{}^{1})+2\sin^2(\delta_{12}{}^{3}-\delta_{11}{}^{1})+\sin^2(\delta_{10}{}^{3}-\delta_{11}{}^{1})],\tag{27}$$

$$1/T_{ee3}=v_{eA}N_A(\pi/k^2)[3\sin^2(\delta_{12}{}^{3}-\delta_{11}{}^{3})],\tag{28}$$

$$1/T_{ee2}=v_{eA}N_A(\pi/k^2)[\sin^2(\delta_{01}{}^{3}-\delta_{00}{}^{1})+\tfrac{3}{2}[\sin^2(\delta_{12}{}^{3}-\delta_{11}{}^{1})+\sin^2(\delta_{11}{}^{3}-\delta_{11}{}^{1})]+\sin^2(\delta_{11}{}^{3}-\delta_{10}{}^{3})+\tfrac{1}{2}\sin^2(\delta_{12}{}^{3}-\delta_{11}{}^{3})],\tag{29}$$

and

$$\frac{\kappa_1}{T_{ee2}}=v_{eA}N_A(\pi/2k^2)[\sin2(\delta_{01}{}^{3}-\delta_{00}{}^{1})+\tfrac{3}{2}[\sin2(\delta_{12}{}^{3}-\delta_{11}{}^{1})+\sin2(\delta_{11}{}^{3}-\delta_{11}{}^{1})]$$
$$+\sin2(\delta_{12}{}^{3}-\delta_{10}{}^{3})+\tfrac{3}{2}\sin2(\delta_{11}{}^{3}-\delta_{12}{}^{3})].\tag{30}$$

These expressions are considerably more complicated than the corresponding expressions [Eq. (9)] when there is no spin-orbit coupling. The relaxation time for the off-diagonal elements of the electron density matrix is no longer simply related to the relaxation time for the diagonal elements. The expression for the ratio of the frequency shifts to the linewidth is more complicated. The corresponding expression for the time rate of change of the alkali-atom density matrix is

$$\frac{d\rho(A)}{dt}=\begin{bmatrix}\dfrac{P(e)-P(A)}{2T_{eA1}}-\dfrac{P(A)+P(e)}{2T_{eA3}} & 0\\[3mm]0 & \dfrac{P(A)-P(e)}{2T_{eA1}}+\dfrac{P(A)+P(e)}{2T_{eA3}}\end{bmatrix}.\tag{31}$$

Here

$$1/T_{eA1}=(N_e/N_A)(1/T_{ee1}),\quad\text{and}\quad 1/T_{eA3}=(N_e/N_A)(1/T_{ee3}).$$

If we now use the phenomenological equations

$$\frac{d\rho(e)}{dt} = \begin{bmatrix} \dfrac{\frac{1}{2}-\rho_{11}(e)}{T_{1e}} & \dfrac{\rho_{12}(e)}{T_{2e}} \\[2ex] -\dfrac{\rho_{21}(e)}{T_{2e}} & \dfrac{\frac{1}{2}-\rho_{22}(e)}{T_{1e}} \end{bmatrix} \tag{32}$$

and

$$\frac{d\rho(A)}{dt} = \begin{bmatrix} \dfrac{\frac{1}{2}-\rho_{11}(A)}{T_{1A}} & -\dfrac{\rho_{12}(A)}{T_{2A}} \\[2ex] -\dfrac{\rho_{21}(A)}{T_{2A}} & \dfrac{\frac{1}{2}-\rho_{22}(A)}{T_{1A}} \end{bmatrix} \tag{33}$$

to represent the other relaxation mechanisms, we can use the procedure of the previous paper to derive an expression for the change in light transmitted by the absorption flask when there is a radio-frequency field which can depolarize the electrons. If we assume that there is a static magnetic field H_0 along the direction of the light beam, and a radio-frequency field $2H_1 \cos\omega t$ perpendicular to the light beam, the change in transmitted light is

$$\delta I_T = A A_\alpha(s) \left(\int_0^\infty I(\nu,0)d\nu \right) \left[\frac{\tau^{-1}}{\tau^{-1}+T_{eA1}^{-1}+T_{eA3}^{-1}+T_{1A}^{-1}} \right]$$

$$\times \left[\frac{T_{eA1}^{-1}-T_{eA3}^{-1}}{T_{1A}^{-1}+T_{eA1}^{-1}+T_{eA3}^{-1}-(T_{eA1}^{-1}-T_{eA3}^{-1})((T_{ee1}^{-1}-T_{ee3}^{-1})/(T_{ee1}^{-1}+T_{ee3}^{-1}+T_{1e}^{-1}))} \right]$$

$$\times \left[\frac{T_{ee1}^{-1}-T_{ee3}^{-1}}{T_{ee1}^{-1}+T_{ee3}^{-1}+T_{1e}^{-1}} \right] \left[\frac{\omega_1^2 \tau_1 \tau_2}{1+\omega_1^2 \tau_1 \tau_2 + (\tau_2)^2(\omega_0-\delta\omega_0-\omega)^2} \right]. \tag{34}$$

Here

$$\tau_1 = \frac{\tau^{-1}+T_{1A}^{-1}+T_{eA1}^{-1}+T_{eA3}^{-1}}{(\tau^{-1}+T_{1A}^{-1}+T_{eA1}^{-1}+T_{eA3}^{-1})(T_{1e}^{-1}+T_{ee1}^{-1}+T_{ee3}^{-1})-(T_{eA1}^{-1}-T_{eA3}^{-1})(T_{ee1}^{-1}-T_{ee3}^{-1})}, \tag{35}$$

and

$$\tau_2^{-1} = T_{2e}^{-1} + T_{ee2}^{-1}. \tag{36}$$

In these equations τ is the pumping time, A is the cross-sectional area of the cylindrical absorption flask, $A_\alpha(s)$ is a function which gives the fraction of the incident light absorbed by the flask, $I(\nu,0)$ is the intensity per unit frequency range of the circularly polarized D_1 light incident on the absorption flask, ω_1 is the resonance frequency of the electrons in the field H_1, ω_0 is the resonance frequency of the electrons in the field H_0, and $\delta\omega_0$ is the frequency shift due to spin exchange collisions.[6] In terms of the phase shifts

$$\delta\omega_0 = P(A)(\kappa_1/T_{ee2}). \tag{37}$$

EXPERIMENTAL PROCEDURE AND RESULTS

The apparatus used in this experiment is described in the previous paper on the rubidium-electron system. The experiments were carried out in a magnetic field of 50 mG. The magnetic field was sufficiently homogeneous that the full width at half-maximum of the

cesium Zeeman transitions (350 cps/mG) was 40 cps. The resonance signal was measured by amplitude modulating the radio-frequency field with a mercury relay and observing the demodulated absorption signal with a lock-in detector. The temperatures of the absorption flasks were measured with a copper-constantan thermocouple which was attached to the side of the bulb. Solid carbon dioxide was employed to reach temperatures below 20°C.

Two types of absorption bulbs were used. The first type was a 500-cm³ spherical flask containing cesium, 41 ± 1 mm Hg of a helium buffer gas, and 2 C of tritium. The free electrons were produced through ionization by the tritium beta rays. The second type of absorption bulb consisted of a 300-cm³ flask which was connected by a neck 1 cm in diameter and 1 cm long to a 25-cm³ bulb. The 25-cm³ bulb was constructed with two glass-covered tungsten electrodes, and contained 40.6 mm Hg of a helium buffer gas. A continuous radio-frequency discharge between these two electrodes provided a source of free electrons. The electrons then diffused through the connecting neck into the main absorption flask. This second type of flask was constructed primarily to ensure that the measurements were made on

---

[6] The corresponding equations in Ref. 5 [Eqs. (77) and (79)] contain a misprint. The expression $T_{ee}/(T_{ee}+T_{1R})$ should read $T_{ee}/(T_{ee}+T_{1e})$.

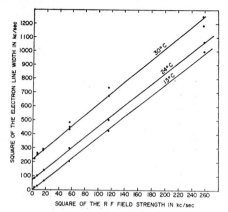

FIG. 1. The square of the full width at half-maximum of the electron line in kc/sec plotted versus the square of the rf field strength in kc/sec for three different temperatures. The slope of these lines is equal to $4\tau_1/\tau_2$; the intercept of the lines is $(1/\pi\tau_2)^2$. The measurements were made in a tritium-helium bulb.

thermal electrons. Identical results were obtained with both types of bulbs. Since there was less background light with the tritium bulbs, they were used for most of the measurements.

The first measurements were directed toward a determination of τ_1 and τ_2 as a function of temperature. According to Eq. (34) the amplitude of the electron resonance signal is described by the equation

$$\delta I_T = (\text{const}) \frac{\omega_1^2 \tau_1 \tau_2}{1 + \omega_1^2 \tau_1 \tau_2 + (\omega_0 - \delta\omega_0 - \omega)^2 (\tau_2)^2}. \quad (38)$$

This equation indicates a method for determining τ_1 and τ_2. A plot of the square of the full width at half-maximum of the electron line versus $(\omega_1/2\pi)^2$ should yield a straight line with a slope of $4\tau_1/\tau_2$ and with a zero radio-frequency intercept of $(1/\pi^2\tau_2^2)$. In order to determine these two relaxation times, measurements were made of the electron linewidth as a function of the strength of the radio-frequency field. Runs were made at various temperatures using both the tritium and the discharge bulbs. The radio-frequency field strength ω_1 was obtained by keeping the radio-frequency oscillator set at the electron frequency and increasing the magnetic field H_0 until the cesium signal was visible on the oscilloscope. The cesium signal was then photographed. This signal showed the characteristic modulation of the pumping light due to the nutation of the cesium moment. Since the magnetic moment of the electron is approximately eight times the atomic moment of the cesium atom (nuclear spin equals $\frac{7}{2}$), ω_1 was obtained from the relationship

$$\omega_1 = 16\pi\nu(\text{cesium}). \quad (39)$$

Figure 1 shows several plots of (linewidth)^2 versus

TABLE I. The values of τ_2 obtained for various bulb temperatures. The values of τ_2 referred to 20°C were obtained from the equation $\tau_2(20°)/\tau_2(T) = N_{Cs}(T)/N_{Cs}(20°)$. Here $N_{Cs}(T)$ is the number of cesium atoms per cm³ at temperature T.

Bulb type	Temperature in °C	τ_2 in sec	τ_2 (20°C) in sec
Tritium-helium	12.5	14.2 ×10⁻⁵	6.5×10⁻⁵
Tritium-helium	16	9.6 ×10⁻⁵	6.3×10⁻⁵
Tritium-helium	20	5.8 ×10⁻⁵	5.8×10⁻⁵
Tritium-helium	24	3.74×10⁻⁵	5.5×10⁻⁵
Tritium-helium	30	2.15×10⁻⁵	5.8×10⁻⁵
Helium -discharge	30	2.15×10⁻⁵	5.8×10⁻⁵

$(\omega_1/2\pi)^2$ for various bulb temperatures. The slopes of the lines indicate that

$$\tau_1/\tau_2 = 1.0 \pm 0.1$$

for all the measured temperatures. Table I summarizes the values of τ_2 determined from the zero radio-frequency field intercepts.

Figure 2 shows a plot of $1/\pi\tau_2$ as a function of temperature. According to Eqs. (36) and (29)

$$1/\tau_2 = 1/T_{2e} + 1/T_{ee2},$$

and

$$\frac{1}{T_{ee2}} \alpha N_A v_{eA} - \alpha \frac{1}{k^2} \frac{p(\text{Cs})}{T^{3/2}}, \quad (40)$$

where $p(\text{Cs})$ is the cesium vapor pressure. The dashed curve is a plot of $p(\text{Cs})T^{-3/2}$ versus temperature and it has been normalized to fit the data in the middle of the temperature range. Table I shows in another fashion the agreement between the measured temperature dependence and the temperature dependence expected if the linewidth is due entirely to spin-exchange collisions. We conclude that $\tau_2 = T_{ee2}$ in

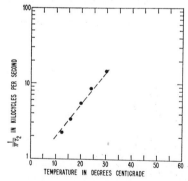

FIG. 2. A plot of $1/\pi\tau_2$ as a function of temperature. The values of $1/\pi\tau_2$ were obtained at each temperature by measuring the zero rf field intercepts of straight line plots such as those shown in Fig. 1. The dashed curve represents the temperature dependence of the function, $p(\text{cesium})T^{-3/2}$. This is the temperature dependence one expects for $1/\pi\tau_2$ if spin-exchange collisions are the principal source of the linewidth.

TABLE II. The measured values of the frequency shift $\delta\nu_0$ at various temperatures. Also listed are the corresponding values of $P(Cs)\kappa$ obtained from the relation $P(Cs)\kappa_1 = 2\pi T_{ee1}\delta\nu_0 = 2\delta\nu_0/\Delta\nu$. Here $P(Cs)$ is the electronic polarization of the cesium and $\Delta\nu$ is the full width at half-maximum of the electron resonance.

Bulb type	Temperature in °C	$\delta\nu_0$ (cps)	$P(Cs)\kappa_1$
Tritium-helium	11	10	−0.011
Tritium-helium	17	23	−0.012
Tritium-helium	20	55	−0.021
Tritium-helium	24.5	65	−0.014
Discharge-helium	30	190	−0.025

the temperature range investigated and that the electron relaxation is dominated by spin-exchange collisions.

The frequency shift due to electron-cesium collisions was measured by first observing the electron resonance frequency with left circularly polarized light and then with right circularly polarized light. This operation changed the sign of the cesium polarization and consequently the direction of the frequency shift. The shift was determined from the equation

$$\delta\nu_0 = \frac{\nu(\text{left}) - \nu(\text{right})}{2}. \tag{41}$$

During measurements of the frequency shift, measurements of the cesium Zeeman frequency were interspersed to correct for drifting of the magnetic field. The electron resonance frequency was higher when left circularly polarized light was incident on the absorption flask and the cesium polarization was positive. Table II summarizes the measured values of the frequency shift. Table II also lists the value of $P(Cs)\kappa_1$ computed from the measured linewidths and frequency shifts by using the equation

$$P(Cs)\kappa_1 = 2\pi T_{ee2}(\delta\nu_0) = 2\delta\nu_0/\Delta\nu, \tag{42}$$

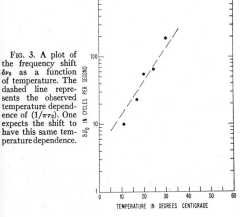

FIG. 3. A plot of the frequency shift $\delta\nu_0$ as a function of temperature. The dashed line represents the observed temperature dependence of $(1/\pi\tau_2)$. One expects the shift to have this same temperature dependence.

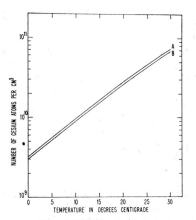

FIG. 4. Plots of the cesium density as a function of temperature. Curve A is derived from the equation (Ref. 7)

$$\log_{10}p(Cs) = (-4041/T) + 11.053 - 1.35\log_{10}T,$$

where $p(Cs)$ is the vapor pressure of cesium in mm Hg and T is the temperature in degrees Kelvin. Curve B is derived from the equation (Ref. 8)

$$\log_{10}p(Cs) = (-4075/T) + 11.38 - 1.45\log_{10}T.$$

where $\Delta\nu$ is the full width at half-maximum of the electron line. The computed values indicate that $2\delta\nu_0/\Delta\nu$ varies slowly with temperature. Figure 3 shows a plot of the measured frequency shifts versus the bulb temperature. Figure 3 also shows the expected temperature dependence if the frequency shift depends only on spin-exchange collisions with the cesium atoms.

Measurements of the relative amplitudes of the cesium Zeeman transitions in a magnetic field sufficiently strong to separate them indicated that the cesium electronic polarization at 20°C was greater than 0.25. This measurement is subject to a systematic error since it is based on a measurement of relative signal amplitudes and not of the absolute signal strength. It is felt that the value 0.25 is a lower limit.

INTERPRETATION

In this section we wish to see what the measurements indicate concerning the cesium electron spin-flip cross section. First let us assume that the scattering is predominantly s wave and that there is no spin-orbit coupling. In this case we can use Eqs. (13) and (14) and the values of the ratio of frequency shift to the linewidth listed in Table II to determine $(\delta_0{}^3 - \delta_0{}^1)$. At 20°C we find that

$$\cot(\delta_0{}^3 - \delta_0{}^1) = -\frac{0.02 \pm 0.01}{P(Cs)}.$$

If we assume that $P(Cs) \geq 0.25$, then

$$-0.01 \geq \cot(\delta_0{}^3 - \delta_0{}^1) \geq -0.12,$$

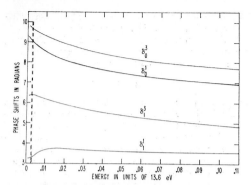

FIG. 5. The singlet and triplet phase shifts for s- and p-wave cesium-electron scattering as calculated by Stone and Reitz (Ref. 4) are plotted as a function of energy in units of 13.6 eV. The dashed lines indicate the energy range of the experiments reported in the present paper, i.e., from 0.0376 to 0.0394 eV.

and it follows that

$$(\delta_0{}^3 - \delta_0{}^1) = -\tfrac{1}{2}\pi + \epsilon \quad \text{or} \quad \tfrac{1}{2}\pi + \epsilon,$$

where ϵ is positive and small.

We can obtain an alternate value for the phase shifts by using the measured values of the linewidth and an expression for the density of cesium atoms in the bulb. There are several expressions for the cesium vapor pressure in the literature; two of these expressions which are considered to be most reliable are plotted in Fig. 4.[7,8] In order to relate the observed linewidth to the theoretical expression, we must average the signal calculated assuming one velocity for the electrons over the electron velocity distribution. The observed signal is a superposition of Lorenzian lines whose widths depend upon the electron velocities. In order to perform this average, we will assume that the electrons have a Maxwell-Boltzmann velocity distribution characterized by the bulb temperature T and that the scattering phase shifts vary slowly with electron temperature. This averaging process yields an expression for the observed linewidth $\Delta\nu$ which is coincidentally the same as that obtained by averaging over a Maxwell-Boltzmann distribution the expression for the linewidth obtained by assuming one velocity for the electrons.

$$\langle \Delta\nu \rangle_{\mathrm{av}} = \left\langle \frac{1}{\pi T_{ee}} \right\rangle_{\mathrm{av}} = N_A \left(\frac{\hbar}{m}\right)^2 \left(\frac{2m}{\pi kT}\right)^{1/2}$$

$$\times \sum_{l=0}^{\infty} (2l+1)\sin^2(\delta_l{}^3 - \delta_l{}^1). \quad (43)$$

[7] G. G. Grau and K. L. Schaefer, *Landolt-Börnstein Zahlenwerte und Funktionen Aus Physik, Chemie, Astronomie, Geophysik, und Technik* (Springer-Verlag, Berlin, 1960), Vol. II, p. 7.
[8] *Metals Reference Handbook*, edited by Colin J. Smithells (Butterworths Scientific Publications Ltd., London, 1955), Vol. II, p. 613.

If we use the observed value of T_{ee} at 20°C and the rubidium density derived from curve A in Fig. 4, we find that

$$\sum_{l=0}^{\infty} (2l+1)\sin^2(\delta_l{}^3 - \delta_l{}^1) = 1.25 \pm 0.1, \quad (44)$$

where the error reflects the uncertainty in the measured linewidths. This result indicates that s-wave scattering alone can not account for the observed spin-flip cross section and that other angular momenta must be present. If we assume there is only s- and p-wave scattering, we should look for simultaneous solutions of the two equations

$$\sin^2(\delta_0{}^3 - \delta_0{}^1) + 3\sin^2(\delta_1{}^3 - \delta_1{}^1) = 1.25 \pm 0.1, \quad (45)$$

and

$$-\frac{1}{2} \frac{\sin 2(\delta_0{}^3 - \delta_0{}^1) + 3\sin 2(\delta_1{}^3 - \delta_1{}^1)}{\sin^2(\delta_0{}^3 - \delta_0{}^1) + 3\sin^2(\delta_1{}^3 - \delta_1{}^1)} = -\frac{0.02 \pm 0.01}{P(\mathrm{Cs})} \quad (46)$$

in order to determine both the s- and p-wave contributions to the scattering. If the cesium polarization is ≥ 0.25, then there are no simultaneous solutions of Eqs. (45) and (46). The observed frequency shift is too small to allow a sufficiently large p-wave contribution to explain the magnitude of the observed spin-flip cross section.

If one believes the vapor-pressure curve, the spin-flip cross section at 20°C is $(3.95 \pm 0.32) \times 10^{-14}$ cm². If one believes the frequency-shift measurements and the theory, one concludes that the scattering is entirely s wave, that the spin-flip cross section is $(3.16 \pm 0.25) \times 10^{-14}$ cm² and that $|\delta_0{}^3 - \delta_0{}^1| \simeq \frac{1}{2}\pi$.

There are at least two ways in which one can rationalize this failure to yield a unique solution. The first is to assume that the density of cesium atoms in the absorption flask is 25% greater than the values calculated from the measured vapor pressure curves. It is difficult to say how reliably one can determine the density of cesium atoms at such low temperatures. Another way is to assume that the spin-exchange theory is oversimplified. As an improvement in this direction we can use the theory which includes the spin-orbit coupling. A short study of the expressions for the relaxation times and frequency shift when there are s waves, p waves, and spin-orbit coupling shows that we now have a sufficient number of parameters to fit all the observations and explain a large spin-flip cross section and a small frequency shift. It would require a detailed calculation to say whether or not these values of the phase shifts are reasonable.

In Fig. 5 we have plotted, as a function of energy, the calculated values of the s- and p-wave phase shifts obtained by Stone and Reitz for elastic collisions between electrons and cesium atoms. The differences of the triplet and singlet phase shifts which they have calculated are too small to explain our results. They predict a spin-flip cross section of 1.58×10^{-14} cm² and a value for the shift parameter κ of -0.2.

Chen and Raether find that their data for the momentum-transfer cross section in the temperature range of 450 to 550°K can be fitted by the equation

$$Q_m = \frac{1.61 \times 10^{-10}}{T} - \frac{9.63 \times 10^{-12}}{T^{1/2}} + 2.03 \times 10^{-13} \text{ cm}^2. \quad (47)$$

If one extrapolates this function to 20°C, one finds that $Q_m = 1.9 \times 10^{-13}$ cm². Q_m is by definition related to the ordinary differential cross section $I(\theta)$ for elastic scattering by the equation

$$Q_m = \int d\Omega (1 - \cos\theta) I(\theta), \quad (48)$$

$$I(\theta) = \tfrac{3}{4}|f_3|^2 + \tfrac{1}{4}|f_1|^2. \quad (49)$$

If one assumes that the scattering at room temperature is exclusively s wave, then one obtains

$$\begin{aligned} Q_m = \sigma_{\text{tot}} &= (\pi/k^2)[3 \sin^2\delta_0^3 + \sin^2\delta_0^1] \\ &= 3.16 \times 10^{-14}[3 \sin^2\delta_0^3 + \sin^2\delta_0^1]. \quad (50) \end{aligned}$$

In any situation, however,

$$3 \sin^2\delta_0^3 + \sin^2\delta_0^1 \leq 4. \quad (51)$$

Hence one would conclude that there is a large p-wave contribution present. The momentum-transfer cross sections measured by Flavin and Meyerand do not overlap the data of Chen and Raether. The results of Flavin and Meyerand indicate that the momentum-transfer cross section decreases with decreasing temperature; the measurements of Chen and Raether show an increase of the cross section with decreasing temperature. There may be a sharp bend in the cross section's dependence on the temperature; in either case, however, one is reluctant to trust an extrapolation of Chen and Raether's data down to 20°C.

CONCLUSIONS

This experiment indicates that there is still some difficulty in understanding the magnitude of the electron–alkali-metal-atom spin-flip cross sections and of the electron frequency shifts due to spin-exchange collisions. It is not clear whether there is some incompleteness in the theory of the frequency shift or whether some of the measurements are in error. For both rubidium and cesium the spin-flip cross sections are large and the frequency shifts are small. In both rubidium and cesium the s-wave part of the scattering seems to be near the unitary limit and

$$|\delta_0^3 - \delta_0^1| \simeq \pi/2.$$

It is not easy to understand this relationship. It is in general difficult to calculate the spin-flip cross section. Most of the scattering depends upon the polarization potential which is the same in both singlet and triplet states. The spin-flip cross section, however, depends upon the difference of the phase shifts and thus possibly upon the difference of two large numbers. It is interesting that the frequency shifts for electron-cesium collisions have the opposite sign from those for electron-rubidium collisions.

ACKNOWLEDGMENTS

We are indebted to Dr. Peter Bender for prepublication copies of some of his work on these problems.

Theory of Spin Exchange between Optically Pumped Rubidium and Foreign Gas Nuclei*

R. M. Herman†

TRW Space Technology Laboratories, Redondo Beach, California

(Received 9 September 1964)

Cross sections for spin exchange between alkali valence electrons and foreign nuclei in collisions of atomic Rb with atomic He, Ne, Kr, and molecular hydrogen are calculated. It is concluded that while classical dipolar hyperfine interactions are negligible, scalar interaction strengths are greatly magnified as a result of electron exchange. Specifically, it is shown that cross sections associated with the latter are as much as 10^5 times those calculated if exchange effects are neglected. For He^3, Ne^{21}, Kr^{83}, H_2, and D_2, the estimated cross sections for mutual spin flip are 1.1×10^{-24}, 1.0×10^{-23}, 1.0×10^{-22}, 3.6×10^{-25}, and 5.5×10^{-26} cm². For He^3 and Ne^{21}, these are comparable in magnitude to the corresponding experimental cross sections for the deplorization of optically oriented Rb. For the other gases considered, they are relatively much smaller, however. Cross sections for Rb electronic spin disorientation through spin-orbit interactions in collisions with molecular hydrogen are also calculated. They are considerably larger than those observed for the disorientation of optically pumped Rb vapor.

I. INTRODUCTION

IN a recent article,[1] the disorientation of atomic Rb electronic spins in collisions with rare-gas atoms was analyzed. There, it was concluded that spin-orbit effects give rise to the observed disorientation of optically oriented Rb vapor in rare-gas buffer atmospheres. In the present discussion, we shall analyze another process of importance in the spin dynamics of alkali vapor–rare-gas mixtures. This is the simultaneous flip of alkali valence electronic and rare-gas nuclear spins under the influence of magnetic hyperfine interactions, in cases where the rare-gas nuclei have nonzero spin. Such a phenomenon has been observed by Bouchiat, Carver, and Varnum,[2] who detected a polarization of He^3 nuclei in mixtures with optically oriented Rb vapor. Unfortunately, the cross section for spin exchange was not reported by those investigators, although in a calculation based on their data, Brewer[3] estimated its magnitude as approximately 4×10^{-26} cm², an order of magnitude smaller than the observed[4] cross section for disorientation of optically pumped Rb by natural He. To further test the relative importance of spin exchange in the depolarization of alkali vapors, Brewer[3] has also measured disorientation cross sections for Rb-H_2 and Rb-D_2 collisions. From his data, he concluded that hyperfine interactions play a relatively minor role in Rb spin disorientation.

In the present paper, cross sections for Rb valence electronic–rare-gas nuclear spin exchange are calculated. Because of exchange correlations, the calculated cross sections are unexpectedly large, in some cases compar-

able in magnitude to observed and predicted spin-orbit relaxation cross sections. This is surprising, in view of existing experimental evidence, as well as in view of the weakness of hyperfine—as compared to spin-orbit—interactions in general. Because of the availability of experimental data[3,5] on Rb spin relaxation associated with H_2 and D_2, calculations of the spin-orbit and spin-exchange depolarization cross sections are also made for these encounters. The results are tabulated, along with existing experimental data, in Tables I and II, Sec. IV.

II. GENERAL CONSIDERATIONS

In the present treatment, the alklai is regarded as a single-electron atom and, for simplicity, we shall neglect the alkali nuclear spin. The hyperfine interactions experienced by the rare-gas nucleus in binary collisions with alkalis are governed by the Hamiltonian[6]

$$\mathcal{3C}' = -2g_n\beta_n\beta \sum_{i=1}^{n} \left\{ \frac{\mathbf{I}\cdot\mathbf{S}_i}{r_{iB}^3} - 3\frac{(\mathbf{I}\cdot\mathbf{r}_{iB})(\mathbf{S}_i\cdot\mathbf{r}_{iB})}{r_{iB}^5} - \frac{8\pi}{3}\delta(\mathbf{r}_{iB})\mathbf{I}\cdot\mathbf{S}_i \right\}, \quad (1)$$

where $\mathbf{I}$ is the rare-gas nuclear spin, $\mathbf{S}_i$ the ith electronic spin (units of $\hbar$), β the Bohr magneton, β_n the nuclear magneton, and g_n the nuclear gyromagnetic ratio. The first two terms in the brace of Eq. (1) represent the polar interaction between two point magnetic dipoles, $\mathbf{r}_{iB}$ being the radius vector extending from the rare-gas nucleus (B) to the ith electron. The third term represents the Fermi contact potential, $\delta(\mathbf{r}_{iB})$ being the three-dimensional delta function in the coordinates of the ith electron relative to the rare-gas nucleus. The summation over i refers to the alkali valence (1) and rare-gas $(2\cdots n)$ electrons.

*Research supported by the TRW Space Technology Laboratories Independent Research Program.
† Present address: Physics Department, The Pennsylvania State University, University Park, Pennsylvania.
[1] R. M. Herman, Phys, Rev. **136**, A1576 (1964), henceforth referred to as I.
[2] M. A. Bouchiat, T. R. Carver, and C. N. Varnum, Phys. Rev. Letters **5**, 373 (1960).
[3] R. G. Brewer, J. Chem. Phys. **37**, 2504 (1962).
[4] R. A. Bernheim, J. Chem. Phys. **36**, 135 (1962).

[5] R. J. McNeal, J. Chem. Phys. **37**, 2726 (1962).
[6] A. Abragam, *The Principles of Nuclear Magnetism* (Oxford University Press, London, 1961).

The conventional technique for estimating spin reorientation cross sections associated with hyperfine interactions appears to be that of (1) estimating the strength of the magnetic interaction between the rare-gas nucleus and the alkali valence electron, thought to be localized at the alkali nuclear site, and (2) then employing standard arguments to estimate the cross sections. In the present treatment, however, we consider primarily the contact interactions. (An estimate of the polar interaction strength in Rb–Ne collisions is made and it is concluded that in general, these interactions are unimportant.) It is shown that electron-exchange effects lead to a marked enhancement of the scalar coupling, thereby causing the associated cross sections to greatly exceed those calculated if one fails to antisymmetrize the electronic eigenfunction for the collision pair. The importance of the exchange-enhanced scalar interaction is dramatized in Table I, where for He^3, Ne^{21}, and Kr^{83}, the depolarization cross sections, as calculated from the contact interaction with exchange effects included, are compared with those calculated on the point-dipole approximation. The former are a few orders of magnitude larger in all cases.

The present treatment of the hyperfine interactions between paramagnetic electrons and neighboring nuclei is not original with the author, having previously been employed by Adrian[7] in his study of magnetic interactions between paramagnetic impurity atoms and lattice nuclei in van der Waals' crystals. The present example of exchange enhancement is possibly more dramatic, however, inasmuch as in the calculation of cross sections it is the *square* of the energy which is of importance.

III. THEORY

Scalar Interactions in Rb–Rare-Gas Collisions

The problem of calculating the scalar interaction strength is, of course, one of first calculating the unpaired spin density at the rare-gas nucleus during collisions. If one were to accept the simple product wave function as a reasonable approximation to the actual many-electron eigenfunction, the effective hyperfine coupling would simply be

$$\mathcal{3C}_{eff}' = (16\pi/3)g_n\beta_n\beta u_1(B)^2 \mathbf{I} \cdot \mathbf{S}, \qquad (2)$$

where $u_1(B)^2$ is the probability density for locating the alkali valence electron at a distance equal to the internuclear separation from the alkali nucleus. The Pauli principle requires the use of antisymmetric many-electron wave functions, however. Accordingly, a more suitable approximation is the Slater function

$$\psi = (1/n!)^{1/2} \det |\varphi_1 \varphi_2 \cdots \varphi_n|, \qquad (3)$$

where the φ_i are spin-orbitals of the rare-gas–alkali valence electronic system, each taken to be functionally unchanged from its form in isolated atoms. By using

[7] F. J. Adrian, J. Chem. Phys. 32, 972 (1960).

the wave function given above, the effective hyperfine coupling

$$\mathcal{3C}_{eff}' = (16\pi/3)g_n\beta_n\beta u_1(B)^2\eta^2 \mathbf{I} \cdot \mathbf{S} \qquad (4)$$

is readily obtained. Here, the *exchange enhancement factor* η is given by

$$\eta(R) = \left(1 - \sum_{i=2}^{n} \frac{\langle i|1\rangle u_i(B)}{u_1(B)}\right), \qquad (5)$$

R being the internuclear separation, the factors $\langle i|1\rangle$ being overlap integrals (which are nonzero only if the spin parts of the spin-orbitals are identical), and $u_i(R)$ the amplitude of the ith orbital at the rare-gas nucleus.

The presence of the exchange terms in Eq. (5) is expected, of course. Somewhat surprising, however, is their magnitude, for the exchange terms involving rare-gas s orbitals are considerably larger than unity, because these orbitals are sharply peaked at their nucleus. By way of example, let us suppose u_1 to be uniform $[=u_1(B)]$ over the volume of a colliding He^3 atom. (This is a good approximation, inasmuch as the alkali orbital can be represented, to good approximation, by

$$u_1 \cong u_1(B) + (du_1/dz)_B(z-z_B) \qquad (6)$$

in the vicinity of the rare-gas, the z axis being coincident with the interatomic axis. While the linear term is important in the enhancement of polar interactions in the heavier rare gases, it does not influence the scalar coupling.) Assuming the He $1s$ orbitals to be hydrogen-like, with effective nuclear charge parameter Z, it is then readily verified that

$$\eta_{He} = (1-8) = -7, \qquad (7a)$$

independent of the value of Z. Because cross sections for spin exchange vary as η^4, application of the Pauli principle is seen to lead directly to a 2400-fold increase in the importance of scalar interactions in causing spin exchange. In heavier rare gases, electrons exist also in higher s orbitals. If we assume each of these to be hydrogen-like ($n=2, 3, \cdots$) as well, each with individual effective nuclear charge parameter (or, alternately, screening constant[8]) we find, similarly,

$$\eta_{Ne} = (1-8+16) = 9, \qquad (7b)$$

$$\eta_A = (1-8+16-24) = -15, \qquad (7c)$$

$$\eta_{Kr} = 17, \qquad (7d)$$

$$\eta_{Xe} = -23. \qquad (7e)$$

For heavier rare gases, under the above assumptions, exchange correlations thus lead to an increase by some 10^5 in the magnitudes of spin flip cross sections governed by the contact potential.

[8] See, for instance, L. Pauling and E. B. Wilson, *Introduction to Quantum Mechanics* (McGraw-Hill Book Company, Inc., New York, 1935).

Now the above estimates for η are too small for the following reasons: (1) When the exact form for u_1 is used in place of Eq. (6), the overlap with rare-gas s orbitals is always found to be larger than is obtained with the approximate form for u_1. These changes are relatively negligable in the numerical calculations which have been performed, however. (2) The actual rare-gas s orbitals are more peaked at their nucleus than are the corresponding hydrogen-like functions. This results from the fact that attractive Coulomb forces are relatively stronger (than those corresponding to the $1/r$ potential) near the nuclei, thus tending to "pull in" the orbitals. In all cases, therefore, the values of η as calculated with accurate rare-gas orbitals exceed those calculated on the assumption of hydrogen-like s orbitals. Using as the Rb valence electronic wave function the single-electronic orbital of Callaway and Morgan,[9] simple hydrogen-like orbitals (effective nuclear charge $Z = 27/16$) for He,[10] Brown's[11] analytic wave functions for Ne, and the self-consistent-field orbitals of Worsley[12] for Kr, refined values of η have been calculated. The results are

$$\eta_{He}(b_0) = (1 - 8.0) = -7.0, \qquad (8a)$$

$$\eta_{He}(b_0) = (1 - 8.0 + 24.0) = 17.0, \qquad (8b)$$

$$\eta_{Kr}(b_0) = (1 - 8.0 + 17.5 - 30.6 + 45.7) = 25.6, \qquad (8c)$$

to be compared with Eqs. (7a), (7b), and (7d), where b_0 is the kinetic radius for the collision pair.

By making the same kinematical approximations, where pertinent, as in I, the spin-flip cross section

$$\sigma \cong 2\varphi_+(b_0)^2 \sigma_{kin} \qquad (9)$$

is obtained for nuclear spin $\frac{1}{2}$, after averaging over initial nuclear spin states (assuming equal populations of magnetic substates) and integration over impact parameter. Here, σ_{kin} is the gas kinetic cross section ($= \pi b_0^2$) and $\varphi_+(b_0)$ is the phase shift experienced in a single encounter in which the impact parameter is equal to b_0, and the nuclear and electronic spins are parallel. It is given approximately by

$$\varphi_+(b_0) \cong (4\pi/3)(g_n\beta_n\beta b_0/\hbar\bar{V}) u_1(b_0)^2 \eta(b_0)^2, \qquad (10)$$

assuming all collisions to take place with mean relative thermal velocity $\bar{V}$. For arbitrary nuclear spin, the more general result

$$\sigma = \frac{2}{3}(8\pi g_n\beta_n\beta u_1(b_0)^2\eta(b_0)^2 b_0/3\hbar\bar{V})^2 I(I+1)\sigma_{kin} \qquad (11)$$

is readily obtained.

Polar Interactions in Rb–Rare-Gas Collisions

In examining the polar interactions, we also find them to be exchange-enhanced when the atoms overlap.

Here, the enhancement is dependent on the overlap between rare-gas p orbitals and u_1 [particularly the linear term in Eq. (6)]. Explicit calculation of the polar interaction strength in heavy rare gases is quite involved, owing to the complicated nature of the spin-density function in the interacting biatomic system and of the integrals which must be evaluated. For He and Ne, however, the situation is simpler. Specifically, in He, polar interaction enhancement is absent because He does not contain electrons in p orbitals. In Ne, only one p orbital must be considered. Using the Rb and Ne wave functions already cited[9,11], exchange effects are found to produce a 50-fold increase in the cross section associated with polar interactions, as compared to a 35 000-fold exchange-dependent increase in the cross section associated with the scalar coupling. This makes the latter more than 100 times the polar-interaction cross section. The relative weakness of the exchange enhancement in polar interactions appears to result from the facts that (1) hyperfine interactions generally tend to be weak for electrons in p orbitals and, to a lesser extent, (2) for Rb, $(du_1/dz)_B$ is small, causing the pertinent overlap integrals to be small. Based on the results for Ne-Rb collisions, we shall assume polar interactions to play a negligible role in all Rb–rare-gas encounters.

Scalar Interactions in Rb–Molecular Hydrogen Collisions

In calculating the spin-flip cross sections for H_2 and D_2, the Wang function,[13] of form

$$\psi(2,3) = (1/2(1-\Delta^2))(u_A(2)u_B(3) \\ + u_A(3)u_B(2))(\alpha_2\beta_3 - \beta_2\alpha_3) \qquad (12)$$

is employed. Here u_A and u_B are hydrogen-like $1s$ functions centered on nuclei A and B of the hydrogen molecule, separated by the equilibrium distance in H_2. The effective charge parameter for the $1s$ functions is 1.166, chosen so as to minimize the electronic ground-state energy. The overlap between the functions u_A and u_B is represented by Δ. The Wang function can be expressed as a linear combination of two Slater-type functions. Accordingly, when the valence electron of Rb is considered, the three-electron wave function can also be represented as a linear combination, thus

$$\psi(1,2,3) = (1/2\sqrt{3}(1-\Delta^2)) \\ \times \{\det|\varphi_1 u_A\alpha u_B\beta| - \det|\varphi_1 u_A\beta u_B\alpha|\}. \qquad (13)$$

A straightforward calculation of the spin density at either nucleus, under the approximation $u_1 = $ constant over the hydrogen molecular volume, then yields for the enhancement factor

$$\eta^2_{H_2, D_2} = \{1 - 8/(1-\Delta)\{1 + u_B(A)/u_A(A)\} \\ + 32/(1-\Delta^2)\{1 - u_B(A)/u_A(A)\}\} = 21.4. \qquad (14)$$

[9] J. Callaway and D. F. Morgan, Jr., Phys. Rev. 112, 334 (1958).
[10] See L. Pauling and E. B. Wilson, Ref. 8, pp. 184–5.
[11] F. W. Brown, Phys. Rev. 44, 214 (1933).
[12] B. H. Worsley, Proc. Roy. Soc. (London) A247, 390 (1958).

[13] See Ref. 8.

The effective contact interaction Hamiltonian now becomes

$$\mathcal{H}_{eff}' = (16\pi/3)g_n\beta_n\beta u_1(H_2)^2\eta_{H_2}{}^2\mathbf{I}\cdot\mathbf{S}, \qquad (15)$$

where $\mathbf{I}=\mathbf{I}_A+\mathbf{I}_B$. In H_2, the possible resultant spins are 0 and 1, with statistical weights $1:3$. For D_2 the possible spins are 0, 1, and 2 with statistical weights $1:3:5$. Accordingly, the statistically weighted average value of the factor $I(I+1)$ appearing in Eq. (11) is $\frac{3}{2}$ for H_2 and 4 for D_2.

IV. RESULTS AND DISCUSSION

The depolarization cross sections, calculated according to Eq. (11) for He^3, Ne^{21}, and Kr^{83} are listed in Table I along with the nuclear spins and gyromagnetic

TABLE I. Cross sections for the disorientation of Rb electronic spins in inert atmospheres.

Isotope	I	g_n	σ (calculated) Exchange-enhanced	σ (calculated) Point dipoles	σ (observed)[a] Total
He^3	$\frac{1}{2}$	-4.25	1.1×10^{-24} cm^2	1.9×10^{-27}	6.2×10^{-25}[b]
Ne^{21}	$\frac{3}{2}$	-0.44	1.0×10^{-23}	5.5×10^{-28}	5.2×10^{-23}[c]
Kr^{83}	$\frac{9}{2}$	-0.22	1.0×10^{-22}	1.8×10^{-27}	5.9×10^{-21}[c]

[a] Natural isotopic abundance.
[b] Reference 4.
[c] Reference 14.

ratios for these isotopes. Also included are the cross sections calculated on the point dipole model as explained previously, and the experimentally observed[4,14] cross sections for the depolarization of optically pumped Rb by natural He, Ne, and Kr. Comparison with Table II of I reveals that for He^3 and Ne^{21} cross sections associated with hyperfine interactions, as computed in the present work, are comparable in magnitude to those which have been observed and calculated for spin-orbit relaxation. The calculated cross section for nuclear spin polarization of He^3 is considerably larger than that estimated by Brewer[3] from the data of Bouchiat et al.[2] The present estimates indicate that it is also reasonable to expect that rare-gas nuclei other than He^3 might be detectably polarized in collisions with optically pumped alkalis.

The situation is somewhat different for H_2 and D_2.

[14] W. Franzen, Phys. Rev. 115, 850 (1959).

Here again, Eq. (11) is used to calculate the cross sections, with the enhancement factor given by Eq. (14), and the statistically averaged values of $I(I+1)$ replacing that factor in Eq. (11). The results are shown in Table II, where we have also tabulated the theo-

TABLE II. Cross sections for the disorientation of Rb electronic spins by molecular hydrogen.

Molecule	g_n	σ (calculated) Exchange-enhanced	σ (calculated) Spin-orbit	σ (observed) Total
H_2	5.59	3.6×10^{-25} cm^2	1.5×10^{-22}	2.2×10^{-24}[a] 3×10^{-24}[b]
D_2	0.96	5.5×10^{-26}	1.5×10^{-22}	4.3×10^{-24}[a]

[a] Reference 3.
[b] Reference 5.

retical spin-orbit cross sections (calculated after the method of I) and the experimentally determined[3,5] cross sections for disorientation of optically pumped Rb vapor. Here, we see that the hyperfine interactions are less important than they are for He^3, primarily because the exchange enhancement is weaker. At the same time, spin-orbit disorientation cross sections are larger, in view of the stronger intermolecular forces experienced by Rb with H_2 and D_2. Somewhat disturbing is the discrepancy between the predicted and observed spin-orbit relaxation rates. Significant improvement is achieved if, instead of using the calculated long-range force constants to obtain the relative strengths of short-range interactions (see I), empirically determined Lennard-Jones parameters[15] are used to give us this comparison. When this is done, the calculated spin-orbit relaxation cross sections become 4.9×10^{-23} and 6.3×10^{-23} cm^2 for H_2 and D_2, while the calculated cross sections for the rare gases are not significantly changed. The hyperfine cross sections are, of course, unaffected by the change, inasmuch as the kinetic radii involved are the Lennard-Jones in all cases.

ACKNOWLEDGMENT

The author takes pleasure in acknowledging helpful discussions with Dr. Robert Neusel.

[15] American Institute of Physics Handbook, edited by D. E. Gray (McGraw-Hill Book Company, Inc., New York, 1957).

From: *Phys. Rev.* **124**, 800–809 (1961)

Pressure, Light, and Temperature Shifts in Optical Detection of 0-0 Hyperfine Resonance of Alkali Metals

M. Arditi

ITT Federal Laboratories, Nutley, New Jersey

AND

T. R. Carver

Palmer Physical Laboratory, Princeton University, Princeton, New Jersey

(Received April 19, 1961)

Precision measurements of the hyperfine splitting of Cs^{133} or Rb^{87}, in a cell with buffer gases and using optical pumping, show a frequency shift when the intensity of the exciting resonance light is varied. Use of high buffer gas pressures will reduce considerably the light intensity shift. Also, in some cases, the magnitude and sign of the light intensity shift can be changed appreciably by varying slightly the frequency of the hyperfine components of the exciting light. Tentative explanations of the light shift are discussed. Frequency shift variations with light intensity, buffer gas pressure, and temperature of the cell, show the existence of an invariant point whose frequency, when reduced to zero pressure and zero field, is very close to the value obtained by the atomic beam resonance method. This invariant point is the basis for a definition of the pressure shift and temperature shift coefficients. Experimental determination of these coefficients is given for Cs^{133} and Rb^{87}.

INTRODUCTION

THE atomic beam technique has been used to measure accurately the hyperfine splitting of numerous paramagnetic atoms. In some cases, the accuracy of the measurements is sufficiently large to form the basis for the definition of a frequency standard. For example, by definition, in the A-1 time scale the Cs^{133} frequency is $\Delta\nu = 9\ 192\ 631\ 770$ Mc/sec. More recently, the accurate measurement of the hyperfine splitting in a simple gas cell containing the alkali metal vapor has also been made possible by the development of several techniques such as the use of nonmagnetic buffer gases to reduce the Doppler width of the line, and the use of optical pumping and optical detection to increase considerably the signal-to-noise ratio of the detection of the microwave transition. However, these techniques, under certain conditions, can produce large frequency shfts and this paper reports precision measurements of such effects under varying conditions of buffer gas ipressure, resonance light intensity, and temperature of the cell. Most detailed measurements

have been made with Cs^{133}, but a few results are given also for Rb^{87}.

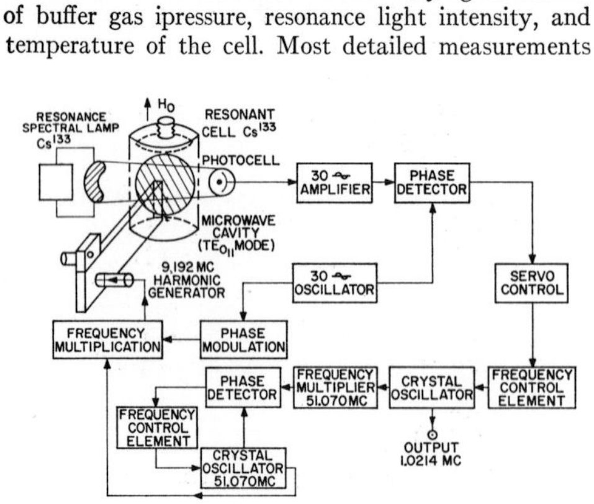

EXPERIMENTAL ARRANGEMENTS

The principles of the double resonance method used for the detection of the microwave transition $\Delta F = 1$, $m_f = 0$ to $m_f = 0$, in the ground state of alkali metal vapors, using optical pumping and optical detection have been previously described.[1] The apparatus used is illustrated in Fig. 1. A sealed-off gas cell contains the alkali vapor metal mixed with buffer gas to reduce Doppler broadening of the microwave transition.[2] A beam of resonance radiation from a resonance lamp is passed through the gas cell and is focused on a photocell. A homogeneous magnetic field of a few tenths of an oersted is produced in the region of the cell. The gas cell is placed in a microwave cavity which is excited by microwave at a frequency corresponding to the energy separation of the hyperfine levels of the ground state. This produces a saturation of these levels and the amount of resonance radiation transmitted through the gas cell is changed. By modulating, at low rate, the frequency of the microwave radiation, the output current of the photocell is modulated at the same rate and, by using this signal in a synchronous phase detector, a null is obtained when the frequency of the microwave radiation is exactly the frequency of the hyperfine resonance. If the output of the phase detector is fed back, in proper phase, to an element controlling the frequency of the microwave radiation, one can obtain a microwave frequency which is locked to the

Fig. 1. Experimental arrangement.

[1] A. Kastler, J. Opt. Soc. Am. **47**, 460 (1957); J. Brossel and A. Kastler, Compt. rend. **229**, 1213 (1949); H. G. Dehmelt, Phys. Rev. **105**, 1487 (1957); W. E. Bell and A. L. Bloom, *ibid*. **109**, 219 (1958); M. Arditi and T. R. Carver, *ibid*. **109**, 1012 (1958), **112**, 449 (1958); P. L. Bender, E. C. Beaty and A. R. Chi, *ibid*. **112**, 450 (1958), Phys. Rev. Letters **1**, 311 (1958).
[2] R. H. Dicke, Phys. Rev. **89**, 472 (1953).

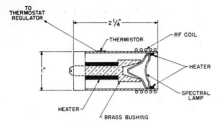

FIG. 2. Resonance lamp.

stable atomic resonance. This principle is used in so-called "gas cell atomic frequency standards."

The gas cell is made of low-loss 707 glass, and filled with pure alkali metal and spectroscopically pure buffer gases. The microwave cavity, excited in the TE_{011} mode, is carefully thermostated to produce a uniform temperature in the cell and the temperature is monitored with a thermocouple.

The light source of resonance radiation is an electrodless discharge produced in a small hemispherical bulb about 1 inch in diameter containing argon at a pressure of a few millimeters Hg and pure alkali metal. It is excited at 60 Mc/sec inside an rf coil and well-thermostated to avoid changes in light intensity due to the alkali metal migrating in the lamp[3] (Fig. 2). With this design the intensity of the light was very stable over a period of more than 3000 hr of continuous operation and because of this stability great accuracy and good reproducibility of the observations were possible.

The microwave frequency is obtained by multiplication from a stable crystal oscillator at $1.0214\cdots$ Mc/sec which is the 9000th subharmonic of the cesium frequency. However, it is known that spurious sidebands in the microwave spectrum can produce systematic errors in the determination of the hyperfine frequency.[4] Since most of these spurious side-bands are produced in the low stages of frequency multiplication, they can be greatly minimized in the microwave spectrum by using, as a driver, a simple crystal oscillator at 51.0701 Mc/sec loosely phase-locked to the more stable oscillator at $1.0214\cdots$ Mc/sec.

In determining the frequency corresponding to the maximum of the absorption curve, in most cases, the signal-to-noise ratio of the optical detection is good enough to observe the signal output of the narrow-band photocell amplifier directly on an oscilloscope, and to measure the frequency corresponding to a null with an accuracy of a few parts in 10^{10}. The use of the synchronous phase detector and servo is most convenient, however, in these cases where the signal-to-noise ratio of the detection does not permit such a direct measure-

ment; however, when using the synchronous phase detector, special care must be taken in adjusting the servo because some relaxation effects taking place in the gas cell can give an out-of-phase component which can produce systematic errors in the position of the servo. Details of the adjustment procedure of the servo to minimize such errors can be found in reference 5. The frequency was measured with the setup shown in Fig. 3. Essentially the frequency of the oscillator driving the gas cell was compared against the frequency of an ultra-stable James Knight crystal oscillator type JKFS-1000 after a multiplication in frequency by a factor of 2500. The ultra-stable oscillator frequency was compared, for calibration, either directly with an Atomichron frequency, or with broadcast frequencies at 133.33 kc/sec from Station A5KA, Fort Monmouth, New Jersey, or at 18 kc/sec from Station NBA, Summit, Canal Zone, both stations being monitored by Atomichrons. An absolute accuracy of a few parts in 10^{10} could thus be obtained in the frequency measurements.

For the $\Delta F=1$, $m_f=0$ to $m_f=0$, magnetic dipole transition, the Breit-Rabi formula shows that the dependence of the frequency with the magnetic field is given by a quadratic term. The magnetic field at the gas cell could be varied by adjusting the current in a pair of Helmholtz coils at right angles around the gas cell. The magnetic field at the cell, inside the resonant cavity, was measured accurately by inducing simultaneously the low frequency Zeeman transitions $\Delta F=0$ $\Delta m_f=1$ with a small auxiliary coil placed near the cell inside the cavity. At resonance the intensity of the detected hyperfine signal is reduced because of a change in the population distribution of the $m_f=0$ levels. An accuracy of ± 5 millioersteds can be obtained easily by this method. In the earth's magnetic field this corresponds to a maximum frequency error of ± 2 parts in 10^{10} for Cs^{133} and ± 3.5 parts in 10^{10} for Rb^{87}.

Since many factors can affect the optical pumping, it is necessary to define carefully the conditions under which the subsequent experimental results were

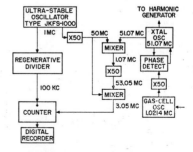

FIG. 3. Schematic of frequency measurement components.

[3] This design is a modification of a model originally developed by P. L. Bender and E. C. Beaty of the National Bureau of Standards.

[4] J. A. Barnes and R. C. Mockler, IRE Trans. on Instrumentation 9, 149 (1960).

[5] M. Arditi, Proc. 15th Symp. Freq. Control 1961 (to be published).

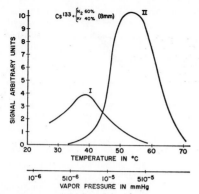

FIG. 4. Signal strength of optically detected 0-0 transition in cesium: I with resonance light filtered through a D_2 filter. II with no outside filtering, or D_1 filtering.

observed. When using unpolarized resonance radiation, it has been found that the optical detection of the 0-0 microwave transition is not only a function of the selective absorption of the hyperfine components of the exciting resonance radiation but also depends on the percentage of the D_1-D_2 components, in a certain range of temperature. This is illustrated in Fig. 4, which shows the detected signal in the case of Cs^{133} in a spherical bulb about $1\frac{1}{2}$ inches in diameter filled with a mixture of nitrogen (60%) and krypton (40%) at a filling pressure of 8 mm Hg. (This mixture has a minimum of pressure shift.) Curve I refers to the signal obtained when using an interferometer filter which lets pass only the D_2 radiation (8521 A). For purpose of comparison in these curves, it should be noted that the D_2 filter absorbed about 80% of the total incident radiation. Curve II refers to the case where no outside filter is used; here, self-filtering of the resonance radiation takes place inside the cell since the D_2 radiation is strongly absorbed above a temperature of

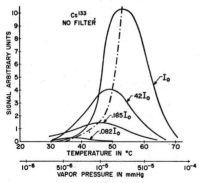

FIG. 5. Signal strength of optically detected 0-0 transition in Cs^{133} as a function of light intensity and cell temperature.

45°C, and only the D_1 radiation is active above that temperature. In this latter case, operation is possible at much higher temperature than when using a D_2 filter. Since a high temperature of ambient operation is required in some applications, this mode of optical pumping has been more particularly studied here. Figure 5 shows the effect of varying the light intensity: It can be seen that in the temperature range between 30° and 45°C, the curves are overlapping due to the conflicting pumping effects of D_1 and D_2 radiations. The position of the maximum of the curves agrees qualitatively with previously published analysis.[6] Also, a shorter length of the cell in the path of the light shifts the maximum of the detected signal toward the higher temperatures.

Somewhat similar effects have been observed in the optical detection of the 0-0 transition of Rb^{87} in a two-inch bulb filled with the natural isotopic mixture of Rb^{85} and Rb^{87} (Fig. 6). The exciting lamp in this

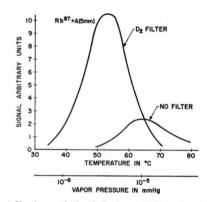

FIG. 6. Signal strength of optically detected 0-0 transition in Rb^{87}.

case was filled with the same mixture as in the resonance cell. The D_2 filter passing the 7800-A radiation has an absorption coefficient of about 62%.

In all the following experiments, the results will be given for Cs^{133} for the condition where no outside filtering of the resonance radiation was used, except otherwise specified. Filtering with a D_2 filter has been used in the experiments with Rb^{87}. Otherwise the experimental arrangement is essentially the same for cesium and rubidium.

The factors producing a frequency shift in the hyperfine resonance frequency will now be studied under these conditions of optical pumping. In actual operation, since these factors are interacting, it is not always possible to separate them clearly, but since most of the effects are proportional to the density of alkali

[6] W. E. Bell, A. Bloom and R. Williams, IRE Trans. on Microwave Theory and Techniques 7, 95 (1959); T. M. Andres, D. J. Farmer and G. T. Inouye, IRE Trans. on Military Electronics 3, 178 (1959).

atoms in the gas cell, it has been found convenient in this study to take the temperature as the variable parameter.

EXPERIMENTAL RESULTS

A. Effect of Buffer Gases

Buffer gases are used in the gas cell, both to obtain a reduction of the Doppler width and to increase the efficiency of optical pumping. However, it has been found previously that the presence of buffer gases produces an appreciable pressure shift. Pressure shifts have been measured in the particular cases of atomic hydrogen,[7,8] deuterium,[8] tritium,[8] sodium 23,[9] potassium 39,[10] rubidium 87,[11,12] and cesium 133.[13] The proportional shifts $\Delta\nu/\nu$ for the various alkalies and for a given buffer gas have the same sign and increase slowly in magnitude with increasing alkali atomic number. The pressure shift depends on the buffer gas.

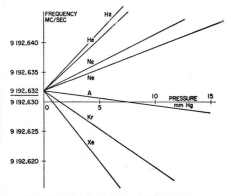

FIG. 7. Pressure-shift of zero-field hyperfine splitting of Cs[133].

Shifts to higher frequencies occur for light atoms such as hydrogen, helium, nitrogen or neon and shifts to lower frequencies occur for heavy atoms such as argon, krypton, or xenon (Fig. 7). Mixtures of gases giving low-pressure shifts can be obtained by the proper combination of buffer gases giving pressure shifts in opposite directions. However, there usually is a residual temperature-dependent shift which is a function of the nature of the buffer gases in the mixture. Details

[7] J. P. Wittke and R. H. Dicke, Phys. Rev. 96, 530 (1954).
[8] L. W. Anderson, F. M. Pipkin, and J. C. Baird, Phys. Rev. Letters 4, 69 (1960). Phys. Rev. 120, 1279 (1960).
[9] M. Arditi and T. R. Carver, Phys. Rev. 109, 1012 (1958); M. Arditi, J. phys. radium 19, 873 (1958).
[10] A. Bloom and J. B. Carr, Phys. Rev. 119, 1946 (1960).
[11] R. H. Dicke, T. R. Carver, C. O. Alley, and N. S. VanderVen, Final report, U. S. Army Signal Corps Engineering Laboratories, 1957 (unpublished).
[12] E. C. Beaty, P. L. Bender, and A. R. Chi, Phys. Rev. Letters 1, 311 (1958).
[13] M. Arditi and T. R. Carver, Phys. Rev. 112, 449 (1958); E. C. Beaty, P. L. Bender, and A. R. Chi, ibid. 112, 450 (1958).

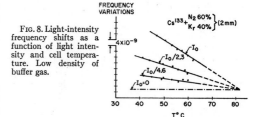

FIG. 8. Light-intensity frequency shifts as a function of light intensity and cell temperature. Low density of buffer gas.

on this temperature-shift will be given in the next sections.

B. Frequency Shifts with Light Intensity Variations

It has been found that, for low buffer gas pressure, varying the intensity of the light source shifts the resonant frequency by a substantial amount. The data may best be expressed in terms of the following plot in Fig. 8, which refers to a sealed-off cesium cell, $1\frac{1}{2}$ inches in diameter and filled with a mixture of nitrogen (60%) and krypton (40%). (This buffer gas mixture was prepared to obtain a minimum of pressure shift, taking into consideration the pressure shifts shown in Fig. 7.) The relative frequency variations have been plotted as a function of the temperature of the cell and for various values of the incident light intensity I_0. The light intensity was varied by means of the interposition of neutral density filters. The following remarks can be made: First, the frequency variations are linear, within the temperature range of the experimentation. (The measurements were stopped when the

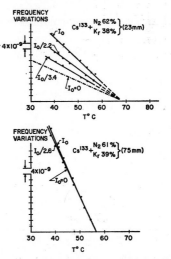

FIG. 9. Light-intensity frequency shifts as a function of light intensity and cell temperature, with increasing density of buffer gas.

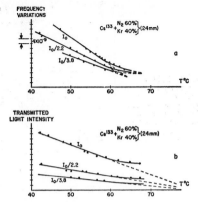

FIG. 10. Light-intensity frequency shifts and corresponding light absorption in a cesium cell.

signal-to-noise ratio of the detection did not permit a determination of the frequency with an accuracy better than ± 1 part in 10^9); second, the frequency shifts are directly proportional to the incident light intensity (the broken line in the curves corresponds to the extrapolated limiting value at $I_0 = 0$); third, the straight lines converge toward a definite point, usually inaccessible to direct observation because of poor signal-to-noise ratio of the detection at this temperature; fourth, in this case, the frequency shifts are positive, i.e., the frequency of the hyperfine splitting is increased when the intensity of the exciting resonant light is increased.

It has been found also that the dispersion of the frequency shifts with light intensity variations is a function of the buffer gas density. As the filling pressure of the buffer gas is increased, the fantail array of the curves becomes narrower and for sufficiently high pressure, the curves merge into one curve, within experimental errors (Fig. 9). A corresponding increase in the light absorption in the gas cell is observed as the buffer gas density is increased. (See Fig. 10. At sufficiently high temperatures the absorption of light is no longer linear, with a corresponding tapering-off of the

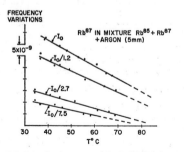

FIG. 11. Light-intensity frequency shifts in Rb^{87} and pure argon.

frequency shifts in this temperature range.) When the buffer gas density is increased, it should be noted that the temperature of the converging point of the linear extrapolations is shifted toward the lower values. This is related to the increased absorption of the resonant light. Also the slope of the extrapolated line corresponding to $I_0 = 0$ changes when the buffer gas density is changed. In describing the pressure shifts and temperature shifts in the following section the shifts are based on such an extrapolation to zero light intensity.

Somewhat similar results have been obtained in the case of Rb^{87} under the conditions of optical pumping previously defined (see Figs. 11 and 12).

C. Pressure-Shift and Temperature-Shift Coefficients

In Fig. 7, which represents the pressure shift of Cs^{133}, the hyperfine frequency was plotted against the

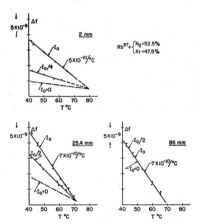

FIG. 12. Light-intensity frequency shifts as a function of light intensity and cell temperature, with Rb^{87} (isotopic mixture of Rb^{87} and Rb^{85}) with increasing density of buffer gas.

filling pressure of the buffer gas, at room temperature, with the cell also at room temperature. Actually the term "pressure shift" is not very well chosen to define the effect. Since, in first approximation, the shift observed depends on the number of collisions between the alkali atoms and the buffer gas molecules, the term "density shift" would be more appropriate. The collision frequency is proportional to $n\sigma(2kT/m)^{\frac{1}{2}}$ and consequently the pressure shift or density shift should be proportional to $T^{\frac{1}{2}}$. In addition to the density shift there is an independent temperature shift. These temperature-shift coefficients as previously defined[14] were the observed shifts in frequency for a given change

[14] E. C. Beaty, P. L. Bender, and A. R. Chi, Phys. Rev. 112, 450 (1958); Phys. Rev. Letters 1, 311 (1958).

in temperature of the whole cell, and this was not measured at constant pressure. However, these simple approximations do not seem to check the experimental data over a large range of temperature. In the light of the experiments previously described, all the data of frequency shifts may be better expressed in terms of a semiempirical formula, as follows:

1. With buffer-gas mixtures having a minimum of pressure or density shift, and at low density for the buffer gas, the frequency of the converging point is very close to the frequency f_0, of the cesium or rubidium atoms as measured by the atomic beam method.

2. With buffer gases at high density, the frequency, $f_{T_{cp}}$, of the converging point is still related to the frequency, f_0, by the relation:

$$f_0 = f_{T_{cp}} - \alpha p T_{cp}/303, \qquad (1)$$

where α is the pressure or density shift in cps per mm Hg, p is the filling pressure in mm Hg at 303°K, and T_{cp} is the temperature of the converging point.

3. The extrapolated line corresponding to $I_0 = 0$ can be considered as the resultant of two linear variations, one due to the density coefficient α, and equal to $\alpha p(T_{cp} - T)/303$, and the other due to the temperature coefficient δ, and equal to $\delta p(T_{cp} - T)$. (See Fig. 13.) The slope of this line is equal to $p\gamma$ in cps per degree, where $\gamma = \alpha/303 + \delta$, and can be positive or negative depending on the relative signs of α and δ (Fig. 14). The frequency, f_T, of a point on the extrapolated line

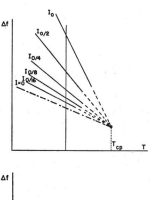

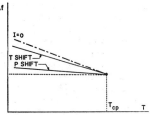

FIG. 13. Linear extrapolation of light intensity shifts versus cell temperature. The converging point T_{cp} is used for the definition of the temperature-shift coefficient, as well as reference point for the pressure-shift.

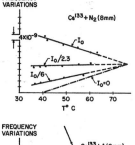

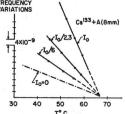

FIG. 14. Light-intensity frequency shifts in Cs^{133} mixed with pure nitrogen or pure argon, showing effect of using a positive pressure-shift or negative-pressure shift buffer gas.

$I_0 = 0$, at a temperature T, can then be expressed by the formula:

$$f_T = f_0 + (\alpha p/303)(2T_{cp} - T) + \delta p(T_{cp} - T), \qquad (2)$$

where $f_0 = 9\ 192\ 631\ 770 \pm 10$ cps (A_1 time) with 313°K $< T <$ 333°K for Cs^{133}, and $f_0 = 6\ 834\ 682\ 600 \pm 15$ cps (A_1 time) with 313°K $< T <$ 343°K for Rb^{87}, and where α and δ are given in Table I for Cs^{133} and in Table II for Rb^{87}.

The values of α and δ can be obtained by making measurements with pure buffer gases or with mixtures of gases. The accuracy is limited by the extrapolations and the uncertainties in the pressure and temperature of the cell, but the values indicated are in good agreement with the measurements of the hyperfine splitting made by atomic beam methods.[15] The values of δ^*, shown for purpose of comparison, correspond to previously published data[14] for a somewhat different definition of the temperature coefficient. In the derivation of the values of α and δ shown in Tables I and II, it has been implicitly assumed that the pressure-shift or temperature-shift coefficients of a gas mixture are the algebraic sum of the pressure or temperature-shift coefficients of the component gases of the mixture. The experimental evidence seems to bear this point of view.

Formula (2) gives a better agreement with the experimental data than formula (3) which is based on the assumption that the density shift varies as $(T)^{\frac{1}{2}}$, since the collision frequency is proportional to $(T)^{\frac{1}{2}}$.

$$f_T = f_0 + \alpha p[2(T_{cp}/303)^{\frac{1}{2}} - (T/303)^{\frac{1}{2}}] + \delta p(T_{cp} - T). \quad (3)$$

Using formula (3) as a definition for α and δ gives the values shown in Table III. Although formulas (2)

[15] L. Essen, J. V. L. Parry, W. Markowitz, and R. G. Hall, Nature 181, 1054 (1958). L. Essen, E. G. Hope, and D. Sutcliffe, ibid. 189, 298 (1961).

TABLE I. Pressure and temperature shifts with buffer gases in Cs[133] [formula (2)].

Gas	α (cps/mm)	$\alpha/303$	δ (cps/mm deg)	δ^*	Remarks
He	+1200	+3.96	−3.6	+1.5	Measured in {He 15%, Ar 85%}
N₂	+840	+2.77	−2.1		Measured directly and in {N₂ 30%, Ar 70%},
					{N₂ 60%, Kr 40%}, {N₂ 70%, Xe 30%}
Ar	−212	−0.70	−0.10	−0.7	Measured directly and in {N₂ 30%, Ar 70%}
Kr	−1360	−4.33	+2.38		Measured in {N₂ 61%, Kr 39%}
Xe	−2350	−7.59	+6.2±0.3		Measured in {N₂ 70%, Xe 30%}
{N₂ 30%, Ar 70%}	+104	+0.34	−0.64		
{He 18%, Ar 82%}	+45	+0.148	−0.72		
{N₂ 70.8%, Xe 29.2%}	−78	−0.26	+0.5±0.1		
{N₂ 62%, Kr 38%}	−0.33	−0.001	−0.39±0.1		

TABLE II. Pressure and temperature shifts with buffer gases in Rb[87] [formula (2)].

Gas	α (cps/mm)	$\alpha/303$	δ (cps/mm deg)	δ^*	Remarks
Ar	−52	−0.171	−0.017	−0.30	Measured directly
{N₂ 52.4%, Kr 47.6%}	−8.3	−0.027	−0.03±0.01		

and (3) give values of α which are very close to each other, the values of δ differ significantly. When cells filled with mixtures of various buffer gases are tested, the experimental results are more accurately represented by formula (2) than by formula (3) (see Table IV). This may be due to the fact that not only the number of collisions between alkali atoms and buffer gas molecules but the energy of the collisions is to be considered in a more detailed theory of the pressure

shift.[16] The temperature T_{cp} of the converging point is related to the absorption of the resonance radiation in the cell, and consequently is a function of the geometry of the cell and of the density of the buffer gas filling the cell (Fig. 15). Similarly the temperature coefficients indicated in the Tables ought to be restricted to the particular size of the cells and the geometry of the light beam used in these experiments.

DISCUSSION OF EXPERIMENTAL RESULTS

The frequency shifts produced by variations of the exciting resonance light intensity are not due to an asymmetrical broadening of the microwave resonance. In the experiments the linewidth of the field insensitive 0-0 microwave transition is rather large, of the order of 600 to 800 cps, and much larger than an expected linewidth of 20 to 30 cps. However, the line shape is quite symmetrical as shown in Fig. 16, which represents the amplitude of the signal at the output of the photocell amplifier versus the microwave frequency.

If the exchange cross section for Cs-Cs or Rb-Rb collisions[11] is indeed about 3.5 to 7×10^{-14} cm² at high

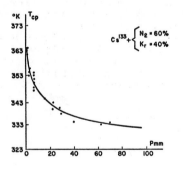

FIG. 15. Dependence of the converging point T_{cp} on the density of the buffer gas used in the resonance cell.

TABLE III. Pressure and temperature shifts with buffer gases in Cs[133] [formula (3)].

Gas	α (cps/mm)	δ (cps/mm deg)
He	+1200	−1.44
N₂	+820	−0.74
Ar	−212	−0.435
Kr	−1320	+0.29
Xe	−2350	+3.68

[16] H. Margenau, P. Fontana, and L. Klein, Phys. Rev. 115, 87 (1959); L. B. Robinson, ibid. 117, 1275 (1960), E. M. Purcell (private communication) R. Bersohn (private communication).

TABLE IV. Pressure and temperature shifts with buffer gases in Cs^{133}.

| | α (cps/mm) Computed | | | δ (cps/mm deg) Computed | | |
Gas	(3)	(2)	Measured	(3)	(2)	Measured
{N_2=62%, Kr=38%}	+7	−4	−0.3	−0.35	−0.40	−0.39
{N_2=65.5%, Kr=24.5%, Xe=10%}	−21	−18	−20	−0.045	−0.202	−0.206
{N_2=67%, Kr=20%, Xe=13%}	−20.4	−14	−10	+0.040	−0.17	−0.18

temperature like 60°C, the exchange collisions lead to a linewidth of this magnitude. However, reduction in rubidium pressure by an order of magnitude does not lead to narrower lines. Also the linewidth is not reduced more than about 20% when the intensity of the incident light is reduced within a ratio of 4 to 1, for example. (The maximum intensity I_0 of the exciting light falling directly on a 927 type photocell screened by a 6-mm Corning filter No. 5850 gives a photocell current of about 2.5 μamp.) This would indicate a very large amount of self-reversal in the emitted light in the lamp. Collisions of the alkali atoms with the walls of the cell contribute very little to the linewidth since cells coated with GE. SC-77 Dri-film, which is known to reduce disorienting effects,[17] give the same linewidth as noncoated cells as soon as a few mm of buffer gas are introduced in the cell. The broadening of the microwave transition may be due to the fact that here there is a great deal of light trapping and filtering in the cell itself while the atoms are simultaneously subjected to the microwave field. Since the filtering and trapping is not homogeneous in the cell along the beam path, it is possible that the resonance is apparently broadened by these inhomogeneities. Somewhat smaller linewidths have been obtained with larger cells when the microwave field was localized to the back of the cell with a microwave horn. Much narrower linewidths have been obtained, under different experimental conditions,[14] when the light filtering was produced essentially in a filter cell separate from the sample cell subjected to the microwave field.

The magnitude of the light-intensity shift observed is somewhat of a "volume effect" involving the whole of the cell, and will vary with the geometry or temperature of the cell and with the density of the buffer gas. As pointed out above, the light trapping and filtering is not homogeneous along the path of the light beam; raising the temperature of the cell will localize the trapping near the input window, where the exciting light beam enters and the effect of light intensity shift in the whole cell will be reduced. This will be true also if the buffer gas density is increased because collisions

between alkali atoms and buffer gas molecules, without loss of orientation, will also permit a more efficient utilization of the incident photons and again will restrict the maximum absorption of light close to the input window. That such a geometrical effect exists can be demonstrated by the following experiment: a second source of resonance light is used at right angle to the main beam of light (Fig. 17). When this source lies in the plane XX' an additional frequency shift is produced; when the source lies in the plane YY' practically no additional effect is observed because in this region the light trapping is so intense that a saturation is produced.

The geometrical aspect of the light intensity shift is also in agreement with the almost linear variation of the frequency shift with incident light intensity and is closely related to the absorption of resonance radiation (Fig. 10).

Although the previous remarks tentatively explain the variations of the light intensity shifts with temperature of the cell or the density of the buffer gas, they do not provide an explanation for the origin of the shift itself. Several models appear to present themselves and will be briefly discussed here.

At first, one is tempted to ascribe the frequency shifts observed with the light intensity variations to a wall effect: collisions of the alkali atoms with the glass walls of the cell could produce a frequency shift from the true resonant frequency of the free alkali atoms.

[17] Non-disorienting wall coatings were originally proposed by R. H. Dicke (see reference 7). Also H. G. Robinson, E.S. Ensberg, and H. G. Dehmelt, Bull. Am. Phys. Soc. 3, 9 (1958). The GE. SC-77 Dri-film coating, a mixture of dimethyldichlorosilicane and methyltrichlorosilicane, was suggested by R. A. Naumann and with it C. Alley obtained strong signals in the detection of the low-frequency Zeeman transitions in Rb^{87}.

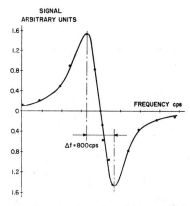

FIG. 16. Line shape of optically detected 0-0 transition in Cs^{133}

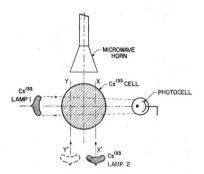

FIG. 17. Double light beam experimental arrangement for investigation of light intensity frequency shifts in a large resonance cell (XX' and YY' represent planes along which auxiliary resonance radiation from lamp 2 is focused).

By increasing the light intensity, atoms farther away from the walls are oriented and contribute more to the detected microwave signal. Since the number of wall collisions per second is reduced as the alkali atoms are farther away from the walls, a frequency shift could thus occur. Also as the density of the buffer gas is increased, the number of wall collisions per second is decreased and the effect of the light intensity should be less pronounced, as found experimentally. However, with this model, the sign of the frequency shift predicted is not in agreement with experimental results; also tests with Dri-film coated cells, filled with buffer gases, show that a light-intensity frequency shift of the same magnitude is obtained than when using uncoated cells filled with the same buffer gas. With a filling of a few mm of buffer gas in the cell, the wall coating effect is almost completely masked by the buffer gas action. Thus it is unlikely that wall collisions contribute significantly to the light intensity shift.

In another model, one could think of a coupling between the ground-state and the excited-state energy levels, through optical pumping, with the retention of a certain amount of coherence in the resonance fluorescent light.[18] The fact that the alkali atoms are submitted to the simultaneous processes of optical pumping and microwave transition could place them in superposition states with both hyperfine levels of the ground state slightly displaced upward, but with the upper level displaced a little more than the lower level, thus producing a positive frequency shift. The reduction of the light intensity shift at high densities of buffer gas could be due to the fact that at these densities the collisions of the alkali atoms in the excited states with buffer gas atoms tend to mix the hyperfine levels, leading to complete intensity pumping rather than to stochastic pumping.

Recently a more satisfactory model, leading to a semiquantitative explanation, has been suggested by

[18] J. N. Dodd, W. N. Fox, G. W. Series, and M. J. Taylor, Proc. Phys. Soc. 74, 789 (1959).

C. Cohen-Tannoudji, with regard to his theoretical work, with J. P. Barrat, on the light shift of the Zeeman sublevels of the mercury isotopes.[19] Frequency shifts of magnetic resonances associated with virtual transitions produced by optical excitation has been observed experimentally.[20] The following explanation[21] has been proposed for the light intensity shift of the hyperfine transition:

"Let 1 and 2 represent the two hyperfine levels of the ground state and e one of the sublevels of the excited states (Fig. 18). The two hyperfine components of one of the doublet lines are represented by the wave numbers k_1 and k_2. Thus k_1 acting on the alkali atoms located in level 1 produces real transitions while producing virtual transitions when acting on atoms located in level 2, since the distance 1–2 is much larger than the Doppler breadth. According to the theory[19] k_1 gives a self-energy $\Delta E'$ to level 2 and the sign of $\Delta E'$ is the sign of $1/(k_1-k_2)$, which in this case is negative. Similarly k_2 gives a self-energy to level 1 with the sign of $1/(k_2-k_1)$, and this is positive. The energy gap between 1 and 2 is thus increased. With this interpretation the exciting resonant light produces simultaneously real and virtual transitions depending on the energy level considered, and a positive frequency shift is obtained when the light intensity increases. Every time an atom in level 1 absorbs a k_1 photon it decreases the number of photons available to produce virtual transitions for atoms located in level 2, and it is conceivable that the factors affecting the optical pumping could greatly influence the magnitude of the light intensity shift observed."

It may be that parts of the proposed models concord in the true explanation of the effect, but the ideas of Cohen-Tannoudji suggest several experiments to test his theory. In particular, a variation of the light-intensity frequency shift could be produced by shifting slightly the hyperfine components of the exciting light compared to the hyperfine components of the resonance cell itself. In one experiment this was verified by placing the light source in a magnetic field; by varying the magnetic field intensity the light shift could be reduced, annulled, or even slightly reversed (Fig. 19). In another experiment, a filter cell was used between the light

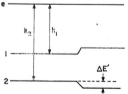

FIG. 18. Virtual transitions induced by radiation k_1 on atoms located on level 2.

[19] J. P. Barrat and C. Cohen-Tannoudji, Compt. rend. 252, 93 (1961); 252, 255 (1961).
[20] C. Cohen-Tannoudji, Compt. rend. 252, 394 (1961).
[21] C. Cohen-Tannoudji (quoted from private communication).

source and the resonance cell. In this case a positive frequency shift of $+7.5\times10^{-9}$, corresponding to a 2 to 1 change in light intensity, was changed to a negative shift of -6.5×10^{-9} when a magnetic field of about 500 gauss was applied to the filter cell. (The isotopic mixture of Rb^{87} and $Rb^{85}+2$ mm argon was used in the light source. The same mixture $+5$ mm argon was used in the filter cell, while the resonance cell was filled with the rubidium isotopic mixture $+4$ mm of nitrogen $53\%+$krypton 47%.) It is interesting to note that the frequency displacement of the hyperfine components produced by a magnetic field of a few hundred gauss is of the order of magnitude of the Doppler breadth of the optical lines.

Other experiments, using various filtering schemes affecting the relative intensity of the hyperfine optical lines used for optical pumping, could be devised with more flexibility if one uses separate filter and sample cells as in the optical pumping of a rubidium 87 sample through a rubidium 85 filter cell.[14] Experiments in this direction have already been performed.[22]

These experiments, although in qualitative agreement with the theory of virtual transitions, are not easily subjected to quantitative treatment since the number of hyperfine components to be considered is rather large and their mutual interaction extremely complex. The authors have therefore felt it useful to publish, at this time, as much of the experimental

---

[22] P. Bender (private communication).

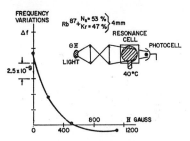

FIG. 19. Light-intensity frequency shifts as a function of magnetic field intensity at the light source: The magnetic field in displacing slightly the hyperfine components of the light source, as compared to the hyperfine components in the resonance cell, can change the magnitude or the sign of the light-intensity frequency shift.

results and tentative conclusions as possible, even though in somewhat empirical form.

ACKNOWLEDGMENTS

We are greatly indebted to Professor A. Kastler, Professor J. Brossel and members of their group at Ecole Normale Superieure, Paris, particularly Mme. M. A. Bouchiat, Dr. J. P. Barrat, and Dr. C. Cohen-Tannoudji for their valuable advices and suggestions. We wish also to thank Dr. F. Reder and Dr. G. M. P. Winkler, Signal Corps, Fort Monmouth, New Jersey, for the temporary loan of an Atomichron, and Dr. P. Bender, National Bureau of Standards, for helpful discussions.

Effects of Helium Buffer Gas Atoms on the Atomic Hydrogen Hyperfine Frequency* †

GEORGE A. CLARKE

Department of Chemistry, Columbia University, New York, New York

(Received August 18, 1961)

Calculations are made for the pressure, mass, and temperature dependence of the atomic hydrogen hyperfine frequency shift arising from the perturbing influence of helium buffer gas atoms. The calculated fractional pressure shift is found to be $+1.73 \times 10^{-9}$ mm Hg^{-1} compared with the experimental value of $+3.7 \times 10^{-9}$ mm Hg^{-1}. From the standpoint of the calculation this discrepancy may be related to a failure of the simple wave function employed to adequately characterize the unpaired electron spin density at the hydrogen nucleus. The results of the calculations for the temperature variation and mass dependence indicate that these are very small effects. The form of the mass dependent quantum statistical correction, used to elucidate the mass effect, suggests that the relatively large variations experimentally observed with other buffer gases, due to hydrogen isotope variation, are in error.

Finally, a calculation is made for the pressure shift from a kinetic theory point of view and the result obtained ($+1.79 \times 10^{-9}$ mm Hg^{-1}) is in fair agreement with the above mentioned quantum statistical calculation.

INTRODUCTION

RECENT experiments by Anderson *et al.*[1] on the determination of the atomic hyperfine frequencies of the hydrogen isotopes in the presence of various buffer gases by an optical pumping method have revealed a dependence of the experimentally determined fractional pressure shifts on the nature of the hydrogen isotopes and on the buffer gases employed. This latter dependence has been shown by Anderson *et al.* to parallel the polarizability of the buffer gases and is characteristic of the effect of buffer gases on other optically pumped atoms[2-5] (see Table I). The ordering reflects the predominating perturbation of the relevant hyperfine levels, but this net effect is in general difficult to predict without recourse to detailed calculation.

The purpose of this note is to report on calculations for the fractional pressure shift and the temperature variation of the frequency shift for hydrogen atoms in the presence of helium buffer gas atoms. Similar calculations[6-8] have been presented for more complicated systems; we present here a nonparametric approach to the problem. In order to elucidate the isotopic mass dependence for this favorable system a quantum statistical correction to the classically averaged fractional pressure shift has also been calculated.

---

* This research was supported by the U. S. Atomic Energy Commission and the U. S. Air Force.

† Preliminary results were reported previously [Bull. Am. Phys. Soc. **6**, 248 (1961)].

[1] L. W. Anderson, F. M. Pipkin, and J. C. Baird, Jr., Phys. Rev. Letters **4**, 69 (1960); Phys. Rev. **120**, 1279 (1960); **122**, 1962 (1961).

[2] M. Arditi and T. R. Carver, Phys. Rev. **109**, 1012 (1958).

[3] E. C. Beaty, P. L. Bender, and A. R. Chi, Phys. Rev. Letters **1**, 311 (1958).

[4] M. Arditi and T. R. Carver, Phys. Rev. **112**, 449 (1958).

[5] E. C. Beaty, P. L. Bender and A. R. Chi, Phys. Rev. **112**, 450 (1958).

[6] F. J. Adrian, J. Chem. Phys. **32**, 972 (1960).

[7] H. Margenau, P. Fontana, and L. Klein, Phys. Rev. **115**, 87 (1959).

[8] L. B. Robinson, Phys. Rev. **117**, 1275 (1960).

FORMALISM

In a dilute hydrogen–helium (H–He) gas mixture in which the gas atoms are only weakly coupled, the interactions at any one atom may be considered independent at any instant. Furthermore, with an extreme dilution of hydrogen atoms in the helium gas we may neglect those effects that arise from hydrogen atoms in close proximity to one another. In the gas mixture, then, we consider that the hydrogen atoms, in a given hyperfine level of the ground state, experience adiabatic interactions with the helium gas atoms such that only level shifts occur at any instant. It is assumed that the sole source of disorientation of these hydrogen atoms would be an externally applied radio-frequency field. In order to calculate some average property (e.g., the hydrogen atom fractional pressure shift) associated with the hydrogen atoms in the gas mixture, it is rewarding if we immediately simplify a formally more difficult problem by imagining the gas mixture to be one in which the distribution of helium gas atoms about each hydrogen atom is independent of the other hydrogen atoms in the gas mixture. By so doing we need only focus attention on a single hydrogen atom in the gas mixture (together with its helium atom distribution) and can readily employ the statistical–mechanical concept of an ensemble average to this situation to calculate the probable value of the property of interest. This result we place in correspondence with an experimentally determined value for the gas mixture.

We can employ another approach to the calculation and we do so in the appendix. There we consider specifically the details of the individual H–He collision processes and relate them to an observed property in a manner familiar to kinetic theory. These two approaches, the statistical–mechanical and the kinetic theory, will be seen to lead to similar results.

Since the interactions experienced by a hydrogen atom in a helium gas may be considered to be pairwise additive, we need only consider the perturbation of the

TABLE I. Fractional pressure shifts (mm Hg$^{-1}\times10^9$) observed for several paramagnetic $^2S_{\frac{1}{2}}$ state atoms in the presence of buffer gases.[1,3,4]

	Pumped atom[a]				
Buffer gas	H	D	T	Rb^{87}	Cs^{133}
He	+3.7			+105.3	+174.0
Ne	+2.1	+2.5	+3.7	+57.4	+70.7
Ar	−4.7	−3.6	−2.4	−7.5	−27.2
Kr				−84.9	−141.4
Xe					−261.1
H$_2$	−0.31			+96.6	+206.7
D$_2$				+98.0	
N$_2$				+76.1	+101.2
CH$_4$				−73.2	
n-C$_6$H$_{12}$				−409.7	
n-C$_7$H$_{16}$				−614.5	

[a] Results for the hydrogen isotopes were obtained at 50°C; those for Cs^{133} and Rb^{87} were obtained at 30°C and "near room temperature," respectively.

hydrogen atom hyperfine level arising from a single helium atom at any instant (the nuclear distribution function relative to the hydrogen atom may be obtained from statistical considerations). In order to do so we may consider the electronic wave function for this or any other interacting subsystem to be given formally as

$$\Psi_{H-He}(\mathbf{r}_H, \mathbf{r}_{He}; \mathbf{R}), \qquad (1)$$

where $\mathbf{r}_H$ and $\mathbf{r}_{He}$ are the set of electron coordinates associated with each atom and $\mathbf{R}$ denotes the implicit dependence of the wave function on the internuclear coordinates. As we will assume that each of the wave functions of the type given by Eq. (1) is a solution of a spin-independent Hamiltonian, each will serve as a valid description in a first-order perturbation theory calculation for the spin-dependent interactions arising from a hydrogen atom in the hyperfine state $F=0$ or $F=1$ merely by a proper choice for the electron spin associated with the hydrogen atom in a basis set. By virtue of the Franck–Condon principle, then, we can examine with equal facility the instantaneous hyper-

fine level separation of a hydrogen atom in the presence of a perturber helium atom.

The spin-independent Hamiltonian (in atomic units) for each of the independently interacting subsystems from which the wave function of Eq. (1) would result is of the form

$$H_0 = (2/R) - \sum_{j>i=1}^{3} \left[\tfrac{1}{2}\nabla_i^2 + (1/r_{iH}) + (2/r_{iHe}) - (1/r_{ij})\right],$$

$$(2)$$

such that

$$H_0\Psi_{H-He}(\mathbf{r}_H, \mathbf{r}_{He}; \mathbf{R}) = E(\mathbf{R})\Psi_{H-He}(\mathbf{r}_H, \mathbf{r}_{He}; \mathbf{R}), \quad (3)$$

and where $E(\mathbf{R})$, when taken relative to the energies of the infinitely separated atoms, is the intermolecular potential energy $V(\mathbf{R})$ for a given set of intermolecular coordinates. We shall assume for the moment that this three-electron problem is completely solved, and will return to it at a more convenient point in the discussion.

Under the experimental condition of a weak applied magnetic field[1] we need only consider as a perturbation correction to Eqs. (2) and (3) that term which arises from the nonzero interaction of the magnetic moments of the individual electrons in the subsystem with the magnetic moment of the hydrogen nucleus, i.e., the Fermi contact term,

$$H_F = (8\pi/3) g_N g_e \beta_N \beta_e \sum_{i=1}^{3} \mathbf{I}_H \cdot \mathbf{S}_i \delta(\mathbf{r}_{iH}). \qquad (4)$$

In Eq. (4) g_N and g_e are nuclear (N) and electronic (e) g factors, β_N and β_e the nuclear and Bohr magnetons, $\mathbf{I}_H$ the nuclear spin vector for the hydrogen nucleus, $\mathbf{S}_i$ the electronic spin vector for the ith electron, and $\delta(\mathbf{r}_{iH})$ the Dirac delta function for the ith electron which vanishes everywhere except at the hydrogen nucleus. The first-order perturbation theory correction to $E(\mathbf{R})$, the variation of a hyperfine level as a function of the internuclear coordinates, is given simply by the expectation value of the Fermi contact term:

$$E_F^{(1)}(\mathbf{R}) = (8\pi/3) g_N g_e \beta_N \beta_e \langle \Psi_{H-He}(\mathbf{r}_H, \mathbf{r}_{He}; \mathbf{R}) \mid \sum_{i=1}^{3} \mathbf{I}_H \cdot \mathbf{S}_i \delta(\mathbf{r}_{iH}) \mid \Psi_{H-He}(\mathbf{r}_H, \mathbf{r}_{He}; \mathbf{R}) \rangle. \qquad (5)$$

The fractional variation of the hyperfine frequency follows immediately from an evaluation of Eq. (5) for the relevant hyperfine levels and may be obtained directly by an evaluation of Eq. (6) for a particular hyperfine level.

$$\frac{\nu(\mathbf{R}) - \nu_0}{\nu_0} = \frac{\Delta\nu(\mathbf{R})}{\nu_0} = \frac{\langle \Psi_{H-He}(\mathbf{r}_H, \mathbf{r}_{He}; \mathbf{R}) \mid \sum_{i=1}^{3} \mathbf{I}_H \cdot \mathbf{S}_i \delta(\mathbf{r}_{iH}) \mid \Psi_{H-He}(\mathbf{r}_H, \mathbf{r}_{He}; \mathbf{R}) \rangle - \nu_0}{\langle \Psi_{H-He}(\mathbf{r}_H, \mathbf{r}_{He}; \infty) \mid \sum_{i=1}^{3} \mathbf{I}_H \cdot \mathbf{S}_i \delta(\mathbf{r}_{iH}) \mid \Psi_{H-He}(\mathbf{r}_H, \mathbf{r}_{He}; \infty) \rangle}. \qquad (6)$$

In Eq. (6) ν_0 is obtained by an evaluation of Eq. (5) with the hydrogen and helium atoms at infinite separation; ν_0 is, apart from a constant, the atomic hyperfine frequency for an isolated hydrogen atom. The ratio $\Delta\nu(\mathbf{R})/\nu_0$ expresses the fractional variation of the hydrogen hyperfine frequency arising from a single interacting helium atom; the quantity of physical interest, the ensemble average fractional frequency shift, from classical statistical considerations can be obtained by multiplication of Eq. (6) by the classical configurational distribution function for a single subsystem times the number of helium atoms in the system and summing over the internuclear coordinates, i.e.,

$$\langle\Delta\nu/\nu_0\rangle=\rho_{\text{He}}\int[\Delta\nu(\mathbf{R})/\nu_0]\exp[-V(\mathbf{R})/kT]d\mathbf{R}. \quad (7)$$

In Eq. (7) ρ_{He} is the number density of helium atoms, $V(\mathbf{R})$ the intermolecular potential energy for a subsystem and k is Boltzmann's constant. Substitution of the equation of state for an ideal gas in Eq. (7) and differentiation with respect to pressure, at constant temperature and volume, gives immediately a quantity desired—the ensemble average fractional pressure shift.

$$(\partial/\partial P)(\langle\Delta\nu/\nu_0\rangle)_{T,V}=(1/kT)\int[\Delta\nu(\mathbf{R})/\nu_0]$$
$$\times\exp[-V(\mathbf{R})/kT]d\mathbf{R}. \quad (8)$$

The temperature variation of the ensemble average fractional frequency shift, at constant buffer gas density, is obtained by differentiation of Eq. (7) with respect to temperature, i.e.,

$$(\partial/\partial T)(\langle\Delta\nu/\nu_0\rangle)_{\rho_{\text{He}},V}=(\rho_{\text{He}}/kT^2)\int[\Delta\nu(\mathbf{R})/\nu_0]$$
$$\times\exp[-V(\mathbf{R})/kT]V(\mathbf{R})d\mathbf{R}. \quad (9)$$

A more convenient quantity, the temperature variation of the frequency shift, is obtained simply by multiplication of Eq. (9) by the atomic hydrogen hyperfine frequency.

In order to exhibit a mass dependence for the fractional pressure shift we may argue that the relative nuclear motion of a H–He subsystem is not sufficiently described classically and should be described instead in quantum mechanical terms—the de Broglie wavelength associated with the relative motion of a H–He subsystem at room temperature is on the order of the distance over which these atoms effectively interact with one another ($\lambda \sim 10^{-8}$ cm).

In the quantum statistical description the subsystem configurational distribution function employed in the ensemble average [Eq. (8)] is no longer correct; in the near-classical limit, however, it has been shown that the distribution function can be described by the classical distribution function modified by correction terms arising from the noncommuting terms in the

TABLE II. Variation of the fractional frequency shift $\Delta\nu(R)/\nu_0$ and intermolecular potential energy $V(R)$ with internuclear separation.

R (a.u.)	$\Delta\nu(R)/\nu_0$	$V(R)$ (a.u.)
1.00	0.017075	0.61420
2.00	0.120229	0.10510
3.00	0.032847	0.01963
4.00	0.006730	0.003455
5.00	0.001196	0.000568
6.00	0.000195	0.000088
7.00	0.000030	0.000013
8.00	0.000005	0.000002
9.00	0.000001	0.000000
10.00	0.000000	0.000000

Hamiltonian for relative mass motion.[9–11] The configurational distribution function in this limit, with only the first nonzero corrections (of order λ^2) included, is proportional to

$$\exp[-V(\mathbf{R})/kT](1+(\lambda^2/6kT)\{(1/2kT)[\nabla V(\mathbf{R})]^2 \\ -\nabla^2 V(\mathbf{R})\}). \quad (10)$$

The thermal de Broglie wavelength (λ) associated with a molecule of reduced mass μ is given by Eq. (11),

$$\lambda=(\hbar^2/2\mu kT)^{\frac{1}{2}}. \quad (11)$$

The quantum-statistical mass dependent correction to the classical ensemble average fractional pressure shift follows then from Eq. (8):

$$\tfrac{1}{6}(\lambda/kT)^2\int[\Delta\nu(\mathbf{R})/\nu_0]\exp[-V(\mathbf{R})/kT] \\ \times\{(1/2kT)[\nabla V(\mathbf{R})]^2-\nabla^2 V(\mathbf{R})\}d\mathbf{R}. \quad (12)$$

QUANTUM MECHANICS OF A SUBSYSTEM

It is now clear that to actually compute the effects of helium buffer gas atoms on the atomic hydrogen hyperfine frequency we must first specify explicitly the intermolecular potential function $[V(\mathbf{R})]$ and the electronic wave function for the H–He subsystem. To simplify this quantum-mechanical problem [Eq. (3)] we choose for the subsystem wave function (suitably normalized) the antisymmetrized product of one-electron spin orbitals, i.e.,

$$\Psi_{\text{H-He}}(\mathbf{r}_{\text{H}}, \mathbf{r}_{\text{He}}; \mathbf{R})=A\,|\,u_{\text{H}}(1)u_{\text{He}}(2)\bar{u}_{\text{He}}(3)\,|. \quad (13)$$

In this first approximation we restrict the basis set to $1s$ hydrogen and hydrogen-like orbitals centered on the hydrogen and helium atoms, respectively, with orbital exponents $z_{\text{H}}=1.0000$ and $z_{\text{He}}=1.6875$. The intermolecular potential energy for this spherically symmetric three-electron problem is obtained from

[9] J. G. Kirkwood, Phys. Rev. 44, 31 (1933).
[10] M. L. Goldberger and E. N. Adams, J. Chem. Phys. 20, 240 (1952).
[11] J. E. Mayer and W. Band, J. Chem. Phys. 15, 141 (1947).

TABLE III. Effects of helium buffer gas atoms on the atomic hydrogen hyperfine frequency at 323°K.

Fractional pressure shift (mm Hg^{-1}) $\times 10^9$	
Classical average	$+1.67$
Quantum average	$+1.73$
Experimental	$+3.7 \pm 0.7$[1]
Temperature variation of frequency shift (cps/mm Hg-°K) $\times 10^3$	
Classical average	$+5.64$

Eq. (3) by an evaluation with the single determinant wave function and is given formally by Eq. (14) as a function of the internuclear separation:

$$E(R) - E(\infty) = V(R)$$

$$= \langle \Psi_{\text{H-He}}(\mathbf{r}_H, \mathbf{r}_{He}; \mathbf{R}) \mid H_0 \mid \Psi_{\text{H-He}}(\mathbf{r}_H, \mathbf{r}_{He}; \mathbf{R}) \rangle$$

$$- \langle \Psi_{\text{H-He}}(\mathbf{r}_H, \mathbf{r}_{He}; \infty) \mid H_0 \mid \Psi_{\text{H-He}}(\mathbf{r}_H, \mathbf{r}_{He}; \infty) \rangle. \quad (14)$$

H_0 is the Hamiltonian given by Eq. (2), and $E(\infty)$ is the energy of the H-He sybsystem at infinite separation, i.e., the energy of the isolated atoms. The calculation for the intermolecular energies with the single determinant wave function has been considered previously[12] ($R \leq 5$ a.u.) and for present purposes we have recalculated some values and extended these results to include larger values of R. As observed previously[12] the results of such a calculation yield a set of energies that increase monotonically with decreasing internuclear separation; the variation of $V(R)$ with R is given in Table II.

The fractional frequency shifts, computed by an evaluation of Eq. (6) with the single determinant wave function, also yield a monotonically increasing variation with decreasing R (to about 2 a.u.) and are tabulated in Table II for several values of R.

In order to facilitate numerical calculations we have expressed [Eq. (15)] the intermolecular energies of Table II in terms of two analytical expressions[12] that satisfactorily characterize these results.

$$V(R) = 4.606e^{-1.760R} + (3.666 \times 10^{-4}/R) - (2.94/R^6)$$

$$2 \leq R \leq 5,$$

$$V(R) = +5542.9688/R^{10} \qquad R \geq 5. \quad (15)$$

RESULTS

The results of numerical evaluation of the integrals for the classical and quantum-statistical ensemble average fractional pressure shift and the temperature variation of the frequency shift, at constant buffer gas density, are given in Table III together with the experimentally determined fractional pressure shift. The calculated temperature effect indicates that the H–He system can be expected to be a rather stable one to modest temperature variations—more so than the

alkali atom systems where observed temperature variations have been found to lie approximately between ±1 cps/mm Hg – °C.[3–5] This result is not surprising in view of the relatively weak distortions of the hydrogen atom in the presence of several different buffer gases (Table I).

The rather poor agreement between the experimentally determined pressure shift and that calculated with the single determinant wave function is indicative of the inadequacy of the wave function. This situation is not significantly altered if we employ, instead, a molecular orbital function formed from the 1s hydrogen and helium atomic orbitals [which differs from Eq. (13) by the incorporation of an additional determinant, $A \mid \mu_H \mu_{He} \bar{\mu}_H \mid$, with a coefficient at any value of R determined from a variational calculation[12]]. Furthermore, any attempt at a recognition of a van der Waals polarization,[6,13] leads naturally to a further reduction in the calculated shift. The basic difficulty of the present calculation appears to be the failure of the subsystem wave function to realistically account for the distortions that arise in the free helium atom and, especially important here, the hydrogen atom electronic orbitals as a result of mutual interaction. For a small atom interaction system it is to be expected, and the experimental result indicates, that the principal interaction experienced by the hydrogen atom electron arises from the Pauli exclusion effect which, with significant orbital overlap, leads to an increase in the unpaired spin density at the hydrogen nucleus and a positive pressure shift. The function given by Eq. (13) is partially deficient in this respect but the calculated shift will not improve measurably[12] unless the basis set of functions is extended to include excited state configurations. Preliminary results obtained by Matsen and Browne[14] for the unpaired electron spin density at the hydrogen nucleus with a more detailed wave function offers much encouragement in view of the experimental result. Their wave function includes the hydrogen and helium atomic orbitals through to and including the 2p Slater orbitals with the nonlinear coefficients obtained from a variational procedure.

The quantum statistical mass correction for the H-He system is small (~4%); since distortions in the electronic charge distribution (with resultant variation in the potential energy of interaction) of a subsystem are not expected to vary significantly from one hydrogen isotope to another, it follows from the form of the quantum correction that somewhat smaller corrections —proportional to the ratio of reduced masses $\mu_{\text{H-He}}/\mu_{\text{D-He}}$ and $\mu_{\text{H-He}}/\mu_{\text{T-He}}$ for the deuterium–helium and tritium–helium systems, respectively— would result for the D–He and T–He systems. With an experimental procedure sensitive to these small variations one could hope to investigate this effect and

[12] E. A. Mason, J. Ross, and P. N. Schatz, J. Chem. Phys. **25**, 626 (1956).

[13] See, for example, T. P. Das and R. Bersohn, Phys. Rev. **102**, 733 (1956).

[14] F. A. Matsen and J. C. Browne (private communication).

its consequences, however, the present experimental uncertainty is such that it renders these mass effects inaccessible. The fractional pressure shifts reported[1] for the hydrogen isotopes in the presence of neon and argon buffer gases appear to exhibit an isotopic mass dependence, but these variations are not at all consistent with a quantum mass effect. If the alterations in the potential energy and electronic charge distribution are indeed negligible, as we should expect, then there is, in the present context, no other apparent mechanism available through which such observed variations in the fractional pressure shifts may arise. We can only conclude, therefore, that these results are in error.

ACKNOWLEDGMENTS

The author gratefully acknowledges his indebtedness to Professor Richard Bersohn for suggesting this problem and for many informative discussions in its pursuit. The author would also like to express his appreciation for the use of the computing facilities made available by the IBM Watson Scientific Computing Laboratory, Columbia University.

APPENDIX

In this section we present an alternative approach to the calculation of the hydrogen atom fractional pressure shift from a kinetic point of view. We shall be concerned here with the details of the collision act, i.e., a H–He encounter.

The instantaneous mean fractional frequency shift of a collection of hydrogen atoms in a unit volume of a H–He gas mixture in which the hydrogen atoms are sufficiently dilute so that they experience at any instant predominantly binary (adiabatic and independent) encounters with the helium atoms in the unit volume is given in terms of a sum of the contributions from the several hydrogen atoms in the unit volume of number N and density ρ_H. Each of these contributions will be dependent upon an instantaneous relative separation R_i for a particular hydrogen atom and helium atom that constitute one of the collision pairs at any given instant. The instantaneous mean fractional frequency shift for a hydrogen atom in the unit volume may be expressed by the following:

$$\frac{\Delta\nu(R_1, R_2, \cdots, R_N)}{\nu_0} = \frac{1}{\rho_H}\sum_{i=1}^{N}\frac{\Delta\nu(R_i)}{\nu_0}. \quad (A1)$$

The function for the ith collision pair, $\Delta\nu(R_i)/\nu_0$, as previously defined, is the fractional frequency shift of a particular hydrogen atom due to a perturbing helium atom with the instantaneous relative separation R_i. The summation extends over all of the hydrogen atoms in the unit volume although only a fraction of these atoms contribute effectively at any given instant. This is of course due to the fact (Table II) that the shift differs from zero only over a very limited range of R. The instantaneous mean fractional frequency shift is

not, however, of interest as it corresponds to a condition other than that physically attainable. A more meaningful quantity that will be associated with an experimentally determined mean shift is the time average of this instantaneous shift over an interval Δt which is long compared with the effective interaction time τ_e but short compared with the mean free time,[15] i.e.,

$$\left\langle\frac{\Delta\nu}{\nu_0}\right\rangle = \frac{1}{\Delta t}\int_{t_0}^{t_0+\Delta t}\frac{\Delta\nu(R_1, R_2, \cdots, R_N)}{\nu_0}dt$$
$$= \frac{1}{\rho_H}\sum_i\frac{1}{\Delta t}\int_{t_0}^{t_0+\Delta t}\frac{\Delta\nu(R_i)}{\nu_0}dt. \quad (A2)$$

In Eq. (A2) the sum is understood to extend over the probable number of H–He encounters that occur in the unit volume within Δt. (A typical Δt under experimental conditions would be on the order of 10^{-10} sec with τ_e on the order of $10^{-12}-10^{-13}$ sec.) In this way a large number of binary encounters are included and the instantaneous fluctuations due to these encounters are smoothed over the interval. Each hydrogen atom can, however, suffer at most a single collision in Δt. An implicit assumption of Eq. (A2) is that the time average is independent of further extensions in the interval Δt.

In order to facilitate the evaluation of the mean shift which is dependent upon the behavior of the hydrogen atom hyperfine levels ($F=0$ and $F=1$) in the individual collision pairs over their respective collision paths we note that the effective interaction interval τ_e is very much smaller than Δt. If we regard for the moment that the encounters are instantaneous, i.e., if we ignore the finite extent of the interactions, then each of the encounters in Δt may be considered as occurring interior to this interval. For convenience we shall proceed with such an assumption so that for any encounter we have only to evaluate an integral

$$\frac{1}{\Delta t}\int_{t_0}^{t_0+\Delta t}\frac{\Delta\nu(R_i)}{\nu_0}dt \quad (A3)$$

over the interval Δt that includes the actual collision act. It follows immediately that we can extend the limits of Eq. (A3) to $\pm\infty$ without error since these included times correspond to conditions prior and subsequent to the particular collision. If the collision, furthermore, is symmetric in the time we then have for the time average fractional frequency shift of a single collision pair the expression

$$\frac{2}{\Delta t}\int_0^\infty\frac{\Delta\nu(R_i)}{\nu_0}dt. \quad (A4)$$

[15] With the relatively long time associated with the measurement we consider that the time average of a single hydrogen atom over a large number of encounters in a time much greater than Δt to be equivalent to this time average of a large number of H–HE encounters in the short time Δt.

Recalling from the equations of motion for pair-wise interacting particles that the time t may be expressed in terms of the several collision constants, we may conveniently replace the integration over t by one over R_i, and thus obtain for the time average shift for a collision pair an equation of the form

$$\frac{\Delta\nu(b_i,\epsilon_i)}{\nu_0}=\frac{2}{\Delta t}\int_{R_0}^{\infty}\frac{\Delta\nu(R_i)}{\nu_0}$$

$$\times\frac{dR_i}{\{(2\epsilon/\mu)[1-(b/R)^2-V(R)/\epsilon]\}^{\frac{1}{2}}}. \quad (A5)$$

R_0 is the internuclear separation at $t=0$, and it corresponds to the distance of closest approach. The reduced mass of the collision pair is μ, b is the impact parameter, and ϵ, obtained from the Hamiltonian for the relative mass motion, is the relative energy of the collision pair. Equation (A5) may be considered to be the time average shift for a collision pair of the collision type (b, ϵ). Given a weighting function that represents the probable number of encounters in the unit volume within Δt of type (b, ϵ) with an impact parameter between b and $b+db$ and relative energy between ϵ and $\epsilon+d\epsilon$ or simply (b, db) and $(\epsilon, d\epsilon)$, the sum over the individual collision pairs in Eq. (A2) may be transformed to a summation of the time average shift with the weighting function over b and ϵ consistent with the set of collisions. If we neglect the effect of external fields of force on the H–He gas mixture, and furthermore assume it to be a random gas (composed of elastic spheres), then from a fundamental assumption in the kinetic theory of gases we obtain for the probable number of H–He encounters per unit volume that occur within Δt with relative energy $(\epsilon, d\epsilon)$ and impact parameter (b, db) the expression[16]

$$\Delta t\rho_H\rho_{He}[32\pi/\mu(kT)^3]^{\frac{1}{2}}\exp(-\epsilon/kT)\epsilon bdbd\epsilon. \quad (A6)$$

ρ_H and ρ_{He} are, respectively, the density of the hydrogen and helium atoms in the gas mixture. It follows immediately from Eqs. (A2), (A4), (A5), and (A6) that the mean hydrogen atom fractional frequency shift in

the H–He gas mixture is given by

$$\langle\Delta\nu/\nu_0\rangle=8\rho_{He}[\pi/(kT)^3]^{\frac{1}{2}}\int_0^{\infty}bdb\int_0^{\infty}\epsilon\exp(-\epsilon/kT)d\epsilon$$

$$\times\int_{R_0}^{\infty}\frac{\Delta\nu(R)}{\nu_0}\frac{dR}{\{\epsilon[1-(b/R)^2-V(R)/\epsilon]\}^{\frac{1}{2}}}. \quad (A7)$$

The range of b over which an effective encounter occurs should, in principle, be given with greater precision but because of the finite range of the shift we need not bother to specify it and we may formally extend the upper limit to $+\infty$ without incurring error.

In the assumed ideal gas condition such that ρ_{He} may be replaced by P/kT, the mean hydrogen atom fractional pressure shift is obtained directly by differentiation of Eq. (A7) with respect to this pressure at constant temperature and volume:

$$(\partial/\partial P)(\langle\Delta\nu/\nu_0\rangle)_{T,V}=8[\pi/(kT)^5]^{\frac{1}{2}}\int_0^{\infty}bdb$$

$$\times\int_0^{\infty}\exp(-\epsilon/kT)\epsilon d\epsilon\int_{R_0}^{\infty}\frac{\Delta\nu(R)}{\nu_0}$$

$$\times\frac{dR}{(\epsilon\{1-(b/R)^2-[V(R)/\epsilon]\})^{\frac{1}{2}}}. \quad (A8)$$

It is to be noted that this classical expression is independent of the reduced mass μ of the colliding H–He atoms.

Using the analytical expressions [Eq. (15)] for the intermolecular energies and the condition on the relative energy ϵ such that at $R=R_0$, $(dR/dt)_{R=R_0}=0$, and therefore

$$\epsilon=V(R_0)/[1-(b/R_0)^2].$$

Equation (A8) has been evaluated and the value of $+1.79\times10^{-9}$ mm Hg^{-1} obtained for the mean hydrogen atom fractional pressure shift.

Although the approach of this calculation for the shift is not equivalent to that previously given, the fair agreement in the two results, which would probably not be altered by an improved electronic wave function for a collision pair (subsystem), nevertheless indicates that the hard sphere interaction approximation employed here is an adequate one.

---

[16] R. H. Fowler, *Statistical Mechanics* (Cambridge University Press, London, 1929), p. 421.

From: *Phys. Rev.* **105**, 1487-1489 (1957)

Slow Spin Relaxation of Optically Polarized Sodium Atoms*

H. G. DEHMELT

Department of Physics, University of Washington, Seattle, Washington

(Received November 29, 1956)

In order to obtain as narrow as possible paramagnetic resonance signals, it is of importance to investigate the conditions under which long relaxation times can be realized. In the present experiment on sodium atoms diffusing in argon gas, relaxation due to sodium-sodium collisions was minimized by employing very low sodium partial vapor pressures (about 10^{-7} mm Hg). While at lower pressures the argon is serving its function well to slow down relaxation by inhibiting wall diffusion, at about 10 cm Hg relaxation due to sodium-argon collisions becomes the decisive factor. Nevertheless it was possible to realize a relaxation time of 0.21 sec for a 1-liter spherical bulb filled with 3 cm argon. About 0.02 sec was found for a 0.1-liter, 40 cm argon sample. In carrying out the experiments, optical pumping by circularly polarized resonance radiation was used to create an orientation of the sodium atoms which then was monitored by measuring the transmission of the pumping radiation through the sample. By suddenly reversing a small axial magnetic field, the polarization of the atoms could be made to reverse too. From the decay rates of this inverted polarization under the combined effects of relaxation and continuing optical pumping, the experimental relaxation times were deduced. The strong signals obtained are indicative of available signal to noise ratios in future radio-frequency resonance reorientation experiments using the transmission monitoring technique. A theoretical analysis of the optical pumping process, including the dynamic aspects and allowing for collisions with argon that the sodium atoms undergo while in the excited state, was carried out and used to describe the experimental data.

* Part of this research was supported by the United States Air Force through the Office of Scientific Research of the Air Research and Development Command.

RECENT paramagnetic resonance *absorption* experiments[1,2] on free atoms diffusing back and forth in an inert buffer gas have created some interest in the spin relaxation processes in these systems. Various mechanisms have been discussed by Wittke and Dicke.[3] Hoping that under favorable conditions wall collisions are the only ones effecting relaxation, one would expect a relaxation time as long as the average time necessary for an atom to diffuse to the wall. This report will deal with experiments on sodium atoms which were contained in argon gas of a pressure between 1 and 40 cm Hg, while the partial sodium pressure was of the order of 10^{-7} mm Hg. Relaxation times as long as 0.21 sec were observed which in future radio-frequency resonance *reorientation* experiments should allow the observation of extraordinarily narrow lines.

The experimental arrangement was the following one. Sodium resonance radiation from a battery-operated GE sodium arc (Na 1) mounted in a Dewar was focused by a large condenser lens through a Polaroid circular polarizing sheet on a spherical absorption vessel. The volume of the thoroughly baked, sealed off vessels containing some metallic sodium and the buffer varied between 0.1 and 1 liter. The vessels were generally heated to such a temperature (130–250°C) that about 50% absorption occurred. The transmitted light[3a] was focused upon a vacuum photocell whose output was amplified by a single-stage broad-band amplifier (0.05 to 1000 cps pass-band) and displayed on an oscilloscope. The earth field in the region of the absorption vessel was cancelled out and a small field of about 0.5 gauss was applied parallel to the light beam by means of a ring coil energized from a short-time-constant circuit. This arrangement now functioned in the following fashion:

As sufficient numbers of circularly polarized quanta are absorbed, the more strongly absorbing magnetic sublevels of the sodium ground state are depopulated while the less absorbing ones are filled up at their expense until a saturation polarization is attained (optical pumping).[4,5] Consequently, while this is going on, the initially transmitted light intensity I_1 will increase to a value $I_1+\Delta I$. If the axial magnetic field is now suddenly reversed, the polarization of the atoms due to its associated magnetization will follow adiabatically. This leads to a nearly instantaneous exchange of the population of the $+m$ with that of the $-m$ levels and now an overpopulation of the more strongly absorbing ones. The result is a sudden decrease of the transmitted intensity from $I_1+\Delta I$ to $I_1-\Delta I$. However, under the continued irradiation it will not take long before the original polarization pointing in the "right"

direction is restored (Fig. 1). The time involved, if depolarizing relaxation effects are assumed to be insignificant, would be expected to be inversely proportional to the incident light intensity I_0. This state of affairs is found to prevail for the high-intensity oscilloscope traces. If one now reduces the light intensity further and further, there will come a time when the inverted polarization will also decay appreciably because of relaxation effects. Figure 2 shows a plot of "decay times" *versus* relative intensity. The values which were obtained from the oscilloscope traces by the construction explained in Fig. 1, converge against a characteristic relaxation time T.

A brief, more quantitative description of the processes sketched above will now be attempted. The optical pumping is appreciably modified by collisions of the excited atoms with the buffer gas. Experimental[6] evidence indicates that about 5 mm of argon is sufficient to disorient largely the orbital angular momenta with respect to the spin and also a fixed direction before re-emission can occur. The situation at lower argon pressures, where only a few collisions in the excited state occur, is rather complex. However, studies of the optical pumping by investigating the polarization of the resonance fluorescence and an analysis of the collision process have recently been undertaken.[7] In the present work, a greatly simplifying assumption will be made which, even in the pressure range of interest here, 1–40 cm Hg, should hold strictly only for sufficiently strong coupling between the sodium nucleus and the electronic momenta. The assumption is that the collisions bring about a completely random redistribution of the populations of the 24 hfs magnetic sublevels of the excited ^2P state regardless of which of them had been excited originally. Under these assumptions the resonance fluorescence is completely depolarized and the rates at which the atoms return to any of the 8 hfs magnetic sublevels of the $^2S_{\frac{1}{2}}$ ground state will be identical and equal to $\frac{1}{8}$ of the sum of the probabilities for all upwards transitions. The probabilities for leaving a given ground-state m level owing to $\Delta m=+1$ transitions to the excited state under the combined influence

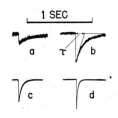

FIG. 1. Oscilloscope traces of transmitted resonance light intensity I_1 *versus* time. The time axis runs from left to right, the scale being the same for all traces. The relative intensity I_0 of the applied resonance light increased for traces *a* to *d* from 4 over 16 and 64 to 160. The sudden intensity drop occurred when the magnetic field, to which the sodium absorption cell was exposed, was instantaneously reversed. The construction shown—for trace *b* only—served to determine the experimental decay times τ.

[1] J. P. Wittke and R. H. Dicke, Phys. Rev. **96**, 530 (1954).
[2] H. G. Dehmelt, Phys. Rev. **99**, 527 (1955).
[3] J. P. Wittke and R. H. Dicke, Phys. Rev. **103**, 620 (1956).
[3a] Compare H. C. Dehmelt, Phys. Rev. **103**, 1125 (1956).
[4] A. Kastler, J. phys. radium **11**, 255 (1950); and Proc. Phys. Soc. (London) **A67**, 853 (1954).
[5] W. B. Hawkins, Phys. Rev. **98**, 478 (1955).

[6] W. Lochte-Holtgreven, Ann. Physik **47**, 362 (1928).
[7] Brossel, Margerie, and Kastler, Compt. rend. **241**, 865 (1955); P. L. Bender, thesis, Princeton University (1956).

of the D_1 and D_2 radiation can be computed from standard formulas[8] for the transition probabilities and are denoted by P_m.

One obtains

$$(P_{-1}:P_0:P_{-1})_{F=1}:(P_{-2}:P_{-1}:P_0:P_{+1}:P_{+2})_{F=2}$$
$$= ((1+5R):(2+4R):(3+3R)):$$
$$((4+2R):(3+3R):(2+4R):(1+5R):6R),$$

R denoting the ratio of the intensities for the D_2 and D_1 components of the radiation which is expected to be close to unity.[5] The time dependence of the relative populations $a_m(t)$ of the m levels will then be described by the 8 simultaneous equations:

$$\dot{a}_m = -a_m P_m + \tfrac{1}{8}\sum a_i P_i + (1/T)(1-a_m).$$

The sum here is over the 8 sublevels of the ground state and $a_m(0)$ has been put equal to 1. The last term takes into account the relaxation processes. For the saturation distribution, $\bar{a}_m$ follows with $P_m \to \infty$ and $\dot{a}_m(\infty)=0$:

$$(\bar{a}_{-1}:\bar{a}_0:\bar{a}_{+1}):(\bar{a}_{-2}:\bar{a}_{-1}:\bar{a}_0:\bar{a}_{+1}:\bar{a}_{+2})$$
$$= (P_{-1}^{-1}:P_0^{-1}:P_{+1}^{-1}):$$
$$(P_{-2}^{-1}:P_{-1}^{-1}:P_0^{-1}:P_{+1}^{-1}:P_{+2}^{-1})$$
$$\approx ((1-\bar{e}):1:(1+\bar{e})):$$
$$((1+2\bar{e}):(1+\bar{e}):1:(1-\bar{e}):(1-2\bar{e})).$$

For the last line and in the following discussion it has been assumed that

$$\bar{e} = (R-1)/(2+4R) \ll 1.$$

Instantaneous population distributions $a_m(t)$ are described in identical fashion as the saturation distribution, except that for $\bar{e}$ one has to substitute $e(t)$ which obeys the relation

$$\dot{e} = cI_0(\bar{e}-e) - (1/T)e,$$

c being a constant depending upon the P_m. The equilibrium value e_I, when the optical pumping is just compensated by relaxation, can be obtained by putting $\dot{e}=0$:

$$e_I = cI_0 T\bar{e}/(cI_0 T+1).$$

[8] E. U. Condon and G. Shortley, *The Theory of Atomic Spectra* (Cambridge University Press, Cambridge, 1935), Chaps. 9 and 16.

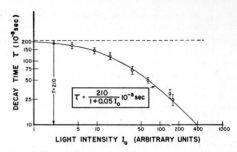

FIG. 2. Plot of the experimental decay time τ of the spin polarization against light intensity I_0. The theoretical curve has been chosen for best fit and allows the determination of the spin relaxation time T as distinct from τ, which still reflects reorientation due to impinging light quanta.

Immediately after the field reversal, we have

$$(\dot{e})_0 = cI_0(\bar{e}+e_I) + (1/T)e_I;$$

from this follows that

$$2e_I/(\dot{e})_0 \equiv \tau = T/(cI_0 T+1),$$

which, as $\Delta I(t)$ can be shown to be proportional to $e(t)$, gives the justification for the determination of τ from the oscilloscope traces, as described in Fig. 1.

So far, quantitative measurements have been undertaken only on a 1-liter, 3-cm Hg argon sample and a 0.1-liter, 40-cm Hg argon sample. No dependence of the relaxation times on temperature, and consequently on sodium vapor pressure, was noticed in either case in the operating range. For both samples the relaxation times found were significantly shorter than the average wall diffusion times of about 0.4 sec and 0.9 sec, respectively. The relaxation times observed, namely 0.21 sec for the 3 cm Hg sample and 0.02 sec for the 40 cm Hg sample are in qualitative agreement with a relaxation mechanism due to sodium argon collisions, which would be expected to be proportional to argon pressure.

The author wishes to thank his colleagues E. A. Uehling and E. M. Henley for clarifying discussions, K. C. Clark and P. Higgs for advice and loans of equipment. Mr. Y. Jonson built the various absorption vessels.

From: *Phys. Rev.* **115**, 850-856 (1959)

Spin Relaxation of Optically Aligned Rubidium Vapor*

W. Franzen

Arthur D. Little, Incorporated, Cambridge, Massachusetts

(Received March 23, 1959)

A new optical method for studying the spin relaxation of optically aligned rubidium vapor is described. In this method, the pumping radiation, consisting of circularly polarized D_1 resonance radiation, is suddenly shut off and then turned on again after a known time interval. The relaxation which takes place during the interval of darkness causes the vapor to become more opaque to the pumping radiation at a rate which is determined by the relaxation time. A large degree of alignment, as well as a relaxation time of about 80 milliseconds, were observed in a closed-off evacuated cylindrical glass cell completely lined, except for 1/200 of the wall area, with a thin film of tetracontane ($C_{40}H_{82}$). The variation of relaxation time with buffer gas pressure was studied in this cell and in an unlined glass cell. From the observations with the unlined cell, diffusion coefficients for rubidium in neon and argon of 0.31 cm²/sec and 0.24 cm²/sec, respectively, can be deduced. Observed cross sections for disorientation collisions between aligned ground-state rubidium atoms and neon, argon, krypton, and xenon atoms are 5.2×10^{-23} cm², 3.7×10^{-22} cm², 5.9×10^{-21} cm², and 1.3×10^{-20} cm², respectively. In the evacuated tetracontane-lined cell, the relaxation time decreased by 30% for a tenfold increase in rubidium vapor pressure. An explanation for this relatively weak dependence is suggested. The longest observed relaxation time was approximately 0.4 seconds in a tetracontane-lined cell filled with neon to a pressure of 3 cm Hg.

INTRODUCTION

A STUDY of the relaxation of alkali metal vapors aligned by optical pumping is particularly interesting for several reasons. In the first place, a relatively large population of oriented atoms is present at temperatures of the order of 300–400°K, corresponding to a degree of alignment achieved by other methods of spin orientation at liquid helium temperatures.[1-5] Furthermore, since the oriented atoms are in the vapor state, they interact with each other and with other gas atoms in the course of isolated binary collisions. The relaxation process is therefore a somewhat more straightforward physical problem than relaxation in condensed systems.

By varying the experimental conditions, such as the partial pressure of an inert buffer gas, or the alkali vapor pressure, the relative frequency of different types of collisions leading to relaxation can be changed and the disorienting interactions can be studied separately. Such a procedure has been followed in the experiment to be described here. The principle of the experimental method can be described as follows.

When circularly polarized resonance radiation is passed through the vapor of an alkali metal, the strongly absorbing magnetic sublevels in the ground state of the alkali atoms tend to get depopulated at the expense of the weakly absorbing levels. This effect is particularly striking when the D_1 line only is present in the pumping radiation.[4,5] As a result of this process, the vapor becomes more transparent to the pumping radiation. By applying a sudden perturbation to the system, it is then possible to obtain information on the relaxation of the vapor by observing its optical transparency as a function of time. Such a method was first used by Dehmelt,[3] who observed the effect on the transmitted light of suddenly reversing a small longitudinal magnetic field. The field reversal reverses the sign of the polarization of the vapor, causing it to become momentarily more opaque. The decay rate of the inverted polarization under the combined effects of relaxation and continued pumping can then be used to deduce the relaxation time of the vapor by separating out the contribution of relaxation.

However, a more reliable measurement of relaxation time is achieved by allowing an aligned vapor to relax in the dark. The change in alignment with time is then determined by relaxation alone, and it is not necessary to separate out any competing effects. To carry out a measurement of this type, we have constructed a mechanical shutter that interrupts the pumping light beam suddenly, and then turns it on again after a variable time interval. The actual interruption time can be measured directly by triggering the sweep of an oscilloscope with the output signal from a photomultiplier tube which is illuminated by light passing through the vapor cell.

When the shutter opens after a short interval of closing, the transparency of the vapor will have changed as a consequence of the partial relaxation of the vapor. This change is reflected in a decreased output signal from the photomultiplier an instant after the re-opening of the shutter. By superimposing the output signals from the photomultiplier corresponding to a series of shutter closing times on a single oscilloscope photograph, the approximately exponential decay of the polarization of the vapor is plotted out directly.

In the case of the rubidium vapor cell used in our experiment, under the most favorable conditions the transmitted light intensity changed by as much as twelve percent as a result of relaxation in the dark. The corresponding amplitude of the Dehmelt-type field reversal transient was somewhat more than twenty percent of the total amount of light passing through the cell. The effects measured here are therefore relatively

* Supported by the U. S. Army Signal Corps Research and Development Laboratory, Fort Monmouth, New Jersey.
[1] A. Kastler, Proc. Phys. Soc. (London) **A67**, 853 (1954).
[2] W. B. Hawkins, Phys. Rev. **98**, 478 (1955).
[3] H. G. Dehmelt, Phys. Rev. **105**, 1487 (1957).
[4] W. E. Bell and A. L. Bloom, Phys. Rev. **107**, 1559 (1957).
[5] W. Franzen and A. G. Emslie, Phys. Rev. **108**, 1453 (1957).

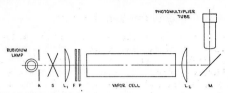

FIG. 1. Schematic diagram of optical system. The symbols have the following significance: *A*-aperture; *S*-shutter; L_1-condensing lens; *F*-interference filter; *P*-circular polarizer; L_2-collimating lens; *M*-mirror.

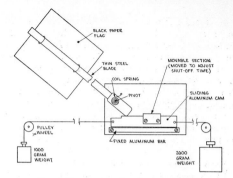

FIG. 2. Construction of mechanical shutter.

large and easily observable, except when the relaxation time is quite short.

APPARATUS

A schematic picture of the optical system employed in this experiment is shown in Fig. 1. As can be seen from this diagram, light from a rubidium spectral lamp passes through an aperture which is in the focal plane of a condensing lens. A mechanical shutter is mounted between the aperture and the lens. The light collected by the lens passes successively through an interference filter and through a circular polarizer and then enters a cylindrical glass cell containing the rubidium vapor. After traversing the cell along its axis, the pumping radiation falls on the face of an infrared-sensitive photomultiplier tube. The entire setup is directed along a magnetic meridian and is surrounded by two rectangular Helmholtz coils which allow both the vertical and the longitudinal magnetic fields to be adjusted at will. The rectangular framework holding the coils is covered with black paper on all sides except one, where an opening is left to allow manipulation of the shutter.

The construction of the mechanical shutter is illustrated in Fig. 2. As shown in this picture, a black paper flag approximately $3\frac{1}{2}$ inches long and $2\frac{1}{2}$ inches wide is fastened to the end of an 8-inch long thin steel blade. The blade is fastened to a pivot at its other end, around which a strong steel spring tends to rotate it. The rotational motion of the blade is arrested, however, by an adjustable metal cam which can slide sideways. There are three stable positions of the steel blade, depending on the position of the cam. In the first position, the paper flag is out of the light beam and below it; in the second position, the flag is directly in the beam, and in the third position, the flag is out of the beam and above it. In operation, the cam is moved from left to right by a modified Atwood's machine, as shown in Fig. 2. By adjusting the position of the middle portion of the cam, the flag will spend a variable length of time in the light beam. In practice, a variation of shutter closing times ranging from 20 to 500 milliseconds could be achieved. To obtain still longer closing times, the cam was moved manually.

Both Philips and Osram spectral lamps operated on direct current were employed as light sources. A three-inch diameter interference filter[6] was used to eliminate the D_2 component from the rubidium resonance radiation. The circular polarizer consisted of a type HN-7 polarizing sheet and a 200-mμ retardation plate.[7]

The vapor cell itself was a cylindrical Pyrex tube, 8 inches long and 2 inches in outside diameter. Both ends of the cell were closed off with flat circular windows cemented to the cylinder with Epoxy resin. The cell was equipped with two 15-mm diam. sidearms projecting vertically upwards and downwards from the center of the cell, respectively. A vacuum and gas filling system was permanently connected to the cell by means of a 2-mm capillary tube attached to the lower sidearm, which contained the rubidium reservoir. The upper sidearm was used to introduce the rubidium metal into the cell, after which the arm was sealed off permanently.

In addition to unlined glass cells, a cell lined with a thin film of tetracontane was used. Tetracontane is a straight-chain saturated hydrocarbon of chemical composition $C_{40}H_{82}$. It therefore belongs in a class with eicosane ($C_{20}H_{42}$) used successfully by Dehmelt recently for a similar purpose.[8] However, tetracontane has the advantage of a higher melting point (approximately 80°C) and of a negligibly small vapor pressure at rubidium vapor temperatures (40 to 50°C).

The tetracontane was distributed over the inside walls of the cell by melting it in an atmosphere of argon, and random shaking of the cell during the course of cooling and solidification. The coverage obtained by this procedure is quite good, as can be judged by placing a drop of distilled water into the cell and observing its lack of adhesion as it rolls about. (In a cell completely coated with a water-repellent material such as tetracontane or polyethylene, a drop of water will not stick at all, but move about like a drop of mercury on a clean glass slide.) However, as explained

---

[6] Spectrolab interference filter type PCB; Spectrolab, Inc., North Hollywood, California.
[7] Purchased from the Polaroid Corporation, Cambridge, Massachusetts.
[8] H. G. Dehmelt, Bull. Am. Phys. Soc. Ser. II, **3**, 9 (1958).

above, in order to install the cell on our optical bench and introduce rubidium metal into it, the upper side arm had to be opened and then sealed off again. As a result, a 15-mm diam. circle at the top of the cell was not covered with tetracontane, comprising approximately 1/200 of the total area of the cell.

The main body of the cell was enclosed in a black-anodized heavy aluminum housing through which warm air was passed in order to maintain an appropriate temperature. The rubidium reservoir in the lower side arm projected out of the housing into a glass beaker filled with warm silicone oil. Thermocouples were used to measure temperatures in various parts of the system.

The glass capillary projecting from the lower side arm could be closed off by means of a Hoke bellows valve. The other side of the valve was attached to a glass gas filling and pressure measuring manifold, which in turn was connected to a metal vacuum system. The glass manifold was equipped with both octoil and mercury manometers. All the rare gases used in the experiment were spectroscopically pure grades obtained from the Linde Air Products Company. No attempt was made to purify these gases any further in the belief that the rubidium vapor itself would be an extremely effective getter for those residual impurities which might shorten the relaxation time.

DEMONSTRATION OF METHOD

To demonstrate the effect of spin relaxation on the transparency of optically aligned rubidium vapor, photographs of shutter transients recorded on a Tektronix oscilloscope have been reproduced in Figs. 3 and 4. In Figs. 3(a) and 3(b), the gain of the vertical amplifier of the oscilloscope has been adjusted so that the entire output of the photomultiplier tube is visible on the face of the cathode-ray tube.

In Fig. 3(a), the vertical component of the earth's magnetic field has been compensated, and the horizontal component is parallel to the direction of light propagation. Under these conditions, optical pumping alignment of the rubidium vapor in the cell is brought about by illumination with circularly polarized D_1 radiation.

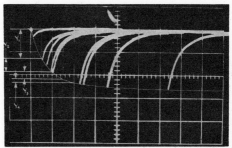

FIG. 4. Enlarged shutter transients to illustrate the approximately exponential decay of the excess transparency of the rubidium vapor, as the vapor is allowed to relax in the dark for a varying length of time. A smooth curve has been drawn with ink through the beginning points of the "recovery" traces. The logarithm of the average decrement of the smooth decay curve is given by $\bar{\delta} = \log\{\frac{1}{3}[(Y_1/Y_2) + (Y_2/Y_3) + (Y_3/Y_4)]\}$. The decay time is then $\tau = T/\bar{\delta}$ where T is the (equal) time interval corresponding to the decrement intervals. (In this photograph, we have used $T = 100$ msec.) This photograph was taken under the following conditions: cell lining, tetracontane; buffer gas, neon at a pressure of 0.58 cm Hg; cell temperature, 48°C; oscilloscope sweep used, 200 msec/scale division.

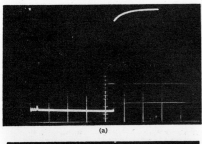

(a)

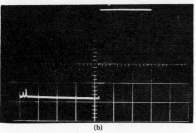

(b)

FIG. 3. Photographs of shutter transients to demonstrate the effect of optical pumping and relaxation on the resonance radiation transmitted through a rubidium vapor cell. Experimental conditions were as follows: cell lining, tetracontane; Buffer gas, neon at a pressure of 0.4 cm Hg; cell temperature, 48°C; oscilloscope sweep speed, 200 msec/scale division. (a) Vertical component of the earth's magnetic field compensated. In this case, there is optical pumping alignment of the vapor. (b) Vertical component of the earth's field not compensated. In this case, there is no optical alignment.

The sweep of the oscilloscope is triggered by the photo-multiplier signal resulting from the sudden decrease of transmitted light intensity at the instant of shutter closing. The electron spot on the cathode-ray tube face thus suddenly moves downward from its previously stationary position in the upper left-hand corner. At the same time, the oscilloscope sweep circuit carries it to the right at a constant rate (thick trace on bottom of photograph). A moment later, the shutter opens again, but the light intensity passing through the cell has now fallen below its pre-closing value. However, the pumping effect of the light gradually realigns the vapor, and the transmitted light intensity returns to its original value after a short time (curved portion of trace in upper right-hand corner of photograph). The vertical motion of the oscilloscope trace at the instants of shutter opening and closing are not visible on this photograph because of the high writing speed resulting from the motion of the shutter and the relatively small aperture opening of the oscilloscope camera.

Figure 3(b) is a photograph taken immediately after Fig. 3(a), with all conditions of operation unchanged, except that the vertical component of the earth's magnetic field is now left uncompensated. Since the dip angle of the earth's magnetic field is rather large (of the order of 75°) in Cambridge, Massachusetts, where this experiment was performed, the resultant field is nearly vertical, and no pumping alignment of the vapor takes place.[2] The light intensity therefore returns to its original value when the shutter opens, as indicated by the horizontal trace in the upper right hand corner. (It is also interesting to observe that the maximum deflection of the oscilloscope trace as a result of the closing of the shutter is now *less* than in Fig. 3(a). This corresponds to the fact that the vapor is more opaque in an unpolarized state. The difference between the levels of the traces at left bottom of the two photographs corresponds exactly to the change in transparency brought about by optical pumping.)

In Fig. 4, the gain of the vertical amplifier of the oscilloscope has been increased in order to emphasize the effect of relaxation. Furthermore, a number of shutter transients with a range of closing times are superimposed on a single photograph. We can regard these oscilloscope records as electronic enlargements of the uppermost portion of Fig. 3(a).

Evidently, the loss in transparency of the vapor as a result of relaxation in the dark approaches a limiting value asymptotically, as we would expect. Superimposed on the end points of the photographed shutter transients is an approximate smooth curve which has been drawn with ink through the beginning points of the thick "recovery" traces. The position of these beginning points on the photograph corresponds to the transmitted light intensity at the instant of shutter opening. We have assumed that the decay curve is exponential in every case. To determine the decay time, the logarithm of the average decrement of each curve has been measured, as shown in Fig. 4.

RESULTS

A summary of the most important results of this experiment is presented in Fig. 5. The experimentally determined spin relaxation time is plotted as a function of buffer gas pressure for an unlined glass cell filled with neon, argon, krypton, and xenon at various pressures, and for a tetracontane-lined cell filled with a variable pressure of neon.

In cells filled with neon and argon (both lined and unlined), relaxation times were determined by measuring the logarithm of the average decrement of the experimentally recorded shutter transients, as explained previously. It is estimated that this procedure yields relaxation times accurate to about ±10%. A constant

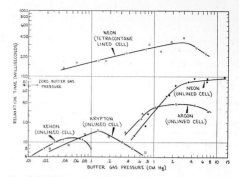

Fig. 5. Rubidium vapor spin relaxation time as a function of buffer gas pressure under various conditions.

logarithmic decrement over the range of shutter intervals recorded on one photograph would be an indication that the relaxation of the vapor is indeed exponential. In practice, the decrement varied in some cases by as much as 20% over the decay curve, indicating some deviation from exponential decay. The series of shutter transients recorded on one photograph were usually taken as quickly as possible, in a time which rarely exceeded one minute. To check the constancy of the light source during this time, field-reversal transients were photographed before and after each series. The amplitude of the observed field-reversal transient is a very sensitive measure of light intensity. (Except for possible variations in light intensity during the process of photographing one series of shutter transients, the measured relaxation time is of course independent of the intensity of the pumping radiation.)

In the case of the unlined cell filled with krypton and xenon, the relaxation times were so short that the shutter transient method could not be employed. In these cases, we therefore photographed field-reversal transients and deduced decay times from the extrapolated slope of such transients, as described by Dehmelt.[3]

Aside from the large differences observed in the effects of the various inert gases on the spin relaxation time, the effect of the tetracontane lining is particularly noteworthy. Evidently, in a cell lined with this material, the variation of relaxation time with buffer gas pressure has a character entirely different from that observed in an unlined glass cell. Furthermore, a considerable degree of alignment and an appreciable relaxation time are achieved in a high vacuum.

Figure 6 shows the variation of the measured relaxation time with cell temperature in an evacuated tetracontane-lined cell. In this case, as in all our observations, the temperature of the rubidium reservoir was maintained consistently about 2°C below the cell temperature. In the scale of vapor pressures indicated in Fig. 6, it has been assumed that the vapor pressure is given directly by the cell temperature. The relatively

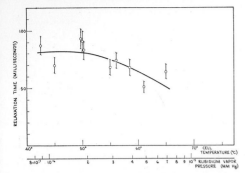

FIG. 6. Variation of relaxation time with rubidium vapor pressure for an evacuated cell lined with tetracontane.

weak dependence of the observed relaxation time on rubidium vapor pressure is remarkable.

It may be of interest to note that a tetracontane-lined evacuated cell was closed off from the gas-filling and vacuum system and operated for several days without observable change in characteristics.

ANALYSIS OF RESULTS AND DISCUSSION

The relaxation of a partially oriented alkali metal vapor in a buffer gas would be expected to take place by electron exchange between colliding alkali atoms, as discussed by Wittke and Dicke[9] and Purcell,[10] by collisions with buffer gas atoms, and by collisions with the cell walls. Experimental evidence for the influence of electron exchange on the width of the hyperfine resonance line in Rb^{87} has been obtained by the Princeton group,[11] who obtained an approximately linear relationship between line width and vapor pressure. From this relationship, they have deduced an effective cross section for exchange collisions σ_{ex} in Rb^{87} of 7 to 10×10^{-14} cm^2. If our cell temperature can indeed be used to compute the rubidium vapor pressure, we would expect a mean time between collisions (corresponding to a relaxation time) of

$$\tau_{ex} = 1/(n\sigma_{ex}\bar{v}_{rel}) = 6.5 \times 10^{-3} \text{ sec}$$

at a cell temperature of 47°C. (This was our usual operating temperature, corresponding to a rubidium vapor pressure of approximately 1.5×10^{-6} mm Hg.) The measured relaxation time in our experiment with an evacuated, tetracontane-lined cell at this temperature was approximately 90×10^{-3} sec, or 14 times as long, as can be seen by inspection of Fig. 6. (Since the cell is in a high vacuum, there is no contribution to the relaxation time from buffer gas collisions in this case, and the only effective relaxation mechanisms are spin exchange collisions between rubidium atoms and wall collisions. The mean time between wall collisions is of the order of 0.2×10^{-3} sec in a cell of the dimensions used in this experiment.)

Furthermore, the data of Fig. 6 seem to indicate a relatively small variation of relaxation time with vapor pressure. On increasing the rubidium vapor pressure from 8×10^{-7} mm Hg to 8×10^{-6} mm Hg, the relaxation time appears to decrease to about $\frac{2}{3}$ of its maximum value, while the relationship observed by the Princeton group would predict a decrease by a factor of 10.

We would like to suggest the following explanation for this discrepancy which is perhaps related to a suggestion made recently by Bender.[12] In a nonradiative binary collision, of which a spin exchange collision between two rubidium atoms is an example, the sum of the z components of the total angular momenta of the colliding atoms must be the same before and after the collision. This means in the first place that in a collision between two atoms which are both in the higher energy hyperfine state ($F = I + \frac{1}{2}$, where I is the nuclear spin) and for which the magnetic quantum number has either its maximum or its minimum value ($m_F = F$ or $m_F = -F$), spin exchange cannot affect the spin orientation of the two atoms. In the second place, if two atoms collide which are in the same hyperfine state both before and after the collision, their combined light absorption probability for D_1 radiation will remain unaffected by the collision. Thus for an atom with nuclear spin $I = \frac{3}{2}$, as Rb^{87} or Na^{23}, the absorption probability for D_1 radiation in the $F = 2$ state is proportional to $2 - m_F$; in the $F = 1$ state it is proportional to $2 + m_F$. For two atoms, both of which are in the $F = 2$ state, the combined absorption probability is therefore proportional to $4 - [m_F^{(1)} + m_F^{(2)}]$, while if they are both in the $F = 1$ state, it is proportional to $4 + [m_F^{(1)} + m_F^{(2)}]$. If $[m_F^{(1)} + m_F^{(2)}]$ is invariant, the amount of light absorbed by the two atoms in the same F state does not change as a result of the collision.

The transmission monitoring technique therefore is not sensitive to Δm-relaxation induced by binary collisions between atoms in the same hyperfine state. Undoubtedly, a certain proportion of the spin relaxation events are of this type, and their occurrence could not be recognized in our experiment. However, such events do affect the $m_F = 0$ states which are of principal interest to the hyperfine resonance experiments.

In view of these observations, we shall attempt to analyze the variation of relaxation time with buffer gas pressure in an unlined glass cell by neglecting the contribution of spin exchange collisions between rubidium atoms to the observed relaxation time. Thus we shall consider only wall and buffer gas collision disorientation in this case.

[9] J. P. Wittke and R. H. Dicke, Phys. Rev. 103, 620 (1956).
[10] R. M. Purcell and G. B. Field, Astrophys. J. 124, 542 (1956).
[11] Dicke, Carver, Alley and Van der Ven, Final Report to the U. S. Army Signal Corps Engineering Laboratory, September 30, 1957 (unpublished).

[12] P. L. Bender, Proceedings of the 12th Annual Frequency Control Symposium, Asbury Park, New Jersey, May 8, 1958 (unpublished), p. 593.

Let us assume that every wall collision results in complete disorientation, i.e., an atom is randomly oriented after striking the glass wall of the cell. Let the density of aligned atoms be n_1 at the instant when the shutter closes. (We can regard "alignment" as being defined by the average value of the absorption probability for D_1 radiation at that instant, so that initially the entire population is "aligned".) If n_2 is the density of randomly oriented atoms which are produced by wall collisions, or by disorienting buffer gas collisions, then by definition $n_2=0$ initially. It is easy to show that the *excess* light transmission through the cell (in excess of the transmission through a cell containing only randomly oriented atoms) is proportional to n_1.

If only the two relaxation mechanisms mentioned above are operative, then n_1 can be described by a diffusion equation containing an absorption term:

$$\partial n_1/\partial t = D\nabla^2 n_1 - kn_1. \tag{1}$$

The equation for n_2 is redundant since $n_1+n_2=n$ = constant. The constant k is given by

$$k = N_0\sigma\bar{v}_{\rm rel}(p/p_0), \tag{2}$$

where N_0 is the density of buffer gas atoms at atmospheric pressure p_0 and at the appropriate rubidium vapor temperature; the actual density at pressure p is $N=N_0(p/p_0)$. σ is the disorientation cross section which characterizes rubidium-buffer gas collisions, and $\bar{v}_{\rm rel}$ is the mean relative velocity of rubidium and buffer gas atoms.

D is the coefficient of diffusion for rubidium atoms in the buffer gas. The pressure dependence of D has the form

$$D = D_0(p_0/p). \tag{3}$$

The solution of Eq. (1) in a cylindrical cell which satisfies the boundary condition that n_1 vanish at the walls is

$$n_1(r,z,t) = \sum_{i=1}^{\infty}\sum_{j=1}^{\infty} A_{ij}\exp\{-[(\mu_i^2+\nu_j^2)D+k]t\}$$
$$\times J_0(\mu_i r)\cos(\nu_j z), \tag{4}$$

where $\nu_j=(2j-1)\pi/L$ and μ_i is defined by $J_0(\mu_i a)=0$, and L and a are the length and radius of the cell respectively.

The simplest approximation that can be made in the absence of detailed knowledge of the initial distribution of n_1 is to consider only the first mode of (4). The relaxation time is then

$$\tau = \frac{1}{(\mu_1^2+\nu_1^2)D+k}$$
$$= \frac{1}{1.28\ {\rm cm}^{-2}D_0(p_0/p)+N_0\sigma\bar{v}_{\rm rel}(p/p_0)}, \tag{5}$$

where we have set $\mu_1 a=2.405$; $a=2.15$ cm; $\nu_1=\pi/L$

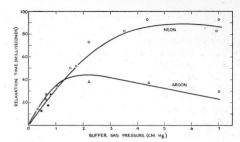

Fig. 7. Relaxation time as a function of buffer gas pressure in an unlined cell filled with neon and argon. The indicated points are experimental points, but the smooth curves are theoretical curves computed on the basis of assumed diffusion coefficients and disorientation cross sections for the two gases, as explained in the text. The solid and open circles refer to the experimental points for neon and the open triangles to those for argon.

and $L=20.0$ cm, which describes the dimensions of our cell. The values of D_0 and σ which give the best fit to the experimental points for neon are 0.31 cm^2/sec and 5.2×10^{-23} cm^2, respectively, and for argon, 0.24 cm^2/sec and 3.7×10^{-22} cm^2, respectively. A plot of Eq. (5) using these parameters has been superimposed on the experimental points for neon and argon in Fig. 7. We have assumed a temperature of 47°C, for which $N_0=2.29\times10^{19}$ cm^{-3}, and mean relative velocities of 6.5×10^4 cm/sec for rubidium-neon and 5.0×10^4 cm/sec for rubidium-argon.

The diffusion coefficients for rubidium diffusing through neon and argon have not been measured previously. The values that we have derived are quite reasonable in comparison with known diffusion coefficients in rare gases. This result, as well as the relatively good fit to the experimental points obtained in Fig. 7, seems to lend strong support to the assumption that complete disorientation is produced in every wall collision in a glass cell.

The disorientation cross section σ for rubidium colliding with neon is astonishingly small; it is smaller than the gas-kinetic collision cross section by a factor of approximately 10^8. In other words, 10^8 collisions with neon are necessary on the average in order to disorient the spin of an aligned rubidium atom in its electronic ground state.

Equation (5) predicts that the relaxation time in a buffer gas should go through a maximum value at a certain gas pressure. For a cell of our geometry, the maximum occurs at 5.4 cm Hg neon pressure; in argon, it occurs at approximately 2.0 cm Hg pressure.

In view of the extremely short relaxation times in krypton and xenon, it was not possible to make measurements over a wide range of pressures. For this reason, we were not able to fit a calculated curve to the experimental data in these cases. However, diffusion coefficients for rubidium in krypton and xenon can be computed from the coefficient in neon by assuming that D_0 is inversely proportional to the product of the gas kinetic collision cross section and the square root of the reduced mass, at a given temperature. (This would be true for a gas of hard spheres, which is a reasonable model for monatomic gases.) This argument leads to diffusion coefficients of 0.16 cm²/sec for rubidium in krypton, and 0.13 cm²/sec for rubidium in xenon. (By the same argument, we would calculate a diffusion coefficient of 0.21 cm²/sec for rubidium in argon, as compared to a measured value of 0.24 cm²/sec.)

We can then calculate approximate disorientation cross sections in krypton and xenon from the experimentally observed maximum relaxation time by use of Eq. (5). The resulting values are 5.9×10^{-21} cm² for krypton and 1.3×10^{-20} cm² for xenon. These cross sections are 100 and 200 times larger, respectively, than the value in neon. Such very large differences in the disorienting properties of the various inert gases are quite surprising.

We shall now turn to a discussion of the relaxation time measured in a tetracontane-lined cell with variable neon buffer gas pressure. As can be seen from Fig. 5, the relaxation time slowly increased with increasing neon pressure, reaching a maximum value of about 0.4 second at a pressure of 3 cm Hg. Evidently, the neon is again inhibiting diffusion to the walls, or to some portion of the walls. In view of the fact that about 1/200 of the total wall area of the cell was left uncovered, as a result of the method of sealing-off the cell employed here, we are not able to judge conclusively whether tetracontane itself, or the uncovered portion of the cell, were the principal remaining causes of wall disorientation.

However, since the ratio of the relaxation time observed in a vacuum (about 80 msec) to the mean cell crossing time for rubidium in a high vacuum (0.2 msec) is about 400, while the ratio of covered to uncovered cell wall area is about 200, we are inclined to attribute the remaining wall relaxation to the uncovered glass. In that case, the variation of relaxation time with buffer gas pressure shown in Fig. 5 can be interpreted in terms of the inhibition of diffusion along the axis of the cell (the z direction) by the neon buffer gas.

If this assumption is correct, considerably longer relaxation times should be observed in a completely lined cell. It is important to emphasize, however, that in view of the need for a rubidium reservoir at one place in the cell, it is not possible to achieve complete coverage in practice; the surface of the liquid alkali metal in the reservoir will certainly always be a cause of complete disorientation. Our cell was constructed so as to enhance the frequency of wall collisions, since this was an important object of our study. In a spherical cell, the ratio of volume to surface area would be more favorable than in our cylindrical cell and still longer relaxation times should be easily attainable.

CONCLUSION

The various rare gases differ considerably in their effect on the spin orientation of ground-state rubidium atoms. This difference in behavior does not appear to have a physical explanation at the present time. Of the gases investigated, neon has by far the smallest disorientation cross section.

The dependence of the observed relaxation time on rubidium vapor pressure is surprisingly weak. An attempt has been made to explain this effect on the basis of a distinction between Δm-relaxation and ΔF-relaxation induced in spin-exchange collisions.

Straight-chain hydrocarbon wall-linings such as tetracontane are very effective in inhibiting relaxation in wall collisions. Tetracontane is a particularly suitable substance in view of its high melting point and very low vapor pressure at rubidium or cesium vapor temperatures. Extremely narrow hyperfine resonance lines should be obtainable in a tetracontane-lined spherical cell filled with neon at a low pressure.

ACKNOWLEDGMENTS

Thanks are due Dr. A. G. Emslie for his sympathetic interest in this work. George Feick and Dr. William E. Cass were very helpful in providing chemical advice in connection with the development of suitable wall coatings. I would like to thank Dr. Ivan Simon for loan of the tetracontane used in the experiment, and William S. Martin for his expert design and construction of the mechanical shutter.

Spin Relaxation and Line Width in Alkali Metal Vapors

Arnold L. Bloom

Varian Associates, Palo Alto, California

(Received November 16, 1959)

Relaxation constants T_1 and T_2 have been computed for experiments involving optical pumping and optical detection in alkali metal vapor. The calculations have been performed for several possible spin relaxation mechanisms; namely, magnetic dipole, electric quadrupole, spin exchange, and the optical pumping process itself. For all of these mechanisms a reorientation experiment will approximately predict a spin resonance line width (equivalent to the statement $T_1 \approx T_2$ for spin-$\frac{1}{2}$ particles.) However, a spin reorientation experiment of the type originally performed by Dehmelt, employing circularly polarized light, gives approximate results because of the nonexponential character of the reorientation. A more suitable experiment is one employing hyperfine population differences and unpolarized light.

INTRODUCTION

THE recent observation of long spin reorientation times in alkali metal vapors in buffer gases,[1] or with buffering wall coatings[2,3] has prompted considerable speculation as to the existence of correspondingly narrow line widths and application to magnetic field and frequency measurements. Implicit in this is the assumption that conditions in the alkali vapor are analogous to those of nuclear magnetic resonance of spin-$\frac{1}{2}$ nuclei in a nonviscous fluid, for which one has

equal times $(T_1 = T_2)$. However, the alkali vapor differs from an ensemble of spin-$\frac{1}{2}$ particles in two important respects; first, because of the strong hyperfine coupling, and secondly, because of the special nature of the observables measured by optical detection. Thus, for example, the quantity measured by the optical detection of hyperfine population differences using unpolarized light[4] is not simply related to classical dynamical variables such as magnetic dipole moment, electric quadrupole moment, etc.

The observed values of reorientation times in alkali vapor, in the limit of vanishing light intensity, are of the

[1] H. G. Dehmelt, Phys. Rev. **105**, 1487 (1957).

[2] H. G. Robinson, E. S. Ensberg, and H. G. Dehmelt, Bull. Am. Phys. Soc. Ser. II, **3**, 9 (1958).

[3] W. Franzen, Phys. Rev. **115**, 850 (1959).

[4] W. E. Bell and A. L. Bloom, Phys. Rev. **109**, 219 (1958); M. Arditi and T. R. Carver, Phys. Rev. **109**, 1012 (1958).

order of 0.1 second.[1-3] If $T_2 = T_1$, then the resonance line widths should be of the order of 3 cps, however published values of line widths, for both Zeeman[5] and hyperfine[6-8] transitions, are about 10 times as great. It seemed worthwhile, therefore, to investigate the relaxation theoretically in enough detail to take the facts of the above paragraph into account and to see if one could account for the observation $T_2 \ll T_1$ without having to make *ad hoc* assumptions about sources of inhomogeneous line broadening.[9] As it turns out, the theory does not predict large differences between T_1 and T_2. More recently, Bender[10] has observed line widths of a few cycles per second for Zeeman resonances in very weak magnetic fields, where all the resonances are superimposed and the signal-to-noise ratio is higher. The conclusions of the present study, although not strictly valid in very weak fields, are nevertheless supported by Bender's results for Zeeman transitions. For hyperfine resonances the situation is less clear. The existence of large secular perturbations giving rise to pressure shifts[6,8] suggests that there may also exist statistical effects, contributing to line broadening, of a sort not considered here.

METHOD

The calculation is for alkali atoms of nuclear spin $\frac{3}{2}$ and strong hyperfine coupling, with the following simplifying assumptions:

1. The thermal energy kT is very large compared to the hyperfine constant so that, in the absence of optical pumping, all ground-state sublevel populations are assumed equal.

2. The applied magnetic field is weak enough so that F, m_F are approximately good quantum numbers but strong enough so that there are no overlapping resonance lines. This condition can be satisfied for all stable alkali isotopes of spin $\frac{3}{2}$ with fields of one gauss or less.

3. The relaxation is assumed to be of the "classical" type,[11] in which the spin is perturbed by an isotropic, fluctuating perturbation field whose Fourier components have uniform intensity from $\omega = 0$ to the correlation frequency $\omega = \omega_c$. We assume ω_c much greater than the hyperfine frequency, although the treatment can be easily modified to suit other situations.

Bloch[12] has given a treatment of relaxation which is

applicable to the present problem. However, the relaxation parameters $\Gamma_{gg'}{}^p$ which he employs are used here only in the case $g = g'$, in which case they merely represent transition probabilities due to the relaxation process. Furthermore we may take $e^{hp/kT} = 0$, where this term occurs in his equations. Because of this we can adopt a simpler notation and merely write $W_{ab} = \epsilon |H_{ab}'|^2$ for the relaxation transition probabilities between levels a and b. H_{ab}' is the matrix element of the relaxation part of the Hamiltonian connecting states a and b, and ϵ is a constant which we will choose to be unity.

The line width of the resonance between states a and b is given in terms of the inverse parameter $(T_2)_{ab}$ by Bloch's[12] equation (3.8) which, simplified, becomes

$$1/(T_2)_{ab} = \sum_k (|H_{ka}'|^2 + |H_{kb}'|^2) - 2H_{aa}'H_{bb}', \quad (1)$$

where k includes all of the magnetic and hyperfine sublevels of the ground $^2S_{\frac{1}{2}}$ state of the atom.

For the calculation of reorientation effects we use Eq. (2.44) of Bloch, but with all off-diagonal elements of the density matrix equal to zero, since resonance effects are not involved in reorientation experiments. We define the following terms: ρ_i is the time-dependent population of state i, ρ_{i0} is the steady-state or equilibrium population, and $\chi_i = \rho_i - \rho_{i0}$. Then Bloch's general equation (2.44) can be simplified for our purposes to the following system of equations:

$$dX_i/dt = -2 \sum_k |H_{ki}'|^2 (X_i - X_k). \quad (2)$$

Now, the quantity observed in an optical detection experiment as proportional to the intensity of transmitted light is a linear combination of the ρ_i's and can be expressed by a "monitoring operator"[13] Q and corresponding observed signal S such that

$$S = \text{Tr}(Q\rho). \quad (3)$$

In a given experimental situation, Q is uncertain to within an additive multiple of the unit operator, equivalent to selection of the "base line" of the indicator output. We shall choose Q so that

$$\text{Tr}(Q\rho_0) = 0; \quad (4)$$

then

$$S = \text{Tr}(QX) = \sum c_i X_i, \quad (5)$$

the c's being constants. By properly weighting and summing the individual equations in (2) we can write,

$$(d/dt)(\sum c_i X_i) = \sum c_i' X_i. \quad (6)$$

For certain fortunate choices of Q and H', and consequently of the c_i's, we may have

$$c_i'/c_i = \text{constant for all } i; \quad (7)$$

in this case Eq. (6) reduces simply to

$$dS/dt = -S/T_1, \quad (8)$$

[5] T. L. Skillman and P. L. Bender, J. Geophys. Research **63**, 513 (1958).

[6] M. Arditi, J. phys. radium **19**, 873 (1958).

[7] E. C. Beaty, P. L. Bender, and A. R. Chi, Phys. Rev. **112**, 450 (1958).

[8] P. L. Bender, E. C. Beaty, and A. R. Chi, Phys. Rev. Letters **1**, 311 (1958).

[9] Doppler broadening represents such a possible mechanism for the hyperfine lines, though not for the Zeeman lines. However, for buffer pressures of 1 cm Hg or above, its effect should be small.

[10] P. L. Bender, Proceedings of the Ann Arbor Conference on Optical Pumping, June, 1959 (University of Michigan, Ann Arbor, 1959), page 111.

[11] N. Bloembergen, E. M. Purcell, and R. V. Pound, Phys. Rev. **73**, 679 (1948).

[12] F. Bloch, Phys. Rev. **102**, 104 (1956).

[13] W. E. Bell and A. L. Bloom, Phys. Rev. **107**, 1559 (1957).

with T_1 a unique relaxation time for this particular experiment. However if (7) does not hold, there is no unique time constant and the relaxation is not only nonexponential but depends in detail on the initial population distribution.

The calculations outlined above have been carried out with four observables for each of three thermal relaxation mechanisms as well as relaxation by the incident light itself. The observables are the following: (a) The line width parameter T_2 of the Zeeman resonance $F=2$, $m_F=2 \to F=2$, $m_F=1$. (b) The T_2 of the field-independent hyperfine resonance $F=2$, $m_F=0 \to F=1$, $m_F=0$. (c) The relaxation time T_1 for reorientation and optical detection by circularly polarized light[1] propagated parallel to the magnetic field and with equal intensity in both hyperfine components. This is precisely the experiment performed by Franzen,[3] in which the light is shut off for varying periods of time and the depolarization due to thermal relaxation is observed. The signal is given by

$$S_m = 2\chi_{2,2} + \chi_{2,1} - \chi_{2,-1} - 2\chi_{2,-2} - \chi_{1,1} + \chi_{1,-1}. \quad (9)$$

Here the subscripts refer to F, m_F, respectively, and $S_m = 0$ if all populations are equal. (d) The T_1 for a reorientation experiment similar to (c) except that the incident light is unpolarized and is filtered so that it can excite atoms out of the $F=1$ state but not out of the $F=2$ state.[8] The signal is given by

$$S_H = 3(\chi_{2,2} + \chi_{2,1} + \chi_{2,0} + \chi_{2,-1} + \chi_{2,-2}) - 5(\chi_{1,1} + \chi_{1,0} + \chi_{1,-1}). \quad (10)$$

The relaxation mechanisms are the following:

(i) Magnetic dipole relaxation. This is most likely the principle contribution to the thermal relaxation process. Besides usual direct collision effects, it includes the perturbation of the hyperfine coupling that occurs during a collision. The matrix elements H_{ik}' are simply the matrix elements for angular momentum operators, which are well known in the literature.[14] Numerical constants are chosen so that hypothetical alkali atoms of spin $\frac{1}{2}$ in the same environment would have unit relaxation times ($T_1 = T_2$).

(ii) Electric quadrupole. The possible importance of this mechanism is not known. Nuclear spins in noble gases are known to have extremely long relaxation times even if the nuclei possess a quadrupole moment[15]; however, the situation may be different in alkali atoms with their valence electron, even if most of the collisions are with noble gas atoms. The quadrupole matrix elements are also well known.[14] Numerical constants used here are arbitrary, since one cannot perform these experiments with a bare nucleus.

(iii) Electron spin exchange, normalized so that $T_1 = 1$ for spin-$\frac{1}{2}$ particles. We have in mind here the mechanism described in detail by Wittke and Dicke,[16] in which the exchange energy during a collision is so large and so dependent on collision parameters that there is no correlation between initial and final states (except conservation of total angular momentum). The matrix elements are the same as in (i) except that diagonal elements and elements connecting states of the same m value are zero. The treatment used here requires that the equilibrium populations be equal, which implies the presence of a large "sink" of unpolarized spins. This is not a usual condition in alkali vapor experiments and we have not investigated the effect of exchange within an already polarized system.[17]

(iv) The incident light itself as a relaxation agent. We assume here an alkali sample with buffer gas, so that there is complete disorientation in the excited state[1] and no correlation between absorption and emission even if the atom returns to the same ground-state sublevel from which it came. Thus in applying Eq. (1), the interference term $2H_{aa}'H_{bb}'$ is zero and $\sum_k H_{ki}'$ is merely the rate of photon absorption in state i. Equation (2) must be replaced by the "pumping equation,"[13]

$$d\rho_i/dt = -\rho_i P_i + \frac{1}{8} \sum_j \rho_j P_j, \quad (11)$$

where $P_i = \sum_k H_{ki}'$. The monitoring operators must be chosen so that $\text{Tr}(Q\rho) = 0$ when the system is completely "pumped" instead of for equal populations. For circularly polarized light, pumping the population into the $F=2$, $m_F=2$ level, the signal is

$$S_m' = \chi_{2,1} + 2\chi_{2,0} + 3\chi_{2,-1} + 4\chi_{2,-2} + 3\chi_{1,1} + 2\chi_{1,0} + \chi_{1,-1}. \quad (12)$$

For hyperfine filtered light it is

$$S_H' = \chi_{1,1} + \chi_{1,0} + \chi_{1,-1}. \quad (13)$$

TABLE I. Relaxation times for various experiments and relaxation mechanisms. Those cases where there is no unique relaxation time are denoted by letters and the corresponding signal equations are given in Table II. "Line width" in the table refers to the type of measurement; the quantity given in T_2.

Experiment	Magnetic dipole	Electric quadrupole	Spin exchange	Light
Zeeman line width	2/5	16/11	1/2	1[a]
$0 \to 0$ line width	1/3	2	1/2	1[b]
Spin reorientation	(a)	(b)	(c)	(d)[a]
Hyperfine reorientation	1/4	2	(e)	8/5[b]

[a] Circularly polarized light.
[b] Hyperfine filtered light.

[14] E. Feenberg and G. E. Pake, *Notes on the Quantum Theory of Angular Momentum* (Addison-Wesley Publishing Company, Cambridge, 1953) and (Stanford University Press, Stanford, 1959).

[15] E. Brun, J. Oeser, H. H. Staub, and C. G. Telschow, Phys. Rev. **93**, 904 (1954).

[16] J. P. Wittke and R. H. Dicke, Phys. Rev. **103**, 620 (1956).

[17] L. W. Anderson, F. M. Pipkin and J. C. Baird, Phys. Rev. **116**, 87 (1959).

TABLE II. Signal equations for the cases specified in Table I. From the definitions, it is possible to replace χ by ρ wherever it appears in Eqs. (a) through (d), but not in Eq. (e). $\dot{S} \equiv dS/dt$.

$$\dot{S}_m = -\tfrac{2}{5}S_m + 4(\chi_{1,1} - \chi_{1,-1}). \tag{a}$$

$$\dot{S}_m = -\tfrac{7}{16}S_m - \tfrac{1}{2}(\chi_{1,1} - \chi_{1,-1}). \tag{b}$$

$$\dot{S}_m = -\tfrac{2}{5}S_m + \tfrac{3}{2}(\chi_{2,1} - \chi_{2,-1}) + \tfrac{5}{2}(\chi_{1,1} - \chi_{1,-1}). \tag{c}$$

$$\dot{S}_m' = \chi_{2,1} + \chi_{1,-1} - 3(\chi_{2,-1} + \chi_{1,1}) - 8\chi_{2,-2}. \tag{d}$$

$$\dot{S}_H = -12(\chi_{2,2} + \chi_{2,-2}) - 6(\chi_{2,1} + \chi_{2,-1}) - 4\chi_{2,0}$$
$$+ 14(\chi_{1,1} + \chi_{1,-1}) + 12\chi_{1,0}. \tag{e}$$

RESULTS

Table I lists those combinations of experiments and interactions for which measurable relaxation times T_1 or T_2 exist, and Table II gives the equations corresponding to Eq. (6) for the other cases.

The lack of a unique relaxation time under any conditions for the Dehmelt spin reorientation experiment is of interest because this is the experiment that has been performed extensively to estimate line widths. The worst situation is that of the incident light as a relaxation agent, Eq. (d). This has been solved on a computer by Franzen and Emslie[18] for certain initial conditions, and the nonexponential character can be seen in their published curves. For the other cases involving spin reorientation, it may be possible to infer approximate values of T_1 under certain conditions. These situations, Eqs. (a), (b), and (c), differ from a purely exponential decay only in the presence of terms representing population differences which may be small in a thoroughly "pumped" sample. Thus, in an experiment such as that of Franzen, if only the initial slope of the decay is used, the result may well be a usable relaxation constant. The values of T_1 derived in this

way are 2/5, 16/7, and 2/5 for magnetic, quadrupole, and spin exchange relaxation, respectively.

CONCLUSIONS

The naive assumption $T_1 \approx T_2$ is shown to be justified in a rough sort of way. However, the Dehmelt[1] type of reorientation experiment is not as well suited to measurement of T_1 as a hyperfine reorientation experiment. This type of experiment has not, to our knowledge, been performed. It differs from the Dehmelt experiment only in the substitution of hyperfine-filtered light for circularly polarized light. Such light is easily available for rubidium[8] and cesium,[7] and with some difficulty for sodium[4,19], and potassium. The hyperfine reorientation should be a relatively foolproof experiment, from the standpoint of experimental difficulties, and will give a unique relaxation time for all cases except spin exchange. Spin-exchange parameters can, however, often be inferred from other experiments, such as exchange with another species of alkali atom not directly involved in the optical pumping process.

With regard to spin reorientation, *if only the initial slope of the decay is used*, then meaningful results are obtainable in Franzen's experiment, and presumably also in Dehmelt's original experiment where T_1 is an extrapolated value taken in the limit of zero light intensity. What is questionable, however, is the value of the initial slope at a *given* light intensity. In a given experimental setup this will probably bear the simple inverse relationship postulated by Dehmelt, but its exact value must depend in some detail on the manner in which the spin reversal was produced.

ACKNOWLEDGMENT

We are indebted to P. L. Bender for valuable discussions on relaxation mechanisms and measurements in alkali metal vapor.

[18] W. Franzen and A. G. Emslie, Phys. Rev. **108**, 1453 (1957).

[19] H. Bucka, Z. Physik **141**, 49 (1955).

The numerical values in the column headed "Magnetic Dipole" in Table I should be multiplied by 4.

A. L. B.

From: *J. Chem. Phys.* **36**, 135–140 (1962)

Spin Relaxation in Optical Pumping*

Robert A. Bernheim†

Department of Chemistry, Columbia University, New York

(Received May 5, 1961)

The spin relaxation of optically aligned rubidium vapor has been studied as a function of helium buffer gas pressure. Relaxation times as long as 0.68 sec were observed in helium at $\frac{1}{2}$-atm pressure. The diffusion constant D_0 for rubidium in helium at 50°C was evaluated as 0.54 cm² sec⁻¹. The disorientation cross section σ for rubidium-helium collisions was found to be 6.2×10^{-25} cm². A mechanism for spin relaxation in optically aligned alkali vapors is proposed and discussed. It is found that the relaxation arises from the coupling of the alkali electron spin to orbital and rotational motion accompanying the collision. The variation of σ for rubidium in the presence of other inert gases is also discussed.

INTRODUCTION

SPIN relaxation of alkali-metal vapors in the presence of inert buffer gases has been previously studied.[1-3] For example, by investigating the spin relaxation of rubidium atoms as a function of the pressure of the inert buffer gas, two parameters may be determined. These are (1) the diffusion coefficient D_0 of rubidium atoms in the inert gas and (2) the disorientation cross section σ of the inert gas.

Regarding rubidium spin relaxation, the effects of all the rare gases except helium have been studied.[2] The results were that D_0 became larger, and σ became smaller as rare gases with lower atomic number were used. The magnitude and variation of σ has hitherto been unexplained. The present research extends the data to include helium and also gives an explanation for the relaxation process.

EXPERIMENTAL PROCEDURE

An apparatus consisting of a light source, interference filter, circular polarizer, vapor cell, and a photocell was used for the experiments and is shown in Fig. 1. The vapor cell containing rubidium metal, 99.7% stated purity, was located at the center of an orthogonal set of Helmholtz coils which were used to eliminate the components of the earth's magnetic field perpendicular to the light path and to apply a small magnetic field parallel to, and in the direction of, the light path. The magnetic field seen by the vapor cell was 0.605 gauss, deduced from the Zeeman splitting of the rubidium hyperfine levels. The light source was an Osram rubidium spectral lamp. The top of the outer glass jacket of the lamp was cut away, and the space between the outer jacket and the inner bulb filled with silicone oil. A stream of air was directed at the outer jacket. This arrangement provided excellent temperature stabilization. The D_2 component of the rubidium

resonance radiation was eliminated with an interference filter.[4] The D_1 component was then circularly polarized by passing it through a type HN-7 polarizing sheet and a 200 mμ retardation sheet.[5] A type 917 photocell was used to measure the intensity of light passing through the apparatus. A system of lenses was used to focus the rubidium resonance radiation on the vapor cell, and the light passing through the vapor cell was focused on the photocell. A shutter, operated with relays, was placed between the lamp and the interference filter.

The method used here for measuring relaxation times has been discussed previously[2] and is briefly summarized as follows. One begins with a vapor cell containing optically pumped rubidium atoms in the presence of a buffer gas. This means that there is an excess population in some of the Zeeman split hyperfine levels of the ground state. This excess is called the degree of alignment or polarization of the rubidium vapor. The pumping radiation passing through the cell is abruptly cut off with a shutter, and the rubidium vapor begins to lose its polarization by colliding with the cell walls and with the buffer gas atoms. The shutter is opened after a time t, and it is found that the transmission of light through the cell has decreased due to rubidium atoms that have lost their polarization and are again able to absorb the pumping radiation. The decrease in intensity of the light passing through the vapor cell is proportional to the number of rubidium atoms that have lost their polarization in the dark. Assuming that the decay is exponential,

$$a = A_0[1 - \exp(-t/\tau)], \tag{1}$$

where a is the above-described decrease in light intensity, emerging from the vapor cell, τ is the relaxation time of the rubidium atoms, t is the time the shutter has been closed, and A_0 is the value of a at $t = \infty$.

All measurements were recorded photographically from an oscilloscope connected to the 917 photocell

---

* Supported by the U. S. Air Force Office of Scientific Research.
† Present address: Department of Chemistry, Pennsylvania State University, University Park, Pennsylvania.

[1] H. G. Dehmelt, Phys. Rev. **105**, 1487 (1957).
[2] W. Franzen, Phys. Rev. **115**, 850 (1959).
[3] A. L. Bloom, Phys. Rev. **118**, 664 (1960).

[4] Spectrolab type PCB; Spectrolab, Inc., North Hollywood, California.
[5] Polaroid Corporation, Cambridge, Massachusetts.

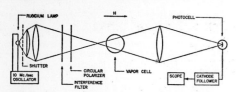

Fig. 1. Schematic diagram of the experimental apparatus. The optical system was arranged such that the image of the rubidium lamp filled the vapor cell as completely as possible. With the lenses used this required that the focal point of the system be just in front of the vapor cell. The optical alignment of the rubidium vapor was found to be at a maximum with the above arrangement.

through a cathode follower circuit. A_0 was evaluated by leaving the shutter closed for at least 10 times τ. In Fig. 2, $\log[(A_0-a)/A_0]$ is plotted as a function of t for a typical measurement. The slope of the resulting straight line gives the relaxation time τ. If there is only one decay time, the extrapolated intercept at $t=0$ should be equal to unity due to the normalization of A_0-a. However, the experimental values in Fig. 2 give an extrapolated value of 0.7 at $t=0$. All measurements gave this same intercept, ±0.1. It will be seen in the next section that this extrapolated value at $t=0$ is a natural consequence of the solution of the differential equation describing the relaxation process.

EXPERIMENTAL RESULTS

The relaxation time τ was measured for rubidium atoms in the presence of different pressures of helium. The vapor cell temperature was 50°C. The results are shown in Fig. 3. The error limits shown are standard deviations for six or more measurements of τ. The points without error limits are average values of τ where less than six but more than three measurements were made. It will be noted that relaxation times up to 0.68 sec can be obtained when the helium pressure is as great as $\frac{1}{2}$ atm.

The solid theoretical curve was calculated in the same manner as was done before.[2] However, due to the spherical shape of the vapor cell the treatment must be slightly modified.

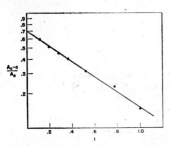

Fig. 2. Typical plot of $\log[A_0-a)/A_0]$ vs t. The above data are for rubidium in helium at a helium pressure of 355 mm and for a vapor cell temperature of 50°C. From the above plot $\tau=0.65$ sec.

The atoms become depolarized by (a) collisions with the walls and (b) collisions with inert-gas atoms. Collisions between alkali atoms do not change the net polarization.[2] If n_1 is the density of aligned atoms then its variation in time will be given by

$$dn_1/dt = D\nabla^2 n_1 - kn_1. \qquad (2)$$

The constant k in the absorption term is given by

$$k = N_0\sigma\bar{v}_{\mathrm{rel}}(p/p_0), \qquad (3)$$

where N_0 is the density of inert gas atoms at atmospheric pressure p_0 and at the temperature of the vapor cell, p is the actual inert gas pressure, $\bar{v}_{\mathrm{rel}}$ is the mean relative velocity of alkali and inert gas atoms, and σ is the disorientation cross section. Actually, σ is an energy-dependent quantity, and in its use here as a constant, a mean value is implied.

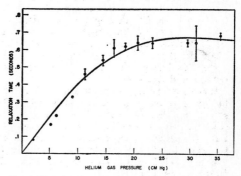

Fig. 3. Variation of rubidium spin relaxation time with helium buffer gas pressure.

The diffusion coefficient D has the form

$$D = D_0(p_0/p), \qquad (4)$$

where D_0 is the diffusion coefficient at atmospheric pressure and 50°C.

Solving Eq. (2) for the boundary condition $n_1=0$ at the walls of a sphere of radius R one obtains

$$n_1(r, \theta, \phi, t) = \sum_{n=0}^{\infty}\sum_{\alpha}\sum_{m=0}^{n}\{P_n^m(\cos\theta)[A_{nm\alpha}\cos m\phi$$
$$+B_{nm\alpha}\sin m\phi](\alpha r)^{-\frac{1}{2}}J_{n+\frac{1}{2}}(\alpha r)\exp[-(D\alpha^2+k)t]\}, \qquad (5)$$

where the summation in α is over the positive roots of $J_{n+\frac{1}{2}}(\alpha R)=0$. If we consider only the first term of the above series solution the relaxation time will be given by

$$\tau = [0.546D_0(p_0/p) + N_0\sigma\bar{v}_{\mathrm{rel}}(p/p_0)]^{-1}, \qquad (6)$$

where to satisfy $J_{\frac{1}{2}}(\alpha R)=0$, $\alpha R=\pi$ and $R=4.25$ cm.

This expression for τ was based on the assumption that only the first term of Eq. (5) contributes to the relaxation. Eq. (5) can be solved for the actual fraction of polarized atoms that relax with the time constant of the first term. To do this one first solves for the coefficient of $(\alpha r)^{-\frac{1}{2}}J_{\frac{1}{2}}(\alpha r)\exp(-t/\tau)$ [the first term of Eq. (5)] which we designate as c_0. Since Eq. (5) is simply an orthogonal set of functions, this is

$$\frac{c_0}{n_1}=\frac{\int_0^R (\alpha r)^{-\frac{1}{2}}J_{\frac{1}{2}}(\alpha r)\,r^2dr}{\int_0^R [(\alpha r)^{-\frac{1}{2}}J_{\frac{1}{2}}(\alpha r)]^2 r^2 dr}. \qquad (7)$$

The density of polarized atoms n_1 has been assumed to be a constant quantity over the bulb at time $t=0$. The fraction of polarized atoms contributing to the first term of Eq. (5) is

$$(c_0/n_1)\langle(\alpha r)^{-\frac{1}{2}}J_{\frac{1}{2}}(\alpha r)\rangle_{Av}=6/\pi^2=0.61, \qquad (8)$$

where the angular brackets denote an average over the sphere. This value manifests itself as the extrapolated intercept as in Fig. 2. The two values agree fairly well, supporting the above assumption of a homogeneous density of polarized atoms at $t=0$.

The remaining fraction of polarized atoms relax via the other modes of Eq. (5). These are too fast to see in the present experiment.

One can determine D_0 and σ by comparing the pressure dependence of Eq. (6) with the observed pressure dependence of τ. At 50°C $N_0=2.27\times10^{19}$ cc^{-1} and $\bar{v}_{rel}=1.34\times10^5$ cm sec^{-1}. The best fit to the experimental data (the solid line in Fig. 3) gives $D_0=0.54$ cm^2 sec^{-1} and $\sigma=6.2\times10^{-25}$ cm^2. These results are listed in Table I along with the previously known values. The magnitude of D_0 and its variation agree quite well with other gas diffusion coefficients.[6,7] However, the values of σ are unusually small and have a pronounced variation. A polarized ribidium atom can sustain about 10^9 collisions with helium atoms before becoming depolarized. If xenon is used, the number of collisions required is decreased by a factor of almost 10^5.

The remaining task is to explain the role of the inert gas in the above relaxation phenomena.

RELAXATION PROCESS

It has been assumed that a disorientation accompanies each collision of a polarized rubidium atom with the walls of the vapor cell. The following discussion is confined solely to the role of the inert gas in the relaxation process. This will include (a) the mechanism of the relaxation process, (b) the magnitude of the disorientation cross section, and (c) its variation with the different species of inert gases.

A. Derivation of the Effective Hamiltonian

The relaxation process must conserve angular momentum among all of the particles, electrons, and

[6] R. E. Walker and A. A. Westenberg, J. Chem. Phys. **29**, 1147 (1958).
[7] I. Amdur and T. F. Schatzki, J. Chem. Phys. **29**, 1425 (1958).

TABLE I. Diffusion coefficients D_0 and disorientation cross sections σ for rubidium atoms in various inert buffer gases.

Buffer gas	D_0 (cm^2/sec)	σ (cm^2)
He	0.54	6.2×10^{-25}
Ne[2]	0.31	5.2×10^{-23}
A[2]	0.24	3.7×10^{-22}
Kr[2]	0.16	5.9×10^{-21}
Xe[2]	0.13	1.3×10^{-20}

nuclei, involved in the collision between a polarized alkali atom and an inert gas atom.

The problem of coupling of angular momentum in molecules has been treated by Van Vleck.[8] His treatment is applied here to the colliding pair of atoms. Omitting the spin-spin part of the interaction which is not pertinent in the alkali-inert gas system, the remaining spin-orbit interaction energy may be written as

$$H_{so}=H_a+H_b, \qquad (9)$$

where

$$H_a=\frac{g\beta}{c}\sum_K\sum_j\left(\frac{Z_K e}{r_{jK}^3}\right)[(\mathbf{r}_j-\mathbf{r}_K)\times(\tfrac{1}{2}\mathbf{v}_j-\mathbf{v}_K)]\cdot\mathbf{s}_j \qquad (10)$$

and

$$H_b=\frac{g\beta}{c}\sum_{k>j}\left(\frac{-e}{r_{jk}^3}\right)[(\mathbf{r}_j-\mathbf{r}_k)\times(\tfrac{1}{2}\mathbf{v}_j-\mathbf{v}_k)]\cdot\mathbf{s}_j. \qquad (11)$$

Capital and lower case subscripts refer to nuclei and electrons, respectively. The coordinate system is fixed in space with its origin at the center of mass of the colliding atoms.

The transition probability for a spin flip of the alkali outer s electron may then be computed by application of first-order time-dependent perturbation theory. It will be shown that the effective Hamiltonian responsible for the spin flip may be written

$$H_{eff}=\sum_j\gamma_j\mathbf{s}_j\cdot\mathbf{J}, \qquad (12)$$

where $\mathbf{J}$ is the total angular momentum (exclusive of spin) of the colliding pair of atoms about their center of mass, and $\mathbf{s}_j$ is the spin of electron j.

It will be shown that the energies involved are the same order of magnitude as the hyperfine interaction in atoms. However, the nuclear spin has been omitted from Eqs. (10)–(11) because it is assumed that the disorientation arises from a spin flip of the odd alkali atom electron via a spin-orbit coupling with the colliding inert-gas atom. The large variation of the disorientation cross section among the inert gases can be explained on this basis, but it would be difficult to explain the variation in terms of an anisotropic hyperfine interaction or a nuclear quadrupole interaction accompanying an alkali–inert-gas collision.

[8] J. H. Van Vleck, Revs. Modern Phys. **23**, 213 (1951).

The coefficients γ_j in Eq. (12) originate from two types of terms, some of which are diagonal in the electronic energy, and some of which are nondiagonal. The following development shows how γ_j may be evaluated. Letting $H_a = H_a' + H_a''$ and $H_b = H_b' + H_b''$, we have

$$H_a' = \frac{g\beta}{c} \sum_K \sum_j \left(\frac{Z_K e}{r_{jK}^3}\right) [(\mathbf{r}_j - \mathbf{r}_K) \times \tfrac{1}{2}\mathbf{v}_j] \cdot \mathbf{s}_j, \quad (13)$$

$$H_a'' = \frac{-g\beta}{c} \sum_K \sum_j \left(\frac{Z_K e}{r_{jK}^3}\right) [(\mathbf{r}_j - \mathbf{r}_K) \times \mathbf{v}_K] \cdot \mathbf{s}_j, \quad (14)$$

$$H_b' = \frac{g\beta}{c} \sum_{k>j} \left(\frac{-e}{r_{jk}^3}\right) [(\mathbf{r}_j - \mathbf{r}_k) \times \tfrac{1}{2}\mathbf{v}_j] \cdot \mathbf{s}_j, \quad (15)$$

$$H_b'' = \frac{-g\beta}{c} \sum_{k>j} \left(\frac{-e}{r_{jk}^3}\right) [(\mathbf{r}_j - \mathbf{r}_k) \times \mathbf{v}_k] \cdot \mathbf{s}_j. \quad (16)$$

The electron spin of the jth electron is interacting in the following way in each of Eqs. (13)–(16): In H_a' it interacts with the electric field due to the nuclear charge, in H_a'' with the magnetic moment arising from the nuclear motion, in H_b' with the electric field due to the charge on the other electrons, and in H_b'' with the magnetic moments arising from the orbital motion of the other electrons.

The only part of the above which contributes to the first-order perturbation are the terms involving nuclear velocities. The nuclear velocity of interest is the velocity with respect to the center of mass, $\boldsymbol{\omega} \times \mathbf{r}_K$, where $\mathbf{r}_K$ is the position vector from the center of mass and $\boldsymbol{\omega}$ is the angular velocity of the pair of atoms during the collision. $\boldsymbol{\omega}$ then may be written as $\mathbf{J}/I$, where I is the moment of inertia of the colliding system and $\mathbf{J}$ is its rotational angular momentum. Substituting this information into H_a'' and noting that the term involving $\mathbf{r}_j \cdot \boldsymbol{\omega}$ contributes only to the nondiagonal elements,

$$H^{(1)} = \frac{-g\beta}{Ic} \sum_K \sum_j \left(\frac{Z_K e}{r_{jK}^3}\right) [\mathbf{r}_j \cdot \mathbf{r}_K - |\mathbf{r}_K|^2] \mathbf{J} \cdot \mathbf{s}_j, \quad (17)$$

for the first-order contribution to H_{eff}.

In considering the second-order interaction, all terms which are very small compared with the first-order interaction will be neglected. Following Van Vleck[8] it is noted that contributions to the second-order interaction will come from terms involving electron velocities and from cross terms between $\mathbf{J}$ and $\mathbf{L}$, where $\mathbf{L}$ is the contribution of the electrons to the angular momentum of the colliding atoms. These latter terms come from the fact that the energy of rigid rotation is really proportional to $(\mathbf{J} - \mathbf{L})^2$ and not $\mathbf{J}^2$. All possible contributions to the second-order interaction arise from cross products of the terms,

$$H_a', \; H_a'', \; H_b', \; H_b'', \quad \text{and} \quad \frac{1}{I}\sum_j \mathbf{l}_j \cdot \mathbf{J}.$$

The only cross products that will give an interaction comparable in magnitude to the first-order interaction will involve an electron term coupled with the rotational term. That this is so may be seen from the size of each interaction. The rotational term is the largest and is the order of $(e^2/a_0)(m/M)$, where m and M are the electron and nuclear masses, respectively. The electron terms are smaller and are the order of $(e^2/a_0)\alpha^2$, where α is the fine-structure constant. The largest term comes from the square of the rotational interaction, but this does not involve a spin flip of the electron. Next in size are the cross terms between rotational interaction and the electron interactions, and these give the main contribution to the second-order energy. All interelectronic cross terms and the terms involving $\mathbf{r}_j \cdot \boldsymbol{\omega}$ from H_a'' will be smaller. Also, H_b'' will not contribute at all because it is a two electron operator and will not connect the same electronic states as will the one-electron $\mathbf{l}_j \cdot \mathbf{J}$ operator. The second-order interaction energy will be

$$H^{(2)} = 2\sum_n \langle 0 \mid H_a' + H_b' \mid n \rangle \langle n \mid \frac{1}{I}\sum_j \mathbf{l}_j \cdot \mathbf{J} \mid 0 \rangle (E_0 - E_n)^{-1}. \quad (18)$$

Introducing the full expressions for H_a' and H_b' and eliminating those terms which average to zero and those terms which are two-electron operators one obtains

$$H^{(2)} = \frac{eg\beta}{Ic} \sum_n \left\{ \langle 0 \mid \sum_K \sum_j \left(\frac{Z_K}{m_j r_{jK}^3}\right) \mathbf{l}_j \cdot \mathbf{s}_j - \sum_{k>j} \left(\frac{1}{r_{jk}^3}\right) \mathbf{l}_j \cdot \mathbf{s}_j \mid n \rangle \right.$$
$$\left. \cdot \langle n \mid \sum_j \mathbf{l}_j \cdot \mathbf{J} \mid 0 \rangle (E_0 - E_n)^{-1} \right\}, \quad (19)$$

where $(1/m_j)\mathbf{l}_j \cdot \mathbf{s}_j$ has replaced $\mathbf{r}_j \times \mathbf{v}_j \cdot \mathbf{s}_j$. If it is now noted that $J_z = 0$ (where z refers to the interatomic axis of a coordinate system mounted on the rotating pair of atoms) and if one uses the proportionality theorems mentioned by Van Vleck, the $\mathbf{s}_j \cdot \mathbf{J}$ term may be separated from Eq. (19). The factor γ_j may then be evaluated by means of Eqs. (17) and (19)

$$\gamma_j = \frac{eg\beta}{Ic} \left[-\sum_K \left(\frac{Z_K}{r_{jK}^3}\right) [\mathbf{r}_j \cdot \mathbf{r}_K - |\mathbf{r}_K|^2] \right.$$
$$+ \sum_n \langle 0 \mid \sum_K \left(\frac{Z_K}{m_j r_{jK}^3}\right) \mathbf{l}_j - \sum_{k>j} \left(\frac{1}{r_{jk}^3}\right) \mathbf{l}_j \mid n \rangle \langle n \mid \mathbf{l}_j \mid 0 \rangle$$
$$\left. \cdot (E_0 - E_n)^{-1} \right]. \quad (20)$$

The summation over n includes all excited states of the colliding system. The effective Hamiltonian for the process leading to a spin flip is given by Eq. (12) with γ_j defined as above.

A numerical evaluation of γ_j (and hence, σ) is beyond the scope of this work, but its order of magnitude can be tested. From the previous discussion of the energies involved it is seen that γ_j is of the order of $(e^2/a_0)\alpha^2(m/M)$, which is comparable to the hyperfine interaction. That this is a reasonable magnitude will be seen in the following section.

B. Transition Probability

The disorientation cross section σ is related to the transition probability P for a spin flip in the following way:

$$\sigma = P\sigma_{\text{kin}}, \qquad (21)$$

where σ_{kin} is the kinetic cross section of the inert-gas atom. Ideally, P may be calculated from first-order time-dependent perturbation theory, in which case it would be proportional to the square of the matrix element of H_{eff},

$$P \propto |\langle 0\beta | H_{\text{eff}} | 0\alpha \rangle|^2, \qquad (22)$$

where α and β are the initial and final spin states of the alkali atom.

As noted above, considerable effort is required to carry out an actual calculation of P. In lieu of this we propose to express P in terms of some magnetic field H_γ which is acting on the magnetic moment of the alkali atom during a collision. H_γ is proportional to the $\gamma\mathbf{J}$ factor in Eq. (12). In first-order time-dependent perturbation theory the interaction amplitude will be

$$a_\beta^{(1)} = \frac{1}{i\hbar}\int_{-\infty}^{t} \langle 0\beta | \mathbf{\mu} \cdot \mathbf{H}_\gamma'(t') | 0\alpha \rangle \exp(i\omega' t')dt', \quad (23)$$

where $\mathbf{H}_\gamma'(t')$ is the magnetic field acting on the alkali atom at time t' and $\mathbf{\mu}$ is the magnetic moment of the alkali atom. A likely description of the magnetic field is that it has a Gaussian distribution over the collision,

$$\mathbf{\mu} \cdot \mathbf{H}_\gamma'(t') = \mathbf{\mu} \cdot \mathbf{H}_\gamma \exp[-(t')^2/\tau_c^2], \qquad (24)$$

where τ_c is the collision time. Since the initial and final electronic states are the same, the phase difference ω' is zero. Letting t go to ∞ and integrating Eq. (23), the transition probability becomes

$$P = |a_\beta^{(1)}|^2 \simeq \pi\mu^2 H_\gamma^2 \tau_c^2/\hbar^2. \qquad (25)$$

For rubidium-helium collisions P can be evaluated experimentally from Eq. (21) to be about 10^{-9}. If the collision time is about 10^{-12} sec, H_γ is found to be of the order of several gauss. For rubidium-xenon collisions H_γ would be several hundred gauss. This admittedly crude approximation approaches the same fields present in hyperfine interactions. Therefore the interaction discussed in the previous section is in the right energy region.

C. Variation of σ

Upon examination of the experimental values of σ, it is found that they can be described in terms of their dependence upon the atomic number of the inert gas

TABLE II. Variation of κ for the rare gases. The values are normalized to κ for helium for purposes of comparison.

Gas	He	Ne	Ar	Kr	Xe
$\kappa/\kappa_{\text{He}}$	[1.00]	0.67	0.82	1.60	1.07

involved. In fact, the variation may be described as

$$\sigma = \kappa Z^3, \qquad (26)$$

where Z is the inert gas atomic number and κ is a proportionality factor. Table II shows the accuracy of this description.

Of course, there are other factors besides the atomic number which enter into an evaluation of P and which are different for the various inert gases. However, it is instructive to point out how the relationship in Eq. (26) might arise. If we think of the alkali electron experiencing a spin-orbit interaction on the inert gas atom, we may use the elementary concept of the spin-orbit interaction in atoms. This is proportional to

$$1/r[\partial V(r)/\partial r]. \qquad (27)$$

Averaged over the cross product of the alkali atom and inert-gas atom electronic wave functions a factor $Z_{\text{eff}}^{\frac{1}{2}}$ is obtained from the $1/r$ part of Eq. (27) and a factor Z_{eff} from $V(r)$. If the effective nuclear charge Z_{eff} is proportional to the inert gas atomic number Z then the spin-orbit part of H_{eff} contributes a factor $Z^{5/2}$. The rotational part of H_{eff} involves the inverse of the moment of inertia I^{-1} of the colliding pair of atoms. On the basis of hard-sphere radii for the atoms I can be calculated, and it is found to be closely proportional to Z^{-1}. Combining $Z^{5/2}$ with Z^{-1} yields $Z^{\frac{3}{2}}$, which when squared in Eq. (22) gives Z^3. This reasoning has its deficiencies, but at the same time gives consistency with the proposed relaxation process.

It should be pointed out that the idea of intermolecular spin orbit perturbation is not a new one.[9] Recently it has been used in discussing the phosphorescent lifetime of benzene in different environments including some rare gases.[10] In Ar, Kr, and Xe at 4.2°K the $^3B_{1u} \rightarrow {}^1A_{1g}$ phosphorescent lifetimes are 16, 1, and 0.07 sec, respectively. The parallel between these results and our σ values is very interesting.

CONCLUSION

The disorientation cross section of helium for polarized rubidium atoms is the smallest known at present. From the discussion of the relaxation process it is seen that this is due to the small amount of spin orbit interaction experienced by the rubidium $5s$ electron during a collision with a helium atom. As the atomic number of the buffer gas atom increases, the

[9] M. Kasha, J. Chem. Phys. **20**, 71 (1952).
[10] M. R. Wright, R. P. Frosch, and G. W. Robinson, J. Chem. Phys. **33**, 934 (1960).

spin-orbit interaction increases, and σ becomes larger. This may also be one reason why wall coatings of long-chain hydrocarbons preserve the alignment of atoms present in a vapor cell. The polarized atoms collide with a layer of hydrogen atoms belonging to the hydrocarbon coating. The hydrogens, being of low atomic number, will not give a large spin-orbit interaction with the polarized atom, hence will not disorient it.

ACKNOWLEDGMENT

The author wishes to express his appreciation to Professor Richard Bersohn whose suggestions and encouragement made this work possible.

Disorientation Cross Sections in Optical Pumping*

ROBERT J. MCNEAL

*Department of Chemistry, Columbia University
New York 27, New York*

(Received August 3, 1962)

CROSS sections for disorientation of rubidium atoms, oriented by optical pumping, have been reported for the inert buffer gases helium[1] and neon, argon, krypton, and xenon.[2] The cross section is roughly proportional to the cube of the atomic number. The disorientation has been described as resulting from a spin-orbit interaction experienced by the rubidium valence electron during the collision with the buffer gas.[1] Disorientation cross sections are reported here for methane, ethane, ethylene, cyclohexane, hydrogen, and nitrogen molecules.

The disorientation cross section and the diffusion coefficient of the rubidium atoms in the buffer gas are obtained by measuring the variation of the relaxation time of the oriented rubidium vapor with buffer gas pressure, as described by Franzen.[2] The experimental apparatus used here has been described by Bernheim.[1] A spherical vapor cell is used, and the relaxation time τ is given by

$$\tau = [0.546 D_0 (p_0/p) + N_0 \bar{v}_{\mathrm{rel}} \sigma (p/p_0)]^{-1}, \qquad (1)$$

where D_0 is the diffusion coefficient at the temperature of the vapor cell, σ is the disorientation cross section, N_0 is the density of buffer gas atoms at atmospheric pressure p_0, and at the temperature of the cell, p is the buffer gas pressure, and $\bar{v}_{\mathrm{rel}}$ is the mean relative velocity of rubidium and buffer gas atoms. D_0 and σ

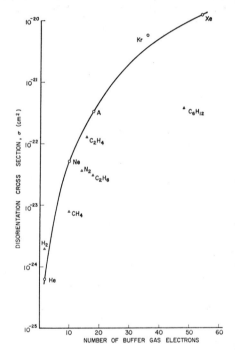

FIG. 1. Variation of disorientation cross section with number of buffer gas electrons. Dots denote previous work[1,2] and triangles the present work.

are obtained by comparing the pressure dependence of Eq. (1) with the observed pressure dependence of τ.

The values of σ and D_0 giving the best fit to the observed pressure dependence of τ are presented in Table I. The range of pressures studied for each gas and the temperature of the cell are also listed. The relaxation time was obtained at no fewer than five pressures for

TABLE I. Disorientation cross sections and diffusion coefficients D_0 for rubidium atoms in various buffer gases with applicable pressure ranges and temperature.

Buffer gas	$D_0 (\mathrm{cm^2/sec})$	$\sigma (\mathrm{cm^2})$	Pressure range (mm)	Temp. (°C)
CH_4	0.5	8×10^{-24}	5–235	60
C_2H_6	0.3	3.8×10^{-23}	14–80	60
C_2H_4	0.24	1.3×10^{-22}	5–100	60
C_6H_{12}	0.10	4.5×10^{-22}	2–26	50
H_2	1.34	3×10^{-24}	1–400	70
N_2	0.33	5.7×10^{-23}	5–95	55

each gas, and at least four measurements were made at each pressure. The measurements of the relaxation time were reproducible to within 20% in most cases.

Figure 1 shows the variation of σ with the total number of buffer gas electrons for all gases reported to date. Choosing this parameter as abscissa reveals the regular variation of σ with rare-gas atomic number and the more irregular behavior observed with the other gases. The number of buffer gas electrons is not expected to be the only important parameter for description of the disorientation process. Clearly, a complete understanding of the magnitude and variation of the cross sections for the different buffer gases requires a more detailed study of the interactions occurring during the collision.

Preliminary results with other buffer gases indicate that disorientation mechanisms other than spin-orbital interactions may be important for some buffer gas molecules. For example, experiments with benzene have indicated that the disorientation cross section of benzene is much larger than for cyclohexane. At comparable pressures the relaxation time in benzene is too short to be measured accurately by the present method. These results suggest that benzene might form a charge-transfer complex, to a very slight degree, with rubidium. Such a complex would be a free radical which would strongly disorient the remaining optically pumped rubidium atoms by spin exchange. Further studies of this effect, and others are now in preparation.

The author wishes to acknowledge the advice and encouragement of Professor Richard Bersohn during the course of this work.

* Supported by the U. S. Air Force Office of Scientific Research.
[1] R. A. Bernheim, J. Chem. Phys. **36**, 135 (1962).
[2] W. Franzen, Phys. Rev. **115**, 850 (1959).

From: *J. Chem. Phys.* **40**, 1678-1683 (1964)

Optical Pumping and Chemical Reactions

R. J. McNeal,* R. A. Bernheim,† R. Bersohn, and M. Dorfman

Department of Chemistry, Columbia University, New York, New York 10027

(Received 13 November 1963)

Optical pumping in this paper refers to the orientation of the angular momenta of atoms and molecules by light. The phenomenon of spin exchange raises the possibility of the use of a gas of pumped atoms as a highly sensitive detector of free radicals. It is shown, however, that a suitable buffer gas may not have atoms of high atomic number, and may not be polar or aromatic and must be extraordinarily inert chemically. Examples are He, Ne, Ar, H_2, N_2, CH_4, C_2H_6, C_2H_4, and—for a short time—CO. These highly stable molecules decompose into radicals at ordinary temperature only under irradiation with vacuum ultraviolet photons or with particles. Optically pumped gases may be useful, therefore, in studying the reactions involved in vacuum uv photolyses of simple hydrocarbons.

INTRODUCTION

THE rate constant for a chemical reaction as usually measured is a statistical average over the translational, rotational, and internal states of the reacting molecules. To obtain more detailed information about a chemical reaction than is contained in the thermally averaged rate constant, one must start with a collection of molecules which has been state selected in some way. That is, the rate constant must be measured for a system of molecules characterized by a nonequilibrium distribution and the chemical kinetic measurements must be made in a time short compared to the relaxation time of the distribution. One type of state selection is performed by the collimating slits which shape an effusing molecular beam so that only a subset of translational states are studied rather than all of them. In this paper we consider the effect of selecting only the spin states of atoms and radicals.

I. SPIN ORIENTATION OF ATOMS AND RADICALS

The most direct way of selecting the spin states of an atom or radical is to pass an already translational state selected beam through an inhomogeneous magnetic field. Although this method is ideal in principle, we want to investigate whether it is possible to study chemical kinetics by establishing a nonequilibrium distribution *in the spins alone.*

A. Orientation by a Large Magnetic Field

In the presence of a magnetic field H, a species with unpaired electrons has an energy of the form $M_J g_J \beta H$,

---

* Now at Department of Chemistry, Harvard University, Cambridge, Massachusetts 02138.

† Now at Department of Chemistry, Pennsylvania State University, University Park, Pennsylvania.

where M_J is the magnetic quantum number, g_J the gyromagnetic ratio, and β is the Bohr magneton. The differences in energy of the $2J+1$ states results in a difference in concentration of the species in the different magnetic energy levels.

As an example, consider the dissociation of a molecule M into two radicals $R\pm$ having quantum numbers $\pm\frac{1}{2}$ referred to the axis of the field H:

$$M = R_+ + R_-. \tag{1}$$

The equilibrium constant for this reaction,

$$K/4 = [R_+][R_-]/[M], \tag{2}$$

is just $\frac{1}{4}$ of the usual equilibrium constant $K = [R]^2[M]^{-1}$, where $[R] = [R_+] + [R_-]$ because $[R_+] = [R_-]$. In the presence of a magnetic field, however,

$$[R_+] = [R_-] \exp(g\beta H/kT) \tag{3}$$

and one can show that

$$[R]^2/[M] = K/4 = K \cosh^2(g\beta H/2kT)$$
$$= K[1 + \frac{1}{4}(g\beta H/kT)^2 + \cdots]. \tag{4}$$

At room temperature for $g=2$ and in a field of 10^5 G, the correction factor in the brackets is 4×10^{-4}. Transient experiments can be envisioned in which the optical absorption of the medium could be studied in the presence of large time-varying magnetic fields. The method is limited in usefulness, obviously, to reaction times longer than the switching times possible for very large fields.

B. Direct Orientation by Light

The anisotropic excitation of a gas of atoms or molecules by a directed beam of light, whether polarized or not, automatically produces a nonuniform distribution among the ground angular momentum quantum states. The molecules are then said to be optically pumped. If, for a radical, the distribution over the magnetic sublevels of the total angular momentum is nonuniform so that the magnetic moment is oriented, then, in general, the radicals are spin oriented. The orientation so produced is useful for studying chemical reactions if and only if the relaxation time of the nonuniform distribution to the almost uniform Boltzmann distribution is longer than the reaction times.

The atoms in which spin orientation in the ground state of the vapor has been produced optically are Na,[1] K,[2] Rb,[2] and Cs.[3] These atoms are in S states and have reasonably large vapor pressures at relatively low temperatures. Other S-state atoms with nonzero spin have not been pumped because of engineering difficulties in fabricating transparent high-temperature vapor cells. On the other hand, non-S ground-state atoms and molecular radicals have not been pumped at all except

in beam experiments. The reasons are discussed in Sec. II.

C. Orientation and Disorientation by Spin Exchange

It is implicit in quantum mechanics that electron exchange takes place on every close molecular collision. Nevertheless, the only direct proof of electron exchange is afforded by the phenomena of spin exchange, If one atomic species is being optically pumped, its spin-density matrix differs greatly from the thermal equilibrium, or Boltzmann, spin-density matrix. If another species with unpaired electrons is present, it will have, at least initially, a Boltzmann spin-density matrix. If the two species are allowed to collide with one another, spin exchange can occur, and the resultant spin-density matrix for each species can be characterized by the same "spin temperature." In the steady state where one species is continually optically pumped this spin temperature will be that of the pumped species. While the spins may change temperatures, both species, of course, retain their initial ambient translational temperature, and the degree of orientation that can be obtained by the above process will depend upon the relative rates of spin relaxation of the two species. For example, if the optically pumped species has a long spin relaxation time while the second species has a very short spin relaxation time, the degree of orientation will be governed by the second species, and the resulting spin temperature will be close to the translational temperature of the gas. If such is the case the second species can act as a "sink" for the net magnetic moment of the optically pumped atoms. On the other hand, if the second species has a relaxation time comparable to that of the optically pumped atoms then it can be successfully oriented by the spin-exchange process. The species which have been oriented in this way are the free electron,[4] Na(^2S),[5] K(^2S),[5] Rb(^2S),[6] H(^2S),[7] N(^4S),[8] P(^4S),[9] and He$^+$(^2S).[10]

The spin-exchange cross sections for the Rb isotopes and Cs have been found [11,12] to be about 2.0×10^{-14} cm². As pointed out by Purcell and Field,[13] the spin-exchange cross sections will in general be comparable to or greater than geometrical cross sections. In a typical collision the colliding atoms will be close to each other for 10^{-13} sec and there will be an exchange energy at the distance of closest approach of about $10^{13}h \sim 0.04$ eV so that the unpaired electrons will exchange at least once during

[1] J. P. Barrat, J. Brossel, and A. Kastler, Compt. Rend. **239**, 1196 (1954).
[2] A. Bloom, J. Phys. Radium **19**, 881 (1958).
[3] A. Blondin and J. P. Barrat, Compt. Rend. **243**, 2041 (1956).

[4] H. G. Dehmelt, Phys. Rev. **109**, 381 (1958).
[5] P. Franken, R. Sands, and J. Hobart, Phys. Rev. Letters **1**, 118 (1958).
[6] R. Novick and H. E. Peters, Phys. Rev. Letters **1**, 54 (1958).
[7] L. W. Anderson, F. M. Pipkin, and J. C. Baird, Jr., Phys. Rev. Letters **1**, 229 (1958).
[8] W. W. Holloway, Jr., and R. Novick, Phys. Rev. Letters **1**, 367 (1958).
[9] R. H. Lambert and F. M. Pipkin, Phys. Rev. **128**, 198 (1962).
[10] H. G. Dehmelt and F. G. Major, Phys. Rev. Letters **8**, 213 (1962).
[11] R. Sands and H. W. Moos, Bull. Am. Phys. Soc. **7**, 433 (1963).
[12] S. M. Jarrett, Phys. Rev. **133**, 111(A) (1964).
[13] E. M. Purcell and G. B. Field, Astrophys. J. **124**, 542 (1956).

TABLE I. Spin disorientation cross section σ for Rb atoms in the presence of various buffer gases.

Buffer gas	σ (cm^2)[a]	Reference
He	6.2×10^{-25}	18
D$_2$	4.3×10^{-24}	20
H$_2$	3×10^{-24}	19
CH$_4$	8×10^{-24}	19
C$_2$H$_6$	3.8×10^{-23}	19
Ne	5.2×10^{-23}	17
N$_2$	5.7×10^{-23}	19
C$_2$H$_4$	1.3×10^{-22}	19
Ar	3.7×10^{-22}	17
C$_6$H$_{12}$	4.5×10^{-22}	19
Kr	5.9×10^{-21}	17
Xe	1.3×10^{-20}	17
C$_6$H$_6$	6×10^{-19}	21
(CH$_3$)$_2$O	3×10^{-18}	21
C$_4$H$_8$O$_2$ (dioxane)	$\sim 4 \times 10^{-18}$	21
NH$_3$	8×10^{-18}	21

[a] The horizontal lines separate the orders of magnitude of the cross section. The data makes clear the fact that pumping is almost impossible in the presence of highly polarizable molecules (Kr, Xe), aromatic molecules (C$_6$H$_6$), or polar molecules (dimethyl ether, dioxane, and ammonia).

the collision at short distances. There is also a small exchange frequency in the much larger region outside the distance of strong interaction. To put it another way the cross section for exchanging electrons between atoms should be comparable to the cross section for changing momentum. Purely magnetic effects are negligible.

In order to examine how spin orientation, produced either directly or by exchange, can be used to study chemical reactions, we must examine the factors which determine the degree of spin orientation that can be obtained in an experiment. The degree of orientation will depend upon the intensity of the pumping radiation and upon the spin relaxation of the oriented species. The intensity of the pumping light can be experimentally controlled, but the spin relaxation depends upon the species being pumped. We now turn our attention to this latter property of the system.

II. RELAXATION MECHANISMS FOR ELECTRONIC SPIN ORIENTATION

A. S-State Atoms

A spin-oriented atom, in general, loses its orientation on collisions with the walls of its container. In most cases the atom is not only relaxed by the surface but is strongly adsorbed by it.[14-16] The alkali atoms in particular are strongly adsorbed by glass and quartz. A paraffin-coated surface[14] is most exceptional in that it does not absorb cesium atoms and gives only a small phase shift on each collision, i.e., 0.09 ± 0.01 radian/collision.

In general, therefore, it is necessary to add a buffer gas such as helium or nitrogen to an optically pumped gas in order to maintain the orientation for a time longer than the transit time of the vessel. Even then the relaxation time for the orientation is finite, of the order of tenths of a second, and it diminishes with increasing gas pressure at higher pressures. The diminution is sufficiently rapid that it is clear that achievement of appreciable orientation in condensed systems by optical pumping is most unlikely.

Extensive measurements have been made of the spin-disorientation cross sections of Rb and other alkali atoms by various buffer gas molecules, and the results[17-21] for Rb are summarized in Table I. The theoretical mechanisms for the relaxation processes for various types of molecules have been discussed by Bernheim[18] and McNeal[21] and may be summarized as follows. The disorientation cross section for nonpolar molecules, which lies in the range $\sim 10^{-25}$ to 10^{-20} cm^2, depends on the square of a spin–rotation interaction which occurs during the collision between a Rb atom and a buffer gas molecule. This interaction has been shown to arise from the spin–orbit interaction of the colliding system of atoms. The very large ($\sim 10^{-18}$ cm^2) cross section for polar molecules in optically pumped rubidium is caused by the virtual excitation of the alkali atom into a P state where spin–orbit interaction can occur. The cross section for these buffer gases varies as $(\mu/R_0^3)^4$, where μ is the dipole moment of the polar buffer gas and R_0 is the average distance of closest approach for zero impact parameter. The cross section also depends on the square of the spin–orbit splitting of the excited P states of the alkali atom.

B. Rapid Destruction of Orientation in Non-S-State Atoms and Free Radicals

Let us consider three types of systems in which electron spin orientation could be produced optically—S-state atoms, which have been discussed above, non-S-state atoms, and molecular radicals. A simple argument shows that only in the first case will the spin orientation persist for a useful length of time. In other words, the spin disorientation cross sections are very large when the molecule or atom possesses any angular momentum other than nuclear or electronic spin. The physical

[14] H. M. Goldenberg, D. Kleppner, and N. F. Ramsey, Phys. Rev. **123**, 530 (1961).
[15] L. Wexler, Rev. Mod. Phys. **30**, 402 (1958).
[16] R. G. Brewer, J. Chem. Phys. **38**, 3015 (1963).
[17] W. Franzen, Phys. Rev. **115**, 850 (1959).
[18] R. A. Bernheim, J. Chem. Phys. **36**, 135 (1962).
[19] R. J. McNeal, J. Chem. Phys. **37**, 2726 (1962).
[20] R. G. Brewer, J. Chem. Phys. **37**, 2504 (1962).
[21] R. J. McNeal, J. Chem. Phys. **40**, 1089 (1964).

reason for this is that if there is an orbital or rotational angular momentum in the system, the associated magnetic moment will produce a magnetic field which will act on the electronic spin. At almost every collision with the walls or a foreign-gas molecule the magnitude or direction of a rotational angular momentum will change. The electron spin is therefore subjected to a magnetic field varying randomly in time with a correlation time τ_c, which is the mean free time between collisions.

Consider, as an example, a radical with an interaction energy $\gamma \mathbf{S} \cdot \mathbf{J} = g\beta \mathbf{S} \cdot \mathbf{H}$, where $\mathbf{H}$ varies randomly.

Following the familiar arguments of Bloembergen et al.,[22] we find for the relaxation rate:

$$1/T_1 = 2\tau_c (\gamma^2/h^2)[J(J+1)/3]. \quad (5)$$

A thermal average of $J(J+1) = kTh^{-2}(I_A + I_B + I_C)$, where I_A, I_B, and I_C are principal moments of inertia, should really be substituted at this point but we substitute instead $J=1$ to obtain a lower limit for the magnitude of the relaxation rate. The values of γ have been measured for only a very few molecules, but we may take the value[23] measured for O_2, -0.0084 cm^{-1}, to be typical. (In O_2 and other triplet molecules the spin–spin interaction would be a much more important source of relaxation but this is irrelevant to the present discussion.)

Taking $|\gamma| \sim 10^{-2}$ cm^{-1} and assuming a mean free time, τ_c of 10^{-8} sec, we find $T_1 = 10^{-9}$ sec. The above calculation is crude but perhaps sufficient to demonstrate that molecular radicals can never be oriented and will always act as a sink for the orientation of S-state atoms. The argument that non-S-state atoms cannot retain their orientation is similar with the interaction $A\mathbf{L} \cdot \mathbf{S}$ replacing $\gamma \mathbf{J} \cdot \mathbf{S}$ but with the restriction that L does not change on collision.

III. OPTICAL PUMPING AND CHEMICAL REACTIONS

A. Optically Pumped Atoms as a Probe for Free Radicals

The preceding discussion shows that it is not possible, except in the absence of collisions, to prepare assemblies of spin-oriented radicals. It is also not feasible to pump directly the electron spins and subsequently retain the orientation of any but atoms whose ground states are S states. These comprise only the alkali atoms, H, N, P, As, Sb, Cr, Mo, Mn, Cu, Ag, and Au. The pumpable atoms in turn can only be present in the gas phase at very low partial pressures, $\sim 10^{-7}$–10^{-5} mm. What then is the utility of optical pumping in chemical reactions?

If we recall that the depolarization cross section for a typical buffer gas like neon is $\sim 10^{-23}$ cm^2 and for a radical $\sim 10^{-14}$ cm^2, we have a ratio of cross sections of 10^{-9} whose physical origin[18] is the factor $(m/M)^2\alpha^2$.

This means that, as compared to a buffer gas at 10^{-2} atm pressure the radicals at a pressure of 10^{-11} atm will make a comparable contribution to the relaxation time. At concentrations of the order of 3×10^8 radicals/cc direct absorption spectroscopy and mass spectroscopy would be useless. In short, the pumped alkali atoms are a unique tool to measure extremely low radical concentrations.

Very small radical concentrations have been measured in the past by comparing the rates of ortho–para H_2 conversion in the presence and absence of a paramagnetic system. A more modern way of performing the same experiment would be to pass ^{3}He through a cell containing optically oriented Rb vapor, thus giving the ^{3}He a nuclear orientation,[24] and then through a reaction vessel, and then to compare the nuclear spin relaxation rates with that of ^{3}He in a similar system without radicals. These methods are based on the fact that electron–nuclear magnetic interactions are larger than nuclear–nuclear magnetic interactions by a factor of M/m and the respective cross sections for spin flips are larger by a factor of $(M/m)^2 \sim 10^6$. The nuclear spin methods are inherently less sensitive but have much greater range of applicability. Unlike the very reactive alkali atoms, ^{3}He atoms would act as passive measuring devices.

B. Choice of Alkali Atom to be Pumped

The atoms whose ground states are S states, other than the alkali atoms, require high temperatures to be maintained in appreciable concentration. Inasmuch as these conditions would tend to destroy the molecules whose reactions are to be studied, these atoms would be less useful than the alkali atoms. As for the latter, Li has not yet been successfully pumped and the other atoms require optimum temperatures as follows: Na(150°C), K(65°C), Rb(48°C), and Cs(30°C). The temperature range in which pumping is feasible is, of course, related to the optimum pressure range.[25] The reason why one cannot separate the temperature range from the pressure range is that the alkali atoms are strongly adsorbed by glass and most other surfaces.[14–16]

For optimum polarization[26] it is necessary to filter out the D_2 component of the alkali atom resonance line from the D_1 component. The intervals in cm^{-1} between the D_1 and D_2 lines are for Na(17.2), K(37.7), Rb(237.6), and Cs(554.1). Interference filters which

[22] N. Bloembergen, E. M. Purcell, and R. V. Pound, Phys. Rev. 73, 679 (1948).
[23] G. Herzberg, Spectra of Diatomic Molecules (D. Van Nostrand, Company, Inc., New York, 1950), p. 223.

[24] M. A. Bouchiat, T. R. Carver, and C. M. Varnum, Phys. Rev. Letters 5, 373 (1960). Alternatively the ^{3}He nuclear moment could be oriented by spin exchange with optically oriented metastable ^{3}He (2^3S_1), cf. G. K. Walters, F. D. Colegrove, and L. D. Schearer, Phys. Rev. Letters 8, 439 (1962).
[25] If the partial pressure is too low, the signal-to-noise ratio will be poor. If the pressure is too high, the pumping radiation will be so strongly absorbed as it travels through the vapor cell that there will be a severe gradient of polarization along the light path. There is, of course, a gradient of polarization in any system caused by the depolarizing effect of the walls, but an additional gradient would seriously complicate interpretation of the results.
[26] W. Franzen and A. G. Emslie, Phys. Rev. 108, 1453 (1957).

can perform the selective filtering are more readily available for Cs and Rb than for Na and K. Finally, because relaxation times depend on the spin–orbit coupling, Rb atoms will have—at the same buffer gas pressure and wall geometry—slightly longer relaxation times than Cs atoms. For these reasons Rb atoms were used in the experiments to be described; it is anticipated that the conclusions drawn would hold for the other alkali atoms.

IV. EXPERIMENTAL PROCEDURES AND RESULTS

We have attempted to utilize the extreme sensitivity of the orientation of optically pumped rubidium atoms to study the kinetics of certain free radical reactions. These experiments have involved several techniques and have been generally unsuccessful. They have, however, served to illustrate several rather unexpected limitations of the general method and to point the way to experiments with more chance of success.

A. Experiments Using Near-Ultraviolet Radiation

Methyl radicals can be produced by photolysis in the near uv of a number of compounds, of which acetone, dimethyl mercury, and azomethane are typical. If optically pumped rubidium is also present in the gaseous mixture, spin exchange between the photolytically produced methyl radicals and the rubidium atoms will occur. The methyl radicals, having rotational angular momentum, would have a fast rate of spin relaxation, as discussed above, and would act as a "sink" for any orientation that rubidium atoms would receive from the pumping radiation. The reduction in orientation of the rubidium atoms would depend upon the spin-exchange cross section and the concentration of methyl radicals. By monitoring the rubidium orientation one would hope to monitor the methyl radical concentration. The time variation in orientation would, in turn, reflect the rate of disappearance of free radicals.

This experiment was tried using the compounds mentioned, $(CH_3)_2CO$, $(CH_3)_2Hg$, and $(CH_3)_2N_2$, as sources of methyl radicals. Unfortunately, when these compounds were admitted to the optical pumping vapor cell the rubidium atoms were immediately disoriented, and, subsequently, reacted with the parent molecules. Studies of the reaction rates of the radical were not possible. These experiments indicate that the optical pumping method of studying free radicals reactions is limited to those radicals derived from parent molecules that are inert to alkali metal atoms when the latter are the optically pumped species.

Other experiments involving near uv photolysis have been performed in an attempt to detect and study triplet-state molecules, which should disorient optically pumped rubidium by the same mechanism as does a free radical which is in a doublet state. One experiment that was attempted was the photolysis of ketene to form CH_2 fragments. If CH_2 is produced as a spin triplet, then strong disorientation of any optically oriented rubidium present would occur, followed by reaction of the CH_2 with rubidium and other species present. If the CH_2 is produced as a spin singlet, then only reaction would occur. However, the parent molecule again proved to be too reactive.

Triplet states also occur as metastable decay products in near-ultraviolet excitation of aromatic hydrocarbons. These molecules were expected to be stable against reaction with alkali metals. However, we have found that benzene and naphthalene and presumably all other aromatic molecules drastically reduce the rubidium orientation and prevent meaningful data from being obtained from an excitation experiment. The reason is presumably the formation of an equilibrium concentration of a Rb–hydrocarbon charge-transfer-complex radical.

The reactivity of the rubidium atoms has frustrated several other types of experiments. It was planned to photolyze $Cr(CO)_6$ into Cr atoms and CO with subsequent orientation of the Cr atoms by spin exchange with Rb. A chemical reaction in which a Cr mirror is produced on the walls of the vapor cell occurs as soon as $Cr(CO)_6$ is exposed to Rb.

B. Experiments in Flowing Systems

One way to defeat the problem posed by the reactivity of the alkali atom with the parent substances of free radicals is to introduce the parent molecules into a flowing buffer gas instead of a stationary system. Thus, a bulb containing rubidium atoms could be placed in a gas flow system consisting of a steadily maintained pressure of a highly purified buffer gas. A small amount of the radical parent could be introduced into the buffer gas stream and photolyzed before entering the rubidium vapor cell. Reaction products would be swept out of the vapor cell by pumps maintaining the flow rate. If the rate of introduction of the radical parent is sufficiently small, conditions could be established for detection and study of the radical.

A prototype of this experiment was performed in which minute quantities of oxygen were introduced into a stream of highly purified N_2 gas flowing through a rubidium vapor cell. Oxygen is a triplet molecule which made it possible to study the characteristics of the flow system detection scheme without having to produce the radicals artificially. The predicted large effect on the rubidium orientation was indeed observed, but it was found that the greatest part of the reaction of the oxygen took place on the walls of the flow chamber, prior to the vapor cell, where large amounts of rubidum are evidently adsorbed. It is concluded that the reaction at the walls of the flow chamber would lead to results impossible to interpret accurately in terms of *gas phase* free radical reactions occurring in the vapor cell.

D. Simple Hydrocarbons and the Vacuum Uv

The central conclusion of our experimental work is that appreciable polarization of alkali atoms can be established with only a limited number of gases—the light noble gases, the simple alkanes and alkenes, N_2, H_2, CO,—and hardly any others. If chemical reactions are to be studied by optical pumping techniques, only these gases will be useful. In turn, these very stable gases will have to be decomposed by photolysis in the vacuum uv or by particle bombardment. Optical pumping may still be very useful in interpreting a limited but important class of reactions.

ACKNOWLEDGMENTS

One of us (Richard Bersohn) is indebted to Professor A. Kastler of Paris for a stimulating stay at his laboratory. Financial support for this work was received from the U.S. Air Force and the U.S. Atomic Energy Commission.

From: *Phys. Rev.* **125**, 1318-1322 (1962)

Alignment of the H_2^+ Molecular Ion by Selective Photodissociation. I*

H. G. Dehmelt and K. B. Jefferts

Department of Physics, University of Washington, Seattle, Washington

(Received September 27, 1961)

On the basis of experimental results obtained by Linlor et al., Fischer, and in this laboratory, demonstrating photodissociation time constants as short as 0.1 sec and trapping times as long as several seconds as practical for the H_2^+ molecular ion, the feasibility is discussed theoretically of a novel technique to align trapped molecular ions and also monitor the alignment by selective photodissociation. First the limiting case of no electronic and nuclear spins and very large rotational quantum numbers is treated, based on the concept that the photodissociation rate R is proportional to the average squared component of the electric light vector perpendicular to the axis of molecular rotation. This angular dependence of R when a bunch of ions created by a short electron bombardment pulse is subsequently irradiated causes the ions in certain magnetic sublevels to decay much more slowly than others. Consequently when conditions for the preservation of

alignment are favorable, the sample becomes increasingly aligned. Furthermore, since a partially aligned sample photodissociates more slowly than an unaligned one, more molecular ions $\bar{N}$ will remain when alignment is allowed to develop than when it is continuously destroyed, resulting in only N ions. Next the nuclear and electronic spins are taken into account and numerical values for the dissociation rates of the 30 magnetic sublevels for the first three rotational states of the H_2^+ ion are evaluated for linear light polarization. One sees that on the basis of a sample of 10^9 H_2^+ ions decaying due to photodissociation to 2×10^7 ions, one might expect an optimum signal $(\bar{N}-N)/N \approx 0.25$ compared to a statistical uncertainty of about 0.0003 for two consecutive pulses. The possibilities inherent in the scheme to observe the rf spectrum of H_2^+ are pointed out.

INTRODUCTION

THE recently developed collision techniques to polarize or align free atoms using electrons,[1,2] photons (optical pumping),[3] or other atoms[4] as collision partners, have so far not been applied to molecules. This note will serve to discuss the feasibility of a new variant which should be capable of aligning certain molecular ions by virtue of the orientation dependence of their photodissociation cross sections. As a specific example, the H_2^+ molecular ion will be treated in some detail here. Since it is the simplest known molecule, there is considerable academic interest in its radiofrequency spectrum. The possible extension to the other hydrogen isotopes widens this interest by providing a potential source for additional information on the structure of these nuclei.

PHOTODISSOCIATION OF TRAPPED H_2^+ IONS

The photodissociation of H_2^+ is due to an electrical dipole transition[5] from the electronic $1s\sigma$ ground (N) state to the first excited repulsive $2p\sigma$ (E) state. It can be effected by visible or ultraviolet light depending on the vibrational excitation of the ground state. Linlor et al.[6] have measured the dissociation cross section as about 10^{-17} cm^2 using the unfiltered output of a 1000-watt high-pressure mercury arc. With this source and reflective cylindrical optics they were able to realize a dissociation time constant T as short as 0.1 sec. Similar times T have been found for trapped H_2^+ ions in this laboratory using a 500-watt HBO 500 mercury arc from the effect of the light for varying irradiation times on resonance signals[7] due to an ion sample created by a short electron burst. Theoretical T values[8] are in agreement with the above experimental values. Even though it might be possible to decrease T to 0.01 sec experimentally, in order to dissociate an appreciable fraction of the irradiated ions special steps will have to

* Supported by a grant of the U. S. Army Research Office (Durham) and by contract funds of the U. S. Navy Office of Naval Research.
[1] H. W. B. Skinner, Proc. Roy. Soc. (London) **A112**, 642 (1926).
[2] H. G. Dehmelt, Phys. Rev. **103**, 1125 (1956).
[3] Alfred Kastler, J. Opt. Soc. Am. **47**, 460 (1957); J. phys. radium **11**, 255 (1950).
[4] H. G. Dehmelt, Proceedings of the Twelfth Annual Frequency Control Symposium May 8, 1958; and J. phys. radium **19**, 866 (1958); P. Franken, R. Sands, and J. Hobart, Phys. Rev. Letters **1**, 118 (1958); R. Novick and H. E. Peters, *ibid.* **1**, 54 (1958); L. W. Anderson, F. M. Pipkin, and J. C. Baird, *ibid.* **1**, 229 (1958).

[5] R. S. Mulliken, J. Chem. Phys. **7**, 20 (1939).
[6] W. Linlor, C. F. Barnett, and R. Reinhardt, University of California Radiation Laboratory Report UCRL-4917, 1957 (unpublished).
[7] E. Fischer, Z. Physik **156**, 1 (1959).
[8] G. Gibson, University of California Radiation Laboratory Report UCRL-4671, 1956 (unpublished).

be taken to trap them for 0.1—1 sec without any collisions occurring during this time. Fischer,[7] using rf quadrupole traps of the type developed in W. Paul's laboratory, reports trapping times as long as 15 msec for N_2^+ ions and a N_2 background pressure of 6×10^{-6} mm Hg corresponding to a $N_2^+ - N_2$ collision time of 0.4 msec. In this laboratory, employing similar techniques but using a sealed-off bakeable tube evacuated by a getter-ion pump and pulsing the electron gun, trapping times of several seconds have been observed for H_2^+ and He^+ ions at background pressures around 10^{-8} mm. These data indicate that it should be possible to make the photodissociation time T short compared to the lifetime against all other reactions, which therefore will be neglected in the following. Next in the order of interest is the number of ions which can be trapped simultaneously. Fischer's[7] data indicate that it should be possible to trap about 10^9 ions without going to extremely large traps. Allowing for decay due to photodissociation to about 10^7 particles the statistical uncertainty in the number of ions counted would amount to 3 parts in 10 000 so that rather small changes in the average ion lifetime due to alignment should be detectable.

ORIENTATION DEPENDENCE WITHOUT ELECTRONIC OR NUCLEAR SPINS

Mulliken[5] has shown that the pulsating electric dipole moment which appears during the electronic transition always lies in the direction of the internuclear axis. In the limit of large rotational quantum numbers K, only the average squared component of the electric light vector $\mathbf{E}$ perpendicular to the axis of rotation $\mathbf{K}$ can be effective in causing the transition at all. That this component has to be further averaged over the molecular rotation is of no concern here. Therefore, one should expect the normalized photodissociation rate R, $\langle R \rangle_{av} = 1$, to be proportional to $\langle \sin^2(\mathbf{K},\mathbf{E}) \rangle_{av}$. Considering an initially unpolarized sample, this angular dependence of the cross section has two consequences. First, as more and more molecules are dissociated, the remaining ones exhibit an increasing alignment. Secondly, since the residual molecules crowd into the long living states, their number $\bar{N}$ decreases more slowly when alignment is allowed to develop than when it is continuously destroyed by some suitable agent. Quantitatively we have for the "no alignment" case $N = N_0 e^{-t/T}$. For the undisturbed case with n initially equally populated substates, $m = 1, 2, \cdots, n$, with varying decay rates R_m

$$\bar{N} = \frac{N_0}{n} \sum_1^n \exp[-(t/T)R_m]; \quad \langle R_m \rangle_{av} = 1.$$

As the "signal," S, resulting when the disaligning agent is switched on and off in otherwise identical cycles, we define $S = (\bar{N} - N)/N$. Since in practical cases the R_m

values lie close to 1, we set $R_m = 1 + \delta_m$ and treat the δ_m as small quantities to obtain the following approximate expression, $\bar{N} \approx N + N(1/2)u^2 \langle \delta_m^2 \rangle_{av}$. Here we have set $t/T = u$ and $\langle \delta_m \rangle_{av} = 0$ has been used. Third and higher powers in δ_m have been neglected, $\langle \delta_m^3 \rangle_{av}$ because it tends to cancel out, the higher ones because they are small. Herewith follows the desired approximate expression, $S \approx (1/2)\langle \delta_m^2 \rangle_{av} u^2$. Of practical interest is further when the optimum ratio of signal to relative statistical fluctuation $N^{-1/2}$ is attained. With $S \propto u^2$ and $N^{1/2} \propto e^{-(u/2)}$ we maximize $S/N^{-1/2} \propto u^2 e^{-(u/2)}$ for the single cycle case and obtain $u = 4$. This leads to the optimum signal $S \approx 8 \langle \delta_m^2 \rangle_{av}$. For the sake of numerical illustration we now evaluate $\langle \delta^2 \rangle_{av}$ for very large K in three experimentally interesting cases. The normalized dissociation rates R are proportional to $\langle \sin^2(\mathbf{K},\mathbf{E}) \rangle_{motion}$, where the average has to be taken over the motion of $\mathbf{K}$ with respect to $\mathbf{E}$ or vice versa. With $\delta = R - 1$ we form $\langle \delta^2 \rangle_{sphere}$, where the average is over all possible orientations of $\mathbf{K}$, that is the whole sphere, to provide a measure of the angular dependence profile of the dissociation rates. The direction of the inevitable residual magnetic field $\mathbf{H}$ is chosen as the Z direction and the angle $(\mathbf{K},\mathbf{Z}) = \Theta$ is a constant of the motion.

(a) The light vector $\mathbf{E}$ is parallel to $\mathbf{H}$ and $(\mathbf{K},\mathbf{E}) = \Theta$. With $\langle \sin^2\Theta \rangle_{sphere} = 2/3$, we have $R_\Theta = (3/2) \sin^2\Theta$, $\delta_\Theta = 1 - (3/2) \sin^2\Theta$, and finally $\langle \delta_\Theta^2 \rangle_{sphere} = (1/5)$, and for the signal $S_{||} = (1/10)u^2$. For $u = 1$ or $t = T$ this corresponds already to the large effect $S_{||} = 0.1$.

(b) The light is linearly polarized perpendicular to $\mathbf{H}$; $\mathbf{E} = E_x$. With $\cos^2(\mathbf{K},\mathbf{E}) = \sin^2\Theta \cos^2\phi$, we have

$$\langle \sin^2(\mathbf{K},\mathbf{E}) \rangle_{av} = 1 - \sin^2\Theta \langle \cos^2\Phi \rangle_{circle} = 1 - (1/2) \sin^2\Theta,$$

where the motion average is over the precession circle. This gives

$$R_\Theta = 3/2 - (3/4) \sin^2\Theta \quad \text{and} \quad -\delta_\Theta = (3/4) \sin^2\Theta - 1/2.$$

Comparing this with δ_Θ for case (a) we get $\langle \delta_\Theta^2 \rangle_{sphere} = (1/20)$ and $S_\perp = (1/40)u^2$.

(c) The light is circularly polarized; $\mathbf{E}$ is perpendicular to $\mathbf{H}$. Here one has to average also over the fast rotation of the $\mathbf{E}$ vector. The result is the same as in case (b).

Case (c) shows that there appears to be no advantage in the use of circular polarization, which is more difficult to realize experimentally. In the following, therefore, we shall limit ourselves to linearly polarized light. Observing the results for cases (a) and (b) shows that turning H from parallel to perpendicular to E provides a convenient experimental way[9] if not to destroy at least to reduce appreciably the molecular alignment. One expects the experimental signal here $S^* = S_{||} - S_\perp$ and with $S_\perp = (1/4)S_{||}$, $S^* = (3/4)S_{||}$.

The above results can also be obtained using the asymptotic M dependence derivable from standard

[9] W. E. Hawkins, Phys. Rev. **98**, 478 (1955).

atomic theory formulas[10] and observing the selection rules[11] $\Delta K=\pm 1$ and $\Delta M=0$. Using in addition sum rules taking into account the statistical weights of the K levels involved, the rates R_{KM} for finite K can be derived. For $\mathbf{E}$ parallel $\mathbf{H}$, one finds in this manner

$$R_{KM}=(3/2)[K(K+1)-M^2]/K(K+1).$$

To justify the use of standard atomic spectra theory ls-coupling intensity formulas here and in the following, we refer in further detail to the fact that the whole KM dependence of the molecular electronic transition $KM-K'M$ matrix element for the case of light polarized parallel to the Z axis is contained in the factor[11]

$$\int P_{K'M}(\cos\theta)\, \cos\theta P_{KM}(\cos\theta)\, \sin\theta d\theta,$$

the angle θ referring to the internuclear axis. This KM dependence is identical to that for a one electron $lm \rightarrow l'm$ atomic electric dipole transition and the selection rule $\Delta K=\pm 1$ applies obviously. That the H_2^+ molecule in the (E) state is falling apart does not create any difficulties since one may invoke a version of the Franck-Condon principle. If one imagines the incident flat white spectrum to be generated by pulses short compared to the dissociation time of the (E) state, about 10^{-13} sec, it must be irrelevant if the state is stable or repulsive. Since for weak light intensities the result can only depend on the power spectrum intensity[12] the specific assumption of short pulses is quite legitimate here. The form of the expression obtained for R_{KM} above suggests writing it as the expectation value of an operator $K^2-K_Z^2$,

$$R_{KM}\propto |(KM|K^2-K_Z^2|KM)|,$$

involving only the KM sublevel of the electronic ground state. This expectation value can be interpreted in analogy to the classical proportionality $R_\Theta \propto \sin^2\Theta$ as a measure of the average squared component of the electric light vector perpendicular to $\mathbf{K}$.

DISSOCIATION RATES FOR THE H_2^+ ION

It is now necessary to take electronic and nuclear spins into account. Theoretical studies of the hyperfine structure of the H_2^+ ion have been undertaken by several authors.[13-15] Dalgarno *et al.* which we will follow here, give approximately the following effective spin Hamiltonian: $H_{eff}[\text{Mc/sec}]=880\mathbf{I}\cdot\mathbf{S}+129I_ZS_Z-150\mathbf{S}\cdot\mathbf{K},$

[10] E. U. Condon and G. H. Shortley, *The Theory of Atomic Spectra* (Cambridge University Press, New York, 1953), p. 387.
[11] G. Herzberg, *Molecular Spectra and Molecular Structure* (D. Van Nostrand Company, Princeton, New Jersey, 1950), Vol. 1. p. 203 and p. 244–247.
[12] Compare P. A. Franken, Phys. Rev. **121**, 508 (1961).
[13] A. Dalgarno, R. N. L. Patterson, and W. B. Somerville (to be published).
[14] M. S. Stephen and S. P. Auffrey, J. Chem. Phys. **31**, 1329 (1959).
[15] M. Mizushima, Astrophys. J. **132**, 493 (1960).

TABLE I. Photodissociation rates R of hfs sublevels of the three lowest rotational states of the H_2^+ molecular ion for electric light vector parallel to static magnetic field. Hfs energies W_F, g factors g_F, and residual population numbers a_4 after irradiation for four dissociation time constants are listed also $a_0=1$.

K	F_2	F	W_F[Mc/sec]	g_F	$|M|$	R	$100a_4$
-2	1/2	3/2		-2/5	3/2	0.650	7.43
					1/2	1.350	0.45
		5/2		+2/5	5/2	0.500	13.50
					3/2	1.100	1.23
					1/2	1.400	0.37
-1	3/2	3/2	+546	+22/45	3/2	1.200	0.82
					1/2	0.800	4.08
		1/2	+544	+10/9	1/2	1.000	1.83
		5/2	+378	+2/5	5/2	0.750	4.98
					3/2	1.050	1.50
					1/2	1.200	0.82
			0				
	1/2	3/2	-898	-2/9	3/2	0.750	4.98
					1/2	1.250	0.67
		1/2	-973	+2/9	1/2	1.000	1.83
0	1/2	1/2		+2	1/2	1.000	1.83

stating that the electron spin-molecular rotation interaction constant is chosen arbitrarily. Their corresponding energy eigenvalues are given in Table I. The naive assumption, that for odd K the nuclear moment resultant $I=1/2+1/2$ couples to the electron spin S via the contact interaction of similar magnitude as in the H-atom plus a smaller dipole-dipole term which in the atom vanishes because of spherical symmetry, is in agreement with this Hamiltonian. Further, one would expect this spin resultant $\mathbf{F_2}=\mathbf{I}+\mathbf{S}$ to couple to the rotation vector $\mathbf{K}$ via an appreciably weaker magnetic interaction to form the final resultant $\mathbf{F}=\mathbf{K}+\mathbf{F_2}$. The corresponding vector model is depicted in Fig. 1. Having established the vector frame of the (N) state, we are now in a position to evaluate the normalized dissociation rates R_{FM} for its sublevels FM. One way is to calculate the individual transition probabilities $|(FM|\cos\theta|F'M)|^2$ and to sum over the appropriate sublevels $F'M$ of the (E) state. Here θ refers to the inter-

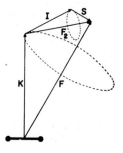

Fig. 1. Vector model for the H_2^+ molecular ion.

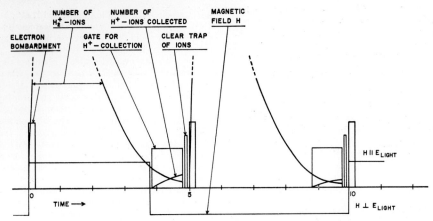

FIG. 2. Periodic sequence of events in pulse scheme to create and detect alignment
of the H$_2^+$ ion by selective photodissociation.

nuclear axis. Noting that in both (N) and (E) state **S** couples most strongly to **I** while the electric light vector interacts with neither, we assume the selection rule $\Delta F_2 = 0$. It is also necessary that $\Delta K = \pm 1$ and $\Delta F = 0$, ± 1. Because of the analogy with the atomic case pointed out earlier standard atomic spectra tables and formulas[16] may be employed in conjunction with suitable sum rules in the same way as one would calculate atomic hfs intensities. We have made the tacit assumption that both (N) and (E) states exhibit the same type of coupling scheme. Actually, because of the summation over the (E) state sublevels, the R_{FM} are independent of this assumption. The numerical values obtained in this way are given in Table I. Another approach, namely evaluating the electronic ground-state expectation values of the operator $K^2 - K_z^2$ constructed earlier, $R_{FM} \propto |(FM|K^2 - K_z^2|FM)|$, gives the same results much quicker. These calculations are most conveniently carried out using a numerical table of the Clebsch-Gordan coefficients,[17] and then normalizing according to

$$\sum_{M=-F}^{M=+F} R_{FM} = 2F + 1.$$

We note that, while the addition of the spin angular momenta on the whole exerts a leveling influence on the angular dependence of the dissociation rates, nevertheless appreciable structure remains. To illustrate the degree of alignment building up in an initially statistical sample, population numbers $a_0 = 1$ at $u = 0$ initially, the residual population numbers a_4 after irradiation for four average dissociation time constants, $u = 4$, are listed in Table I also. To evaluate the

corresponding optimum signal $\mathcal{S}$ as defined before we have to make assumptions concerning the relative populations A_K of the K levels. Assuming that the ionization process does not change K, these populations[18] are the same as for the H$_2$ molecules from which the ions are formed. The corresponding values, for room temperature, are listed in Table II, together with $\langle \delta_K^2 \rangle_{\mathrm{av}}$ values averaged separately over all the M_F sublevels of each K state. The proper average $\langle \delta^2 \rangle_{\mathrm{av}} = \sum A_K \langle \delta_K^2 \rangle_{\mathrm{av}}$, $\sum A_K = 1$, yields $\mathcal{S} = 8 \langle \delta^2 \rangle_{\mathrm{av}} = 0.34$.

EXPERIMENTAL WORK IN PROGRESS

The first experimental goal will be to demonstrate any alignment. The partial destruction of alignment when the magnetic field direction is switched through 90° will be employed in the following scheme, compare Fig. 2. H$_2^+$ ions which are created by short electron bombardment pulses and trapped are continuously irradiated with linear polarized light from a suitable high intensity arc. Consecutive ion bunches are subjected to a small magnetic field alternately parallel and perpendicular to the electric light vector for a time $t \approx 4T$, then counted whereupon the trap is cleared of ions. The relative difference in ion numbers counted S^* should then be $S^* = S_{||} - S_\perp$. Assuming the relation $S_\perp = \frac{1}{4} S_{||}$ to hold quite generally we have with our

TABLE II. Rotational level populations A_K and average quadratic dissociation rate deviations $\langle \delta_K^2 \rangle_{\mathrm{av}}$.

K	A_K	$\langle \delta_K^2 \rangle_{\mathrm{av}}$	$A_K \langle \delta_K^2 \rangle_{\mathrm{av}}$	$\langle \delta^2 \rangle_{\mathrm{av}}$
0	0.145	0	0	
1	0.728	0.0349	0.0254	0.0423
2	0.127	0.133	0.0169	

[16] Reference 10, p. 241–243, and 387.
[17] E. G. and E. R. Cohen, North American Aviation Report NAA-SR-2123 (unpublished).

[18] Compare T. R. Carson, Proc. Roy. Soc. (London) **68**, 900 (1954); note that H$_2$ molecule and H$_2^+$ ion have the same symmetry.

TABLE III. Vibrational level populations and approximate photodissociation threshold wavelength for H_2^+.

Vibrational level ν	0	1	2	3	4	5	6-∞
Population[a]	0.071	0.172	0.190	0.171	0.130	0.086	0.180
Threshold (mμ)	$\cdots$	$\cdots$	$\cdots$	247	286	326	380

[a] After G. Gibson, reference 8.

numerical optimum value $S_{11} = 0.34$, $\mathcal{S} = 0.25$. Combined with the minimum background uncertainty estimated earlier, this would correspond to a signal to noise ratio of about 500 on the basis of comparison of only two ion bunches. There is, however, another obstacle to be overcome, not mentioned before. When using practical high-power light sources,[19] it is not possible to obtain much output below 2500 A. This coincides roughly with the threshold wavelength for photoionization out of the third vibrational level, $\nu = 3$, of the H_2^+ ion; see Table III. In order to achieve roughly the same dissociation rate for all the higher vibrational levels, $\nu \geqq 4$, it would be desirable to have a flat spectrum above about 2600 A with zero intensity below this wavelength; then still about 40% of the H_2^+ ions created from room temperature H_2 molecules would be dissociable by the incident light and our alignment analysis would apply to them. Since the alignment in our numerical example is bought at the loss of about 98% of the dissociable ions and the detection method is based on counting remaining ions, clearly it would be very desirable to eliminate the large undissociable background. Experimentally, this is possible as follows. After the alignment period, duration $4T$, not the remaining H_2^+ ions are counted, but one collects instead the H^+ photodissociation products for the duration T and counts them. This effects essentially without loss counting only the residual dissociable fraction of the remaining H_2^+ ions. These considerations lead to the periodic sequence of events sketched in Fig. 2. It should be obvious that rf transitions between any two hfs levels with different dissociation rates R_{FM} could partially take the place of the alternating H field. The low-field $\Delta F = 0$ transitions for which approximate g factors are listed in Table I should be comparatively easy to detect. In order to detect the weaker $\Delta F = \pm 1$ transitions, it might be desirable to integrate over 100 or more cycles and thereby decrease the theoretical minimum detectable signal to 5×10^{-5} or less. Experimental linewidth as low as 10 to 100 cps might be realizable.

ACKNOWLEDGMENTS

The authors are indebted for stimulating and clarifying discussion to many members of this Department, especially to Professor F. Chilton and also to Dr. G. H. Dunn.

[19] Since a single monochromatic lightpulse from a commercial ruby laser may contain as many as 10^{19} photons, while the H_2^+ photodissociation cross section is about 10^{-17} cm^2, nearly complete dissociation of the molecules in certain vibrational levels could be achieved in this way too. Under some conditions this type laser may have advantages over the conventional continuous broadband light sources considered here.

From: *Phys. Rev. Letters* **3**, 544-545 (1959)

SELF-ABSORPTION AND TRAPPING OF SHARP-LINE RESONANCE RADIATION IN RUBY

F. Varsanyi, D. L. Wood, and A. L. Schawlow

Bell Telephone Laboratories, Murray Hill, New Jersey

(Received November 12, 1959)

As an aid in planning a microwave-optical double resonance experiment,[1,2] we have examined by high-resolution optical spectroscopy the details of the sharp-line fluorescence of ruby (Cr^{3+} in Al_2O_3).

The only transition which appears in the fluorescence of dilute ruby at 4°K is from $^2E(\bar{E})$ to $^4A_2$ and appears at 6934 A. Selection rules for this transition have been calculated,[3] and partially verified for absorption.[4] The Zeeman levels to be discussed here are those occurring

for a magnetic field parallel to the symmetry axis and are shown in Fig. 1.

Figure 2(a) gives the predicted and observed intensities for a dilute ruby containing about 10^{-6} Cr per Al, and showing no color. For the theoretical patterns complete thermalization among the Zeeman levels is assumed in both ground and excited states. The figure shows that the selection rules predicting a 3:2 ratio of components α to γ and of δ to β are confirmed. Moreover, use of the α to δ and γ to β ratios shows that the population of atoms in the upper Zeeman level of the excited state is only slightly above that of a Boltzmann distribution. The effective spin temperature is 1.77°K. If it is assumed (although this is doubtful) that the excita-

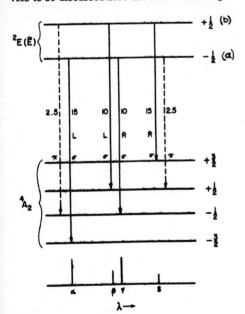

FIG. 1. Energy levels and transition probabilities for Zeeman levels involved in the resonance lines of ruby. $H \parallel c$ axis.

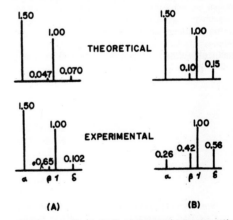

FIG. 2. (a) Theoretical and observed intensity ratio of Zeeman components in very dilute ruby sample (white sapphire). $H = 30\,000$ gauss; $T = 1.58$°K. (b) Theoretical and observed intensity ratio of Zeeman components in ruby containing 0.05% Cr_2O_3. $H = 30\,000$ gauss; $T = 2.1$°K.

tion process populates the two levels equally, and that the actual population is obtained by a balance between spin-lattice relaxation and radiative decay, the spin-lattice relaxation time is about 2×10^{-4} second. Also the crystal may have been heated above the helium bath temperature by the exciting radiation, so the actual relaxation time may be somewhat less. In any case, it seems that there is nearly complete thermalization between the Zeeman levels of the excited state during its relatively long lifetime of several milliseconds.

The great disparity between calculated and observed intensities for a ruby containing 0.05% Cr_2O_3 by weight is shown in Fig. 2(b). This disparity is explained by self-absorption which differs from one component to the next because of the Boltzmann population distribution of the ground-state levels. Thus component α terminates on the ground level ($m = -3/2$), which is populated by 85% of the atoms and is strongly absorbed. At the other extreme the component δ terminates on the +3/2 level, which is 8.3 cm^{-1} above it, and contains only 0.3% of the atoms, so that δ is much *less* absorbed. While self-absorption is often encountered in gaseous luminescence, it is seldom possible for a gas to be cold enough to have appreciably different populations in individual Zeeman levels.

Quantitatively, we find that an absorption coefficient of about 25 cm^{-1} for the α component produces satisfactory agreement with the observed intensity ratio of γ to α in the 0.05% ruby spectrum. A direct absorption measurement at 77°K, where only half of the atoms are in the ±3/2 state and line widths have increased from 0.25 to 0.32 cm^{-1}, gave $k = 13$ cm^{-1} in good agreement. The

radiative lifetime of the excited state was also measured in the very dilute sample, and in finely divided and dispersed 0.05% ruby, and was found to be 4.3 ± 0.3 milliseconds. This gives an oscillator strength $f = 7.5 \times 10^{-7}$ for the same transition, which then gives $k = 11$ cm^{-1} for 0.05% ruby. This satisfactory agreement indicates that the observed lifetime is indeed predominantly radiative.

It has been possible in the 0.05% ruby to observe for the first time in a solid the trapping of resonance radiation. At 77°K the radiative lifetime is found to vary smoothly from 4.3×10^{-3} second for a fine, dispersed powder to 15×10^{-3} second for a whole boule, a very long lifetime. The observation of trapping confirms the predominantly radiative character of the decay of the excited state, and the strong self-absorption of the resonance radiation. The ratio of lifetimes with and without trapping is only about 4, showing that other modes of decay such as radiation in vibrational sidebands and nonradiative processes also occur.

We are indebted to D. G. Thomas for the use of his spectrograph and magnet, to A. M. Clogston, S. Geschwind, and S. Sugano for helpful discussions, and to G. E. Devlin for extensive experimental assistance.

---

[1]Geschwind, Collins, and Schawlow, following Letter [Phys. Rev. Letters **3**, 545 (1959)].

[2]Brossel, Geschwind, and Schawlow, this issue [Phys. Rev. Letters **3**, 548 (1959)].

[3]S. Sugano and Y. Tanabe, J. Phys. Soc. (Japan) **13**, 880 (1958).

[4]S. Sugano and I. Tsujikawa, J. Phys. Soc. (Japan) **13**, 889 (1958).

OPTICAL DETECTION OF PARAMAGNETIC RESONANCE IN AN EXCITED STATE OF Cr³⁺ IN Al₂O₃

S. Geschwind, R. J. Collins, and A. L. Schawlow
Bell Telephone Laboratories, Murray Hill, New Jersey
(Received November 12, 1959)

We have observed paramagnetic resonance in an excited metastable state of Cr^{3+} in Al_2O_3 by a method of optical detection which should have wide applicability to the general problem of studying paramagnetic resonance in excited states of ions in solids. This method makes use of the selective reabsorption in the ground-state

Zeeman levels of the fluorescent light from the excited states in solids at very low temperatures.[1] Referring to Fig. 1 of the preceding Letter,[1] at 1.6°K, the lower of the two Zeeman levels of the excited state $\bar{E}(^2E)$ will be much more heavily populated. Let us first assume there is no reabsorption so that the theoretical intensities for transitions to the Zeeman levels of the $^4A_2$ ground state are as given by Sugano and Tanabe.[2] In this case, when the sample is irradiated with microwave energy of the proper frequency so as to excite ions in the lower Zeeman level of $\bar{E}(^2E)$ to the upper Zeeman level, the ions upon radiating to the ground state emit two σ lines, δ, β of relative intensity 3:2 just as they do in radiating from the lower Zeeman level of the excited state (α, γ). In this case, the total emitted light in σ polarization would remain constant, i.e., it is independent of the relative population of the magnetic sublevels of the excited state. Similarly for the π component. On the other hand, if there is reabsorption of the fluorescent light, components β and δ originating from level b will be less strongly absorbed than α and γ due to the larger Boltzmann populations of the lower Zeeman levels in the ground state at low temperatures. Then, by inducing microwave transitions between the magnetic sublevels of the excited state so as to raise ions from level a to b, we can increase the total light output and thereby detect paramagnetic resonance in the upper state.[3] In contrast to standard optical double resonance techniques in gases, where normally a change in linear or circular polarization is detected along the field direction,[4] this method of utilizing selective reabsorption enables one to observe a change in the light in linear polarization in the much more convenient direction at right angles to the field.

The sample was a $\frac{1}{8}$-in. diameter by $\frac{1}{4}$-in. long cylinder of ruby, containing 0.05% of Cr, whose c axis was perpendicular to the axis of the cylinder. It was placed along the axis of a cylindrical $TE_{0,1,2}$ mode K-band cavity with a hole cut in one end wall for continuous vertical illumination from below by a 200-watt Osram mercury lamp. The ions were continuously excited to the metastable state by absorption of the 5461A and the 4000A light from the mercury lamp and subsequent decay by radiationless transitions to the metastable state. The metastable state $2\bar{A}(^2E)$, 30 cm^{-1} above, is virtually depopulated at 1.6°K, i.e., the thermalization of the metastable states in the radiationless decay is much faster than the radiative lifetime of these states. Slots were cut in the side wall of the cavity to view the fluorescent light which was detected by a photomultiplier preceded by a polaroid, collimating lens, and narrow band interference filter of 70A half-width centered at 6934 A. The microwaves were chopped with a 30-cps square wave and the resulting 30-cps component in the fluorescent light, as one swept the dc magnetic field through the excited state resonance, was recorded using standard lock-in detection techniques. A recorder trace of the increase in σ light is shown in Fig. 1. The line width is 17 gauss and is comparable to the widths observed in the ground-state resonances. We estimate that this signal arises from approximately 10^{10} Cr^{3+} ions in the excited state.

The excited state can be represented by an effective spin Hamiltonian

$$\mathcal{H} = \mu_\beta \vec{H} \cdot \tilde{g} \cdot \vec{S}', \tag{1}$$

where $\vec{S}'$ is an effective spin of $\frac{1}{2}$. The energy levels of the excited state are given by $W = \pm \frac{1}{2} g \mu_\beta H$, where $g = (g_\parallel^2 \cos^2\theta + g_\perp^2 \sin^2\theta)^{1/2}$. The variation of the dc magnetic field required for resonance, H_{res}, as a function of the angle θ between the c axis and H_{res}, is shown in Fig. 2. $1/H_{res}$ is seen to vary as $\cos\theta$ within the accuracy of our measurements,[5] with the components of the g tensor given by $g_\parallel = (-)2.445 \pm 0.001$ and $|g_\perp| < 0.06$. While the sign of $g_\parallel$ has not actually been measured by using microwaves of circular polarization, theoretical analysis by Clogston[6] indicates that it is negative.

The actual increase in the total fluorescent signal when the Zeeman levels of the excited state were saturated amounted to 2.5% of the total fluorescence. This very large light signal made it possible to measure directly the relaxation time T_1 in the excited state. Figure 3(a) is an oscillogram of a sample of the microwave power, square-wave modulated at 50 cps, incident on the cavity. Figure 3(b) is an oscillogram of the

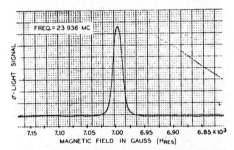

FIG. 1. Recorder trace of increase in σ component of fluorescent light as magnetic field is swept through resonance of excited $\bar{E}(^2E)$ state. This signal corresponds to approximately 10^{10} Cr^{3+} ions in the excited state. H is parallel to the c axis.

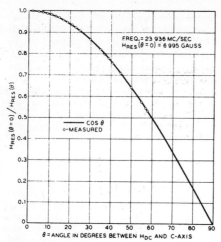

FIG. 2. Variation of magnetic resonance of $\bar{E}(^2E)$ state with angle θ between the applied field and the c axis of the crystal.

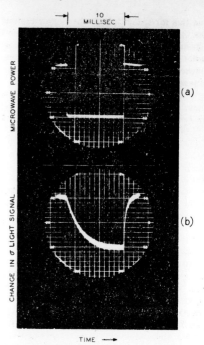

FIG. 3. (a) Oscillogram of microwave power square-wave modulated at 30 cps. The lower portion of the square-wave corresponds to the microwave-power-off part of the cycle. (b) Corresponding change in the σ component of the fluorescent light signal. From the decay of the increased fluorescent light signal when the microwave power is turned off, T_1 for the excited state ions is found to be 2.3 milliseconds.

corresponding light signal. From the decay of the light signal with microwave power off, we determine T_1 to be 2.3 milliseconds. T_1 need not necessarily be a spin-lattice relaxation time; it is, however, the time taken for the magnetic sublevels of the excited state to thermalize when saturated, irrespective of the process, i.e., direct spin-lattice, cross-relaxation to ground-state spins, or even radiative relaxation. It is this latter radiative lifetime τ which sets an upper limit on the nonradiative T_1 which can be observed. Since τ is known to be about 8×10^{-3} sec, the value of T_1 of 2.3×10^{-3} sec can be assumed to be mainly connected with nonradiative thermalization. Further evidence for this is the speedup in T_1 to $\sim 1.6 \times 10^{-3}$ sec at certain angles θ where the energy separation of the excited state approaches the Zeeman separation of some of the ground-state levels.

From a study of the saturation of the light signal with microwave power, the value of microwave power where $(\vec{\mu} \cdot \vec{H}_{rf}/\hbar)^2 T_1 T_2 \sim 1$ was determined. Since we know T_1 and T_2 (the latter from the line width) we could determine $\vec{\mu}$, the magnetic dipole moment matrix element for the transition, if we knew $\vec{H}_{rf}$ as a function of the microwave power level incident on the cavity. As it is difficult to know the exact field configu-

ration in the ruby, we made a rough estimate of $\vec{\mu}$ by comparing the ratio of powers needed to saturate the excited state compared to the ground state, using the values of T_1 and T_2 for the ground state from other work. We find the ratio of the transition probabilities to be approximately 0.005. Even this small transition probability is relatively large compared to that originally predicted theoretically.

We have also detected the ground-state resonances, by monitoring the change in fluorescent light when these resonances are swept through, again due to selective reabsorption. However, these are of secondary interest in this case.

We wish to thank A. M. Clogston for stimulating

From: *Phys. Rev. Letters* **3**, 548-549 (1959)   267

our interest in the problem of studying excited states in solids by paramagnetic resonance. We are grateful to D. Linn for his extensive experimental assistance and to Professor J. Brossel, A. Javan, W. B. Mims, H. E. D. Scovil, and Professor S. Sugano for helpful discussions.

[1]Varsanyi, Wood, and Schawlow, preceding Letter [Phys. Rev. Letters **3**, 544 (1959)].
[2]S. Sugano and Y. Tanabe, J. Phys. Soc. (Japan)

13, 880 (1958).
[3]The principle of this method was also suggested independently by Professor J. Brossel.
[4]F. Bitter and J. Brossel, Phys. Rev. **86**, 308 (1952).
[5]S. F. Jacobs, thesis, 1957, John Hopkins University (unpublished), earlier established the approximate $\cos\theta$ variation of the $\bar{E}(^2E)$ Zeeman pattern from the optical Zeeman spectrum. Our work confirms this with an order of magnitude greater accuracy characteristic of microwaves. We are grateful to Professor G. H. Dieke for making this work available to us.
[6]A. M. Clogston (private communication).

OPTICAL DETECTION OF PARAMAGNETIC RESONANCE IN CRYSTALS AT LOW TEMPERATURES

J. Brossel,[*] S. Geschwind, and A. L. Schawlow
Bell Telephone Laboratories, Murray Hill, New Jersey
(Received November 12, 1959)

Paramagnetic resonance absorption has been extensively used to determine the structure of the ground state of paramagnetic ions in different crystal fields. As is well known, many absorption and fluorescence spectra of ions in a crystal lattice show very sharp optical lines besides the usual broad bands. The Zeeman effect of these lines has been observed in some cases, and the components are often strongly polarized.

A method of detection of magnetic resonance in the fluorescent state which utilizes the selective reabsorption of the components of the fluorescent radiation at low temperatures has been described in the preceding Letter.[1] We wish to discuss extensions of this method to other cases which may arise, as well as to indicate where the more conventional double resonance[2] techniques may be applied to the study of paramagnetic ions in crystal lattices. In addition, we want to point out that optical detection of magnetic resonances in the ground state may have some merits of its own.

The first step in doing resonance in an excited state is to obtain a population difference between the Zeeman substates. We will use the case of ruby to illustrate the different possibilities. Referring to Fig. 1 of Varsanyi, Wood, and Schawlow,[3] two cases may arise:

(A) Thermalization is fast. — This we feel will be the most common case. It is what happens in ruby, i.e., the Boltzmann distribution is reached between (a) and (b) before the atoms radiate. The fluorescent state can be reached in any con-venient way and one can rely on thermal relaxation to achieve the population difference. Absorption of light in any of the broad bands is particularly convenient because it can be filtered out at detection and need not come from a preferred direction.

(B) Thermalization is slow. — In this case, a population difference between the Zeeman levels of the excited state can be achieved, just as is done in gaseous double resonance experiments, by pumping with polarized resonance light. However, in a solid at low temperatures and high enough fields, one can even use unpolarized resonance radiation, because the lowest Zeeman level of the ground state is far more populated than the others, so that absorption will populate level (a) more than level (b).

Having obtained a population difference between the Zeeman levels of the excited state, the next step is to detect the change in this population on passing through magnetic resonance by observing the fluorescent light. At low temperatures selective reabsorption may be utilized as shown in the preceding Letter.

At temperatures very much above 4°K, however, selective reabsorption will not occur. In addition, selective reabsorption will be absent from a fluorescent line whose width is greater than the total Zeeman splitting of the ground state. In these cases, it follows from the transition probabilities shown in Fig. 1 of reference 3, and as explained in the preceding Letter, that the total light output is independent of the population difference in the upper state and so will be unaffected by microwave transitions in the excited state. However, a microwave transition can nonetheless be detected by comparing the ratio of right circular (R) to left circular (L) light emitted in fluorescence; in particular (R) light will increase at resonance. The same thing will happen for all Kramers doublets. There is the experimental difficulty of looking along the direction of the field, at high fields where the Boltzmann factor is favorable. Moreover, the crystal must be strain free so as not to depolarize the light; but the method works even when the components of the optical Zeeman pattern overlap.

In studying resonance in the excited state by the selective reabsorption method, ground state resonances will often show up also; as they did in ruby, due to the change in population of the absorbing levels arising from the microwave resonance. This may be confusing under some circumstances. A way to see only the excited state is to operate with a ruby so dilute that no reabsorption takes place, and observe its fluorescence through a selectively absorbing ruby outside the rf field, but in the same magnetic field and at the same low temperature.

At liquid helium temperatures, optical detection of magnetic resonance in the ground state can be accomplished in several ways. The change of paramagnetic to diamagnetic Faraday effect has been used previously.[4] The absorption of circularly polarized light may be used, since as is seen from Fig. 1 of reference 3, component (a) is more absorbed, i.e., circularly left light is absorbed in the ruby 6934A line, to a greater extent than other polarizations. Resonance in the ground state between level 1 and any other will increase the amount of transmitted left light. One can operate at low fields. The light source may have "broad line" characteristics, but the light must travel along the field.

The same absorption method will apply to linearly polarized (σ or π) 6934A light, traveling perpendicular to the magnetic field, or even in the absence of a field.[5] However, with the condition just defined, transitions $-\frac{1}{2} \to +\frac{1}{2}$ and $-\frac{3}{2} \to +\frac{3}{2}$

will not appear, as seen from the optical transition probabilities (although they should appear if H were not along the optic axis). They can be observed with a suitable "narrow line" light source, emitting the Zeeman components with unequal intensities. This last case requires that the Zeeman components of the line be well separated and that that fairly high fields be used.

Optical detection of ground state resonances could prove useful in many cases. For example, many satellite lines have been seen in the optical spectrum of Cr^{3+} in Al_2O_3 and MgO which are attributed[6] to Cr^{3+} pairs, as well as to an added axial field component due to charge compensation in the case of MgO. Such pairs and centers have indeed been identified by standard paramagnetic resonance techniques.[7] Therefore, by doing double-resonance type experiments on these optical satellites in such a way that only ground-state transitions are observed, a correlation can be made between the particular optical satellite and the type of center with which it is associated. In addition, optical detection of ground-state resonances will be helpful in unraveling unidentified paramagnetic resonance spectra which are associated with different types of centers; for, by studying the ground-state resonances of a particular optical satellite, one selects only that part of the total paramagnetic resonance spectrum associated with only one type of center.

———————

* Permanent address, Ecole Normale Supérieure, Paris, France.

[1] Geschwind, Collins, and Schawlow, preceding Letter [Phys. Rev. Letters 3, 545 (1959)].

[2] F. Bitter and J. Brossel, Phys. Rev. 86, 308 (1952); A. Kastler, J. Opt. Soc. Am. 47, 460 (1957).

[3] Varsanyi, Wood, and Schawlow, this issue [Phys. Rev. Letters 3, 544 (1959)].

[4] J. M. Daniels and H. Wesemeyer, Can. J. Phys. 36, 406 (1958).

[5] I. Wieder, Phys. Rev. Letters 3, 468 (1959).

[6] Schawlow, Wood, and Clogston, Phys. Rev. Letters 3, 271 (1959).

[7] J. E. Wertz and P. Auzins, Phys. Rev. 106, 484 (1958); J. H. E. Griffiths and J. W. Orton, Proc. Phys. Soc. (London) 73, 948 (1959); private communications from M. Peter and from J. C. Gill.

From: *Phys. Rev. Letters* **13**, 567-568 (1964)   269

OBSERVATION OF A PHOTON ECHO*

N. A. Kurnit,[†] I. D. Abella, and S. R. Hartmann[‡]

Columbia Radiation Laboratory, Columbia University, New York, New York

(Received 2 September 1964)

An experiment has been performed in which a ruby crystal has been made to emit spontaneously a short, intense burst of radiation, which we will call a photon echo, after being excited by two short, intense light pulses at 6935 Å from a Q-switched ruby laser.[1] In Fig. 1, oscilloscope photographs show the output of a photomultiplier which monitors the radiation from the ruby-crystal sample. In the three cases shown, for excitation pulse separations of 80, 110, and 140 nsec, the time between the echo and the previous excitation pulse is very nearly equal to the time separation of the excitation pulses. This behavior is similar to that observed in nuclear magnetic spin echo experiments.[2]

The purpose of the first excitation pulse is to create a superradiant state[3] which, because of its large oscillating macroscopic electric dipole moment, radiates strongly until it either decays to the ground state or loses phase coherence. In this experiment the dephasing process is dominant and is caused primarily by inhomogeneous crystal strains. After the dipole moment has dephased, a second excitation pulse is applied which essentially performs a time-reversal operation so that the system now starts rephasing. At a time after the second excitation pulse equal to the time separation of the pulses, the rephasing process is complete and the system again exhibits a macroscopic electric dipole moment resulting in a burst of coherent radiation.

A schematic outline of the experimental setup

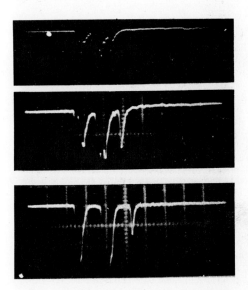

FIG. 1. Oscilloscope photographs of the output from a photomultiplier which monitors the radiation from the ruby sample. The horizontal time scale is 100 nsec/div, and time increases to the right. The excitation pulses appear broadened due to detector saturation. The positions of the echoes imply that these pulses occur ≈ 15 nsec later than indicated above. This is due to an observed build-up time of ≈ 10 nsec for the overall giant pulse, with an additional 5 nsec delay likely for the particular modes responsible for the photon echo.

is given in Fig. 2. The Q-switched ruby laser is triggered to produce an intense light pulse of approximately 10 nsec duration. This pulse (~200 kW) is split by a beam splitter so that one part is focused directly onto an area of ≈ 0.05 cm^2 of a 1-mm thick ruby crystal (0.005% Cr), while the other part of the beam is directed into an optical delay line[4] to obtain the second pulse. The various mirrors and lenses are adjusted so that both pulses are focused at the same area of the ruby crystal, but it is important that the paths of the two pulses make some small but nonzero angle, φ, with respect to each other. In this case, it can be shown that the angle (see Fig. 2) at which the excited crystal will radiate its echo is $\approx 2\varphi$ (in the plane defined by the excitation pulses), thereby allowing an aperture to pass the echo but preventing the large initial pulses from overloading the photomultiplier. The angle φ was $\approx 3°$ in this experiment. The echo leaves the ruby crystal along the dashed line and enters the lens which images the sample crystal on the face of the phototube. A Kerr-cell shutter is placed before the phototube to reduce the amount of scattered light from the excitation pulses. It is activated by a 100-nsec pulse to permit observation of the echo. Not shown in Fig. 2 are a pair of coils, which can provide a magnetic field of 250 gauss along the direction of the incident excitation pulses, and Dewars for keeping the ruby sample at liquid He temperature and the ruby laser crystal at liquid N$_2$ temperature. Cooling the ruby sample to liquid He temperature is necessary in order to obtain relaxation times[5] which are not short compared to the excitation pulse separation, while the laser crystal need only be cooled to the point where the R_1 lines in the sample and the laser crystal overlap.[6]

Several experiments were performed in order to ascertain that the observed echo was originating from the sample crystal and was not the result of a spurious reflection going back through the delay line and onto the detector. (1) The paths of the two excitation pulses were lengthened at a-a (Fig. 2) by 2 m with no increase in the delay of the echo. (2) If a magnetic field greater than ≈ 50 gauss (of either sign) is applied to the ruby sample along the optic axis and parallel to the incident light direction an echo is obtained, while no echo is obtained in zero magnetic field. (3) No echo is observed when the optic axis of the ruby sample is rotated by as little as 3° (or as much as 30°) with respect to the incident light di-

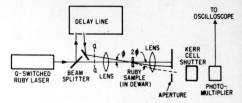

FIG. 2. Schematic experimental arrangement.

rection unless the magnetic field is rotated parallel to the optic axis. The maximum rotation allowed by our experimental setup is 30°. The optic axis in the sample crystal is $\approx 15°$ to the normal of the surface of the crystal. (4) The crystal was warmed slowly by allowing the He to boil off, and it was found that a few minutes later the echo was lost. To check the possibility of the echo being an ion pulse in the photomultiplier caused by the intense excitation pulses (the results of Fig. 1 argue against this possibility), the $B-$ applied to the photomultiplier was varied between 1500 and 2000 volts with no apparent effect on the position or shape of the echo. Other experiments have been performed which also show that the observation of the echo is a genuine physical effect and will be reported in a later paper.

We would like to thank Professor R. Mieher and Professor R. Novick for helpful discussions. We are grateful to Professor R. Gross who lent us his Kerr cell for this experiment.

*Work supported by the Army Research Office (Durham) under contract No. DA-31-124-ARO-D-224, and by the Joint Services (U. S. Army, Air Force Office of Scientific Research, and Office of Naval Research).
†In partial fulfillment of the requirements for the Ph.D. in physics at Columbia University.
‡Alfred P. Sloan Fellow.
[1]See, for example, F. J. McClung and R. W. Hellwarth, J. Appl. Phys. <u>33</u>, 838 (1962).
[2]E. L. Hahn, Phys. Rev. <u>80</u>, 580 (1950).
[3]R. H. Dicke, Phys. Rev. <u>93</u>, 99 (1954).
[4]Based on a mirror design by J. U. White, J. Opt. Soc. Am. <u>32</u>, 285 (1942).
[5]The relaxation time of the echo is determined principally by relaxation in the excited $^2E(\bar{E})$ state and has been studied theoretically by D. E. McCumber and M. D. Sturge, J. Appl. Phys. <u>34</u>, 1682 (1963).
[6]Absorption experiments performed in this laboratory have shown a sizeable overlap of the R_1 lines in ruby crystals at liquid N$_2$ and He temperatures. See also A. L. Schawlow, in <u>Advances in Quantum Electronics,</u> edited by J. Singer (Columbia University Press, New York, 1961), 2nd ed., p. 50.

Index